CO-AUI-866

MAGILL'S
SURVEY
OF
SCIENCE

#22509048

Ref
QH
307.2
.M34
1991
v.3

MAGILL'S SURVEY OF SCIENCE

LIFE SCIENCE SERIES

Volume 3
895-1376
Positive and Negative Eukaryotic Transcriptional Control—
Mammalian Hormones

Edited by

FRANK N. MAGILL

Consulting Editor
LAURA L. MAYS HOOPES

94344

SALEM PRESS

Pasadena, California   Englewood Cliffs, New Jersey

THE GRAHAM LIBRARY
TBC-ELLENDALE, N. D. 58436

Copyright © 1991, by SALEM PRESS
All rights in this book are reserved. No part of this work
may be used or reproduced in any manner whatsoever or
transmitted in any form or by any means, electronic or
mechanical, including photocopy, recording, or any information storage and retrieval system, without written
permission from the copyright owner except in the case
of brief quotations embodied in critical articles and
reviews. For information address the publisher, Salem
Press, Inc., P.O. Box 50062, Pasadena, California 91105.

∞ The paper used in these volumes conforms to the
American National Standard for Permanence of Paper
for Printed Library Materials, Z39.48-1984.

Library of Congress Cataloging-in-Publication Data
Magill's survey of science. Life science series/edited by
Frank N. Magill, consulting editor, Laura L. Mays Hoopes.
  p. cm.
  Includes bibliographical references.
  Includes index.
  1. Life sciences. I. Magill, Frank Northen, 1907-
QH307.2.M34 1991   90-19102
574—dc20   CIP
ISBN 0-89356-612-8 (set)
ISBN 0-89356-615-2 (volume 3)

PRINTED IN THE UNITED STATES OF AMERICA

CONTENTS

LIFE SCIENCE

MAGILL'S
SURVEY
OF
SCIENCE

POSITIVE AND NEGATIVE EUKARYOTIC TRANSCRIPTIONAL CONTROL

Type of life science: Genetic regulation in eukaryotes
Other fields of study: Animal physiology, developmental biology (embryology), and plant physiology

Transcription is the synthesis of RNA using a DNA template. The regulation of transription in eukaryotes involves a number of specific DNA sequences and proteins that bind to those sequences. A complete understanding of the regulation of transcription in eukaryotes will bring scientists closer to understanding cell function and the development of organisms.

Principal terms

ENHANCER ELEMENT: a DNA sequence that activates transcription from the promoter linked to it; an enhancer may be a long distance from the gene it controls, and it can function in either orientation

MESSENGER RNA: an RNA molecule transcribed from the DNA sequence of a gene from which a protein is translated by the action of ribosomes

PROMOTER: in eukaryotes, the region adjacent to a gene where transcription factors and regulatory proteins bind to control gene transcription; once transcription factors are bound, RNA polymerase can bind

REGULATORY GENE: a gene whose protein product is involved in turning on or off the transcription of another gene or genes

REGULATORY PROTEIN: protein which functions to turn on or off the transcription of a gene or genes

RIBONUCLEIC ACID (RNA): a type of molecule consisting of a single, linear strand of nucleotides whose order is determined by the deoxyribonucleic acid (DNA) from which it is copied; the three major types of RNA are messenger RNA, transfer RNA, and ribosomal RNA, and all three types play an important role in protein synthesis (translation)

RNA POLYMERASE: an enzyme that catalyzes the synthesis of an RNA molecule from a DNA template

SILENCER ELEMENT: similar to an enhancer element, but represses gene transcription rather than activating it

TRANSCRIPTION: synthesis of RNA using a DNA template

TRANSCRIPTION FACTOR: a protein which binds to a promoter element, thereby facilitating the binding of the RNA polymerase enzyme

Summary of the Phenomenon

Transcription is the process whereby a molecule of ribonucleic acid (RNA) is synthesized using a deoxyribonucleic acid (DNA) template. There are three major classes of RNA: messenger RNA (mRNA), transfer RNA (tRNA), and ribosomal RNA (rRNA). The DNA templates for these molecules are defined as the genes for those molecules. A messenger RNA molecule carries the genetic information from the DNA for the structure of a protein. The information in the messenger RNA is decoded into the amino acid sequence of the protein for which it codes in a process called translation. Neither the ribosomal RNA nor transfer RNA molecule is translated.

The total DNA content of an organism—its genome—encodes all the RNA and protein molecules that are used to construct its cells. In a multicellular eukaryotic organism, every cell contains the complete set of DNA sequences that can specify the structure, function, and reproduction of the organism; however, only a fraction of the DNA sequences (that is, only some of the genes) are active in a given cell, and this means that there must be mechanisms for controlling gene transcription in a specific way.

Transcription (gene expression) is the target of sophisticated regulatory mechanisms that determine whether the gene is transcribed and how much of the RNA product is produced. Both positive and negative regulatory mechanisms are known. Positive regulatory mechanisms bring about the activation of genes (that is, they turn genes on), whereas negative regulatory mechanisms repress genes (that is, they turn genes off).

In eukaryotic cells, the DNA is organized into linear chromosomes consisting of DNA associated with specific proteins called histones to produce the highly ordered, compact structures seen under the microscope. Given the tight association of DNA with the histones, mechanisms for transcriptional regulation must function at the chromosome level, not merely the DNA level. When a gene is activated, the chromosome structure becomes less compacted in the region of the gene because of a loosening of the association between DNA and the histones. It is not known how the changes in chromosome organization occur when a gene becomes activated. Since DNA tightly bound to histones is typically not active in transcription, however, histones may be considered to be general negative regulators of gene transcription.

More important are the specific regulatory mechanisms involved in the activation and repression of transcription at the gene level. The focus will be on protein-coding genes because the initiation of mRNA synthesis is a primary control point in the regulation of differential gene expression. Protein-coding genes in eukaryotes are transcribed by the enzyme RNA polymerase II, one of three types of RNA polymerase molecules found in eukaryotic cells.

In bacteria, key transcriptional regulatory sequences are found at only two specific regions upstream from the start of RNA transcription: namely, at ten and thirty-five base pairs away from the transcription start site in the opposite direction from the direction of transcription. These sites specify where the RNA polymerase molecule binds to the DNA and initiates transcription. In eukaryotic cells, a protein-coding gene may have a large assortment of regulatory elements for transcription by RNA polymerase II located both upstream and downstream (that is, within the transcribed sequence of the gene) of the RNA initiation site for the gene. Each gene in an animal cell, for example, has a particular combination of positive and negative regulatory elements adjacent to it that are uniquely arranged as to number, type, and arrangement on the DNA. These regulatory elements are DNA sequences that are binding sites for specific transcription factors and regulatory factors, that is, proteins involved in the activation or repression of transcription from the gene. Generally, the regulatory elements are located within several hundred base pairs from the site of initiation of transcription, usually upstream from that point. Some regulatory elements, however, are one thousand to thirty thousand base pairs away. The regulatory region immediately adjacent to the transcription start site is called the promoter, while the more distant regulatory elements are called enhancers.

The DNA sequence elements that constitute eukaryotic promoters—promoter elements—have been studied extensively. In animal cells, certain promoter elements are found adjacent to many protein-coding genes. Named for the general DNA base sequences they contain, these promoter elements include the TATA, GC, and CCAAT sequences, with the TATA element closest to (about twenty-five to thrity-five base pairs upstream) and the CCAAT element farthest from the transcription initiation site. In prokaryotes, a TATA element is found in promoters and serves as a site where the enzyme RNA polymerase binds and orients itself for gene transcription. In eukaryotes, the RNA polymerase II does not bind directly to the DNA sequences of the promoter. Instead, special proteins, called transcription factors, first bind to the promoter elements to facilitate binding of RNA polymerase II and the subsequent transcription of the gene.

The promoter elements just described are general DNA sequences that are required for transcription to commence. Whether transcription occurs typically depends on other DNA sequences associated with the gene. There are promoter elements to which specific regulatory proteins bind and either turn transcription on (positive regulatory elements) or turn transcription off (negative regulatory elements). These regulatory elements are specialized with respect to the genes they control in that they bind the signaling molecule that is responsible for regulating the expression of the gene. For example, certain sets of genes are activated when steroid hormones act on the cell. The hormone molecule binds to a specific receptor protein in the cell, and that hormone-receptor complex binds to specific promoter elements to cause a regulatory change in gene transcription.

Depending on the particular gene, there can be one, a few, or many regulatory promoter elements, since there may be one, a few, or many regulatory proteins that control the expression of the gene under various conditions. The regulatory proteins show remarkable specificity in binding to their specific regulatory element in the DNA and to no others, thus ensuring careful control of which genes are activated and repressed.

While the promoter elements are crucial for determining whether transcription can occur, enhancer elements are also required for maximal transcription of the gene to occur. An enhancer element, by definition, activates transcription from the promoter linked to it, even though the enhancer may be some distance away. Whereas the promoter elements must be arranged on the DNA in one orientation in order for transcription of the gene to occur, enhancer elements function in either orientation. Also, the enhancer elements function at a large distance from the gene, often more than one thousand base pairs from the promoter. In animal cells, enhancer elements can activate genes when they are either upstream or downstream from the RNA initiation site. In most cases, though, the enhancer elements are found upstream of the gene. Similar elements that have essentially the same properties as enhancer elements, except that they repress rather than activate gene transcription, are called silencer elements.

The mechanism of enhancer action is not well understood. It is clear that regulatory proteins bind to the enhancer elements, and which regulatory proteins bind depends on the DNA sequence of the enhancer element. A model for how the enhancers affect transcription from a distance is that specific regulatory proteins bind to the enhancer element and the DNA then forms a loop so that the enhancer-bound regulatory proteins interact with the regulatory proteins and transcription factors bound to the promoter elements. Through the interactions of the proteins, transcription is either activated or repressed.

Some details are known about the regulatory elements that control gene transcription. First, each of the enhancer and promoter elements has a modular design, consisting of specific DNA sequences, each about eight to fifteen pairs long. Each element binds a corresponding regulatory protein. Some of the regulatory proteins are found in most or all cell types, while others are found in only a limited number of cell types. Second, some of the gene regulatory proteins activate transcription when they bind to the enhancer or promoter element, while others repress transcription. The net effect of a regulatory element on transcription therefore depends on the combination of different proteins bound. If positive regulatory proteins are bound at both the enhancer and promoter elements, the result is activation of transcription. If, however, a negative regulatory protein binds to the enhancer and a positive regulatory protein binds to the promoter element, the result will depend on the interaction between the two regulatory proteins. If the negative regulatory protein has a strong effect, the effect will be repression of the gene. In this latter case, the enhancer is acting as a silencer element. Third, enhancer elements and promoter elements appear to bind many of the same proteins. This implies that both types of regulatory elements affect transcription by a similar mechanism, probably involving interactions of the regulatory proteins as described before. Finally, there appears to be a relatively small number of regulatory proteins that control transcription. Therefore, by combining a few regulatory proteins in particular ways, the transcription of different arrays of genes is regulated, and a large number of cell types is specified.

In sum, the regulation of transcription in eukaryotic cells involves an array of regulatory sequences located around the transcription start points of genes, and an array of regulatory proteins that interacts with those sequences. Transcription control results from specific interactions between DNA and proteins as well as between different proteins.

Methods of Study

Much of the present understanding of the regulation of gene transcription in eukaryotes has come through the application of recombinant DNA techniques—that is, the cloning and determination of specific DNA sequences from an organism's genome. For a number of cloned genes, scientists have sequenced the DNA adjacent to the transcription initiation site to determine if there are identical or similar DNA sequences (called consensus sequences) that might be responsible for regulating gene expression. In this way, a number of promoter elements were identified.

Once genes and their adjacent regions are cloned, specific DNA sequences can be altered by making simple base pair changes or deletions in the test tube and testing for their effects on transcription activity. One assay system is to prepare extracts from the cells that are capable of carrying out accurate transcription in the test tube. The extracts contain RNA polymerase, transcription factors, and other proteins needed for transcription regulation to occur. With this system, the effect of specific sequence changes on transcription can be measured. In this way, the sequences of essential promoter elements are determined.

A second assay system is to introduce the altered cloned sequence back into cells. Once it is in the cell, the transcriptional activity of the gene is assayed in an environment in which all the transcriptional and regulatory factors are present under normal conditions. The cell also, however, contains copies of the gene being studied. To get around this, new DNA fragments are made in the test tube by cutting and joining segments of DNA using recombinant DNA technology. The new DNA fragments consist of the region adjacent to the gene (which contains the potential regulatory elements) joined to a gene—called a reporter gene—whose product is not normally made by the cell and which is easily assayed. By joining an array of altered upstream sequences of genes to a reporter gene, scientists can identify important regulatory and enhancer elements for those genes. For example, deletion of an enhancer element results in a significant decrease in transcription of the gene.

From the two approaches described, specific DNA sequences implicated in the regulation of gene transcription were determined. Those regulatory and enhancer sequences were then identified as binding sites for specific proteins by other procedures. For example, a cloned fragment of DNA containing a potential protein binding site is analyzed by gel electrophoresis in the presence or absence of cell extracts that contain regulatory proteins. In gel electrophoresis, DNA migrates in an electric field in a gel-like matrix at a rate which depends on its length. If a protein binds to the DNA fragment, that fragment will migrate more slowly in the gel—its migration is retarded. This gel retardation assay has resulted in the identification of large numbers of specific DNA binding proteins, including transcription factors, and regulatory proteins that control transcription. For a number of these proteins, the genes have been cloned and detailed information is available about how they bind to DNA.

Context

The genome of an organism—its total DNA content—specifies the growth, development, function, and reproduction of that organism. In both prokaryotic and eukaryotic organisms, sophisticated mechanisms of gene regulation have evolved that determine which genes are turned on at a given time so that not all the genes in the genome are transcribed at once.

In eukaryotes, the regulation of expression of most genes occurs at the transcription level. DNA sequences next to the gene bind specific regulatory proteins which determine whether transcription is initiated by RNA polymerase and, if it is, how much transcription of the gene occurs at a given time. For protein-coding genes, the proteins that result from translating the mRNA molecules are important for the functioning of the cell in which they are produced. In multicellular eukaryotes, such as animals and plants, different cell types often differ markedly in both their appearance and their function. A neuron (nerve cell), for example, is very different from a skin cell, yet both contain the same set of genes. These different cell types result from the presence of different arrays of proteins in those cells and differences in relative amounts of those proteins. These differences stem directly from the effects of the gene regulatory systems on transcription.

Interestingly, the protein contents of different cell types are surprisingly similar, indicating that a relatively few protein differences specify the morphology and function of those cell types. This means that the regulation of the transcription of certain key genes is an important determinant of what the cell is in terms of function. Furthermore, certain genes must be transcribed in all cell types to produce the proteins which provide functions common to all cells.

In considering the development of a multicellular eukaryotic organism, another level of complexity must be imposed beyond that of the regulation of transcription at the level of the gene. That is, the transcriptional regulatory systems must be carefully coordinated in time and space so that the determination of cell types in tissues and organs associated with development and differentiation can be accomplished. Regulation in time is important so that, for example, adult structures are not produced prematurely, and regulation in space is important so that, for example, an eye does not develop in the wrong location. Moreover, once the cell type is determined, the gene regulatory mechanisms involved in creating the unique characteristics of the cells are stably maintained in that cell and all progeny cells derived from it.

In sum, transcription is the first step in the pathway within a cell by which proteins are made. Transcriptional regulation directs the fate of a eukaryotic cell. While the detailed mechanisms by which the regulation of transcription of an individual gene are becoming more clearly understood, comparatively little is known about the coordinated regulatory events that must accompany the development and differentiation of an organism.

Bibliography

Alberts, Bruce, Dennis Bray, Julian Lewis, Martin Raff, Keith Roberts, and James Watson. *Molecular Biology of the Cell*. 2d ed. New York: Garland, 1989. An excellent college cell-biology text in which the molecular biology details of cell biology are presented with a high degree of clarity. A discussion of transcription, including RNA polymerases, transcription factors, and RNA processing, is given in chapter 9, "The Cell Nucleus," and the regulation of gene expression is broadly treated in chapter 10, "Control of Gene Expresssion," including a presentation of examples of transcriptional control mechanisms involved in development and differentiation.

Darnell, James, Harvey Lodish, and David Baltimore. *Molecular Cell Biology*. New York: Scientific American Books, 1986. A clearly written, well-illustrated, comprehensive college-level cell-biology text. Chapter 12, "Gene Control in Eukaryotes," provides a detailed discussion of gene control in eukaryotes, particularly animal cells, and puts transcriptional regulation in the broader framework of the multilevels of regulation of gene expression in the cell.

Gilbert, Scott. *Developmental Biology*. 2d ed. Sunderland, Mass.: Sinauer Associates, 1988. An intermediate-level college developmental biology text that includes a very good discussion of the molecular aspects of developmental processes in eukaryotes. Chapter 11, "Transcriptional Regulation of Gene Expression: Transcriptional Changes During Development," presents a general discussion of selective gene transcription in developing eukaryotic systems, while chapter 12, "Transcriptional Regulation of Gene Expression: The Mechanisms of Differential Gene Transcription," describes the organization of eukaryotic protein-coding genes and the structure and function of adjacent and nearby sequences that are important for transcription regulation.

Lewin, Benjamin. *Genes IV*. Cambridge, Mass.: Cell Press, 1990. An advanced college molecular biology text that presents an extremely detailed discussion of the most current molecular information. In chapter 29, "Building the Transcription Complex," there is an up-to-date review of the molecular components needed for transcription to take place, including regulatory elements. The regulation of gene transcription as it relates to the development of an organism is presented in chapter 38, "Gene Regulation in Development: Gradients and Cascades."

Russell, Peter. *Genetics*. 2d ed. Glenview, Ill.: Scott, Foresman, 1990. An intermediate-level college genetics text that presents the experimental basis of scientists' understanding of genetic processes in a logical way. In chapter 11,

"Transcription," the general concepts of transcription in eukaryotes are described in detail, and in chapter 21, "Regulation of Gene Expression and Development in Eukaryotes," the regulation of gene expression is broadly described.

Watson, James, Nancy Hopkins, Jeffrey Roberts, Joan Steitz, and Alan Weiner. *Molecular Biology of the Gene*. 4th ed. Menlo Park, Calif.: Benjamin/Cummings, 1987. A popular undergraduate text that presents the molecular biology of gene structure and function in a well-written lavishly illustrated fashion. The principles of transcription are lucidly described in chapter 13, "The Synthesis of RNA upon DNA Templates." In chapter 18, "Yeasts as the *E. coli* of Eukaryotic Cells," is a discussion of transcription, of the regulatory sequences involved in the regulation of transcription, and of the mechanisms of transcriptional regulation of selected genes the model eukaryote, yeast. Gene regulation during development and differentiation are described in chapter 22, "The Molecular Biology of Development."

Peter J. Russell

Cross-References

Chromatin Structure for Active Genes, 445; Chromosomes, 462; Cloning to Produce Recombinant DNA, 505; DNA Sequencing, 698; Eukaryotic Gene Organization, 871; Eukaryotic Transcriptional Control: Steroid Hormones, 887; Eukaryotic Gene Regulation, 1111; Prokaryotic Gene Regulation, 1119; Nuclear Structure, 1972; Transcription of DNA to Form RNA, 2632.

EVOLUTION: A HISTORICAL PERSPECTIVE

Type of life science: Evolutionary biology
Other fields of study: Botany, invertebrate biology, and zoology

Evolution is the process of change in biological populations. Historically, it is also the theory that biological species undergo sufficient change with time to give rise to new species.

Principal terms

ADAPTATION: the possession by organisms of characteristics that suit them to their environment or their way of life

CATASTROPHISM: a geological theory explaining the earth's history as resulting from great cataclysms (floods, earthquakes, and the like) on a scale not now observed

DARWINISM: branching evolution brought about by natural selection

ESSENTIALISM (TYPOLOGY): the Platonic-Aristotelian belief that each species is characterized by an unchanging "essence" incapable of evolutionary change

GENOTYPE: the hereditary characteristics of an organism

GEOFFROYISM: an early theory of evolution in which heritable change was thought to be directly induced by the environment

LAMARCKISM: an early evolutionary theory in which voluntary use or disuse of organs was thought to be capable of producing heritable changes

NATURAL SELECTION: heritable differences in the ability of several genotypes to produce viable offspring, and the changes in genotypic proportions that result from these differences

SCALE OF BEING (CHAIN OF BEING): an arrangement of life forms in a single linear sequence from "lower" to "higher"

UNIFORMITARIANISM: a geological theory explaining the earth's history using processes that can be seen at work today

Summary of the Phenomenon

Evolution is the theory that biological species undergo sufficient change with time to give rise to new species. The concept of evolution has ancient roots. Anaximander suggested in the sixth century B.C. that life had originated in the seas and that humans had evolved from fish. Empedocles (fifth century B.C.) and Lucretius (first century B.C.), in a sense, grasped the concepts of adaptation and natural selection. They taught that bodies had originally formed from the random combination of parts, but that only harmoniously functioning combinations could survive and reproduce. Lucretius even said that the mythical centaur, half horse and half human, could never have existed because the human teeth and stomach would be incapable of chewing and digesting the kind of grassy food needed to nourish the horse's body.

For two thousand years, however, evolution was considered an impossibility. Plato's theory of forms (also called his "theory of ideas") gave rise to the notion that each species had an unchanging "essence" incapable of evolutionary change. As a result, most scientists from Aristotle to Carolus Linnaeus in the eighteenth century insisted upon the immutability of species. Many of these scientists tried to arrange all species in a single linear sequence known as the scale of being (also called the chain of being or *scala naturae*), a concept supported well into the nineteenth century by many philosophers and theologians as well. The sequence in this scale of being was usually interpreted as a static "ladder of perfection" in God's creation, arranged from higher to lower forms. The scale had to be continuous, for any gap would detract from the perfection of God's creation. Much exploration was devoted to searching for "missing links" in the chain, but it was generally agreed that the entire system was static and incapable of evolutionary change. Pierre-Louis Moreau de Maupertius, in the eighteenth century, and Jean-Baptiste Lamarck were among the scientists who tried to reinterpret the scale of being as an evolutionary sequence, but this single-sequence idea was later replaced by Charles Darwin's concept of branching evolution. Georges Cuvier finally showed that the major groups of animals had such strikingly different anatomical structures that no possible scale of being could connect them all; the idea of a scale of being lost most of its scientific support as a result.

The theory that new biological species could arise from changes in existing species was not readily accepted at first. Linnaeus and other classical biologists emphasized the immutability of species under the Platonic-Aristotelian concept of essentialism. Those who believed in the concept of evolution realized that no such idea could gain acceptance until a suitable mechanism of evolution could be found. Many possible mechanisms were therefore proposed. Étienne Geoffroy Saint-Hilaire proposed that the environment directly induced physiological changes, which he thought would be inherited, a theory now known as Geoffroyism. Lamarck proposed that there was an overall linear ascent of the scale of being but that organisms could also adapt to local environments by voluntary exercise, which would strengthen the organs used; unused organs would deteriorate. He thought that the characteristics acquired by use and disuse would be passed on to later generations, but the inheritance of acquired characteristics was later disproved. Central to both these explanations was the concept of adaptation, or the possession by organisms of characteristics that suit them to their environments or to their ways of life. In eighteenth century England, the Reverend William Paley and his numerous scientific supporters believed that such adaptations could be explained only by the action of an omnipotent, benevolent God. In criticizing Lamarck, the supporters of Paley pointed out that birds migrated toward warmer climates before winter set in and that the heart of the human fetus had features that anticipated the changes of function that take place at birth. No amount of use and disuse could explain these cases of anticipation, they claimed; only an omniscient God who could foretell future events could have designed things with their future utility in mind.

The nineteenth century witnessed a number of books asserting that living species had evolved from earlier ones. Before 1859, these works were often more geological than biological in content. Most successful among them was the anonymously published *Vestiges of the Natural History of Creation* (1844), written by Robert Chambers. Books of this genre sold well but contained many flaws. They proposed no mechanism to account for evolutionary change. They supported the outmoded concept of a scale of being, often as a single sequence of evolutionary "progress." In geology, they supported the outmoded theory of catastrophism, an idea that the history of the earth had been characterized by great cataclysmic upheavals. From 1830 on, however, that theory was being replaced by the modern theory of uniformitarianism, championed by Charles Lyell. Charles Darwin read these books and knew their faults, especially their lack of a mechanism that was compatible with Lyell's geology. In his own work, Darwin carefully tried to avoid the shortcomings of these books.

Darwin brought about the greatest revolution in biological thought by proposing both a theory of branching evolution and a mechanism of natural selection to explain how it occurred. Much of Darwin's evidence was gathered during his voyage around the world aboard HMS *Beagle*. Darwin's stop in the Galápagos Islands and his study of tortoises and finchlike birds on these islands is usually credited with convincing him that evolution was a branching process and that adaptation to local environments was an essential part of the evolutionary process. Adaptation, he later concluded, came about through natural selection, a process that killed the maladapted variations and allowed only the well-adapted ones to survive and pass on their hereditary traits. After returning to England from his voyage, Darwin raised pigeons, consulted with various animal breeders about changes in domestic breeds, and investigated other phenomena that later enabled him to demonstrate natural selection and its power to produce evolutionary change.

Darwin's greatest contribution was that he proposed a suitable mechanism by which permanent organic change could take place. All living species, he said, were quite variable, and much of this variation was heritable. Also, most organisms produce far more eggs, sperm, seeds, or offspring than can possibly survive, and the vast majority of them die. In this process, some variations face certain death while others survive in greater or lesser proportion. Darwin called the result of this process "natural selection," the capacity of some hereditary variations (now called genotypes) to leave more viable offspring than others, with many leaving none at all. Darwin used this theory of natural selection to explain the form of branching evolution that has become generally accepted among scientists.

Darwin delayed the publication of his book for seventeen years after he wrote his first manuscript version. He might have waited even longer, except that his hand was forced. From the East Indies, another British scientist, Alfred Russell Wallace, had written out a description of the very same theory and submitted it to Darwin for his

THE GRAHAM LIBRARY
TBC - ELLENDALE, N. D. 58436

94344

comments. Darwin showed Wallace's letter to Lyell, who urged that both Darwin's and Wallace's contributions be published, along with documented evidence showing that both had arrived at the same ideas independently. Darwin's great book, *On the Origin of Species by Means of Natural Selection*, was published in 1859, and it quickly won most of the scientific community to a support of the concept of branching evolution. In his later years, Darwin also published *The Descent of Man and Selection in Relation to Sex* (1871), in which he outlined his theory of sexual selection. According to this theory, the agent that determines the composition of the next generation may often be the opposite sex. An organism may be well adapted to live, but unless it can mate and leave offspring, it will not contribute to the next or to future generations.

In the early 1900's, the rise of Mendelian genetics (named for botanist Gregor Mendel) initially resulted in challenges to Darwinism. Hugo de Vries proposed that evolution occurred by random mutations, which were not necessarily adaptive. This idea was subsequently rejected, and Mendelian genetics was reconciled with Darwinism during the period from 1930 to 1942. According to this modern synthetic theory of evolution, mutations initially occur at random, but natural selection eliminates most of them and alters the proportions among those that survive. Over many generations, the accumulation of heritable traits produces the kind of adaptive change that Darwin and others had described. The process of branching evolution through speciation is also an important part of the modern synthesis.

The branching of the evolutionary tree has resulted in the proliferation of species from the common ancestor of each group, a process called adaptive radiation. Ultimately, all species are believed to have descended from a single common ancestor. Because of the branching nature of the evolutionary process, no one evolutionary sequence can be singled out as representing any overall trend; rather, there have been different trends in different groups. Evolution is also an opportunistic process, in the sense that it follows the path of least resistance in each case. Instead of moving in straight lines toward a predetermined goal, evolving lineages often trace meandering or circuitous paths in which each change represents a momentary increase in adaptation. Species that cannot adapt to changing conditions die out and become extinct.

Methods of Study

Evolution is studied by a variety of methods. The ongoing process of evolution is studied in the field by ecologists, who examine various adaptations, including behavior and physiology as well as anatomy. These adaptations are also studied by botanists, who examine plants; zoologists, who examine animals; and various specialists, who work on particular kinds of animals or plants (for example, entomologists, who study insects). Some investigators capture specimens in the field, then bring back samples to the laboratory in order to examine chromosomes or analyze proteins using electrophoresis. Through these methods, scientists learn how the ongoing process of evolutionary change is working today within species or at the species level on time scales of only one or a few generations.

The long-term results of evolutionary processes are studied among living species by comparative anatomists and embryologists. Extinct organisms are studied by paleontologists, scientists who examine fossils. Biogeographers study past and present geographic distributions. All these types of scientists make comparisons among species in order to determine the sequence of events that took place in the evolutionary past. One method of reconstructing the branching sequences of evolution is to find homologies, deep-seated resemblances that reflect common ancestry. Once the sequences are established, functional analysis can be used to suggest possible adaptive reasons for any changes that took place. The sequences of evolutionary events reconstructed by these scientists represent the history of life on the earth. This history spans many species, families, and whole orders and classes, and it covers great intervals of past geologic time, measured in many millions of years.

Context

The historical development of evolutionary theory should be viewed in two contexts: that of biological science and that of cultural history. The concept of evolution had been talked about for many years before 1859 and was usually rejected because no suitable mechanism had gained widespread acceptance. The fact that the phenomenon of natural selection was independently discovered by two Englishmen shows both that the time was ripe for the discovery and that the circumstances were right in late nineteenth century England.

Evolutionary biology is itself the context into which all the other biological sciences fit. Other biologists, including physiologists and molecular biologists, study how certain processes work, but it is evolutionists who study the reasons why these processes came to work in one way and not another. Organisms and their cells are built one way and not another because their structures have evolved in a particular direction and can only be explained as the result of an evolutionary process. Not only does each biological system need to function properly, but it also must have been able to achieve its present method of functioning as the result of a long, historical, evolutionary process in which a previous method of functioning changed into the present one. If there were two or more ways of accomplishing the same result, a particular species used one of them because its ancestors were more easily capable of evolving this one method than another.

Everything in biology is thus a detail in the ongoing history of life on the earth, because every living system evolves. Living organisms and the processes that make them function are all products of the evolutionary process and can be understood only in that context. As biologist Theodosius Dobzhansky once said, "Nothing in biology makes sense, except in the light of evolution."

Bibliography

Darwin, Charles R. *On the Origin of Species by Means of Natural Selection: Or, the Preservation of the Favoured Races in the Struggle for Life.* London: John Murray, 1859. This is the original edition, still worth reading. It is better than the more widely reprinted sixth edition, in which Darwin's more forceful statements were toned down as a response to criticism that is no longer greatly valued by biologists. Some knowledge of zoology, geology, and geography would definitely increase any reader's understanding and appreciation of this book. Darwin provided no bibliography, but some modern editors have supplied one.

Dobzhansky, Theodosius G. *Genetics of the Evolutionary Process.* New York: Columbia University Press, 1970. Although somewhat technical in places, this book is extremely well written, and a careful reader should be able to understand it all without any formal background. It is an excellent (and very detailed) outline of the evolutionary process in terms of genetic changes. It contains much information about the genus *Drosophila* (fruit flies), on which Dobzhansky was an expert. Its bibliography is very comprehensive.

Gould, Stephen J. *Ever Since Darwin.* New York: W. W. Norton, 1977.

——————. *The Panda's Thumb.* New York: W. W. Norton, 1980.

——————. *The Flamingo's Smile.* New York: W. W. Norton, 1985. These three books all consist of essays reprinted (and occasionally updated) from *Natural History* magazine. All are well written and directed to a general audience; no previous background is assumed. Although Gould has occasionally supported unorthodox viewpoints, most of the views represented here have become accepted into the mainstream with the passage of time. Gould's easy, familiar style makes for lively reading and he uses esoteric cases and seemingly inconsequential details to make important points about evolution in general. The bibliographies are wide-ranging but are confined to the topics of the individual essays.

Minkoff, Eli C. *Evolutionary Biology.* Reading, Mass.: Addison-Wesley, 1983. A comprehensive general textbook on evolutionary biology, including its historical aspects. The history of evolutionary theories and the mechanisms of the evolutionary process are described in detail. Many examples are given, and the book is profusely illustrated; it assumes no prior knowledge. Contains an excellent bibliography, arranged by topic.

Simpson, George G. *The Meaning of Evolution.* Rev. ed. New Haven, Conn.: Yale University Press, 1967. Covers only the large-scale aspects of evolution as seen through the fossil record, omitting the details of the genetic mechanisms covered in Dobzhansky's book. The few illustrations are used well. Many important evolutionary concepts are explained, making this a good introduction to the subject. Readable and intended for a general audience.

Williams, George C. *Adaptation and Natural Selection: A Critique of Some Current Evolutionary Thought.* Princeton, N.J.: Princeton University Press, 1966. As its title implies, this book is a critical essay of evolutionary thought, with emphasis on adaptation, natural selection, and the relationship between them. It aims at a college-level readership. The book has an adequate bibliography but few illustrations.

Eli C. Minkoff

Cross-References

Adaptive Radiation, 29; Clines, Hybrid Zones, and Introgression, 498; Development: An Evolutionary Perspective, 615; DNA Hybridization Analysis of Relatedness, 686; Convergent and Divergent Evolution, 910; Cultural Evolution, 918; Punctuated Equilibrium versus Continuous Evolution, 926; Extinction, 953; Gene Flow, 1097; Gene Mutation and Repair, 1103; The Hardy-Weinberg Law of Genetic Equilibrium, 1262; Isolating Mechanisms in Evolution, 1493; Isozyme Analysis by Electrophoresis, 1500; The Origin of Life, 1572; Natural Selection, 1870; Neoteny and Other Heterochronic Effects, 1885; Speciation and the Species Concept, 2521; Systematics, 2594.

CONVERGENT AND DIVERGENT EVOLUTION

Type of life science: Evolutionary biology
Other fields of study: Botany, ecology, invertebrate biology, and zoology

The phenomena of convergent and divergent evolution have produced a number of good examples of natural selection at work. Thus, they provide results which can be studied in detail of environment/species interactions which solidly validate aspects of basic evolutionary theory. Examples abound in the earth's fossil record as well as in a number of living plant and animal species.

Principal terms

ADAPTIVE RADIATION: the successful invasion by a species into a number of ecological niches previously unavailable to it; the different niches' selective pressures eventually result in a number of new, morphologically distinct species

ANALOGUE: an individual structure shared by two or more species that is of only superficial similarity; thus, it is not indicative of a common ancestor

CLADE: a type of grouping of living or extinct species along lines of shared, unique structures, or homologues, indicative of a common ancestor; helpful in establishing evolutionary relationships

CONVERGENCE: the evolution of a similar morphology by unrelated or only distantly related species caused by both having adapted to similar life-styles in similar environments

DIVERGENCE: the evolution of increasing morphological differences between an ancestral species and offshoot species caused by differing adaptive pressures

ENVIRONMENTAL CONSTRAINTS (PRESSURES): the physical demands placed upon any species by its surroudings that ultimately determine the success or failure of its adaptations and consequently its success as a species

HOMOLOGUE: an individual structure shared by two or more different species that is indicative of a common ancestor

MONOPHYLETIC: a group of species that is believed to have a common ancestor; thus, the species are all members of a clade

POLYPHYLETIC: a group of species believed not to have a common ancestor; thus, they are not members of a clade but are probably a product of convergent evolution

SPECIES: a population of similar individuals, possessing a similar set of biological characteristics, that are capable of interbreeding and producing fertile offspring

Summary of the Phenomenon

Biological species have been defined as populations of organisms that are capable of successfully interbreeding (producing fertile offspring) only with other members of the same species. Members of any species possess unique sets of biological characteristics, termed "characters." These characters are physical expressions of a genetic code unique to members of that species. The code represents an extremely complex and thorough set of instructions for equipping an individual organism with the body and the behavioral knowledge it requires for success in the particular environment to which its species has adapted.

Thus, because of natural selection acting upon many past generations of that species, living members are fine-tuned to a specific ecological niche, or econiche, of the greater ecosystem of which the species is a member. When conditions within the ecosystem change (a general climatic change, for example) or when other scenarios occur, such as when a smaller subpopulation of the species migrates into new, ecologically different territory or becomes isolated in some way, selective pressure is brought to bear upon members of the group or subgroup. Random mutation is a mechanism by which selective pressure is thought to be brought about. Such mutations are changes in the genetic code that occur spontaneously in some individuals within the species in an ongoing manner. Most random mutations are insignificant phenomena with regard to the species as a whole, because most have either a neutral or negative survival value: Either they do not help the individual possessing them to survive or they are counteradaptive to an extreme degree and prove fatal. Consequently, mutations in general are not usually transmitted beyond the generation in which they occur or beyond the affected member or members. In certain scenarios, however, mutations that have a positive survival value can spread throughout the population. This is believed to be especially true when a smaller, isolated subgroup of the population is dealing with a changed or new environmental situation. Such processes are thought, for example, to have been instrumental in the evolution of groups of closely related but now morphologically distinct species found in isolated, midocean island groups. These adaptive radiations of species that are monophyletic and thus share a relatively recent common ancestor are good examples of the process of evolutionary divergence at work.

In one of the best-known cases, studies have traced the presumed paths of divergence among a set of island bird species. This particular radiation produced a number of new species possessing novel adaptive morphologies evolved to exploit new econiches. This is the classic example of Darwin's finches. Darwin's finches are a group of closely related birds, numbering about fourteen species, found on the various islands of the Galápagos Archipelago, which straddles the equator. The islands are remote from any large body of land that would typically harbor similar birds: South America lies about 960 kilometers to the east across an unbroken stretch of the Pacific Ocean. In 1835, Charles Darwin, author of the highly influential work on organic evolution, *On the Origin of Species* (1859), visited the islands while employed as a naturalist on a British scientific voyage. His studies of the flora and fauna of these islands provided him with many observations that directly influenced his later writings.

Darwin's studies of the Galápagos finches convinced him, and generations of subsequent scientists, that the finches are a clear example of divergent evolution in operation. The scenario he deduced is that probably only one ancestral species arrived from South America by ocean currents or winds, established itself, and began to exploit the numerous, as yet unoccupied, econiches that the volcanic islands provided. In the relative ecological vacuum that the original finch species found among the islands, adaptive radiation occurred, resulting in the present, diverse species. The species of Darwin's finches found today on the islands exhibit a great variety of beak types, many of which are atypical of finch-type birds in general but rather are typical of birds found among totally different avian family classifications. Typical finches are noted for beaks adapted for the crushing of seeds—the diet of the usual members of the finch family, such as the familiar North American cardinal. Among the dozen or so Galápagos finches can be found a wide assortment of beaks adapted for obtaining or processing a much greater variety of diets. Darwin's finches include species with beaks and behaviors adapted for diets of insects, seeds, cacti, and other vegetal matter. The adaptive radiation in the case of the Galápagos finches was relatively easy to work out because of the obvious environmental factors involved (the islands' remoteness and general barrenness) and the unusual variety of adaptations that the finches had made. Establishing the details of evolutionary divergence in other living ecosystems can be confusing because the numbers and types of econiches and interacting species are often far more numerous and diverse—for example, the lush and intricate ecosystem of a large, tropical rain forest such as the Amazon.

Myriad examples of evolutionary divergence exist between both living plant and animal species throughout existing ecosystems in the modern world. The fossil record, however, also can be studied, to examine the phenomenon between extinct plant and animal groups. This record of past life-forms preserved in the crustal rocks of the earth provides numerous examples of diverging species as organisms adapted to changing general conditions or spread into novel environments. An example is the many species of ceratopsian dinosaurs found in the latter part of the Cretaceous period of the Mesozoic era of the earth's history. Although the earlier ancestral forms appear to be bipedal and possess no significant armor, the later radiation of ceratopsians is well known by way of such impressive animals as *Triceratops*, a typical ceratopsian: a heavy, quadrapedal herbivore with a large, horned and beaked skull with a defensive, bony frill. Many variations on the basic late ceratopsian body architecture evolved through divergence. Varieties included such forms as *Pentaceratops*, *Torosaurus*, *Styracosaurus*, *Chasmosaurus*, and *Centrosaurus*, among many others. In all these later animals, the basic morphology regarding body, tail, and limbs remained the same. All forms also retained the typical massive, beaked head. What diverged were such morphological features as number and length of facial horns and length and degree of ornamentation of the frill. One of the important things that study of such fossil forms shows is that such past examples of evolutionary divergence eloquently underscore the continuity of the evolutionary process through time down to the present living world. This continuity further reinforces the validity of basic evolutionary theory in general.

A related phenomenon concerning adaptive evolution is the phenomenon of evolutionary convergence. This process can be described briefly as the evolution of similar body structures in two or more species that are only quite distantly related; they therefore come to resemble each other, sometimes to a startling degree of at least outward sameness. These sets of similar-looking but polyphyletic species frequently even display similar behavioral characteristics. All similarities found in convergence cases are believed to be attributable to the fact that the various species involved have adapted to a similar econiche within a similar ecosystem. Because in nature, form follows function and the morphology of an animal or plant is the product of environmental pressures that continuously favor the better-adapted organism, it is easy to understand how convergence can take place. Like divergence, the evidence for convergence can be traced not only among the many participants in contemporary biospace but also over the course of vast stretches of past time.

One of the classic examples of convergence is a threefold example that, conveniently, not only includes representatives from three different classes of vertebrates but also spans many millions of years of time and includes an extinct group. This is the textbook example that compares and contrasts the morphology of sharks, a type of cartilaginous fish; ichthyosaurs, an extinct type of marine reptile; and dolphins, marine mammals like whales. All three groups possess numerous member species, both fossil and alive (except for ichthyosaurs), which resemble each other in body plan and life-style. All three groups include species which lead (or led) an open ocean, fish-eating existence. Consequently, the forms of their bodies came to follow the functions dictated by their environment—sometimes termed their environmental constraints. All three groups' general body plan began to approach a hydrodynamic ideal for a water-living animal: a streamlined fusiform, or spindle shape, efficient in passing through an aqueous medium. Besides this feature, pelagic, or open ocean-living, sharks, ichthyosaurs, and dolphins all evolved a dorsal fin to act as a vertical stabilizer for water travel. In addition, each group evolved a propulsive tail and a pectoral fin necessary for the demands of constant swimming and steering in water. Even more remarkable in this comprehensive example, dolphins' and ichthyosaurs' ancestors were both originally land-dwelling vertebrates that returned to the marine environment. This case presents an inclusive and persuasive argument for the reality of the phenomenon of convergent evolution.

As with the use of both living and extinct examples in the discussion of divergent evolution, the existence of fossil as well as contemporary species that display convergent morphology is convincing evidence for the process of adaptive evolution. Again, a continuity across vast stretches of time exists that connects evolutionary phenomena in a continuum.

Methods of Study

Research in the field of adaptive evolution, especially the phenomena of divergence and convergence of species, began centuries ago with the simple process of recognizing relationships in the surrounding environment between living plants and animals. The search for a unifying order to tie the complex web of animal and plant life together in some meaningful manner was for a long time a part of natural science. The modern theory of organic evolution fulfills this goal admirably in many respects. The methods used to illuminate the intricacies of evolution still encompass the type of keen, analytical observation of phenomena and reflection on their causes and effects that characterized Darwin's studies on the voyage of HMS *Beagle*. Observation, collection of specimens for comparison, classification of specimens according to a meaningful scheme, and, finally, an attempt to sort out the processes involved in a way that agrees with the dictates of strict logic, are hallmarks of the scientific method at work.

Researchers investigating evolutionary divergence and convergence have powerful aids in the form of increasingly sophisticated technology. The main focus of their work is the correct interpretation of the path that various lineages took over time to arrive at known, living forms or extinct forms. In the case of living forms, technology originally developed in the field of medicine has been pressed into service to help establish relationships. For example, detailed analyses of various body tissues and fluids have been employed. Blood types have been traced with varying degrees of success, as have various proteins. Powerful optical microscopes are employed to analyze various tissue types and their structures. Since the invention of scanning electron microscopes, these more powerful instruments have further aided in probing the compositions and textures of animal and plant tissues to determine affinities among various species. In addition to these methods, very sophisticated laboratory techniques are now used to unravel and analyze deoxyribonucleic acid (DNA) strands and to try to determine the actual genetic encoding possessed by a particular organism. All these methods help establish more clearly the picture of biological relationships in regard to ancestries.

This physiological approach is obviously of limited utility with regard to fossil species. Except for such instances as the various ice age animals that were frozen in such environments as the tundra, extinct life-forms cannot be analyzed by medical means, as the original tissue has been transformed or destroyed by geological processes. In the case of most fossil forms, hard body parts such as bones and teeth (for vertebrates) and exoskeletons (in the case of invertebrates) must be analyzed in a more structural way to determine possible evolutionary relationships.

Context

The clarification of the paths that various animal and plant lineages took during the process of their evolution further confirms the validity of basic organic evolutionary theory such as natural selection and adaptation. Study of divergent and convergent species is part of the ongoing study of living organisms that make up the functional ecosystems of which humankind is also a part. Learning more about these ecosystems and the parts that all the member species play within them is extremely important to humanity in the light of the contemporary world picture of pollution, overpopulation, and industrialization. The past and present disruption and destruction of many local ecosystems by human activity has had extremely negative and often unforeseen effects for humans as well as other species. To avert this trend and to prevent the even more disastrous effects that the collapse of major global ecosystems would have should become a goal of all responsible humans in both the scientific and nonscientific communities. The increased insight into how ecosystems operate from the species interaction approach is one of the positive byproducts that studies of divergent and convergent evolution among species provide.

Bibliography

Carroll, Robert L. *Vertebrate Paleontology and Evolution*. New York: W. H. Freeman, 1988. A thorough treatment of the complex subject of vertebrate evolution. Each vertebrate order is covered by an entire chapter. Each chapter, profusely illustrated with excellent anatomical drawings, discusses at length each order's biological characteristics, adaptations, and occurrence in the fossil record. There are also a number of other chapters that clearly explain evolutionary concepts in an understandable way. Convergence and divergence are treated within the greater context of biological evolutionary phenomena.

Cvancara, Alan M. *Sleuthing Fossils: The Art of Investigating Past Life*. New York: John Wiley & Sons, 1989. Intended as a portable reference book aimed primarily at amateur fossil collectors and nonprofessional enthusiasts, this "how to" book also is designed as an authoritative introduction to the subject of the total fossil record of the earth and its implications for the subject of organic evolution. The author, a geology professor, succeeds in clearly explaining many of the intricacies of the topic, including divergence and convergence (explained in chapter 2). Good black-and-white photographs enhance the text, along with some graphs and drawings. Little science background is assumed, except for a very basic high school level. Nevertheless, even scientifically sophisticated adults should find this book enjoyable and informative.

Eaton, Theodore H., Jr. *Evolution*. New York: W. W. Norton, 1970. An extremely thorough work on the subject, intended as a college-level textbook. Great emphasis is placed on the role that genetics and population dynamics play in the phenomenon of organic evolution. Chapters on behavior and adaptation and geographical distribution help clarify how all the complicated factors involved in speciation interact with one another. Illustrations are not as integral a part of the text as with some other books but are well chosen.

McLoughlin, John C. *The Tree of Animal Life*. New York: Dodd, Mead, 1981. In less than 160 pages, the author makes a good summary of the evolution of animal life. Beginning with single-celled organisms and progressing upward through the various stages of complexity until the higher vertebrates are discussed, McLoughlin condenses billions of years of evolution in a way that can be easily followed by readers with the most minimal scientific background. The author is also an accomplished natural science illustrator, and many effective line drawings enhance and expand upon the meaning of the text. In the process of explaining various adaptive radiations and selective pressures, evolutionary divergence and convergence are touched upon effectively. Recommended for all readers with an interest in the general subject.

Orians, Gordon H., and Otto T. Solbrig, eds. *Convergent Evolution in Warm Deserts*. Stroudsburg, Pa.: Dowden, Hutchinson & Ross, 1977. A series of summaries of a large-scale, comparative study undertaken by more than twenty different scientists from both South and North America. The study aimed at determining the degree of actual convergence attained by the flora and fauna in two geographically remote deserts: the Sonoran in the American Southwest and the Monte in Argentina. The deserts analyzed were chosen because of their similar topographies, soils, and climatic conditions. Photographs, drawings, diagrams, and charts help make this book an exceptionally useful reference on the subject.

Paul, Gregory S. *Predatory Dinosaurs of the World*. New York: Simon & Schuster, 1988. A meticulously thorough book that covers almost every conceivable aspect of theropod, or flesh-eating, dinosaurs. The surmised ecology, anatomy, ancestry, and life-styles of all known groups are covered. Related topics such as the theorized evolution of the groups discussed are also dealt with substantially but in a clear and unconfusing manner. Enhanced by a large number of beautifully rendered drawings, also done by the author. The subject of evolutionary convergence and divergence among the theropods is adroitly explained, primarily in chapter 8.

Rhodes, Frank H. T. *Evolution: A Golden Guide*. New York: Golden Press, 1974. Part of a series of paperback guidebooks to the natural sciences which, although heavily illustrated, are well written, organized, authoritative, and extremely informative sources for the general reader. The book holds the reader's attention from beginning to end with colorful original artwork and photographs designed to mesh effectively with the succinct but information-packed text. The basic elements of modern evolutionary theory, including convergence and divergence, are presented with appropriate examples from the living world and the fossil record. A portable and understandable guide to the subject.

Savage, R. J. G. *Mammal Evolution: An Illustrated Guide*. New York: Facts on File, 1986. Presents mammalian evolution in a colorful, highly illustrative manner, with frequent use of lifelike reconstructions of extinct forms going about their hypothesized daily lives. Skeletal and dental diagrams are also frequently used to explain the evolutionary adaptations and innovations of various groups. The authoritative text succeeds in clarifying the various concepts and points of evolutionary theory covered, among which are convergence and divergence. A clearly written reference work for scientifically inclined high school and college students.

Wills, Christopher. *The Wisdom of the Genes: New Pathways in Evolution*. New

York: Basic Books, 1989. Informs the reader of the thinking and findings concerning the evolutionary process from the perspective of genetics. Divergence and convergence are treated as phenomena within the broad context of patterns of biological inheritance. A well-written book that clearly elucidates the concepts and examples presented. Concludes with a glossary. A good introduction to the subject, it assumes some basic biological knowledge.

Frederick M. Surowiec

Cross-References

Adaptations and Their Mechanisms, 22; Adaptive Radiation, 29; The Biosphere, Biomes, and Habitats, 210; Birds, 217; Competition, 541; Ecological Niches, 729; Ecological Principles, 736; Evolution: A Historical Perspective, 903; Extinction, 953; Lower Invertebrate Animals, 1483; Isolating Mechanisms in Evolution, 1493; Mammals, 1662; Natural Selection, 1870; Predation, 2178; Reptiles, 2361; Speciation and the Species Concept, 2521.

CULTURAL EVOLUTION

Types of life science: Anthropology and evolutionary biology
Other field of study: Ethology

Cultural evolution describes the changes apparent both in individual human soci-eties and in human culture as a whole. Both philosophically and scientifically, it raises basic questions about humanity and about the nature, origin, and future of culture.

Principal terms
CULTURE: the institutions, ideas, arts, manners, morals, and emotional habits of a given group of people at a given period
DIALECTIC: the logical examination of opinions, beliefs, or ideas in order to determine their validity
EMPIRICISM: the belief that experience—and in science, experimentation and observation—is the source of knowledge
GENETIC CODE: the biological means of transmitting physical traits from parent to offspring through the deoxyribonucleic acid (DNA) molecules in the nucleus of cells
ORTHOGENESIS: the theory that every culture undergoes the same evolutionary development despite the variations in environments among cultures
PROGRESS: the assumption of advancement toward a higher or better state, usually with the further assumption that ideal conditions can be obtained through reason and will
RATIONALISM: the practice of regarding reason as the only authority in determining a course of action or testing the acceptability of an idea or custom
SOCIOBIOLOGY: the empirical search for biological mechanisms that activate social behavior

Summary of the Phenomenon
Cultural evolution comprises a series of related theories intended to explain change and diversity in human society. The theories fall into two basic categories: those that proceed from an assumption of progress and those that attempt to de-scribe change empirically. Controversy has surrounded both the methods and pur-poses of the theories, so that social scientists and biological evolutionists remain di-vided about their validity.

Although the idea that the human race has progressed from simple to complex societies occurred no later than Aristotle's time, the modern idea of cultural evolu-tion began in the eighteenth century. The focus was philosophical and concerned the mind, so that culture was equated with the capacities and methods of thought. Rationalist philosophers such as Immanuel Kant, David Hume, and G. W. F. Hegel posited that culture evolved from simple, primitive forms in earlier ages, during which people reacted to phenomena rather than thought about them and so lived with little or no use of reason. Modern civilization was to these philosophers the product of reason, and, as the methods of reasoning developed, the mind and culture could improve. Thus, these rationalist theories depended upon a belief in progress, that the species somehow improves, and in continuity, that evolution is uninterrupted. Although philosophers increasingly drew evidence from comparisons of cultures and from biology and geology to support their arguments, progress and continuity provided the springboards for their speculations.

Nineteenth century thinkers also proceeded from assumptions of progress and continuity but more eagerly sought empirical evidence for their ideas. Unlike their forebears, whose concern was almost exclusively European culture, they studied societies throughout the world. This era saw the growth of anthropology and sociology as disciplines separate from philosophy and more particularly concerned with describing the structures of both modern and ancient societies and with comparing the elements of differing societies.

Classification of societies dominated the research, and these classifications led to proposals of evolutionary sequences. Based upon descriptions of societies that had been described in literature and through field research, anthropologists in Great Britain and the United States delineated "stages," or "ethnical periods," through which societies evolve after having dispersed from a single origin. The names attached to the stages varied somewhat, but they were generally thought to progress from a nomadic hunter-gatherer society (savagery), to agrarianism (barbarism), and then to industrial manufacture (modern civilization). This scheme was thought to be universal, and a society could only achieve the stages in sequence.

Such theories treated culture as a grand concept to be studied as a whole and evolution as orthogenic, but other investigators concentrated on single societies in order to make detailed analyses. These sociological philosophers, among them Herbert Spencer in England and Émile Durkheim in France, believed societies to be self-contained units made up of mutually dependent parts, including individual people, groups, and institutions. A society was thought to grow like an organism: Just as organisms evolve when groups of cells specialize to perform discrete functions such as blood circulation and elimination of wastes, so were societies thought to evolve as people banded together to specialize in such functions as farming, manufacture, or government. They therefore defined evolution as the tendency toward greater diversity, specialization, and productivity.

Although both the anthropological and sociological theories developed largely independent of studies in biology, the publication of Charles Darwin's *On the Origin of Species* (1859) provided an analogy that seemed to confirm the concept of cultural evolution. That is, evolution appeared to be a fundamental natural movement from simplicity in organization to complexity and from unity to diversity. Cultural evolution proponents found Darwin's "great tree" metaphor especially useful. The trunk, branches, and twigs of a tree, Darwin said, are like the families, genera, and species of living things, and so societies also appeared to be the ramifications of developments from a single, primordial culture.

While the study of culture became more inductive and particular, philosophers continued to produce macrotheories about evolution. Karl Marx and Friedrich Engels systematized the economic and political forces motivating all cultural change and used their system to predict that the capitalism then prevalent in Europe would give way to an evolutionary advance in the form of communism.

Social theorists in the early twentieth century rejected the sweeping evolutionary systems and sharply criticized their predecessors for reductive argumentation and biased conclusions. A handful of academics, however, tried to release cultural evolution theory from such previous assumptions as progress and continuity and to develop it into a strictly empirical theory. They conceived of their task as the attempt to describe how societies adapt to their environments; how specific cultural traits could be transmitted from one society to another; and how accidents (for example, natural catastrophes), scientific discoveries, and unconscious processes can influence development. Thereby, they could avoid the drawbacks of orthogenesis and its assumption of uniform, irreversible change, and instead accommodate a greater variety of data, which suggested that some societies reach stable plateaus of development while others become more complex in fits and starts. Furthermore, these scientists distinguished between specific or adaptive evolution, the means by which any society adjusts to its environment, and general evolution, which is the progress of human culture as a whole.

All theories up to the mid-twentieth century presumed that greater sophistication and diversity in culture occurs only after the human mind has evolved, but in the second half of that century scientists challenged that assumption. In 1971, anthropologist Clifford Geertz insisted that the mind is not distinct from culture in a way that would mean the former could precede the latter; instead, culture is an ingredient in the development of the mind. In the mid-1970's, some scientists proposed that geneticists and biologists should collaborate to examine the relation of heredity to cultural change. Although they denied that they sought to identify "superior" hereditary types, critics denounced these sociobiologists as deterministic and potentially racist, repudiating the idea that genes can in any way transmit or shape cultural features. Nevertheless, gene-culture studies continue, and Charles J. Lumsden, Edward O. Wilson, and others seek to prove that genes and culture coevolve in that certain genes will be passed on if their bearers practice certain cultural features in preference to others.

According to Lumsden and Wilson, the genetic code creates the properties and structures of the human brain that constitute the mind and limit the ways in which the mind can develop. Certain of these genetically determined "epigenetic rules" lead individuals to make cultural choices that improve their chances of survival and thereby increase the likelihood that they will produce children with a similar genetic makeup. From generation to generation, the genes prescribing successful epigenetic rules will proliferate as individuals are nurtured by the cultural practices for which their genes suit them. Similarly, if cultural practices suddenly change for some reason, those genetic traits will predominate that can adapt to the change best.

Lumsden and Wilson advanced gene-culture coevolution as a hypothesis to be explored and tested, a possibly fruitful new approach to the centuries-old questions about how change occurs and how human societies began, yet many scientists have interpreted their arguments to mean strictly that genes cause cultural traits, and since no such gene or group of genes has yet been identified, they treat gene-culture coevolution cautiously at best.

Methods of Study

Cultural evolution theories have shifted from their beginning emphasis upon deductive logic founded on ideological theories of progress to the more recent empirical descriptions of increasingly specific and varied physical data. The philosophers who took up the question of societal change in the eighteenth century relied on logic, illustrated with historical examples, to substantiate their theories. Hegel, for example, argued that the history of culture entailed a series of conflicts and resolutions as the natural progression toward an ideal society. His dialectic involved a received societal condition, or thesis, against which an opposing condition, or antithesis, develops; the resulting conflict resolves when a new synthesis of cultural elements is achieved. Similarly, Marx and Engels based their development theory of culture on analyses of societal and economic organization; they argued that class struggle leads to new arrangements of wealth and power. Such methods of analysis and prediction described the revolutionary upheavals of politics and ideologies but did little to explain specific cultural traits.

The desire to account for the differences between cultures, as for example between American Indian and European cultures, inspired investigations based upon phenomena rather than abstract dialectic. Accordingly, languages, social customs, religious practices, literature, crafts, and familial structures, in addition to economic and political institutions, became the foci of study. The tools of analysis were not entirely scientific, however, and researchers often compared the societies they studied to Western culture to evaluate them, so that conclusions were colored by preconceptions in order to conform with hierarchical "stage" theories or organismic models parallel to Darwinian evolution. Meanwhile, social philosophers examined epistemological questions—that is, how knowledge can be defined, how it is acquired, and how it is transmitted—in order to trace the progress of culture. The prevalent assumptions held that industrialized, mercantile European culture was the most advanced form and that other forms had been retarded in earlier stages of evolution.

The mid-twentieth century reexamination of cultural evolution sought universal ingredients of culture that would allow analyses of specific cultures without the bias of superiority that comes from using one cultural form as a measure or from hierarchical schemas. Leslie A. White, for example, found the fundamental element of human culture to be the ability to create and manipulate symbols in order to communicate facts and ideas. Similarly, Margaret Mead believed that cultural evolution could be hastened by conscious choices and the influence of exceptionally talented people; therefore, she studied the conditions that could produce clusters of such people, such as scientists dedicated to solving problems of major significance. Marshall D. Sahlins and Elman R. Service distinguished between specific evolution and general evolution in order to encourage particularized studies of cultural traits without either abandoning the idea that humanity evolves generally or allowing theories of overall evolution to distort research data with a priori criteria.

The wedding of genetic to sociological research has intensified the search for and incorporation of physical data to augment descriptions of culture features and comparative studies. L. L. Cavalli-Sforza has called for analyses of cultural evolution through discussions of specific traits, with the aid of mathematical models, to characterize the forces of mutation, selection, migration, and drift in cultural features, much as a geneticist looks for such forces in biological evolution of species. Lumsden and Wilson draw the connection between culture and genes even more closely; they examine the relation between the survival of genetic codes (manifested in inherited traits) and cultural features in order to isolate mutual influences. They draw from demographics, deoxyribonucleic acid (DNA) research, anthropology, sociology, and paleontology for evidence, applying mathematics to rationalize the data.

Context

At least as early as Plato in the *Republic* and Aristotle in the *Nichomachian Ethics* (both dated to the late fourth century B.C.), thinkers have sought ways to perfect societies, and their deliberations have thereby involved them in the nature and origins of society. Interest in ideal societies faded during the Middle Ages, when Christian doctrine taught that human society is a corruption of the paradise in Eden, but it bloomed again when Renaissance and Enlightenment philosophers reapplied Platonic and Aristotelian thought to ethics and politics. The belief that even if utopia is unattainable culture and society can be improved has never disappeared from the idea of cultural evolution and has sometimes surfaced in sinister forms.

The rationalists of the eighteenth century clearly assumed that humankind should attend to conditions on earth, not merely prepare for life after death as Christianity prescribed. They also assumed that reason alone was sufficient to promulgate principles by which people should live in harmony. Almost without exception, such thinkers reached the conclusion that the culture that approached perfection the most, or was most capable of perfection, was their own European culture. This chauvinism persisted through the nineteenth century and seemingly received support from Darwinian evolution.

Chauvinism and too free a use of the analogy between the evolution of organisms and that of culture had tragic results. The struggle among individuals in a species and between species for survival in an environment seemed convincingly to mirror the struggle among persons, classes, or societies to obtain wealth or power. Thus, the doctrine of Social Darwinism held that superior people naturally prosper, while inferiors live in poverty and ignorance. In the British and American societies of the the late nineteenth century especially, "the survival of the fittest" (Spencer's phrase, not Darwin's) meant that the economy of a nation ought to be free of government regulation, such as those that might aid the poor, protect workers from exploitation, or forbid monopolies. Governmental noninterference was a central tenet of laissez-faire capitalism, because it let struggle and progress, thought to be inevitable and beneficial, take their course. At the same time, the assumption that Western industrial culture was the "highest" appeared to justify to major powers such as Great Britain, France, and Germany the conquest and subjugation of weaker societies. It was considered the "white man's burden" to impress Western culture on non-Western nations.

The racist conclusion that the white race is superior and the social abuses of capitalism that were the by-products of Social Darwinism led anthropologists and sociologists in the early twentieth century to reject it and neglect evolution as a whole and avoid any use of such judgments as "primitive" and "superior." That Adolf Hitler made use of white supremacy arguments for his policies helped further repel scientists.

Nevertheless, cultural evolution revived as a respectable theory in the 1960's. Although social scientists shunned the appearance of making value judgments about cultures, some still thought that a detailed understanding of evolutionary processes would give policymakers the basis for rational, long-term programs to better society. Sahlins and Service conclude *Evolution and Culture* (1960) by urging Americans to abandon the containment policy for Communism, increase investment capital to undeveloped nations, and lift trade barriers in order to abolish the cause of strife, despotism, and militarism.

The taint of determinism and racism still adheres to cultural evolution studies. When Wilson first proposed that sociology and biology join forces to examine the relation between genes and cultural behavior, a vocal opposition sprang up at once, referring to the example of World War II Germany. Proponents of gene-culture coevolution have not succeeded completely in extricating themselves from the controversy.

Their explicit purpose is scientific analysis, yet, like the majority of thinkers before them, they cannot resist speculating about the practical application of gene-culture coevolution. Lumsden and Wilson's *Promethean Fire: Reflections on the Origin of Mind* (1983) ends with the argument that epigenetic rules shape human behavior regardless of knowledge about them but that knowledge at least will give humanity precise language with which to debate features of culture in order to agree on universal goals, ethical truths, and the essence of humanness. The assumption that universals exist and that rational debate about them can clarify the practice and purpose of culture seems little changed from eighteenth century rationalism.

Bibliography

Bowler, Peter J. *Evolution: The History of an Idea*. Berkeley: University of California Press, 1984. The primary focus of this history is on biological evolution, but the author takes up all associated ideas as they occurred, including cultural evolution. He relates theories of society to theories of organic growth. The exposition is both technical and clear, written from a historical rather than scientific viewpoint for a general college-educated audience accustomed to complex reasoning.

Geertz, Clifford. "The Growth of Culture and the Evolution of Mind." In *The Interpretation of Cultures*. New York: Basic Books, 1973. By a famous cultural anthropologist, this essay was one of the first attempts to link closely the evolution of the human mind to the evolution of culture. Specifically, he argues that cultural resources help foster mental development. Geertz writes entertainingly and provocatively, making the essay a challenging introduction to some of the basic concepts of late twentieth century evolutionary thought.

Ingold, Tim. *Evolution and Social Life*. Cambridge, England: Cambridge University Press, 1986. Ingold proposes a synthesis of ideas after examining the biological, historical, and anthropological arguments concerning the nature of the mind and culture. He focuses on the relation between culture and consciousness, tackling such enduring problems as how to define consciousness, how it is distinguished from animal consciousness, and the interplay between innate and acquired behavior. The book is nontechnical but deals with concepts that require familiarity with modern philosophy and biology.

Lopreato, Joseph. *Human Nature and Biocultural Evolution*. Boston: Allen & Unwin, 1984. A frank defense of biological and cultural coevolution, the book first summarizes the controversies that have troubled evolutionists since the first theories of progress were advanced. Lopreato makes biting, sometimes sarcastic attacks on those with whom he disagrees, and jargon will obscure his arguments for many readers, yet the book offers a valuable resource in methods of analyzing cultural evolution assumptions and formulations.

Lumsden, Charles J., and Edward O. Wilson. *Genes, Mind, and Culture: The Coevolutionary Process*. Cambridge, Mass.: Harvard University Press, 1981. Written by the scientists at the center of the sociobiology controversy, the book presents the basic premises and main lines of reasoning in favor of gene-culture coevolution. Although helpful graphs and illustrations are included, the argument relies on technical vocabulary and advanced mathematics.

_____. *Promethean Fire: Reflections on the Origin of Mind*. Cambridge, Mass.: Harvard University Press, 1983. This book is a nontechnical version of the previously mentioned volume and is intended for a general audience. Imaginatively, charmingly, the authors try to diffuse the accusations from some scientists that gene-cultural coevolution is a subtle disguise for biological determinism, but the book is still an entertaining survey of the theory.

Sahlins, Marshall D., and Elman R. Service, eds. *Evolution and Culture*. Ann

Arbor: University of Michigan Press, 1960. When it was released, this book marked an advance in the movement to make cultural evolution a respectable theory after years of unpopularity. The authors distinguish between "general evolution" and "specific or adaptive evolution" in order to avoid the appearance of championing the value-laden view that come cultures are superior to others. The book is readable, concise, and, in the last chapter, intensely earnest in arguing that evolution theory can guide rulers and policymakers to farsighted decisions.

White, Leslie A. *The Evolution of Culture: The Development of Civilization to the Fall of Rome*. New York: McGraw-Hill, 1959. White advanced the idea that the human manipulation of symbols gave rise to culture at a time when the whole idea of cultural evolution was in disrepute, so the book represents an attempt to resuscitate an idea and bring more conceptual rigor to it. The attempt won a modest victory, introducing valuable distinctions in types of dispersion and influence not considered before, even though the tone is imperious.

Roger Smith

Cross-References

Adaptations and Their Mechanisms, 22; Altruism, 73; Development: An Evolutionary Perspective, 615; Emotions, 765; Ethology, 858; Evolution: A Historical Perspective, 903; Hominids, 1321; *Homo sapiens* and the Diversification of Humans, 1329; Learning, 1548; Mammalian Social Systems, 1655; Memory, 1683; Natural Selection, 1870.

PUNCTUATED EQUILIBRIUM VERSUS CONTINUOUS EVOLUTION

Type of life science: Evolutionary biology
Other fields of study: Genetics and systematics (taxonomy)

According to classical evolutionary theory, new species arise by gradual transformation of ancestral ones. Speciation theory of the 1950's and 1960's, however, predicted that new species arise from small populations isolated from the main population, where they diverge rapidly. In 1972, Niles Eldredge and Stephen Jay Gould applied this concept to the fossil record, predicting that species should arise suddenly ("punctuated" by a speciation event) rather than gradually, and then persist virtually unchanged for millions of years in "equilibrium" before becoming extinct or speciating again.

Principal terms

ALLOPATRIC: refers to populations of organisms living in different places and separated by a barrier that prevents interbreeding

GRADUALISM: the idea that transformation from ancestor to descendant species is a slow, gradual process spanning millions of years

MACROEVOLUTION: large-scale evolutionary processes that result in major changes in organisms and allow them to change rapidly, occupy new adaptive niches, or develop novel body plans

MICROEVOLUTION: small-scale evolutionary processes resulting from gradual substitution of genes and resulting in very subtle changes in organisms

PUNCTUATED EQUILIBRIUM: the idea that new species form during relatively short (a few generations) speciation events and then persist for millions of years unchanged until they go extinct

SPECIATION: the process by which new species arise from old species, either by splitting off from their ancestor or by the transforming of the ancestor into the descendant

SPECIES SELECTION: the idea that species are independent entities with their own properties, such as birth (speciation) and death (extinction); a higher level of selection above that of natural selection is postulated to take place on the species level

STASIS: the long-term stability and lack of change in fossil species, often spanning millions of years of geologic time

SYMPATRIC: refers to populations of organisms living in the same place, not separated by a barrier that would prevent interbreeding

Summary of the Phenomenon

Although Charles Darwin's most influential work was entitled *On the Origin of Species* (1859), in fact it did not address the problem in the title. Darwin was concerned with showing that evolution had occurred and that species could change, but he did not deal with the problem of how new species formed. For nearly a century, no other biologists addressed this problem either. Darwin (and many of his successors) believed that species formed by gradual transformation of existing ancestral species, and this viewpoint ("gradualism") was deeply entrenched in the biology and paleontology books for a century. In this view, species are not real entities but merely arbitrary segments of continuously evolving lineages that are always in the process of change through time. Paleontologists tried to document examples of this kind of gradual evolution in fossils, but remarkably few examples were found.

By the 1950's and 1960's, however, systematists (led by Ernst Mayr) began to study species in the wild and therefore saw them in a different light. They noticed that most species do not gradually transform into new ones in the wild but instead have fairly sharp boundaries. These limits are established by their ability and willingness to interbreed with each other. Those individuals that can interbreed are members of the same species, and those that cannot are of different species. When a population is divided and separated so that formerly interbreeding individuals develop differences that prevent interbreeding, then a new species is formed. Mayr showed that, in nature, large populations of individuals living together "sympatric" conditions) interbreed freely, so that evolutionary novelties are swamped out and new species cannot arise. When a large population becomes split by some sort of barrier so that there are two different populations ("allopatric" conditions), however, the smaller populations become isolated from interbreeding with the main population. If these allopatric, isolated populations have some sort of unusual gene, their numbers may be small enough that this gene can spread through the whole population in a few generations, giving rise to a new species. Then, when the isolated population is reintroduced to the main population, it has developed a barrier to interbreeding, and a new species becomes established. This concept is known as the allopatric speciation model.

The allopatric speciation model was well known and accepted by most biologists by the 1960's. It predicted that species arise in a few generations from small populations on the fringe of the range of the species, not in the main body of the population. It also predicted that the new species, once it arises on the periphery, will appear suddenly in the main area as a new species in competition with its ancestor. These models of speciation also treated species as "real" entities, which recognize one another in nature and are stable over long periods of time once they become established. Yet, these ideas did not penetrate the thought of paleontologists for more than a decade after biologists had accepted them. In 1972, Niles Eldredge and Stephen J. Gould proposed that the allopatric speciation model would make very different predictions about species in the fossil record than the prevailing dogma that they must change gradually and continuously through time. In their paper, they described a model of "punctuated equilibrium." Species should arise suddenly in the fossil record ("punctuation"), followed by long periods of no change ("equilibrium," or "stasis") until they went extinct or speciated again. They challenged paleontologists to examine their biases about the fossil record and to see if in fact most fossils evolved gradually or rapidly, followed by long periods of stasis.

In the years since that paper, hundreds of studies have been done on many different groups of fossil organisms. Although some of the data were inadequate to test the hypotheses, many good studies have shown quite clearly that punctuated equilibrium describes the evolution of many multicellular organisms. The few exceptions are in the gradual evolution of size (which was specifically exempted by Eldredge and Gould) and in unicellular organisms, which have both sexual and asexual modes of reproduction. Many of the classic studies of gradualism in oysters, heart urchins, horses, and even humans have even been shown to support a model of stasis punctuated by rapid change. The model is still controversial, however, and there are still many who dispute both the model and the data that support it.

One of the more surprising implications of the model is that long periods of stasis are not predicted by classical evolutionary theory. In neo-Darwinian theory, species are highly flexible, capable of changing in response to environmental changes. Yet, the fossil record clearly shows that most species persist unchanged for millions of years, even when other evidence clearly shows climatic changes taking place. Instead of passively changing in response to the environment, most species stubbornly persist unchanged until they either go extinct, disappear locally, or change rapidly to some new species. They are not infinitely flexible, and no adequate mechanism has yet been proposed to explain the ability of species to maintain themselves in homeostasis in spite of environmental changes and apparent strong natural selection. Naturally, this idea intrigues paleontologists, since it suggests processes that can only be observed in the fossil record and were not predicted from studies of living organisms.

The punctuated equilibrium model has led to even more interesting ideas. If species are real, stable entities that form by speciation events and split into multiple lineages, then multiple species will be formed and compete with one another. Perhaps some species have properties (such as the ability to speciate rapidly, disperse widely, or survive extinction events) that give them advantages over other species. In this case, there might be competition and selection between species, which was called "species selection" by Steven Stanley in 1975. Some evolutionary biologists are convinced that species selection is a fundamentally different process from that of simple natural selection that operates on individuals. In species selection, the fundamental unit is the species; in natural selection, the fundamental unit is the individual. In species selection, new diversity is created by speciation and pruned by extinction; in natural selection, new diversity is created by mutation and eliminated by death of individuals. There are many other such parallels, but many evolutionary biologists believe that the processes are distinct. Indeed, since species are composed of populations of individuals, species selection operates on a higher level than natural selection.

If species selection is a valid description of processes occurring in nature, then it may be one of the most important elements of evolution. Most evolutionary studies in the past have concentrated on small-scale, or microevolutionary, change, such as the gradual, minute changes in fruit flies or bacteria after generations of breeding. Many evolutionary biologists are convinced, however, that microevolutionary processes are insufficient to explain the large-scale, or macroevolutionary, processes in the evolution of entirely new body plans, such as birds evolving from dinosaurs. In other words, traditional neo-Darwinism says that all evolution is merely microevolution on a larger scale, whereas some evolutionary biologists consider some changes too large for microevolution. They require different kinds of processes for macroevolution to take place. If there is a difference between natural selection (a microevolutionary process) and species selection (a macroevolutionary process), then species selection might be a mechanism for the large-scale changes in the earth's history, such as great adaptive radiations or mass extinctions. Naturally, such radical ideas are still controversial, but they are taken seriously by a growing number of paleontologists and evolutionary biologists. If they are supported by further research, then there may be some radical changes in evolutionary biology.

Methods of Study

Determining patterns of evolution requires a very careful, detailed study of the fossil record. To establish whether organisms evolve in a punctuated or gradual mode, many criteria must be met. The taxonomy of the fossils must be well understood, and there must be large enough samples at many successive stratigraphic levels. To estimate the time spanned by the study, there must be some form of dating that allows the numerical age of each sample to be estimated. It is also important to have multiple sequences of these fossils in a number of different areas to rule out the effects of migration of different animals across a given study area. Once the appropriate samples have been selected, then the investigator should measure as many different features as possible. Too many studies in the past have looked at only one feature and therefore established very little. In particular, changes in size alone are not sufficient to establish gradualism, since these phenomena can be explained by many other means. Finally, many studies in the past have failed because they picked one particular lineage or group and selectively ignored all the rest of the fossils in a given area. The question is no longer whether one or more cases of gradualism or punctuation occurs (they both do) but which is predominant among all the organisms in a given study area. Thus, the best studies look at the entire assemblage of fossils in a given area over a long stratigraphic interval before they try to answer the question of which tempo and mode of evolution is prevalent.

Context

Since the 1940's, evolutionary biology has been dominated by the neo-Darwinian "synthesis" of genetics, systematics, and paleontology. In more recent years, many of the accepted neo-Darwinian mechanisms of evolution have been challenged from many sides. Punctuated equilibrium and species selection represent the challenge of the fossil record to neo-Darwinian gradualism and overemphasis on the power of natural selection. If fossils show rapid change and long-term stasis over millions of years, then there is no currently understood evolutionary mechanism for this sort of stability in the face of environmental selection. A more general theory of evolution may be called for, and, in more recent years, paleontologists, molecular biologists, and systematists have all been indicating that such a radical rethinking of evolutionary biology is on the way. Evolutionary biology as it has been presented in textbooks and popular books in the second half of the twentieth century may be completely revamped by the end of that century.

Bibliography

Eldredge, Niles. *Time Frames: The Rethinking of Darwinian Evolution and the Theory of Punctuated Equilibria*. New York: Simon & Schuster, 1985. A general introduction to the development of punctuated equilibria by one of its original authors, with an excellent discussion of its implications for evolutionary biology. This text is the best book with which to begin reading about this topic.

Eldredge, Niles, and Stephen J. Gould. "Punctuated Equilibria: An Alternative to Phyletic Gradualism." In *Models in Paleobiology*, edited by T. J. M. Schopf. San Francisco: Freeman, Cooper, 1972. The classic article that started the whole revolution in evolutionary paleobiology. Even though it was intended for a scholarly audience, it is so well written and clearly presented that it is readable even for a layperson. It was reprinted in Eldredge's *Time Frames*.

Gould, Stephen J. "The Meaning of Punctuated Equilibria and Its Role in Validating a Hierarchical Approach to Macroevolution." In *Perspectives on Evolution*, edited by Roger Milkman. Sunderland, Mass.: Sinauer Associates, 1982. Gould's clearest defense and discussion of the macroevolutionary implications of punctuated equilibria and species selection.

Gould, Stephen J., and Niles Eldredge. "Punctuated Equilibrium: The Tempo and Mode of Evolution Reconsidered." *Paleobiology* 3 (1977): 115-151. Five years after the original article, the same authors evaluate the criticisms and new research that the paper generated and suggest an agenda for future research.

Hoffman, Antoni. *Arguments on Evolution: A Paleontologist's Perspective*. New York: Oxford University Press, 1988. One of the harshest and most cogent of the critics of punctuated equilibria. In this book, Hoffman details his objections to the whole model. Although some of his criticisms are well taken, others miss some of the most important points or overlook key evidence.

Levinton, Jeffrey S. *Genetics, Paleontology, and Macroevolution*. Cambridge, England: Cambridge University Press, 1988. A thorough discussion of the topic by one of the leading critics of punctuated equilibria; unfortunately, he misses some of the central points of the species selection argument.

Mayr, Ernst. *Animal Species and Evolution*. Cambridge, Mass.: Harvard University

Press, 1963. The classic study of speciation theory by the foremost proponent of the allopatric speciation model. This book dominated speciation theory for more than forty years from its first edition, *Systematics and the Origin of Species*, in 1942.

Stanley, Steven M. *Macroevolution: Pattern and Process*. San Francisco: W. H. Freeman, 1979. Although written for the technical audience, it is extremely clear and well illustrated and conveys much of the excitement of the new school of macroevolutionary thought. Much of it will be interesting to the general reader.

_____. *The New Evolutionary Timetable: Fossils, Genes, and the Origin of Species*. New York: Basic Books, 1979. Along with Eldredge's *Time Frames*, one of the best introductions to the subject for the nontechnical reader. Stanley gives a good background on evolutionary biology before punctuated equilibria and illustrates his points with many well-chosen examples.

Donald R. Prothero

Cross-References

Evolution: A Historical Perspective, 903; Convergent and Divergent Evolution, 910; Extinction, 953; Gene Flow, 1097; Isolating Mechanisms in Evolution, 1493; Natural Selection, 1870; Speciation and the Species Concept, 2521.

EXCRETION OF NITROGENOUS WASTES

Type of life science: Animal physiology
Other field of study: Biochemistry

Nitrogenous wastes, primarily breakdown products of amino acids, are toxic. They are modified to a form that can be excreted while the water and salt balance of body fluids is preserved. The usual forms for excretion are ammonia, uric acid, and urea.

Principal terms

AMMONIA: the most toxic and most soluble form of nitrogenous waste; its molecular formula is NH_3

CREATININE: the nitrogen-containing metabolic breakdown product of the energy-storage molecule creatine phosphate that is found in the brain and muscles

GLOMERULAR FILTRATION: the process by which small molecules are forced from the glomerular capillary and enter the nephron

NITROGENOUS WASTES: the nitrogen-containing molecules resulting from the breakdown of amino acids, purines, and creatine

TUBULAR ABSORPTION or REABSORPTION: the process of transferring molecules or ions from the fluid in the nephron tubule to the blood vessels surrounding the nephron

TUBULAR SECRETION: the process of transferring unfiltered molecules from the blood vessels surrounding the nephron to the nephron's tubule

UREA: an element less toxic than ammonia and more soluble than uric acid

URIC ACID: the least soluble form of nitrogenous waste

URINE FORMATION: the result of the processes of glomerular filtration, tubular absorption, tubular secretion, and concentration of tubular fluid and ureteral urine for excretion

Summary of the Phenomenon

Organisms are composed of cells, and within these cells dynamic processes are always occurring. Metabolism is the total of all the chemical reactions of the organism. Part of metabolism is the building of molecules for use by the cell, which is called anabolism. Molecules that are no longer necessary are broken down into smaller parts, which can become raw material for further anabolism or that must be excreted from the organism. This process is called catabolism and often includes the release of energy for use in cellular processes.

Excretion is the removal of unusable or excess materials from an organism. In multicellular animals, this term usually is reserved for the elimination of solid waste by the digestive system and of liquid waste by the urinary system. The digestive system eliminates undigested materials that have been ingested. The urinary system eliminates unusable or excess materials that have accumulated in the blood.

The cells of the liver secrete urea, a toxic nitrogenous waste, into the circulatory system. If urea were to accumulate, all the organism's cells would be unable to function, and, therefore, it must be eliminated from the body. Urea is carried in the blood until it reaches the urinary system. The urinary system filters excess materials and wastes from the blood vessels passing through the kidney, the primary site of urine formation; kidney cells also secrete some nitrogenous wastes. All are excreted from the body in the urine.

Urine is the end product of a number of separate processes that occur in all parts of the urinary system. The urinary system is composed of the (usually paired) kidneys, the ureters (tubes carrying the urine to the urinary bladder), and the urinary bladder, the site of urine storage. The urinary systems of vertebrates differ in their details and complexity. A cloaca is a common chamber into which gastrointestinal egesta (feces), urine, and reproductive cells pass prior to release from the body. It is found in some fishes, amphibians, reptiles, birds, and monotreme mammals such as the platypus. Urine can be stored and modified within the cloaca before leaving the body. In marsupial and placental mammals, the urine leaves the bladder through a tube called the urethra without further modification.

Ammonia is the simplest nitrogenous waste. It results from the breakdown of amino acids, the molecules that form proteins. Ammonia is the most toxic and most soluble form of nitrogenous waste. In multicellular organisms, it can be formed within the cells of the kidney itself. Generally, simple organisms living in an aquatic habitat use ammonia as their primary excretion product because it diffuses rapidly from the cells to the environment. Some freshwater fishes, which can afford to excrete great quantities of water, use ammonia as their primary nitrogenous waste product. Organisisms whose primary nitrogenous waste product is ammonia are called ammonotelic.

Urea is less toxic and less soluble than ammonia, which means that more urea can be carried safely in the blood of the organism and that less water is required to excrete it than ammonia. Urea requires special enzymes for its formation within liver cells, limiting the types of organisms that can use it as a nitrogenous waste product. Marsupial and placental mammals are examples of animals that primarily excrete urea. Organisms that excrete urea are called ureotelic.

Uric acid is formed when purines, such as adenine and guanine, are metabolized in cells. Urates are salts formed by combining uric acid with metal ions; both uric acid and urates are excreted. Uric acid can be formed within the cells of the kidney, but urates form within the tubule. Both uric acid and urates are nontoxic and insoluble. Therefore, they do not require much water for excretion, an important factor for birds, which would fly less efficiently if they had to carry about the extra weight of water required to keep urea in solution, and for reptiles, which often live in arid environments where water is not available. Animals that excrete nitrogenous wastes primarily in the form of uric acid or urates are called uricotelic.

Another nitrogenous waste is creatinine. The energy storage molecule creatine phosphate provides a ready source of phosphate for reenergizing adenosine triphosphate (ATP) without the necessity for complex chemical reactions in muscles and the brain. After the phosphate is transferred to ATP, creatine is degraded to creatinine and eliminated. Only a small amount of this nitrogen-containing molecule is found in normal urine.

The fine structure of the kidney determines the efficiency with which nitrogenous wastes are excreted. The functional unit of the kidney is the nephron. In vertebrates, the nephron can vary from a simple straight tube to a complexly folded tube with thick and thin regions that vary in their functions. In general, birds and mammals have complexly folded nephrons, with several specialized regions. The functions of some of the regions are only generally understood. The nephron has a closed end, the Bowman's capsule, which is usually curved around a capillary (thin-walled blood vessel). The capillary is called the glomerulus and may vary from almost straight to twined and tuftlike.

The capillary delivers blood to the nephron. The blood is under pressure, which can vary depending on the forcefulness of the heart's contraction and the constriction or dilation of blood vessels. This pressure forces water and small molecules, such as salt ions and sugars (generally called solutes), out of the glomerulus and through tiny pores into the Bowman's capsule. Large molecules, such as proteins, cannot be forced between the capillary wall's cells and remain within the blood vessel. Eventually, the proteins, which attract water to themselves, prevent any more water from leaving the capillary tuft.

Inside the nephron tubule, the pressure is low. The water and filtered solutes flow from the region of high pressure near the capillary tuft to the region of lower pressure within the nephron. Within the nephron, two other processes alter the tubular fluid. Water is withdrawn, thus concentrating the solutes. Some of the salts and sugars, which are needed within the body, are removed from the concentrated solution. Most of this reabsorption occurs in the proximal tubule, the portion of the nephron closest to the Bowman's capsule.

In all uricotelic vertebrates (birds, reptiles, and some amphibians), uric acid is secreted by tubule cells into tubular fluid. Uric acid can also be withdrawn from the tubular fluid (especially by mammalian kidneys). The transport is usually an exchange of anions (negatively charged ions), such as bicarbonate or hydroxyl ions, which will contribute to adjusting the pH balance of the urine.

Urea is freely filtered, and, in mammals, normally about half the filtered urea is reabsorbed. In fact, its presence in the medulla, or inner region, of the kidney around the tubules helps absorb water from the tubular fluid. This absorption is an important step in concentrating the urine so that as little water as possible is wasted. The urine that leaves the nephron can be further concentrated. The permeability of the wall of the collecting duct depends upon the amount of antidiuretic hormone (ADH) circulating in the blood. When water must be conserved, ADH concentration rises and the permeability of the collecting duct cells to water increases. Water can leave the collecting duct and return to the blood. Solutes remain behind and become even more concentrated in the urine. In mammals, this process is the final stage in urine formation. The urine passes from the kidney into the ureter and is stored in the urinary bladder until micturition (the scientific term for urination).

In birds, reptiles, and some amphibians, further modification of the urine can take place in the bladder and cloaca. Water can be removed, urates can form and precipitate out of solution, and salts can be exchanged, which is particularly important for creatures in a dry habitat that need to retain water.

In ureotelic vertebrates, urine is a fluid. Depending on the availability of water to the animal and the diet, the fluid may be hypoosmotic (lower in solute content) to the blood plasma, isoosmotic (having the same concentration), or hyperosmotic (having a higher solute concentration than the plasma).

In uricotelic vertebrates, the urine is usually semisolid. The whitish excretion of birds is composed of urates. It is usually somewhat fluid but dries to a paste. The solid matter in the excreta is usually the egesta (feces), which are excreted from the body at the same time as urine in animals with a cloaca.

Methods of Study

Studying the contents of urine outside the subject's body is easier than studying the changes that occur within the urinary system, but the latter reveals more information. Urine can be collected directly by allowing the subject to urinate into a container, which is sealed against evaporation by oil, or from a catheter (a small-diameter tube) inserted into the urethra to drain the bladder. Far more is, therefore, known about the ability of organisms to concentrate urine and conserve water than is known about the mechanisms used to remove water and certain solutes while concentrating others.

After the urine is obtained, it is analyzed for water content and for the concentrations of particular ions or molecules of interest. This analysis can tell the biologist how much the organism can concentrate its urine and conserve water when necessary. Medical doctors can determine whether the kidney is functioning properly by determining the concentration of ions or molecules that are usually absorbed and retained in the body. Blood tests also determine whether the kidney is excreting properly. The blood urea nitrogen (BUN) test determines whether urea is removed by the kidneys or is accumulating in the blood.

More precise understanding of the excretion process is important in determining how the kidney functions, and several methods of testing are used. Clearance studies use a substance such as inulin, a plant carbohydrate, which is not metabolized and filters from the glomerulus like water does. A known concentration is injected into the bloodstream, and samples of urine and blood are obtained at the same time. The concentrations of inulin are then determined. If the kidney is functioning properly, they should be the same. The concentrations of other molecules, such as urea, should be different, because the kidney can absorb and secrete urea. In humans, about 50 percent of filtered urea is absorbed. If the blood sample does not have twice the urea that the urine sample has, the kidney may not be functioning properly.

Levels of creatinine, a normally occurring breakdown product of creatine, are tested in humans. Although about 1 percent of the creatinine present in urine is the result of secretion, the amount of creatinine in the urine approximates the amount filtered. If an unexpected change occurs, other tests can be done to determine the problem.

When investigating animals, however, other, more precise, methods can be used. The kidney can be excised, sliced into thin sections, and the slices placed on a slide, with a drop of a solution applied. The concentrations and movements of substances, particularly dyes, then can be monitored. If different sections of the tubule can be sampled, the site of alteration of concentration of the molecule of interest can be determined.

Small mammals, such as rats and hamsters, have kidneys in which some portions of the nephron are visible using a microscope. Micropuncture can be used to obtain samples under free-flow conditions by using micromanipulators and extremely fine pipettes. Microperfusion techniques can be used also. Several methods are available, depending on the information desired. One simple method involves injecting a droplet of oil into the tubule. A second micropipette injects the test solution into the middle of the oil droplet, splitting it in two. A stopwatch and microscope are used to determine when the two ends of the oil droplet meet. This test allows an approximation of the rate of absorption in the studied portion of the nephron. Another technique is to inject an oil droplet near the capsule end of the nephron. A perfusate is pumped into the tubule beyond the oil droplet. At various points along the nephron, samples are withdrawn and their contents analyzed.

In organisms that have a renal portal system, a network of blood vessels that serves only the kidney, a substance can be introduced to the renal portal artery and affect only the kidney, and a sample can be removed from the renal portal vein. The concentrations of the substance of interest can be measured from blood and urine samples. A toxic substance, such as urea, may be used at higher concentrations than would be safe for the whole animal. Kidney structures can be examined to determine their functioning in its presence.

By using all these methods, physiologists have discovered that urea is filtered freely into the tubules. Even in ureotelic species, a certain proportion of the filtered urea is reabsorbed in the proximal tubule and in the collecting duct. This reabsorption is a passive process in most species, although the reabsorption from the collecting duct is increased when antidiuretic hormone (ADH) is present. Secretion is most often thought to result from urea synthesis within the tubules.

Urates are secreted into the tubule of uricotelic species. This secretion occurs along the entire first portion of the nephron, the proximal tubule. In mammals, urates are secreted in the second half of the proximal tubule. Mammals do not use urate as a major excretory product, however, and some can also be absorbed.

Ammonia is rarely found in the blood of most vertebrates. Any that is secreted is thought to be secreted from the cells of the proximal tubule. It is often used to adjust the pH (acid-base balance) of urine.

Context

Organisms build proteins from raw materials. When their usefulness is over, the proteins are broken down into raw materials, amino acids. Amino acids cannot be stored in the body, and, if there is an excess of any amino acid, it must be broken down further into energy and waste products, ammonia and urea. (Uric acid and creatinine also result from such catabolic processes.) Because these breakdown processes are a normal part of living, organisms have mechanisms to dispose of these wastes. If some error in metabolism or excretion should occur, nitrogenous wastes can accumulate in the blood, a condition called uremia.

Since all proteins are composed of amino acids, the higher the diet is in protein the more the livers of mammals produce urea. It is less toxic than ammonia and, thus, can circulate at rather high concentrations in the plasma. Most is filtered into the tubules, where about half is reabsorbed and about half is excreted. Urea itself is responsible for the efficiency of urea excretion. In the early portions of the nephron, urea freely diffuses out of the tubule with water. In the last segments of the nephron and in the collecting duct, however, urea does not pass freely from the tubule. The urea that has been reabsorbed remains around these later segments of the urinary system, creating a high osmotic pressure, which helps withdraw excess water and concentrate the urine. It also allows greater quantities of urea to remain in the urine as the concentration is occurring.

Putting kidney patients on a low-protein diet often delays the course of kidney disease and, consequently, the need for dialysis. Less protein means lowered urea production, which reduces pressure on the kidneys to eliminate large quantities of urea. The plasma concentration of uric acid rises in the disease gout. Uric acid is less soluble than urea, and it precipitates at high concentrations. When the blood level becomes very high, uric acid crystals deposit in joints, particularly the great toe, and other tissues, causing inflammation and pain. Drugs that inhibit the reabsorption of uric acid are often used to increase its excretion in urine. Urates can also precipitate in the kidney, forming kidney stones, also known as renal calculi. The stones cause considerable pain and cannot easily be excreted. Usually acid beverages, such as cranberry juice, are prescribed in an attempt to dissolve the stones. If that fails, lithotripsy or laser light can be used to pulverize the stones so that they can pass from the kidney.

Bibliography

Cameron, Stewart. *Kidney Disease*. Oxford, England: Oxford University Press, 1981. This small book presents information about kidney functions as well as the symptoms and signs of disease conditions affecting the kidney. There are chapters on kidney transplantation and dialysis. In addition, an appendix includes a helpful list of addresses and telephone numbers of groups involved in kidney research as well as those involved in supporting the kidney patient and family.

Medical World News. "Kidney Stones Get Green Light." *Science Digest* 3 (January, 1990): 82-83. This article contains a brief discussion of the use of green laser light to break up kidney stones (renal calculi) so that they can be painlessly excreted.

Mommson, Thomas P., and Patrick J. Walsh. "Evolution of Urea Synthesis in Vertebrates: The Piscine Connection." *Science* 243 (January 5, 1989): 72-75. A technical article describing urea synthesis and its evolution in toadfish species.

Phillips, Robert H. *Coping with Kidney Failure.* Garden City Park, N.Y.: Avery, 1987. This clearly written book presents overviews of kidney functions, kidney transplantations, and dialysis. It considers the life-style changes and emotional consequences of kidney failure and its effects on social interactions.

Purvis, William K., and Gordon H. Orians. *Life: The Science of Biology.* Sunderland, Mass.: Sinauer Associates, 1987. Chapter 25, "Excretion and Osmoregulation," covers the various invertebrate and vertebrate excretory structures. In a clear and simple fashion, it illustrates how urine formation is related to an animal's adaptation to environments from the ocean to deserts.

SerVaas, Cory. "Kidney Care." *Saturday Evening Post* 258 (March, 1986): 106-108. A brief article describing the buildup of urea in the blood of patients in early renal failure. The high-protein diet eaten constantly by most Americans produces high renal blood pressure in normal individuals. Physicians are using protein-restricted diets to decrease urea formation and thus eliminate one of the causes of diuresis.

Smith, Homer W. *From Fish to Philosopher.* Garden City, N.Y.: Doubleday, 1961. A casual exploration of salt balance and excretory physiology, written by one of the foremost biologists investigating vertebrate evolution.

Wallace, Robert A. *Biology: The World of Life.* Glenview, Ill.: Scott, Foresman, 1987. Chapter 17, "Homeostasis and the Internal Environment," presents a concise discussion of the interactions of the body and the environment to maintain dynamic equilibrium. The contributions of the excretory system are presented on pages 335-341.

Judith O. Rebach

Cross-References

Active Transport and Cotransport, 15; Catabolism of Fats and Proteins, 337; Kidneys and Other Excretory Structures, 1514; Metabolic Pathways, 1691; Metabolic Rates, 1699; Osmoregulation, 2015; Osmosis, Free Diffusion, and Facilitated Diffusion, 2022; Proteins, 2272; Water Retention and Excretion, 2709.

EXERGONIC AND ENDERGONIC REACTIONS

Type of life science: Biochemistry
Other field of study: Biophysics

Reactions are either exergonic and spontaneous or endergonic and nonspontaneous. The spontaneity, as well as the concentrations of reactants and products at equilibrium, depends on the amount of free energy released or required for the reaction to occur. Adenosine triphosphate (ATP) is the primary energy carrier in physiological reactions, as it can undergo hydrolysis to adenosine diphosphate (ADP).

Principal terms

ADENOSINE DIPHOSPHATE (ADP): one of the products of hydrolysis of adenosine triphosphate (ATP), the other one being the phosphate anion; it can regenerate ATP in an endergonic reaction

ADENOSINE TRIPHOSPHATE (ATP): the predominant energy supplier of metabolic energy; it hydrolyzes to produce adenosine diphosphate (ADP) and phosphate in an exergonic reaction

COUPLING: a mechanism whereby endergonic, thermodynamically unfavorable, reactions are made possible by input of energy provided by another, exothermic, reaction; the net sum of free energy in these two reactions should be negative in sign

ENDERGONIC REACTION: a reaction whose products' free energy is higher than that of the reactants; as a result, the reaction is not spontaneous and is thermodynamically unfavorable

EXERGONIC REACTION: a reaction whose products' free energy is lower than that of the reactants; the reaction is considered spontaneous and is thermodynamically favorable

GIBBS FREE ENERGY: the intrinsic energy associated with the molecular structure of a compound; a negative value in a reaction suggests spontaneity, while a positive value is an indication of an endergonic reaction

MYOSIN: the major contractible protein in muscle that catalyzes the hydrolysis of ATP to ADP and phosphate

Summary of the Phenomenon

The primary source of energy for life on Earth is the sun, which is responsible for photosynthesis: the process that transforms radiant energy into chemical energy. Chemical energy is stored in biomolecules, which can then be used as the fuel to provide the energy needs for life to be sustained. Such biomolecules include sugars (or carbohydrates), proteins, and lipids (or fats). Thus, it is of great importance for the body to be able to conserve, release, and utilize chemical energy. No chemical or physical change can exhibit complete conversion of energy from one form to another. Bioenergetics is the science that studies the description of the basic mechanisms that govern the production and use of energy by organisms. These mechanisms describe the most likely pathways through which reactions can occur and consequent biological functions can be feasible.

A chemical reaction can be described in general terms as occurring when reactants interact, thereby creating new products. The energy (often measured in calories) contained in the molecular structure of a compound is called Gibbs free energy (after the scientist W. Gibbs, who developed the concept) and is the free energy available to perform useful work. The difference between the free energy of the products and the free energy of the reactants is called the change in free energy and is fundamental in determining if a reaction can take place on its own. Thus, if the difference is negative in sign, energy is released and the free energy content is lowered. The reaction is then called exergonic and is spontaneous. On the other hand, if the difference is a positive number, free energy is required, and the reaction is called endergonic and is considered nonspontaneous. As a result, when the value for the standard free energy of a reaction is about +4.1 calories per mole, the ratio of products over reactants at equilibrium is about one thousand to one. The reverse holds if the standard free energy of a reaction in an endergonic reaction is about −4.1 calories per mole; the ratio of products over reactants at equilibrium in this case is one to one thousand. Under physiological conditions, the relative ratio of reactants and products decides which direction the reaction will proceed as well as the concentrations that are going to be present at equilibrium.

Photosynthesis and respiration are two of the most important biochemical processes. Photosynthesis involves the formation of glucose, a basic carbohydrate, and molecular oxygen from the ultraviolet-light-catalyzed reaction of carbon dioxide and water. Respiration deals with the transfer and consumption of atmospheric oxygen in the cells and its transformation into water; at the same time, the waste product, carbon dioxide, is removed from the cells and, subsequently, from the lungs via expiration. Both processes are exergonic despite the fact that the former one involves formation of oxygen, while the latter one oxygen consumption. It should be noted, therefore, that the processes are not reversible, although a first look might indicate that they are. In other words, not all processes involving oxygen consumption are exergonic, nor are all oxygen-forming processes endergonic. As a rule, the value of the Gibbs free energy for a reaction is independent of the path and depends solely on the nature of the reactants and their concentrations. It is noteworthy that in biochemical reactions, positive values for the free energy difference are not uncommon.

Consider the following two reactions, which together allow the conversion of compound A to compound C via the intermediary formation and consumption of compound B.

$$A \rightarrow B \ \text{(free energy} = 1,360 \ \text{calories)}$$
$$B \rightarrow C \ \text{(free energy} = -2,760 \ \text{calories)}$$

The first reaction is endergonic and is not spontaneous, since the free energy for the reaction is a positive number. The second reaction will go on its own (since its free energy is a negative number) and will remove B as soon as it is formed, leading to the overall "net" reaction.

$$A \rightarrow C \text{ (free energy } = -2,760 + 1,360 = -1,400 \text{ calories)}$$

The "net" reaction, therefore, is an exergonic one and is favorable because the free energy of the second reaction was transferred to the first, thus enabling it to proceed in a forward direction.

The principal carrier of energy for all forms of energy is adenosine triphosphate (ATP), which was first isolated from muscle by Cyrus H. Fiske and Yellapragada SubbaRow (in the United States) and Karl Lohman, independently (in Germany). For some time thereafter, ATP was believed to be concerned only with muscular contraction. In the 1930's, however, two other German biochemists, Otto Warburg and Otto Meyerhof, demonstrated that ATP is generated from adenosine diphosphate (ADP) in the anaerobic (absence of air) transformation of glucose to lactic acid in muscle. Later, it was proved that ATP is also generated from ADP during aerobic oxidation in animal tissues. The hydrolysis of ATP to ADP and phosphate by myosin was discovered by Engelhardt and M. N. Lyubimova.

ATP's role in energy was recognized by Fritz Lipmann, the 1953 Nobel Prize laureate in Physiology or Medicine, who nevertheless expressed his inability to give very definite answers that can explain "how high phosphate group [produced from ATP] potential operates as the promoter of various processes." He made, however, a comparison of the metabolic cycle with a machine that generates electrical current, the phosphate "current," which plays a part similar to the electrical current in the life of human beings, serving as the all-purpose type of energy. The ATP structure proposed by Lohman in 1930 was confirmed through a chemical synthesis by Alexander Todd and his coworkers in 1948. ATP, ADP, and adenosine monophosphate (AMP), the hydrolysis product of ADP, are widely distributed in both the animal and plant kingdoms. In the intracellular fluid, ATP combines with the abundant magnesium ions to form the $MgATP^{-2}$ complex, which is the active form of ATP in the enzymatic reactions in the cell.

As the supplier of the metabolic energy, ATP hydrolyzes (reacts with water) to give ADP and phosphate anion at pH 7. The reaction is exergonic and releases 7,300 calories per mole; it is catalyzed by myosin, the major contractible protein of the muscle. Since the forward reaction (ATP yielding ADP) is an exergonic reaction, the reverse (ADP producing ATP) is an endergonic process, an ideal relationship because many biochemical processes are highly exergonic. As a result, ADP can be converted to ATP, thus absorbing much of the heat produced by the exergonic reaction, which would otherwise make life intolerable for the cell. At the same time, the energy stored in the newly formed ATP can be used in a coupled mechanism to carry out a variety of energy-requiring processes. This cycle in life uses ATP as an energy intermediate. First, the excess energy from the various oxidative reactions of the cell is absorbed by ADP to produce ATP. Then, ATP is converted back to ADP and releases energy to be used in biosynthesis, movement, transport, waste disposal, communication, and other endergonic processes.

The enigma is why ATP, and not any other molecule, is used. Although no complete justification is available, there are several points that support its significance. First, there is the high stability of the ATP molecule at the physiological pH (around 7.4) toward uncatalyzed hydrolysis and decomposition. This stability guarantees the preservation of the extra energy in the molecule to be used in coupling with the endergonic reactions. Second, there is the presence of ATP in substantial amounts during the transmission of genetic information. Finally, there is the value of the free energy involved in the ATP-ADP transformation, which is located in the range of energies of most exergonic and endergonic reactions in the biological system. As a result, it can play the role of an intermediate quite easily.

Methods of Study

The value for the Gibbs free energy in reactions performed in vitro (outside the body) is different from the value obtained in vivo (in the body). This aberration occurs because many reactions, as they occur in nature, involve pH participation. If one uses the in vitro free energy measurements, the value of pH is set at 0, which is unrealistic for a living cell, in which the pH is approximately 7.

The value of Gibbs free energy (and thus, the prediction that the reaction can be exergonic or endergonic) can also be calculated from the value of the equilibrium constant. The equilibrium constant, which relates logarithmically the concentrations of reactants and products to the Gibbs free energy, can be calculated by means of various methods, such as spectrophotometry. In spectrophotometry, the quantity of light absorbed by a compound at a specific wavelength is directly related to the concentration of the compound. Thus, if a reactant and a product of a reaction absorb light at different wavelengths, their respective concentrations can be calculated and the equilibrium constant computed. The common types of electromagnetic radiation used are the ultraviolet and visible regions.

The Gibbs free energy can also be calculated electrochemically, provided that an oxidation-reduction reaction is involved. The basis for this relationship is the capability of doing useful work by transferring electrons from the part of the system that undergoes oxidation (loss of electrons) to the part that undergoes reduction (gain of electrons). Such a system is called an electrochemical cell, and the net potential is merely a measure of the difference between each part of the system that undergoes oxidation and reduction. The Gibbs free energy is directly related to the net standard oxidation-reduction potential (measured in volts) and the number of electrons per molecule involved in this transfer.

The separation of ATP from ADP and AMP was achieved via chromatography. Thus, samples containing all three components were placed on a special paper, called chromatogram, which in many aspects is similar to filter paper. A solvent was allowed to flow downward from the top edge of the paper and carry the samples with it by capillary action at varying speeds. Such a procedure would demonstrate whether ATP was involved in a specific biochemical reaction, depending on whether the presence of ADP (and/or AMP) was detected.

The methods used to determine the Gibbs free energy of a biochemical reaction were used first in vitro and were then used (with approximations) in vivo. Each of those methods—whether spectrophotometric, electrochemical, or chromatographic—gave an insight to the basic reactions of a living organism and helped in the detailed comprehension of the endergonic and exergonic reactions.

Context

The energy produced by cells in their reactions is transformed into chemical energy, which is used in doing mechanical work, such as muscular contraction, and the osmotic work required to transport materials in and out of the cell. It is also used in the synthesis of cell components. Although the body may produce heat by muscular work, the living cell operates at a constant temperature and pressure at a practically neutral pH. It is important to realize that the cell cannot withstand the release of great amounts of heat, since any rise of temperature leads to a deviation from the ideal physiological conditions.

A portion of the chemical energy formed in the cell is stored in the form of high-energy compounds. Such compounds are extremely valuable, since they can drive essential reactions in the metabolic cycles of carbohydrates, lipids, and proteins. Many of the reactions in the cell have a positive Gibbs free energy and, because they are endergonic, will not proceed without assistance. That is accomplished by coupling to a highly exergonic reaction, such as the hydrolysis of ATP to ADP. Coupling is possible only when the net sum of the free energies of the two reactions is negative in sign. It can also occur between a highly exergonic reaction and a slightly exergonic one, which is so weak that it does not proceed sufficiently and therefore does not produce high concentrations of the product. The role of ATP can also be illustrated in the contraction of a relaxed muscle. The energy released by the hydrolysis of ATP to ADP by means of myosin is adequate for this process, which, without it, is thermodynamically unfavorable.

Equally important is the process whereby ATP is produced: the citric acid cycle and oxidative phosphorylation, in which fuels are completely oxidized to carbon dioxide and ATP. The energy change, which involves the relative amounts of ATP, ADP, and AMP, plays a significant role in the regulation of metabolism. Thus, a high energy change inhibits the catabolic pathways (which generate ATP) and stimulates the anabolic pathways (which utilize ATP).

In everyday terms, ATP may be thought of as something similar to a charged storage battery, whose discharged form is ADP (or AMP). Much as the discharge of a storage battery can permit external work through the release of energy in the form of electric current, the conversion of ATP is used to perform chemical work: the synthesis of needed materials or the performance of essential processes.

Bibliography

Armstrong, Frank Bradley, and Thomas Peter Bennett. *Biochemistry*. New York: Oxford University Press, 1979. Chapter 14, "Energy and Life," stresses the importance of ATP in life as an energy carrier. It also includes a list of suggested readings on bioenergetics, such as articles in *Scientific American*.

Kilgour, Gordon L. *Fundamentals of Biochemistry*. New York: Van Nostrand, 1981. Chapter 6, "Biochemical Energetics: An Introduction," treats thermodynamics in a simple manner and includes a list of additional readings at the end of the chapter. The roles of ATP and related compounds are covered in a special section.

Lehninger, Albert L. *Biochemistry*. 2d ed. New York: Worth, 1975. The classic textbook for undergraduate biochemistry. Chapter 15, "Bioenergetic Principles and the ATP Cycle," gives a complete picture of the thermodynamic principles and biochemistry on an intermediate level. A list of scientific articles and books is at the end of the chapter.

——————. "Energy Transformation in the Cell." *Scientific American* 205 (September, 1961): 102-114. This article involves a series of schemes and explains the paths through which the living cell converts the energy of foodstuff into a form that can be utilized and stored. It also gives a historical outline of the progress in identifying the role of ATP as the storage battery of the living system.

Malm, Miriam. *Fundamentals of Organic and Biochemistry*. New York: Van Nostrand, 1980. An excellent text for introductory biochemistry and organic chemistry. Unit 12, "Energy and Biochemical Reactions: ATP and Energy Flow," links ATP and nucleotides with the basic thermodynamics concepts.

Routh, Joseph I. *Introduction to Biochemistry*. 2d ed. Philadelphia: W. B. Saunders, 1978. Chapter 8, "Biochemical Energy," is an intermediate-level description of thermodynamics as related to the living cell. It includes a section, "World of ATP," in which the history of the recognition of ATP's role in life is discussed.

Stumpf, Paul K. "ATP." *Scientific American* 188 (April, 1953): 85-90. This article describes ATP's participation in biochemical reactions and cellular energy systems. It includes schemes and a picture of ATP crystals.

Paris Svoronos

Cross-References

ATP and Other Energetic Molecules, 134; Biochemical Pathway Analysis, 163; Chemical Elements of Living Systems, 417; Enzymes and Ribozymes, 851; Intermediates, Monomers, and Polymers, 1452; Metabolic Pathways, 1691; Thermodynamics in Biology, 2625.

EXOSKELETONS

Type of life science: Animal anatomy
Other field of study: Invertebrate biology

The exoskeleton is one of the distinctive primary features of members of the phylum Arthropoda. The evolution of the exoskeleton cuticle is thought to have been important in this group's successful adaptation to many diverse environments. The exoskeleton's intricate structure has provided advantages enabling the arthropods to have thrived for hundreds of millions of years.

Principal terms

ARTHROPODA: an invertebrate animal phylum that comprises about a dozen classes, including the Crustacea, Insecta, and Arachnida; members possess chitinous exoskeletons and jointed, segmented appendages

CHITIN: a celluloselike, crystalline material that makes up anywhere from 25 percent to 60 percent of the dry weight of the cuticle

CUTICLE: the outer arthropod exoskeleton consisting of several layers of secreted organic matter, primarily nonliving chitin

ENDOCUTICLE: usually the thickest layer of the cuticle, found just outside the living epidermal cell layer and is made of untanned proteins and chitin

EPICUTICLE: the outermost and thinnest layer of the arthropod cuticle, composed mainly of the hardened protein cuticulin

EPIDERMIS: a living cellular layer that secretes the greater part of the cuticle and is responsible for dissolving and absorbing the cuticle during molting (also termed the hypodermis)

EXOCUTICLE: a thick middle layer in the cuticle made up of both chitin and rigid, tanned proteins termed sclerotin

EXOSKELETON: a jointed and segmented, relatively thin, hard covering that surrounds and protects the entire inner body in most arthropods

INTEGUMENTARY PROCESSES: surface outgrowths from the cuticle, primarily rigid nonarticulated processes or movable articulated processes

SCLEROTIN: a hard, horny protein constituent of the exocuticle found in arthropods such as insects; it is superficially similar to vertebrate horn or keratin

Summary of the Phenomenon

The evolution of invertebrate animals possessing rigid, hard exoskeletons represented a great advance for members of the phylum Arthropoda. The development of such exoskeletons—in comparison with less solid structures, such as the hydrostatic skeleton of coelenterates—gave arthopods several distinct evolutionary advantages over other invertebrate phyla. Hydrostatic skeletons, such as those possessed by sea anemones, operate by the animal's musculature being arranged in a pattern that surrounds an enclosed volume of fluid. Contraction of any one section of the muscular system creates a fluid pressure in the central cavity that is consequently transmitted in an omnidirectional manner to the rest of the body. Arthropodic exoskeletons, on the other hand, are consistently rigid and much harder because they are composed to some extent of crystalline substances. Flexibility of movement is attained by multiple jointings in the limb system and in other appendages in the body such as feeding and sensory apparatuses.

As a consequence of two distinctive features—a hard, rigid exoskeleton and jointed appendages and other body parts—arthropods have become one of the most successful of all animal groups; indeed, it is by these two features that they are taxonomically defined. Biologists sometimes term the enhancement of the annelid (worm) body plan of segmentation by arthropod improvement "arthropodization." Because of it, the ancestors of the present immense spectrum of arthropod species successfully adapted to myriad ecological niches in the sea, on land, and in the air. Arthropod species account for more than three quarters of all known animal species. In fact, the class Insecta, one of a number of classes within the arthropod phylum, numbers at least 700,000 known species, with new species being discovered yearly, mostly in the tropics.

The immense success of arthropods is, to a great extent, the result of the advantages provided by the composition and structure of the seemingly simple surface architecture that is the arthropod exoskeleton. This exoskeleton not only provides a substantial chemical and physical barrier between the animal and the external environment, protecting the internal organs and fluids, but also allows a degree of temperature and osmotic regulation. In addition, the exoskeleton helps deter predation, provides a solid base of attachment for an internal muscular system, and offers a good site for the location of various sense organs. One of the most noteworthy evolutionary advantages of the exoskeleton is its service as a solid base of muscle attachment. The arthropod limbs act as a system of mechanical levers that are a much more efficient locomotive system than that of evolutionarily older and less sophisticated invertebrate locomotive systems such as that of the annelids. Because of exoskeletons and the structurally strong, jointed appendages that exoskeletons permit, arthropods possess an internal, muscular body wall broken down into separate muscles having an arrangement allowing contractions that are more localized in time and space than annelid or coelenterate muscle behavior. This more modular approach to the musculature allows arthropods to react to their environment to use energy more efficiently and with greater precision of movement and response. In fact, the inner surface of the exoskeleton acts as a limited type of endoskeleton, or inner skeleton, in that it provides good anchoring sites for muscle attachement, thus further increasing the leverage power of arthropod limbs and appendages.

The exoskeleton itself can be divided into several distinct units based on function and composition. These are composed of consecutive layers that surround the animal in an arrangement similar to a medieval knight's suit of armor. Like the armor suit, the outermost exoskeleton is, in a typical arthropod, very rigid and hard; movement is possible only because both protective systems are composed of plates or body-contoured segments that incorporate narrow, flexible jointings allowing motion. The motion is usually narrowly defined in extent and direction, and it is this quality that gives both armored humans and many arthropods their often distinctively awkward and ungainly mode of movement. The larger terrestrial beetles and marine forms such as crabs and lobsters are ready examples of this. Some arthropods are nevertheless adroit and delicate in their movements, as shown by various arthropod aerialists such as the dragonflies and butterflies.

Insects can, in many ways, be considered typical arthropods and are therefore useful as models for a discussion of the exoskeleton as found among all arthropods. All the various layers of the exoskeleton, both living and nonliving, are as a whole variously termed the integument or cuticle. These layers are the skin or surface of the animal. The innermost layer of the exoskeleton is termed the epidermis, or hypodermis, and is made of living cells. The epidermis is immediately external to a basement membrane that separates the epidermis from the inner body, with its organs and fluids. The epidermis is responsible for secreting the layers external to it, which are organic but actually nonliving material. From the epidermis outward, these layers in insects consist of the endocuticle, the exocuticle, and the epicuticle. (Some biologists use the term procuticle to describe the endocuticle and use epicuticle to mean both the epicuticle and the exocuticle.) Whatever precise terms may be employed, the general concept is that layers of material closer to the epidermis are more flexible and less chemically hardened than layers that are found closer to the actual exterior of the animal. The endocuticle is usually the thickest cuticle layer and is constituted of protein mixed with a material called chitin. Chitin is a celluloselike, crystalline material that makes up anywhere from 25 percent to 60 percent of the dry weight of the cuticle. It has many useful properties, such as resistance to concentrated alkalies and acids. In chemical composition, chitin is a nitrogenous polysaccharide. Chitin itself can be a relatively soft and flexible material that gains hardness in the outermost arthropod exoskeleton in several ways. One way is by using the presence of a material termed sclerotin. The process of hardening through the agency of sclerotin is called sclerotinization and involves a molecular change in the organization of the protein part of the cuticle. The outermost chitin found in the exocuticle of insects, for example, is thoroughly sclerotinized, which characteristically results in a darkening of the chitin. The other method by which chitin hardens is the deposition of calcium carbonate, primarily in the form of calcite. This is the process found among marine arthropods such as the Crustacea: crabs, lobsters, and shrimp, for example. This process, called calcification, occurs among Crustacea starting in their epicuticle, or outermost exoskeletal layer, and works inward to the exocuticle and finally the endocuticle.

Besides the darkening caused by sclerotinization, coloration of the cuticle is effected in two basic ways. One is simple pigmentation caused by the presence of colored compounds found within the cuticle itself. The other is through the presence of extremely fine parallel ridges found on the epicuticle. These ridges break normal white light into its constituent wavelengths by prismatic diffraction in the same way that raindrops create rainbows. It is by this means that the effect of spectacularly iridescent rainbow hues found on many insects' wings and bodies is achieved.

Adding to the complexity of the cuticle are great numbers of sensory organs that project from or extend through the various exoskeletal layers. Prominent among these sensory structures are tactile hairs, bristles, and spines found all over the general body surface and on limb surfaces. These sensory structures, or setae, are movable and are set into thin, flexible disks on the cuticle surface itself. When one of these projections is moved, its base mechanically stimulates one or more sensory cells, setting off stimuli to which the arthropod can respond.

While the exoskeleton is wonderfully evolved to protect the arthropod and to enhance its locomotive and sensory abilities, its overall rigid structure presents some inherent drawbacks. Perhaps chief among these is the fact that its formidable rigidity and solidity are a limitation to an individual's physical growth throughout its lifetime. Growth, in fact, is probably an arthropod's single most difficult physiological problem. This is true because once formed and hardened, an exoskeleton cannot be enlarged as the animal within enlarges with time. The physiologic solution among arthropods is the process termed ecdysis, or molting.

This process is intrinsically dangerous to the arthropod, as it leaves each individual extremely vulnerable to predation during, and immediately following, molting. It has been estimated that as much as 80 to 90 percent of arthropod mortality occurs during ecdysis. The process takes place in stages. Prior to the shedding of the old exoskeleton, a new, soft cuticle is formed beneath the old one. The new cuticle has not been started along either the sclerotinization or calcification process and therefore is still soft and pliable. As the new cuticle is forming, the lower section of the old cuticle is partially dissolved by corrosive fluids secreted by cutaneous glands situated below the new cuticle. Immediately prior to the shedding, also termed casting, of the old exoskeletal cuticle, the arthropod stops feeding and absorbs more than the usual amount of water and oxygen. Its body begins to swell, and the animal makes spasmodic movements to shake off the old cuticle, most of the base of which has been removed by the corrosive process. Eventually, the old exoskeleton is effectively disconnected from the arthropod's body, and the animal extricates itself from the remains. At this point, its new exoskeleton is soft and very pliable, and its movements are limited. Consequently, the individual is extremely vulnerable to predation as well as serious damage from tearing through abrasive or sharp-edged materials in its environment. It takes some time before the animal's cuticle has hardened and thickened enough for it to resume its normal activities. In the meantime, the exoskeleton—which normally provides a great degree of protection and mobility—acts as a hindrance and danger to the arthropod.

Methods of Study

The two main approaches used to study the arthropod exoskeleton are the same types of study used by researchers in nearly all branches of the life sciences: field studies and laboratory studies. In the field approach, living arthropods are observed in nature. The specific techniques employed include both still and motion photography in various light—normal, infrared, and ultraviolet. It is important to combine the observational database with later structural analyses of specific arthropod body parts, such as exoskeletons, to ascertain how the anatomical components actually function in the natural setting. Actual physical collections are necessary for study by laboratory workers, who subject the specimens to a range of tests to determine their qualities and features in comparison with similar species and with the normal parameters that are known for previously collected members of the same species.

Specimens are often dissected—or in some cases, vivisected (disassembled while alive)—in order to record useful data such as chemical composition of exoskeletons, metabolic rates, and the estimated age of the sample. In the case of specimens raised in captivity, more precise data can be gained as the precise age, food type, and daily or hourly intake are known with great precision.

A wide range of techniques are employed in the laboratory to analyze the structural components of exoskeletons. Among them, optical microscopy has traditionally been the primary approach. Working with dissected parts, frequently cut and chemically stained to facilitate viewing or bring out certain features selectively, researchers have used powerful microscopes capable of magnifying by a factor of many hundreds to see tiny subcomponent structures found within exoskeletal tissue. Optical microscopes have also been used to take a close look at associated cellular and noncellular organic matter, such as chitin and sclerotin. Providing an exponential increase in magnification for study, however, has been the advent of scanning electron microscopes (SEMs). These are instruments that use a beam of focused electrons to scan an object and form a three-dimensional image on a cathode-ray tube. The SEM reads both the pattern of electrons scattered by the object and the secondary electrons produced by it. This greatly enhanced ability to see smaller objects with great clarity allows scientists to see very small target sections of exoskeletal tissue, measured in microns (millionths of a meter) in circumference. Researchers can examine in minute detail the structures and interrelationships of the various layers of the arthropod cuticle.

Because the hard arthropod exoskeleton fossilizes more readily than the remains of many other animals, the evolutionary history of the phylum Arthropoda is abundantly represented in the fossil record. Much more is known about this phylum than other invertebrate phyla because of this phenomenon. Entire classes of arthropods that have left no modern descendants are known today because their substantial body armor appears in various marine strata. Examples of this are well documented in the remains of the extinct marine groups of the trilobites (similar to modern horseshoe crabs) and the eurypterids (giant "water scorpions"). In the case of the trilobites, many fossils are actually the result of cast-off exoskeletal moltings rather than the carcass of the dead animal. This illustrates the fact that, for hundreds of millions of years, arthropods have maintained a life-style and evolutionary approach to physiological problems that are similar to those of modern forms. X-ray photography has been employed successfully to penetrate the hard, mineralized fossils of extinct and ancestral forms of modern arthropods, showing in good detail the internal structures of exoskeletons and other tissues. Radiographic images produced by this technique demonstrate the continuity of structure and life shared by members of this extremely successful phylum for a period extending beyond the early Cambrian period (500 million years before the present).

Context

The exoskeleton is an evolutionary advantage shared by all arthropods. This advantage, along with their body and limb segmentation, has allowed them to move into myriad ecological niches, first in the sea and later on land, in fresh water, and finally in the air. As a phylum, arthropods are arguably the most successful of all metazoan animal phyla; they exceed all others combined in terms of the number of species, diversity, and the number of individual organisims. This ubiquity in all biomes and climates and in virtually every conceivable niche in every ecosystem makes them a force that has a constant influence on human life.

Humankind has many relationships with arthropods. Among them are their functions and roles as a food source, as contenders for common food sources, as a primary component of the food chain for numerous other animals (vertebrate and invertebrate, domestic and wild), as a parasitic disease vector for microbial parasites, as a major agent of plant pollination in many useful and ornamental plants, and even as inspiration for art and mechanical and materials engineering.

Crustacean arthropods such as lobsters, shrimp, and crabs are delicacies and dietary staples around the world. In some cultures, insects are considered both as staples and delicacies. At the same time, plagues of locusts, beetles, and other insect arthropods can spell disaster for whole societies. Crustacean arthropods also cost humans billions of dollars in ship damage resulting from hull-loving barnacles. They also provide a vast amount of protein for insects and other arthropods as well as for birds, mammals, and fish. These vertebrates simultaneously provide food, serve as work animals and companions, and provide recreational activities and even inspiration. At the same time, some arthropods (lice, ticks, and other parasites) kill, sicken, and weaken people, pets, and livestock. In addition, arthropods serve as avenues of disease transmission in the form of malaria and other contagion. Yet without the many coadapted arthropods and their interactive plants, flowering plant pollination in its many forms would be much more difficult or even impossible. Finally, insects and other arthropods have for ages been an inspiration for human art and literary expression. Jewelry, painting, poetry, and sculpture have portrayed the exoskeleton-clad forms of insects and other arthropods since the time of the ancient Egyptians. The mechanical efficiency of many arthropods, attributable in part to their exoskeletons, is a wonder. The flying abilities of insects and the leverage systems of crustaceans are engineering marvels that have inspired blueprints for new types of vehicles, useful robots, and other functional devices.

Bibliography

Barrington, E. J. W. *Invertebrate Structure and Function*. Boston: Houghton Mifflin, 1967. This textbook is written in an easy-to-understand but authoritative manner. Chapter 7, "Movement and Arthropodization," is very useful to readers interested in exoskeletons; several good schematic diagrams illustrating the various layers constituting exoskeletons are included. Written for advanced high school or college students who have a good foundation in the life sciences.

Boardman, Richard S., Alan H. Cheetham, and Albert J. Rowell, eds. *Fossil Invertebrates*. Palo Alto, Calif.: Blackwell Scientific Publications, 1987. An extremely thorough and exhaustively detailed treatment of all known types of fossil invertebrates, with an emphasis on metazoans. Chapter 13, "Phylum Arthropoda," is of prime interest because it includes a comprehensive description of exoskeletons and what is known of their evolution from the fossil record in extinct and extant taxonomic classes. Features numerous expert drawings, diagrams, and black-and-white photographs. It is suitable for readers who have a solid foundation in natural history.

Buchsbaum, Ralph. *Animals Without Backbones*. 2d ed. Chicago: University of Chicago Press, 1965. This is a text intended for the beginning college student or layman that provides a detailed overview of all the phyla and major classes of invertebrate animals. Chapter 22, "Jointed-legged Animals," defines and explains the arthropod cuticle and its composition layer by layer. Chapter 23, "The Lobster and Other Arthropods," is also useful because of its many explanations of the functions of this typical marine arthropod's exoskeleton.

Clarkson, E. N. K. *Invertebrate Palaeontology and Evolution*. 2d ed. Boston: Allen & Unwin, 1986. Intended as a college-level textbook for introductory courses in invertebrate paleontology, this book nevertheless is a very useful source of information on exoskeletons for all readers having a serious interest in the subject. Chapter 11, "Arthropods," is the main focus of useful information, with subsection 11.2, "Classification and General Morphology," treating the subject in the greatest detail.

Hutchins, Ross E. *Insects*. Englewood Cliffs, N.J.: Prentice-Hall, 1966. Intended for the general natural science reader who has an interest in insect life. Chapter 1, "The World of Insects," features a basic explanatory treatment of insect exoskeletons. Chapter 17, "Of Light and Color," contains a lengthy discussion of the phenomena of insect coloration in its two forms: pigmentation and prismatic (surface-structure) light diffraction. Numerous black-and-white photographs of insects and small or microscopic insect body structures enhance the easily read text.

Lanham, Url. *The Insects*. New York: Columbia University Press, 1964. Designed for the general reader. It is written in a low-key but clear and authoritative style that succeeds at conveying many complex subjects. Chapter 3, "The Outside," is an informative discussion of insect external structures beginning with the nature of the exoskeleton itself. Black-and-white drawings and diagrams help to complete textual explanations in this chapter as well as each of the others throughout the book.

Laverack, M. S., and J. Dando. *Essential Invertebrate Zoology*. 2d ed. New York: John Wiley & Sons, 1979. This book is designed as a main or supplemental text for a high school or college introductory biology course. Profusely illustrated throughout with clearly drawn, cross-sectional diagrams of representative species of thirty-three invertebrate phyla, the book is a useful source of information for nonacademic readers as well. Chapter 23, "Phylum Arthropoda," has a section describing the exoskeleton and its components, complete with a special, explanatory diagram.

Mash, Kaye. *How Invertebrates Live*. New York: E. P. Dutton, 1977. A wonderful introduction to the subject of invertebrates written for the nonacademic reader. The author presupposes no prior scientific background and handles each subtopic and subject in a clear and down-to-earth manner. It is abundantly illustrated throughout with beautiful color photographs that are reproduced with good definition. Chapter 3, "Skeletons and Movement," is the main chapter dealing with the topic of exoskeletons and the problems and advantages of those groups of animals having them.

Richards, O. W., and R. G. Davies. *Imms' Outlines of Entomology*. 6th ed. London: Chapman and Hall, 1978. Although intended as an elementary text in insect science, the book is extremely useful as a basic introduction to any readers who have an interest in these animals' morphology. Two chapters in particular are a good source of information on insect exoskeletons. Both chapter 1, "Introduction," and chapter 2, "Anatomy and Physiology," explain clearly various aspects of exoskeleton composition and the evolutionary advantages it provides.

Wigglesworth, Vincent B. *Insect Physiology*. 6th ed. New York: John Wiley & Sons, 1966. A short but information-packed book on the physiology of this important class of arthropods. Chapter 1, "The Integument," will prove useful to readers who want to know more about the exoskeleton and how this unique and important structure benefits numerous species of insects. Although intended originally as a college or high school text or supplement, the book will enhance the understanding of any interested reader because of its clear and concise style.

Frederick M. Surowiec

Cross-References

Animal Cell Types, 105; Circulatory Systems of Invertebrates, 476; Endocrine Systems in Invertebrates, 793; Endoskeletons, 843; Evolution: A Historical Perspective, 903; Histological Analysis, 1299; Histology, 1307; Higher Invertebrate Animals, 1475; Lower Invertebrate Animals, 1483; Muscle Anatomy in Invertebrates, 1814.

EXTINCTION

Type of life science: Evolutionary biology
Other field of study: Genetics

"Extinction" means the total disappearance (by dying out) of all members of a species of plants or animals. Two types of extinctions are recognized by scientists: "background" extinction, in which a species disappears for one or more reasons, and "mass" extinctions, which occur when many different species disappear in a relatively short period of time.

Principal terms

CATASTROPHISM: a scientific theory which postulates that the geological features of the earth and life thereon have been drastically affected by natural disasters of huge proportions in past ages

FOSSIL: a remnant, impression, or trace of an animal or plant of a past geological age that has been preserved in the earth's crust

GENE: an element of the germ plasm that controls transmission of a hereditary characteristic by specifying the structure of a particular protein or by controlling the function of other genetic material

GENE POOL: the whole body of genes in an interbreeding population that includes each gene at a certain frequency in relation to other genes

SPECIES: a category of biological classification ranking immediately below the genus or subgenus, comprising related organisms or populations potentially capable of interbreeding

UNIFORMITARIANISM: a scientific theory that all processes which have affected the earth and living creatures thereon in the past are presently at work and observable by scientists

Summary of the Phenomenon

In 1796, a French naturalist, Georges Cuvier, demonstrated incontrovertibly that many species of once-living plants and animals had completely disappeared from the earth. Cuvier was also the first to recognize that many of the extinct species he identified had disappeared at approximately the same time—a mass extinction. He and his successors attributed extinctions to catastrophic events, such as the biblical flood. The catastrophists held the field of scientific opinion concerning extinction until the publication of Charles Lyell's *Principles of Geology* (1830-1833), which proclaimed the doctrine of uniformitarianism. Lyell maintained that no processes have affected the earth (including its flora and fauna) that are not presently observable. He denied that any spectacular cataclysms had occurred.

Lyell's arguments convinced geologists, but the problem of extinctions remained: What could cause a plant or animal species to die out? In 1859, Charles Darwin offered a biological explanation for extinctions that seemed to answer all questions. In *On the Origin of Species*, Darwin suggested that all life-forms engage in a perpetual struggle for survival. The best-adapted species therefore survive and perpetuate themselves. The less-adapted species are outcompeted and disappear. Darwin's ideas seemed to fit well with the doctrine of uniformitarianism, but the problem of mass extinctions remained. He suggested no reasons why great numbers of very different species should disappear at approximately the same time.

Although his ideas were not accepted for many years after Darwin, another scientist proposed a possible solution to the puzzle of mass extinctions as early as 1837. Louis Agassiz produced evidence that the earth has periodically undergone periods of extreme cold, with much of its surface covered by glaciers. Agassiz's glaciers are presently in existence, move very slowly, and thus fit well with the uniformitarian view. His glaciers might also explain mass extinction in evolutionary terms, since plants and animals that could not adapt to changing climate would be outcompeted by other species that could adapt, and, thus, the less-flexible species would disappear.

Uniformitarian views about extinction received a further boost in the twentieth century with the proposal of the theory of continental drift, which has evolved into the modern theory of plate tectonics. Scientists have demonstrated that the land-masses of the earth are in constant motion relative to one another and to the poles of the planet. Over millions of years, the present landmasses have occupied very different positions on the earth's surface, often drifting quite near the polar regions, causing massive climatic changes. In addition, scientists have demonstrated that landmasses have subsided to be covered by the seas and have risen to create dry land from ocean floors. These massive changes would also have a profound effect on flora and fauna, creating constant competition and struggle for survival.

Many contemporary biologists believe that background extinctions may be the result of genetic rather than strictly climatic factors. In simple terms, extinction results from an excess of deaths over births in a given species. This excess represents, in biological terms, a reduction in the characteristics of a species that allow it to adapt to its environment. Those characteristics, biologists argue, are brought about through natural selection, a process that favors the genes that give the organism an advantage in the struggle for survival. Since natural selection has produced not only the species itself but its ancestors as well, any change in environment must work against the existing organisms. In the new process of changed environment, new gene combinations will result that will produce an organism better adapted to the changed environment. If, however, these genetic changes do not occur rapidly enough, adaptation will not take place and the species will become extinct.

Another possibility results if an organism is too well adapted to its environment. The gene pool of a species usually combines those genes that work well with one another to produce a well-adapted individual. Some biologists have observed a tendency within the gene pools of some species to resist genetic adaptation when environmental changes occur. Thus, genetic changes that could impart greater chances for survival of the individual in times of environmental turbulence do not occur. This effect also occurs when groups of genes are linked together (usually by a chromosomal inversion) in such a way as to prevent new gene combinations that might impart the ability to adjust to changed environmental conditions. This phenomenon actually retards the ability of a species to survive and may lead to extinctions.

Genetics may also explain mass extinctions. One biologist has theorized that species which live in environments that change very little over long periods of time probably have low genetic variability (a gene pool in which nonutilitarian genes have disappeared). Conversely, species in changeable environments should have much more genetic diversity, allowing them to cope with rapidly altering living conditions. If that is true, then mass extinctions might result from a rapid environmental change after a very long period of stability. When the change came, the theory goes, widespread extinctions of many species resulted. Most geneticists, however, reject this theory of mass extinctions. The species in unstable environments may actually have less genetic variability than those in stable environments. Biologists therefore have not been able to advance a plausible genetic explanation for mass extinctions.

Geologists have identified a number of what they call "mass extinction events." The first such event known to paleontologists occurred 440 million years ago at the end of the Ordovician period, during which more than 22 percent of all families and 57 percent of all genera disappeared. Another mass extinction occurred during the Devonian period, 370 million years ago, during which more than 20 percent of all marine families disappeared. The greatest of all mass extinctions occurred 248 million years ago, at the end of the Permian period. During that event, 52 percent of all marine families, 83 percent of all genera, and a frightening 95 percent of all species became extinct. During this event, land animals and plants vanished along with marine flora and fauna. Yet another "great dying" took place during the Triassic period, approximately 215 million years ago, when 20 percent of all marine families and 48 percent of all genera disappeared.

The mass extinction known most widely outside the scientific community occurred at the end of the Cretaceous period, about 65 million years ago. During this event, the dinosaurs vanished, along with 50 percent of all marine genera. A number of less-spectacular mass extinctions have taken place in the earth's long history, including a relatively recent one at the end of the Pleistocene epoch, which included among its victims such well-known extinct animals as the woolly mammoth and the so-called saber-toothed tiger.

Some paleobiologists and archaeologists are convinced that many of the Pleistocene extinctions were caused by the activities of human beings. They point out that the extinction of most of the large North American land mammals coincided with one theoretical date for the appearance of humans in the Western Hemisphere, approximately 11,500 years ago. According to these scientists, especially efficient human hunters were responsible for those extinctions; however, this theory seems unlikely as an explanation for all the Pleistocene extinctions. Many species in areas other than North America disappeared at the same time, most of which would have had little or no value as game. In addition, there are huge "boneyards" containing fossils of the extinct species in areas as far separated as Alaska and Florida that apparently died at the same time from causes that seem to be related to some great natural cataclysm.

The species of flora and fauna that disappeared in each of these mass extinctions apparently died at approximately the same time, and scientists were at a loss to explain them until 1980. In that year, a scientific team led by Nobel laureate Luis Alvarez presented what seems to be irrefutable evidence that the extinction of the dinosaurs coincided with the collision of a huge asteroid or comet with the earth. The evidence is based on a layer of clay that separates the rock formations associated with the dinosaurs from the overlying formations, which contain fossils from the era of mammals. The clay contains large amounts of iridium and other elements that are scarce in the crust of the earth but common in asteroids and comets.

Many scientists now contend that the collision between the earth and a large extraterrestrial body would have thrown enormous quantities of dust into the atmosphere, sufficient to block out the sun's radiation for an extended period of time. The resulting sub-zero weather would have had devastating effects on flora and fauna, including even the seemingly invincible dinosaurs. Shortly after the evidence for the collision appeared, other scientists presented evidence for an even more frightening phenomenon—periodicity of extinction events.

A scientist charting the occurrence of mass extinction events showed that they seem to occur at regularly spaced intervals, approximately every 26 to 30 million years. Almost immediately after the presentation of the evidence for periodicity, new scientific studies demonstrated more evidence that several mass extinctions other than the one during which the dinosaurs disappeared are also associated with unusually high concentrations of iridium. Taken together, these data seem to indicate that most, perhaps all, mass extinctions are caused by extraterrestrial agents and recur on a regular basis. If that is indeed the case, the implications for all the sciences, including evolutionary biology, are profound.

Methods of Study

Scientists from several different disciplines are currently studying extinctions, including mass extinctions, in a variety of ways. Many biologists believe that the most effective way to understand background extinctions is to examine those that have taken place in historic times. Geologists and paleontologists are subjecting the fossil record to a new and rigorous examination, armed with new, supersensitive techniques for ascertaining the ages of the rocks in which fossils occur in an attempt to understand mass extinctions better. These new techniques are the products of research in nuclear physics. Ecologists are particularly examining currently endangered flora and fauna, which may soon disappear. Even some astronomers are actively engaged in research into mass extinctions, scanning the heavens with powerful telescopes in search of an extraterrestrial agent that might explain the apparent periodicity of mass extinction events.

Biologists studying recent background extinctions conclude that virtually all of them are the results of the activities of humankind. The great auk, the last-known specimens of which were killed by Icelandic fishermen in 1844; the Tasmanian tiger cat, the last-known specimen of which died in captivity in 1934; and many other species are examples of human-caused extinctions. These studies lend validity to the theory that at least some of the many extinctions during the Pleistocene resulted from the hunting activities of prehistoric peoples. More disturbing are studies which show that such modern phenomena as acid rain and ozone depletion, both results of industrialization, may be doing irreparable damage to the environment, which could result in another mass extinction event in the very near future. Indeed, some biologists and ecologists believe that such an event has already begun.

A number of geologists and paleontologists, using new dating techniques based on the rate of radioactive decay in rocks, are reassessing the ages traditionally assigned to fossils by less sophisticated techniques in the past. These studies should eventually reveal whether the mass extinction events of the remote past occurred in a very short or over a relatively longer period of time. Other geologists are searching for impact craters, to lend further credence to the theory that at least some and perhaps all mass extinctions resulted from periodic collisions between the earth and large celestial bodies.

A team of physicists (including astrophysicists), engaged in an ongoing search for a hypothetical dark companion to our sun, has postulated that the orbit of this presently undiscovered body may periodically disrupt the comet cluster on the outer fringes of the solar system, resulting in many comets being diverted into an intersection with the earth's orbit. If their search is successful, it will provide powerful substantiating evidence for the collision theory, with sobering implications. Some physicists have even proposed ways to prevent future collisions between the earth and large heavenly bodies.

Context

The implications of background and mass extinctions are profound. If, as an overwhelming mass of evidence seems to indicate, the activities of humankind are a major cause of recent background extinctions, then those activities may soon lead to an ecological disaster of gigantic proportions. At present rates of disappearance, as many as two million species currently in existence will disappear by the middle of the twenty-first century. Many biologists warn that the world's rain forests may become extinct by the end of the twentieth century. Rain forests are not only a primary source of the oxygen in our atmosphere but also a major supplier of medicines. Almost 20 percent of all currently used drugs come from tropical plants. Not only will humankind lose the source of medicines that relieve pain, antibiotics, drugs that treat heart disease, and more than a thousand plants that produce agents that are apparently effective against many forms of cancer, it will also lose other, potentially more effective substances that have yet to be discovered. Botanists report that less than 10 percent of tropical plants have been tested for medicinal value.

In addition, many wild tropical fruits and vegetables are resistant to droughts and to many diseases that affect their temperate-climate relatives. Botanists have used them in the past to introduce beneficial genes into the breeding lines of important food crops such as corn and rice. The loss of the rain forests could mean the loss of the ability to make those sorts of adjustments needed to feed an ever-burgeoning population.

Unless immediate steps are taken, plant extinctions on the scale envisioned by many botanists may also cause massive climatic changes. Some ecologists and geophysicists warn that if the tropical forests disappear, the result will be the "greenhouse effect." The greenhouse effect refers to a global increase in temperatures that may make many temperate regions (such as the American Midwest) that are presently heavily cultivated unsuitable for large-scale agriculture, causing world food shortages of catastrophic proportions. Some geologists believe that the greenhouse effect could also melt the polar ice caps, raising sea levels to the point that many coastal regions and many large cities would be inundated.

Of less immediate, but nevertheless great, concern is the theory that mass extinction events in the fossil record have resulted from collisions between the earth and asteroids or comets. Even if the theory is correct, however, there is no cause for alarm in the near future. If these collisions occur every 26 to 30 millon years, the next one is not due until approximately A.D. 16 million. Although the chances of such an object striking the earth at any given time are almost infinitely remote, one need only look at the crater-pocked surface of the moon to know that such collisions can occur and have taken place.

The implications of the collision theory for evolutionary biology, however, are far-reaching. If the theory is correct, then the struggle for survival is not the most important feature of evolution. No matter how well adapted to its environment a species may be, survival of a collision would be largely a matter of chance. If the theory proves to be correct, biologists will need to rewrite the textbooks on evolution.

Bibliography

Corliss, William R., ed. *Strange Planet: A Sourcebook of Unusual Geological Facts.* Glen Arm, Md.: Sourcebook Project, 1975. Corliss' book is a compilation of articles, most from scientific journals, which deal with little-known or poorly understood geologic phenomena. Included throughout are articles concerned with mass extinctions and their possible causes. The articles all present data which strongly suggest that only cataclysmic events could have caused mass extinctions.

Elliot, David K., ed. *Dynamics of Extinction.* New York: John Wiley & Sons, 1986. The twelve articles in Elliot's book address the subject of background extinctions and mass extinctions from several perspectives, including the problem of apparent periodicity (suggesting an extraterrestrial agent), climatic causation of extinctions, contemporary extinctions (the destructiveness of modern technology and its environmental consequences), and possible approaches to further study and understanding of the causes of extinctions. The lack of anything approaching unanimity among the authors whose articles appear in the book concerning the causes and effects of extinctions indicates the dire need for further, interdisciplinary study of the subject.

Gore, Rick. "Extinctions." *National Geographic* 175 (June, 1989): 662-698. This article, beautifully illustrated with photographs and diagrams, reviews the various theories of mass extinctions. It includes interviews with researchers who espouse differing points of view on the causes of extinctions.

Martin, Paul S., and Richard G. Klein, eds. *Quaternary Extinctions: A Prehistoric Revolution.* Tucson: University of Arizona Press, 1984. This book contains thirty-eight articles, which analyze the most recent mass extinction event from many perspectives. Various articles examine the influence of humankind on extinctions in many parts of the world, the influence of climatic changes, and the influence of seafloor rising/land subsidence. The articles demonstrate the complexity of the problem of extinctions and the lack of a scientific consensus on their causes.

Muller, Richard. *Nemesis: The Death Star.* New York: Weidenfeld & Nicolson, 1988. Muller provides a fascinating account of the origin and evolution of the currently controversial theory that the dinosaurs became extinct because of the collision of the earth with an asteroid or comet. He then details the development of the theory that our sun has a presently undiscovered dark companion (he has named it Nemesis) that causes the disruption of either the asteroids or (more likely) the comet cluster every 26 to 30 million years. This disruption results in periodic collisions between the celestial objects and the earth, causing mass extinctions of terrestrial life.

Soule, M. E., ed. *Conservation Biology Revisited.* Sunderland, Mass.: Sinauer Associates, 1986. Most of the articles in Soule's book relate to threats to the ecosystem caused by a number of factors and the ways in which those threats may be countered. There are particularly good articles concerning the depletion of tropical forests and the potential greenhouse effect.

Stanley, Steven M. *Extinction.* New York: Scientific American Library, 1987. Stanley's book is an excellent account of extinctions in general and major mass extinctions in particular. He makes a strong case for gradual climatic changes being the primary agent in extinctions but acknowledges that catastrophic events and the activities of humankind may have played significant roles in some extinction events.

Paul Madden

Cross- References

Adaptive Radiation, 29; The Biosphere, Biomes, and Habitats, 210; Ecological Niches, 729; Ecological Principles, 736; Evolution: A Historical Perspective, 903; The Greenhouse Effect, 1225; The Hardy-Weinberg Law of Genetic Equilibrium, 1262; Natural Selection, 1870; Predation, 2178.

EXTRANUCLEAR INHERITANCE

Type of life science: Genetics
Other fields of study: Microbiology and the origin of life (paleontology)

Extranuclear inheritance is a non-Mendelian form of heredity that involves genetic information located in cytoplasmic organelles such as mitochondria. Cytoplasmic genes are of interest in understanding evolution, genetic diseases, and the relationship between genetics and embryology.

Principal terms

CHROMOSOMES: the threadlike structures that carry linear arrays of genes; in higher organisms, the chromosomes consist of deoxyribonucleic acid (DNA) molecules complexed with ribonucleic acid (RNA) and proteins

CYTOPLASM: the aqueous phase of the cell in which organelles such as mitochondria and ribosomes are suspended; it contains proteins, RNA, metabolites, waste products, and electrolytes

ENDOSYMBIONT THEORY: the idea that cellular organelles such as mitochondria have evolved from free-living organisms that began to live symbiotically within the cells of another organism

EUKARYOTES: organisms made up of cells containing a distinct nucleus bounded by a membrane and a cell sap containing various membrane-bound organelles such as mitochondria

GENE: the fundamental physical unit of inheritance; a specific DNA sequence that codes for a single gene product

GENOME: the total complement of genetic material carried by an organism

MITOCHONDRIA: organelles found in the cytoplasm of almost all eukaryotic cells that serve as the basic energy-producing machinery of the cell

NUCLEUS: a structure found in eukaryotic cells that contains the chromosomes

ORGANELLES: subcellular structures serving specific functions for the cell; cell organelles include mitochondria, chloroplasts, plastids, endoplasmic reticulum, centrioles, and lysosomes

Summary of the Phenomenon

Extranuclear inheritance is a non-Mendelian form of heredity that involves genetic information located in cytoplasmic organelles such as mitochondria rather than genes located on the chromosomes found in the cell nucleus. Extranuclear genes located in mitochondria and chloroplasts are the most extensively studied examples of extranuclear inheritance. Both parents contribute equally to the inheritance of nuclear genes, but extranuclear genes are more likely to be transmitted through the maternal line because the egg is rich in cytoplasmic organelles, whereas the sperm contributes only its nucleus to the fertilized egg. Therefore, extranuclear genes do not follow Gregor Mendel's statistical laws of segregation and recombination. Cytoplasmic genes are of interest in understanding evolution, genetic diseases, and the relationship between genetics and embryology.

Since the rediscovery of Mendel's principles, research in genetics has been guided by the belief that the fundamental units of inheritance are located on chromosomes in the cell nucleus. T. H. Morgan, one of the founders of modern genetics, declared that the cytoplasm could be ignored genetically. Yet, some biologists resisted the concept of a "nuclear monopoly" over inheritance. Embryologists, in particular, argued that nuclear genes, identical in every cell, could not explain how cells differentiated from one another in the course of development. They argued that differences between cells in the developing embryo must have a basis in the cytoplasm. Trying to formulate a compromise, some biologists suggested that Mendelian genes play a role in determining individual characteristics, while cytoplasmic determinants are responsible for more fundamental aspects of plants and animals. The discovery of a wide variety of cytoplasmic entities seemed to support the concept that cytoplasmic factors played a role in development and heredity.

In the 1940's, Boris Ephrussi's work on "petite" mutants in yeast suggested that inheritance of this trait depended on some factor in the cytoplasm rather than the nucleus. Yeast cells with the petite mutation produce abnormally small colonies when grown on a solid medium with glucose as the energy source. Petite mutants grow slowly because they lack important membrane-bound enzymes belonging to the respiratory system.

Similar studies have been made of slow-growing mutants of the bread mold *Neurospora*. Inheritance of the trait known as "poky" shows a non-Mendelian pattern. Microinjection of purified mitochondria from poky into normal strains has also been used to demonstrate the cytoplasmic inheritance of this trait.

As early as 1909, geneticists were reporting examples of non-Mendelian inheritance in higher plants, usually green and white variegated patterns. These patterns seemed to be related to the behavior of the chloroplasts, organelles that contain the photosynthesizing apparatus of green plants. Because of the chloroplasts' rather large size, scientists have been able to study their behavior in dividing cells with the light microscope since the 1880's. Like mitochondria, chloroplasts contain their own deoxyribonucleic acid (DNA) and ribonucleic acid (RNA). Although chloroplasts contain significant genetic factors, they do not seem to be totally autonomous; nuclear genes are required for some aspects of chloroplast development. Another interesting case of extranuclear inheritance in plants is that of cytoplasmic male sterility. Many species of plants seem to produce strains with cytoplasmically inherited pollen sterility.

Advances in experimental methods made in the 1960's allowed scientists to demonstrate that organelles located in the cytoplasm contain DNA. This finding came as a great surprise to most biologists. In 1966, the first vertebrate mitochondrial DNA was isolated and characterized. Like bacterial DNA, mitochondrial DNA generally consists of a single double helix of "naked," circular DNA. The mitochondrial genome is usually smaller than that of even the simplest bacteria. Most of the proteins in the mitochondrion are encoded in nuclear genes, but mitochondrial DNA contains genes for mitochondrial ribosomal RNAs, transfer RNAs, and some of the proteins of the respiratory-enzyme complexes found in the inner membrane of the mitochondrion.

The DNA found in chloroplasts and mitochondria is chemically distinct from the DNA in the nucleus. Moreover, the extranuclear genetic systems behave differently from those within the nucleus. Even more surprising is the finding that mitochondria have their own version of the genetic code, which was previously thought to be common to all organisms, from virus to human. In general, the DNA found in cytoplasmic organelles has a rather limited coding capacity. Thus, by identifying the functions under the control of mitochondrial or chloroplast genes, all other functions carried on by the organelle can be assigned to the nuclear genome. Coordinating the contributions of the organelle and the nuclear genomes is undoubtedly a complex process.

In addition to the genes found in mitochondria and chloroplasts, extranuclear factors are found in various kinds of endosymbionts and bacterial plasmids. Some biologists think that all organelles may have evolved from various kinds of symbiotic relationships. An endosymbiont is an organism that lives within the cells of another organism. Endosymbionts may be bacteria, algae, fungi, protozoa, or viruses. Unlike the mitochondria and chloroplasts, some endosymbionts seem to have retained independent genetic systems. The "killer" particles in paramecia, discovered by T. M. Sonneborn in the 1930's, provide a historically significant example. After many years of controversy, the killer particles were identified as bacterial symbionts. These cytoplasmic entities are not integral parts of the host cell, because the paramecia are quite capable of living and reproducing without them. Certain peculiar non-Mendelian conditions found in fruit flies also appear to be caused by endosymbionts.

Although bacteria lack a nucleus, their circular DNA is usually referred to as the bacterial chromosome. Some bacteria also contain separate DNA circles smaller than the bacterial chromosome. In the 1950's, Joshua Lederberg proposed the name "plasmid" for such extrachromosomal hereditary determinants. Some of the most interesting examples of these entities are the F (fertility) factor, the R (resistance transfer) factors, and the Col (colicin) factors. Resistance transfer factors can transmit resistance to antibiotics between bacteria of different species and genera. Col factors, toxic proteins produced by bacteria that kill other bacteria, were studied as toxins for many years before their genetic basis was discovered. While bacterial plasmids are by definition extranuclear genetic components, they are quite different from the genomes of the cytoplasmic organelles found in higher organisms. Yet, because of their simplicity, the bacterial systems are better understood and can serve as models for the kinds of studies that should be performed for extranuclear genes in higher organisms as techniques improve.

The recognition of extranuclear genetic systems raises very interesting questions about the possible evolutionary advantage of maintaining such genetic complexity within the cell. In contrast to the remarkable universality of the nuclear genetic system, extranuclear genetic systems are quite diverse in function and mechanisms of transmission. Although extranuclear genes control only a small fraction of the total hereditary material of the cell, in eukaryotic organisms the genes found in mitochondria and chloroplasts are clearly essential for maintaining life.

Methods of Study

The existence of non-Mendelian inheritance was suggested by the work of Karl Correns and Erwin Baur in 1909, but direct genetic evidence accumulated slowly until the 1960's, when the advances in biochemistry, biophysics, Mendelian genetics, and molecular genetics were brought to bear on the problem. Initially, cytoplasmic genes were identified by their failure to follow Mendel's rules, but the criteria for recognizing cytoplasmic genes were vague and indirect. Biologists looking for evidence of cytoplasmic inheritance carried out reciprocal crosses between different varieties, species, and genera of higher plants. It is interesting that Correns, who is remembered as one of the rediscoverers of Mendel, carried out many experiments on plants that provided examples of non-Mendelian inheritance. Others found evidence of cytoplasmic inheritance in wasps selected for differences in pigmentation. Studies of reciprocal crosses in some mosses also seemed to show cytoplasmic inheritance.

The methods now used to study extranuclear factors are very diverse. Some are based on the classical hybridization techniques of genetics and cytoplasmic genetic analysis, but others depend on the tools of biochemistry, molecular biology, and electron microscopy. The principal methods of study include analysis of non-Mendelian behaviors, such as "maternal inheritance"; differences in the results of reciprocal crosses; independence of nuclear and cytoplasmic gene assortment in suitable systems; microinjection techniques; infectivity in appropriate systems; somatic segregation during vegetative or clonal growth; and direct biochemical identification of extranuclear genetic factors.

In reciprocal hybridization experiments (crosses between organisms that differ in a specific trait), the distribution of that trait in the progeny should be the same regardless of whether the female or the male parent contributed the gene being tested if the gene is located in the nucleus, because both parents contribute equal chromosomal material. If the reciprocal crosses are different, extranuclear factors may be involved, because the female parent usually contributes much more cytoplasm than the male. In species in which the nuclear chromosomes have been well mapped, the absence of linkage with known chromosomally located genes can also be used as an indication of extranuclear inheritance.

Crosses made between different species of plants provided evidence of non-Mendelian patterns of inheritance for traits that were apparently transmitted through female reproductive cells. Yet, "maternal effects" as a result of the orientation of various constituents of the egg cytoplasm (such as the direction of coiling of the shell of certain snails) might account for such results. A series of repeated back-crosses can be used to distinguish between the inheritance of cytoplasmic genes and maternal effects caused by the arrangement of factors in a particular egg.

The kinds of hybridization experiments possible with plant species cannot be performed with animals, but it is sometimes possible to fertilize the enucleated egg of one species with the sperm of another. Such experiments posed difficult technical problems and the possibility that not all nuclear material was removed. Neverthe-less, such embryological experiments did seem to provide good evidence that cer-tain characters were cytoplasmic.

Heterokaryon formation and microinjection techniques have been used in studies of extranuclear factors in molds and amoebas. For example, when different strains of mold are brought in contact, their hyphae (branching tubular cells) may unite, producing heterokaryons (hyphae with two different kinds of nuclei and a mixture of cytoplasm). It is then possible to separate the two kinds of nuclei and look for signs of recombination between nuclear genes and cytoplasmic factors. A related technique can be used in amoebas. Nuclei from one cell are injected into another cell. The new cell can then be divided into daughter cells having only a single nu-cleus. Microinjection techniques can also be used to inject cytoplasmic components such as mitochondria into different cells to establish novel nuclear-cytoplasmic interactions. Such experiments have been successful in molds, paramecia, and amoebas.

In order to characterize the genome of cellular organelles, however, scientists had to purify and isolate them from other parts of the cell. One method of accomplish-ing this separation is known as differential centrifugation, that is, centrifugation carried out over a series of increasing speeds. Heavier components such as nuclei and unbroken cells precipitate at relatively low speeds; as the speed is increased, lighter entities such as mitochondria will come down. Similarly, the DNAs of cyto-plasmic organelles were separated and characterized by using cesium chloride den-sity gradients in the ultracentrifuge. Nuclear and organelle DNAs could be sepa-rated because of difference in their composition and structure (organelle DNA is generally circular). The distinctive base composition of organelle DNAs provided further evidence of their unique genetic identity.

Ruth Sager was one of the first scientists to demonstrate the value of a unified approach to the study of cytoplasmic genes. Her research combined genetic analysis of the recombination and linkage of cytoplasmic genes with biophysical studies of organelle DNA and biochemical studies of chloroplast mutations. Sager stressed the importance of using cytoplasmic mutants as an analytical tool that can reveal the interdependent network of nuclear and organelle gene products and signals.

Using the powerful techniques of molecular biology, scientists can directly exam-ine the behavior of nuclear and cytoplasmic genes, determining which characters of the organelles are controlled by nuclear DNA and investigating how nuclear and cytoplasmic genetic systems interact. For example, hybridization experiments can determine whether RNAs found in organelles are complementary to nucleic acid sequences on the organelle DNA.

Specific inhibitors of organelle transcription and translation are also being used to study the activity of organelle gene. For example, mitochondrial protein synthesis is blocked by antibacterial antibiotics such as chloramphenicol and tetracycline; it is not affected by cycloheximide, which blocks the activity of cytoplasmic ribosomes. Therefore, one protein-synthesizing system can be blocked while the other is labeled with radioactive (labeled) isotopes. These methods have enabled scientists to determine which system does what and to identify products of mitochondrial DNA.

Context

Developments in cytoplasmic genetics may have significant impact both on basic science and on important practical applications in human genetics, medical research, and agriculture. Studies of cytoplasmic inheritance may help to bridge the gap between genetics and embryology. Before the identification of cytoplasmic DNAs, systematic investigations of cytoplasmic genetics in a microbial system were carried out with the green alga *Chlamydomonas*. They led to the demonstration of recombination and linkage of cytoplasmic genes and the recognition of the first cytoplasmic linkage group, or "chromosome." Although cytoplasmic genes can be studied by methods independent of the existence of DNA, geneticists had been generally skeptical about the existence or significance of cytoplasmic genes. Suddenly, scientists were certain that if cytoplasmic DNAs exist, cytoplasmic genes must exist. Since the 1960's, investigators of cytoplasmic genetic systems have been trying to integrate evidence from genetic, biophysical, and biochemical studies of cytoplasmic genetic systems.

Studies of extranuclear inheritance are significant with respect to the question of the evolution of cells of higher organisms. These discoveries have complicated the genetic landscape with an assortment of entities and factors having no obvious place in prevailing theories of the evolution of the higher forms of life. Somehow, evolutionary and genetic theory must cope with interactions between mutually dependent nuclear and cytoplasmic genetic systems maintained within the confines of each cell.

Although organelle DNAs clearly play an important part in cell organization, it was difficult to pinpoint the essential roles of organelle DNA and protein-synthesizing systems. Many technical difficulties, and the traditionally low priority of this field, meant that the techniques for dealing with the complexities of the system emerged only slowly. Studies of cytoplasmic genetics will doubtless have significant applications in medical science and agriculture as well as an impact on understanding of the evolution of genetic control mechanisms. For example, M. M. Rhoades's work on maize in the 1940's forced American geneticists to take note of research on cytoplasmic genes, while plant breeders began to use cytoplasmically inherited pollen sterility in the production of hybrid seed. Cytoplasmic pollen sterility is a useful trait to incorporate into commercial inbred lines because it ensures cross-pollination and thus simplifies seed production. (Unfortunately, a toxin-producing fungus to which the major corn cytoplasmic gene for pollen sterility was susceptible destroyed more than 50 percent of the corn crop in certain areas of the United States in 1970. This disaster prompted a return to hand-detasseling.)

Hemoflagellates, such as trypanosomids, are a group of parasitic protozoa responsible for African sleeping sickness, leishmaniasis, and Chagas' disease, among other afflictions. The trypanosomes typically contain a specialized organelle called a kinetoplast, a DNA-containing organelle that is similar to a mitochondrion. Certain acridine dyes appear to block differentially the replication of kinetoplast DNA; the trypanosome then loses respiratory functions and dies. Thus, it should be possible to find drugs that act on the kinetoplast DNA with minimal effects on the host.

Little is known about the effects of cytoplasmic gene mutations on embryological development, but there are suggestive cases. Some complex disorders suggest cytoplasmic transmission through the maternal line, rather than simple sex-linkage. In 1988, scientists reported that a deletion found in human mitochondrial DNA was responsible for an interesting series of related muscle disorders. It is apparently the first example of a new type of genetic disease, but other unsolved riddles concerning diseases with peculiar, confusing patterns of inheritance might eventually be resolved by analysis of mitochondrial DNA in affected individuals. The defects found so far have been spontaneous mutations rather than established inherited disorders. When the defects occur during development, the disorder will appear only in cells derived from the first mutant cell. If the defect appears early in development, almost all the cells will be affected; if the mutation occurs at a later stage, the defect will be more limited. For example, specific deletions in mitochondrial DNA appear to cause a variety of eye disorders.

In 1987, studies of mitochondrial DNA resulted in headlines proclaiming that scientists had found Adam and Eve, or at least a female common ancestor of modern human beings who had lived some 200,000 years ago. This ancestral mother of the human race was dubbed "Mitochondrial Eve." Thus, the molecular biology of mitochondrial DNA has been added to the study of ancient bones and tools as a means of studying humankind's most ancient ancestors and constructing family trees. Mitochondrial DNA is of interest as a special tool for tracing family trees because it is inherited only from the mother, in contrast to nuclear DNA, which is inherited from both parents. Yet, many problems are unresolved and the accuracy of the results is questionable.

Some scientists argue that mitochondrial DNA is simply an evolutionary dead end, a vestige of the past, with very little reason for its continued existence. Mitochondrial genetic systems are very simple when compared to the nuclear apparatus, but they have proved to be very diverse when studied by sophisticated modern methodology. Thus, the study of the mitochondrial system may provide a valuable model system in which to retrace the evolutionary pathways that led to the mechanisms of gene expression in modern bacteria and eukaryotes.

Bibliography

Beale, Geoffrey, and Jonathan Knowles. *Extranuclear Genetics*. Baltimore: University Park Press, 1978. Emphasis on study of genetic properties of mitochondria and chloroplasts and examples of extranuclear heredity in higher organisms and bacteria. References include original publications and major review articles. Index, diagrams, and illustrations. Appropriate for college and high school students with some knowledge of biology and genetics.

De Duve, Christian. *A Guided Tour of the Living Cell*. New York: Scientific American Books, 1984. A beautifully illustrated guide to the finest details of cellular architecture. The two-volume text is based on a distinguished lecture series addressed to high school students. The cytosol and its organelles are discussed in great detail with remarkable clarity and humor. Illustrations, informative and amusing diagrams, and index.

Gillham, Nicholas W. *Organelle Heredity*. New York: Raven Press, 1978. This text is basically about genetics, but the emphasis is on organelle DNA, transcription and translation within chloroplasts and mitochondria, and the biogenesis of these organelles. Genetic theories are presented in a clear and direct fashion that will make them comprehensible and exciting to the nongeneticist. Many illustrations, tables, graphs, simplified diagrams, references, and index.

Grivell, Leslie A. "Mitochondrial DNA." *Scientific American* 248 (March, 1983): 78-89. A well-written article, with excellent illustrations, diagrams and lucid explanations of the genetic system of mitochondria.

Harris, Henry. *Nucleus and Cytoplasm*. 3d ed. London: Oxford University Press, 1974. Good overview of the role of nucleus and cytoplasm, addressed to a general audience. Describes the major advances in molecular biology that have had an impact on the study of nucleus and cytoplasm: development of assays for the biological activity of messenger RNAs, analysis of transcriptional and translational controls, and studies of cell fusion. Illustrations, author index, subject index, and references.

Margulis, Lynn. *Symbiosis in Cell Evolution: Life and Its Environment on the Early Earth*. San Francisco: W. H. Freeman, 1981. Beautifully written exposition of the endosymbiotic theory and a comprehensive, if sometimes speculative, discussion of the evolution of life. Illustrations, references, and index.

Sager, Ruth. *Cytoplasmic Genes and Organelles*. New York: Academic Press, 1972. Sager was the first geneticist to provide evidence of recombination and linkage of cytoplasmic genes and one of the first to isolate and characterize chloroplast DNA. This text provided the first thorough survey of cytoplasmic genetics. Suitable for students and professionals as an introduction to the subject. Covers historical and conceptual aspects of cytoplasmic genetics, biophysical studies of chloroplast DNA, genetic analysis, and biochemical studies of chloroplast mutations. Illustrations, tables, diagrams, lists of useful review articles and important references, glossary, and subject index.

Sapp, Jan. *Beyond the Gene: Cytoplasmic Inheritance and the Struggle for Author-*

ity in Genetics. New York: Oxford University Press, 1987. History of the battle between Mendelian geneticists in the early twentieth century and advocates of cytoplasmic inheritance. Sapp argues that the "nuclear monopoly" deliberately tried to gain scientific authority by excluding competing theories. Provides valuable background information on the work and careers of early leaders in the field of extranuclear inheritance, such as Boris Ephrussi and T. M. Sonneborn. Bibliography and index.

Stewart, Alistair D., and David M. Hunt. *The Genetic Basis of Development*. New York: Halsted Press, 1982. Part of a series covering selected areas of biology for undergraduate students. Uses a multidisciplinary approach to genetics, biochemistry, and developmental biology. Deals with maternal effects in various animals, nuclear-cytoplasmic interactions, and cell fusion experiments. Illustrations, diagrams, tables, references, and index.

Tierney, John, and Lynda Wright. "The Search for Adam and Eve." *Newsweek* 111 (January 11, 1988): 46-52. A well-written account of an exciting, but still controversial, new method of tracing human ancestry through the female line by use of mitochondrial DNA. Illustrations and helpful diagrams.

Lois N. Magner

Cross-References

Chloroplasts and Other Plastids, 431; DNA Replication, 692; Eukaryotic Gene Organization, 871; Evolution: A Historical Perspective, 903; Genes and Nucleic Acids, 1134; Genes and Polypeptide Chains, 1141; The Genetic Code, 1148; Genetics: A Historical Perspective, 1177; The Origin of Life, 1572; Mitochondria, 1745; Prebiotic Evolution in the Laboratory, 2170.

FERTILIZATION

Type of life science: Developmental biology (embryology)
Other fields of study: Biochemistry, cell biology (cytology), and genetics

Fertilization is the process whereby two highly specialized cells (the egg and the sperm) join together. As a result, novel combinations of genes from both parents are united in a common cell, which develops into the embryo. Fertilization of eggs in culture is used to correct some types of human infertility.

Principal terms

ACROSOME: a membrane-bound bag of enzymes at the head of the sperm; these enzymes are released at fertilization and chemically create a path to the egg

CAPACITATION: a change in the sperm brought about by contact with secretions of the female reproductive tract; capacitated sperm have the "capacity," or capability, to fertilize the egg

CLEAVAGE: the series of rapid cell divisions of the fertilized egg that form the early embryo; cleavage occurs without intervening growth of the cells

CORTICAL GRANULE: a membrane-bound bag of enzymes underneath the surface of the egg; the enzymes are released at fertilization and participate in blocking fertilization by a second sperm

EGG: the reproductive cell of the female produced in the ovary; also known as an "oocyte" or "ootid"

GAMETE: a generic term for both the egg and the sperm

HAPLOID: the condition of a cell having only one copy of each chromosome; haploid eggs and sperm are formed from diploid parent cells by the process of meiosis

MEIOSIS: the process of cell division in the formation of eggs and sperm; it results in the reduction of the number of chromosomes by half

PARTHENOGENESIS: literally, "virgin birth"; the process of triggering the activation and development of an egg without sperm; numerous chemical and physical factors can cause parthenogenesis

POLYSPERMY: the condition of fertilization of an egg by more than one sperm; polyspermy is lethal in most species and is prevented by processes that occur at fertilization

PRONUCLEI: haploid nuclei in the fertilized egg that fuse together to form the diploid nucleus of the new organism

ZYGOTE: another term for a fertilized egg

Summary of the Phenomenon

Fertilization is the means whereby two parent organisms combine parts of their genetic heritage into a new organism, their offspring. Organisms do this by creating very specialized cells (eggs in females, sperm in males) that fuse together in the process of fertilization to produce a new cell, the fertilized egg, or zygote, which then develops into an embryo.

The process of producing eggs and sperm involves a type of cell division peculiar to gametes (eggs and sperm) that is called meiosis. Most cells of the organism are diploid, which means that for each chromosome (composed of serially linked genes of deoxyribonucleic acid, or DNA), there are two copies. One copy is inherited from the individual's mother, and one from the father. Since eggs and sperm are produced from diploid cells, it is necessary that they reduce the number of chromosomes by half so that the diploid state will be restored at fertilization. These "reduction divisions" occur during meiosis and produce "haploid" eggs and sperm.

The haploid cell in the testis of a male is not a sperm until it completes some elaborate modifications. These modifications prepare the sperm for its mission at fertilization. They involve the transformation of cell organelles into highly specialized sperm components. The two centrioles organize the construction of a long tail capable of whiplike movement. The numerous mitochondria in the cell fuse together to form one large mitochondrion, which coils inside the tail. The mitochondria produce the high-energy molecule adenosine triphosphate (ATP), used by the sperm tail to power its movement. The nucleus, which contains the haploid number of chromosomes, condenses into a very compact and streamlined mass. Finally, the lysosomes (small, membrane-bound bags of enzymes) coalesce into one large lysosome, called the acrosome, at the head of the sperm. The enzymes in the acrosome are used to digest a path for the sperm through the protective coatings of the egg.

No less than the sperm, the egg is also highly specialized for its role in fertilization. Unlike the sperm, however, the egg is also specialized to become the embryo. It is the very large egg, not the sperm, that cleaves (divides) and is transformed into an embryo after fertilization. The egg grows within the ovary before the meiotic divisions occur, dramatically increasing the volume of its cytoplasm. The nucleus of the egg is very active throughout growth. By the processes of transcription, ribonucleic acid (RNA) is copied from the nuclear DNA. By the process of translation, this messenger RNA (mRNA) is used to make protein. Much of the RNA that is made in the active nucleus is used to produce protein for the growth of the egg cytoplasm, and much is stored in the egg for use after fertilization. Depending on the species of animal, the egg may also store yolk produced outside the egg. In the case of the bird, large amounts of yolk produced in the liver are transported to the growing egg.

Depending on the species, the meiotic divisions of the egg occur just before or just after fertilization. The cell divisions are very unequal, preserving most of the egg's cytoplasm while discarding chromosomes in very small cells called polar bodies. A specialization of the egg, very similar to the acrosome in the sperm, is formed in preparation for fertilization. The egg's lysosomes accumulate just below the surface. These "cortical granules" release their contents from the egg at fertilization, which is important in preventing fertilization by more than one sperm, a lethal condition called polyspermy.

The actual process of fertilization involves a number of successive membrane fusions. Eggs and sperm, the acrosome, and the cortical granules are all bounded by membranes. The cellular membrane is essentially an oily film on the surface of the watery cytoplasm. Just as oil droplets can coalesce, so two membranes can fuse and become confluent. Fertilization can be thought of as four successive membrane fusions.

First, the sperm's acrosome membrane fuses with the sperm's cell membrane. As a result, the enzymes within the acrosome spill out and digest their way through the various coatings surrounding the egg. In many species (the sea urchin included), a long acrosomal process (projection) forms from the elongation of microtubules underneath the acrosome. This "acrosomal reaction" also exposes proteins on the acrosomal membrane's inner surface. One of these proteins is a receptor protein whose shape matches a receptor glycoprotein on the egg's surface. As a result of the interaction of these receptors, the binding of the sperm to the egg is very specific. This specificity explains why sperm can usually only fertilize eggs of the same species.

Sperm develop the capacity to undergo the acrosomal reaction and fertilize the egg only after they have interacted with secretions of the female reproductive tract. In the case of species such as the sea urchin and frog, in which fertilization occurs outside the body, the "jelly" secreted around the egg as its passes through the female's oviduct and uterus is necessary for sperm "capacitation." In mammals, sperm are capacitated by interacting with the fluids in the female uterus. These fluids may remove molecules that coat the sperm and prevent sperm from interacting with molecules that trigger the acrosomal reaction.

Once the capacitated sperm has fired its acrosome and bound to the egg's surface, the second membrane fusion occurs. The membrane of the sperm fuses with the cell membrane of the egg. At the moment these membranes become one, the egg and the sperm no longer exist. In their place is the diploid "zygote."

The third membrane fusion is between the cortical granules in the periphery of the egg (zygote) with the egg's cell membrane. As with the acrosomal reaction in the sperm, the cortical granule reaction releases enzymes outside the egg. Eggs are surrounded by a nonliving coat made of cross-linked proteins and glycoproteins. Typically, this coat is closely attached to the egg membrane and referred to as the "vitelline envelope." The enzymes released from the cortical granules digest away the receptors in the vitelline envelope, which prevents the attachments of further sperm and thus blocks polyspermy. The enzymes also digest the protein moorings of the vitelline envelope, allowing it to expand away from the surface of the zygote from the influx of water. In species that do not form such a dramatic "fertilization envelope," there is still a biochemical alteration of the surrounding coat that accomplishes the same end of preventing polyspermy.

When the egg and sperm membranes are united, the sperm nucleus expands to form a typical nucleus. Not typical, however, is the fact that both the egg and sperm nuclei are haploid. In the fourth and last membrane fusion event, the haploid "pronuclei" fuse together to form a diploid nucleus. The first nucleus of the new individual is thereby formed, fertilization is complete, and cleavage commences.

With regard to the genetic contributions to the new individual, the egg and the sperm are equal. Both bring a haploid constellation of chromosomes to produce the new diploid individual. With regard to the cleavage divisions of the embryo, however, the role played by the egg is paramount to that of the sperm. In essence, the early embryo is a developing egg. The sperm activates the process, and there is a latent genetic stamp from the sperm, but the sperm otherwise plays no role in the cleavage divisions.

When fertilization occurs, a series of reactions is triggered in the cytoplasm of the egg (zygote). These reactions are known collectively as "activation." Since fertilization is the fusion of the membranes of the egg and sperm, the first change in this series occurs in the zygote membrane. Sodium ions suddenly enter the egg. Because sodium ions have a positive electrical charge, their addition changes the net electrical charge difference across the membrane and prevents the fusion of a second sperm. This reaction is called the "early" block to polyspermy; it is much quicker, but less effective, than the "late" block to polyspermy brought about by the cortical granule reaction.

A second change occurs in the cytoplasm when calcium ions are released from inside the egg. The release of calcium causes the cortical granule reaction. The cortical granule reaction begins at the site where the sperm fertilizes the egg and moves in all directions around the egg. As a result, a fertilization envelope forms or (depending on the species) the egg coat is modified. In either case, additional sperm are prevented from binding to and penetrating the egg. This action is the "late" block to polyspermy.

Shortly after the cortical granule reaction has occurred, there is a measurable increase in the pH of the cytoplasm (pH is a measure of the concentration of hydrogen ions—protons—in a solution): A high pH is alkaline, and a low pH is acidic; pH 7 is neutral. This increase in the pH of the cytoplasm is caused by the release of protons ("fertilization acid") from the zygote. The release of fertilization acid and the consequent increase in the pH of the cytoplasm have important effects on the cytoplasm. The unfertilized egg of most species is not very active. The egg is not growing or dividing, and there is very little measurable metabolic activity. This sluggishness changes at fertilization: There is an increase in the rate of oxygen consumption, an increase in the rate of protein synthesis, and the replication of the zygote's DNA in preparation for the first cleavage division.

Methods of Study

In studying the process of fertilization in animals, the most important consideration is the species that is studied. There are many important similarities in different species, and most of the principles are universal, but caution is still advisable in extending any result from one species to another.

The favorite research organism for the study of fertilization is the sea urchin. (Other animals, such as frogs, fish, and mice have been employed with great success, but none so successfully as the sea urchin.) During the breeding season of a given species of sea urchin, eggs and sperm are easily obtained in large quantities from adult animals. Eggs and sperm fertilize readily when they are combined in a dish containing sea water. The formation of a fertilization envelope is easily seen with the microscope as confirmation of successful fertilization. Subsequent development to the larval stage is rapid and requires no special culture conditions.

Many of the phenomena described above were first observed in sea urchins and extended to other species. The cortical granules and acrosomes, as well as their disappearance at fertilization, are easily seen in sections of eggs and sperm prepared for the electron microscope. Antibodies have been used to identify specific proteins in these sections and to pinpoint their locations within the cell. Electron microscopy can also be used to describe and chronicle changes in the sperm head as it transforms into the male pronucleus.

The binding of egg and sperm has been studied biochemically. The receptor protein in sea urchin sperm ("bindin") has been isolated, its molecular weight measured by the technique of electrophoresis, and its location targeted on the acrosomal process. The corresponding receptor on the egg has been identified as a glycoprotein on the vitelline envelope. If isolated bindin receptor from egg vitelline envelopes is present during fertilization, it will block fertilization by attaching to the sperms' bindin molecules. This type of "competition reaction" has been used to demonstrate that the interaction of egg and sperm receptors is very specific: Bindin receptors isolated from one species will not block fertilization in another species.

The role of calcium in the fertilization process can be confirmed by the use of specific chemicals. A calcium ionophore (a chemical that allows calcium ions to pass through the cell membrane unimpeded) will cause parthenogenesis: The cortical granule reaction in sea urchin eggs occurs in the complete absence of sperm. A protein called "aquorin" can be used to confirm the release of calcium inside the egg at fertilization. Aquorin will fluoresce (release light) when it combines with calcium. If aquorin is injected into an egg, and the egg is then fertilized, the release of calcium causes the egg literally to light up.

The increase in the pH of the cytoplasm of the fertilized egg can be observed indirectly by measuring a decrease in the pH of the sea water in which eggs are suspended (the release of fertilization acid) or directly by inserting miniature pH electrodes into the egg cytoplasm. The importance of this increase in the pH of the cytoplasm to the activation of the egg is demonstrated by observing the effects of simple ammonia on unfertilized eggs. Ammonia is alkaline. It penetrates the egg and directly increases the pH of the cytoplasm, which in turn causes the increase in protein synthesis that normally occurs after sperm fertilization.

Protein synthesis in cells is measured by the use of radioactive amino acids.

Because proteins are composed of amino acids, these radioactive amino acids are incorporated into newly synthesized protein by the cell. Radioactive proteins can be measured by precipitating them with strong acid and counting the radioactivity in the precipitate by use of a liquid scintillation counter.

The increase in protein synthesis in sea urchin eggs at fertilization occurs even when the pronuclei are physically removed or when the process of RNA synthesis is blocked with the poison actinomycin. The synthesis of protein requires messenger RNA, and mRNA is copied from nuclear DNA. Since protein synthesis increases without the presence or activity of the nuclear DNA, the only conclusion is that RNA is stored within the cytoplasm as the egg grows. Furthermore, this RNA must be stored in an inactive, or "masked," form during the growth of the egg and activated, or "unmasked," at the time of fertilization.

The favored hypothesis is that mRNA is masked by a protein coat. The increase in the pH of the cytoplasm causes the protein mask to come off the RNA and makes the mRNA available for translation into protein by the ribosomes of the cell. Proteins are very sensitive to pH and change their shape with changes in pH. The increase in pH at fertilization is therefore the likely cause for the increase in protein synthesis. Cleavage of the egg is dependent on this protein synthesis, since poisons that inhibit protein synthesis will (unlike inhibitors of RNA synthesis) prevent cleavage.

Studies of fertilization are more difficult to perform with mammals than with sea urchins because fertilization in mammals occurs inside the reproductive tract of the female. Mimicking this environment and fertilizing eggs in a culture dish (called in vitro fertilization, *in vitro* being the Latin phrase for "in glass") requires painstaking care, rigorous sterile technique, and the development of a very complex culture medium.

Experimental analyses of the fertilization process in mammals have concentrated on the mouse. Biochemical techniques have identified the sperm receptor on the egg coats of mice. Mouse eggs (and the eggs of all mammals) are surrounded by a glycoprotein coat called the "zona pellucida." Electrophoresis has shown that the zona pellucida of mice is composed of three proteins, one of which has been shown to be the sperm receptor and to trigger the acrosomal reaction. That means that the receptor on the sperm, unlike sea urchin bindin, is not inside the acrosome. The sperm receptor has been identified as an enzyme in the sperm membrane that recognizes a single sugar on the carbohydrate portion of the glycoprotein. Once bound to the heads of capacitated sperm, this glycoprotein blocks fertilization.

Context

The study of fertilization involves several fundamental cellular processes: exocytosis, receptor interactions, cell fusion, the intracellular role of calcium, and the regulation of protein synthesis, chromosomal replication, and cell division. The egg and the sperm and their interactions are therefore useful paradigms for the general study of the cell.

More practically, the study of fertilization has allowed the development of the clinical practice of in vitro fertilization (IVF) of human eggs as a cure for certain types of human infertility. The most common type of infertility amenable to this type of solution is blockage of the female Fallopian tubes. The Fallopian tubes (or oviducts) are that part of the female's reproducive tract that transports the egg from the ovary, where it is produced, to the uterus, where it develops into a fetus. Fertilization normally occurs within the Fallopian tube. If the Fallopian tubes are missing or physically blocked, conception is impossible.

The process of in vitro fertilization involves several steps. First, the woman is injected with a regimen of hormones that causes the ovary to release mature eggs. These eggs are recovered surgically by a process called laparotomy: A small incision is made at the navel, the ovary is examined, and any eggs are removed. These eggs are then mixed with ejaculated sperm. The sperm fertilize the eggs, and the eggs are cultured for several days until they reach a stage of development that corresponds to the embryonic stage that enters the uterus. Finally, an embryo is transferred into the woman's uterus through the cervix. The embryo implants into the wall of the uterus, and an otherwise normal pregnancy ensues.

The first infant to result from this procedure was born in England in 1978. Since that time, numerous IVF clinics have sprung up around the world. Despite the fact that the success rate for pregnancy is still quite low (approximately 20 percent) and the procedure is quite expensive, there is considerable demand for the procedure. Further research into the process of egg maturation, sperm capacitation, fertilization, and early development should increase the success rate in the future.

Bibliography

Austin, C. R., and R. V. Short, eds. *Reproduction in Mammals: I. Germ Cells and Fertilization*. 2d ed. Cambridge, England: Cambridge University Press, 1982. One book in a series of seven, this anthology of essays for the general reader includes the process of gametogenesis, the role of hormones in ovulation, and the process of fertilization in mammals. Illustrated.

Edwards, Robert, and Patrick Steptoe. *A Matter of Life*. New York: Morrow, 1980. A personal account by the two British scientists responsible for the first successful human "test tube baby," Louise Brown. This book is as much a chronicle of the political and social conflicts that their work engendered as it is a scientific story. Illustrated, photographs.

Epel, David. "The Program of Fertilization." *Scientific American* 237 (May, 1977): 128-138. A description of the events of fertilization in the sea urchin, this essay concentrates on the chain of cause and effect leading from the penetration of the sperm to the first division of the embryo. Excellent diagrams and electron micrographs.

Gilbert, Scott F. *Developmental Biology*. 2d ed. Sunderland, Mass.: Sinauer Associates, 1988. Chapter 2, "Fertilization: Beginning a New Organism," and chapter 22, "The Saga of the Germ Line," provide a detailed but readable account of fertilization and gametogenesis in representative species. Contains short boxed essays on research issues related to the topic. Illustrated. Excellent list of references to the scientific literature.

Grobstein, Clifford. "External Human Fertilization." *Scientific American* 240 (June, 1980): 57- 67. A lucid description of the process of in vitro fertilization in humans and a discussion of many of the ethical and political issues involved.

Harden, Garrett. "Some Biological Insights into Abortion." *BioScience* 32 (October, 1982): 720-727. An invaluable contribution to the debate about abortion. From a biological perspective, the author takes issue with the notion that life begins at fertilization, arguing that the development of each generation is a continuous process and that discrete boundaries, such as fertilization, are biologically arbitrary.

Wassarman, Paul M. "Fertilization in Mammals." *Scientific American* 259 (December, 1988): 78-84. A detailed description of the discovery of the zona pellucida proteins in mouse eggs and their role in the fertilization process by the scientist chiefly responsible for the work. Excellent illustrations and photographs of the fertilization process.

Ralph A. Sorensen

Cross-References

Birth, 226; Chromosomes, 462; Cleavage, Gastrulation, and Neurulation, 490; Conception, 562; Gametogenesis, 1061; Growth in Animal Development, 1240; Membrane Potential, 1674; Mitosis and Meiosis, 1753; Plasma Membranes, 2134; The Female Reproductive System, 2346; The Male Reproductive System, 2354.

JAWED BONY FISHES

Type of life science: Systematics (taxonomy)
Other fields of study: Animal anatomy and zoology

Bony fishes constitute one of the seven living classes of vertebrates. There are approximately twenty thousand recognized living species, nearly as many as all other vertebrates combined.

Principal terms

CTENOID SCALES: thin, flat, bony scales with tiny spines on the exposed rear edge, found on sunfish, perch, sea bass, and other advanced teleosts

CYCLOID SCALES: thin, flat bony scales with a smooth surface; rounded in shape, found on herrings, minnows, trout, and other primitive teleosts

GANOID SCALES: thick, diamond-shaped, bony scales that are covered with ganoine, a hard inorganic substance; found on bichirs, gars, and other primitive bony fishes

OSTEICHTHYES: the taxonomic class in which the bony fishes are placed; contains species related to the ancestors of higher vertebrates

PECTORAL FINS: paired fins found near the head end of the fish body; related to the forelimbs of higher vertebrates

PELVIC FINS: paired fins found either near the tail end of the fish body or below the pectoral fins; related to the hindlimbs of higher vertebrates

SWIM BLADDER: the hydrostatic (buoyancy) organ of teleost fishes derived from the lung of more primitive bony fishes

TELEOSTS: members of the infraclass Teleostei, the most advanced of the ray-finned fishes; they compose the vast majority of living bony fish species

VERTEBRATES: members of the chordate subphylum Vertebrata; characterized by the possession of a vertebral column made of cartilage or bone

Summary of the Phenomenon

The Osteichthyes, or bony fishes, constitute the largest and most diverse of the classes of vertebrates. Like the jawless and cartilaginous fishes, they are characterized by gills, fins, and a dependence on water as a medium in which to live. Unlike those fishes, however, they typically possess a skeleton made of bone. Additional features characteristic of most bony fishes include a lateral line system, scales, osmoregulation (salt balance) by means of salt retention or secretion, and a bony operculum (gill cover) over the gill openings.

The fossil record of bony fishes begins nearly 400 million years ago in the early

Devonian geological period, mostly in freshwater deposits. Thus there is reason to believe that bony fishes originated in freshwater habitats. Living bony fish species inhabit both freshwater habitats (58 percent of species) and marine habitats (41 percent), and some (1 percent) move between the two environments on a regular basis. This distribution does not reflect the relative proportions of these environments, since 97 percent of the earth's water is in the oceans and only 0.001 percent is in freshwater lakes, rivers, and streams (the rest is ice, groundwater, and atmospheric water). Rather, the high diversity of freshwater species is a reflection of the ease with which freshwater populations become isolated and evolve into new species.

There are four subclasses of bony fishes: Dipneusti (or Dipnoi), Crossopterygii, Brachiopterygii, and Actinopterygii. The first three of these include a total of only eighteen primitive living species. Subclass Actinopterygii includes all the rest. The Dipneusti, or lungfishes, are named for their possession of lungs, an ancestral characteristic suggesting that the earliest steps of bony fish evolution took place in tropical fresh waters subject to stagnation. Modern lungfishes (six species) are able to cope with such conditions by swallowing air and exchanging respiratory gases (oxygen and carbon dioxide) in the lung. Once considered closely related to terrestrial vertebrates, they are now believed to share certain similarities merely because of convergence (independent evolution of characteristics that appear similar).

The Crossopterygii, or fringe-finned fishes, were the dominant freshwater predators of the Devonian period. One fossil subgroup, the rhipidistians, had many features intermediate between fishes and ancestral amphibians, including tooth structure, lobed fins, and a jaw connected directly to the skull. Therefore, they are believed to represent a link between fishes and higher vertebrates. The other subgroup, the coelacanths, was also believed to be extinct (for 70 million years) until a coelacanth was taken from deep water off South Africa in 1938. This species, *Latimeria chalumnae*, is the only known living crossopterygian fish, and is of great interest as a kind of "living fossil."

The Brachiopterygii, or bichirs, include eleven living species known from swamps and rivers in tropical Africa. Though they share some characteristics with the other bony fish subclasses, they have some distinct features that warrant placing them in a separate subclass. One such feature is a dorsal fin consisting of many separate finlets, each supported by a single spine.

The Actinopterygii, or ray-finned fishes, comprise three major infraclasses: the Chondrostei, Holostei, and Teleostei. Chondrosteans, which have reverted to a largely cartilaginous skeleton, include the sturgeons (twenty-three species) and paddlefishes (two species). One species, the beluga sturgeon (*Huso huso*), source of the famous Russian caviar, may be the largest living Osteichthyes species. It is known to achieve a length of 8.5 meters and a weight of nearly 1,300 kilograms.

Holosteans include eight species: seven gar and one bowfin species, all known from North America. These freshwater piscivors (fish predators) are characterized by a skeleton made entirely of bone, but they do have certain other features in common with their more primitive ancestors, such as the ability to breathe air (with the swim bladder) and ganoid scales (also found in sturgeons).

The vast majority of ray-finned fishes, hence, of bony fishes—and indeed nearly half of all living vertebrates—belong to the infraclass Teleostei. It includes nineteen to twenty thousand living species. Among the features characteristic of teleosts are cycloid or stenoid scales (though some are scaleless), a swim bladder (lost in many bottom fishes), highly maneuverable fins, and a homocercal tail (meaning that its upper and lower lobes are symmetrical). Teleosts are represented by an amazing range of body sizes and shapes. A large number of species are quite small, enabling them to occupy niches (ways of living) unavailable to other fishes. The smallest known fish, in fact the smallest vertebrate of any kind, is a goby from the Indian Ocean, *Trimmatom nanus*, which matures at 8 to 10 millimeters in length.

There are several common body shape categories among teleosts which relate strongly to the fishes' habits. "Rover-predators" have the fusiform (streamlined) body shape that is perhaps most typically fishlike. Fins are distributed evenly around the body, and the mouth is terminal (at the end of the snout). This category includes minnows, basses, tunas, and others that typically are constantly moving—searching for and pursuing prey. "Lie-in-wait predators" tend to be more elongated, with the unpaired fins far back on the body, favoring a sudden lunge for their prey. The pike, barracuda, and needlefish typify this category.

"Bottom fishes" include a wide variety of shapes. Some are flattened for lying in close contact with the bottom (as are flatfishes such as flounder), some have flattened heads and sensory barbels (filaments with taste buds) near the mouth (as do catfishes), and some have fleshy lips for sucking food from the bottom sediment (as do suckers). A number of bottom-fish species have structures, usually modified pelvic fins, that enable them to cling to the bottom in areas with strong currents (sculpins and clingfishes have these).

"Surface-oriented fishes" tend to be small, with upward-pointing mouths, heads flattened from top to bottom, and large eyes. The mosquitofish, killifish, and flying fish belong to this category. "Deep-bodied fishes" are laterally flattened and have pectoral fins high on the body, with pelvic fins immediately below. This arrangement favors maneuverability in tight quarters such as coral reefs, thick plant beds, or dense schools of their own species. Examples include angelfishes, surgeonfishes, and freshwater sunfishes. "Eel-like fishes" have highly elongated bodies, tapering or rounded tails, and small, embedded scales (or no scales at all). They are adapted for maneuvering through crevices and holes in reefs and rocks and for burrowing in sediments. Eels, loaches, and gunnels typify this category.

Teleosts occupy habitats ranging from torrential streams high in the Himalayas to the bottom of the deepest oceanic trenches. They are found in the world's highest large lake (Lake Titicaca) and deepest lake (Lake Baikal). Some blind species live in the total darkness of underground caves. One *Tilapia* species lives in hot soda lakes in Africa at 44 degrees Celsius, while the Antarctic icefish *Trematomus* lives at −2 degrees Celsius.

The vast majority of teleost fishes, both marine and freshwater, are tropical.

Southeast Asia contains the greatest number of freshwater fish species, but the Amazon and its tributaries contain almost as many (and perhaps many hundreds more, still undiscovered). Marine teleosts are most diverse in the Indo-Pacific region, especially in the area from New Guinea to Queensland, Australia. A single collection made in the Great Barrier Reef off northeastern Australia may contain one hundred or more species. Some marine teleost species have a nearly worldwide distribution, while certain freshwater species have highly restricted ranges. The Devil's Hole pupfish (*Cyprinodon diabolis*), for example, is found only in one small spring in Nevada.

Many teleosts have highly specialized associations with other organisms. Some live among the stinging tentacles of sea anemones (the clownfish *Amphiprion*), within the gut of sea cucumbers (the pearlfish *Carapus*), within the mantle cavity of giant snails (the conchfish *Astrapogon*), or among the stinging tentacles of the Portuguese man-of-war jellyfish (the man-of-war fish *Nomeus*).

Reproduction among teleosts is incredibly varied. Most species are egg-layers, often producing an enormous number of eggs. The female ocean sunfish *Mola mola* may produce up to 300 million eggs, making it the most fecund vertebrate of all. Some species are livebearers, such as the platyfishes, swordtails, and surfperches. Some species are oral brooders, incubating the eggs in the mouth of the male (as in many cardinalfishes) or of the female (as in many cichlids). In one South American cichlid species, *Symphysodon discus*, the female "nurses" its young with a whitish milklike substance secreted by the skin.

Many teleost species are hermaphroditic. A few of these are synchronous hermaphrodites (functioning as male and female at the same time), such as the hamlet *Hypoplectrus*, but many more are sequential hermaphrodites (first one sex, then the other), such as the sea bass *Serranus*. In some coral reef fishes in the wrasse family, a dominant male mates with a harem of females. If this male is removed, the largest female becomes male and takes over the missing male's behavioral and reproductive function.

In a few species, all individuals are female, as in the Amazon molly *Poecilia formosa*. It has been shown that this species is a "sexual parasite" of two related "host" species. Sperm from host males are required to activate development of Amazon molly eggs, but male and female chromosomes (genetic material) do not join, and the offspring are all genetically uniform females.

Methods of Study

The scientific study of bony fishes dates back to Aristotle, who was the first to note, for example, that the sea bass is hermaphroditic. The "father of ichthyology" in more recent times was Peter Artedi (1705-1735), whose classification system was used by Carolus Linnaeus (1707-1778) in his *Systema Naturae*, which became the basis for all future classification systems.

Bony fish classification depends on the study of taxonomic features, or characters, which vary from one species, or group of species, to another. Useful characters include countable features (meristic characters), such as the number of fin supports (rays) or the number of scales in the lateral line, and measurable features (morphometric characters), such as the relative lengths of body parts. Such studies are typically done on museum specimens that are preserved in alcohol solution after fixation in formaldehyde solution. Dissecting tools, microscopes, and even X-ray machines are used for revealing meristic and morphometric characters. For studying bones, dry skeletons are sometimes prepared, or (especially for small species) specimens are "cleared and stained." This latter technique involves clearing the flesh with potassium hydroxide and staining the bones with Alizarin red stain.

Other techniques use samples of living tissue for finding taxonomic characters. Karyotyping (analysis of the chromosomes) and enzyme electrophoresis (using an electric field to separate similar proteins) are also important sources of taxonomic information.

Specimens for taxonomic studies are collected by means of netting, trapping, catching with hook and line, and spearing. Specialized techniques include electro-fishing (use of an electric shocking device) for stream fishes, and ichthyocide (fish poison such as rotenone) for coral reef fishes.

Understanding the evolutionary history and classification of the Osteichthyes also depends on paleontological studies (the study of fossils). Bony fishes are well represented in the fossil record because of the superior fossilizing nature of their bony skeletons. Many fish biologists are concerned with matters other than taxonomy. Because of the economic importance of both marine and freshwater bony fishes, the science of fisheries biology (concerned with the management and exploitation of fish populations) is of great significance. Fish populations are often studied with "age and growth" techniques. Age (determined by scale analysis), length, and weight data can be used to calculate growth and mortality rates, age at maturity, and life span. Other techniques for studying fish populations involve tagging individuals (useful for making estimates of population size) and even using tiny radio transmitters that can be followed by aircraft (useful for studying fish migrations).

Ecologists and ethologists (behavioral biologists) are also active in fish studies, particularly since the invention of Scuba diving, which allows direct observation of fishes in their natural habitat. An example of an important discovery made possible by Scuba diving is cleaning symbiosis, common in coral reef areas. This symbiosis (an association involving members of two different species) involves a "cleaner" species (often a goby or wrasse), which feeds on the external parasites and diseased tissue of a host ("cleanee") species, which visits the cleaner for this service.

Context

Bony fishes are by far the most numerous of all vertebrates. They are also arguably the most diverse in terms of body form, reproductive habits, symbiotic relationships, and other characteristics. Yet much remains to be learned. Virtually every ichthyological expedition into the Amazon region, for example, returns with specimens of previously unknown species. Some ichthyologists estimate that perhaps five or ten thousand undiscovered teleosts remain in unexplored streams and remote coral reefs.

Many biological mysteries remain about even some of the most familiar species. A good example is the American eel, *Anguilla rostrata*. This predatory species spends most of its life in the rivers, streams, and lakes of eastern North America, where it is often one of the dominant species. After six to twelve years in these habitats, the adult eels swim to the ocean and apparently migrate more than five thousand kilometers to spawn in deep water in the Sargasso Sea (an area in the western Atlantic south of Bermuda).

This general location of eel spawning has been inferred from the appearance there of the tiniest eel larvae (called leptocephali, these were once considered a separate species). The larvae become larger and larger as they drift in the Gulf Stream toward the North American coast. This much has been known since 1922. The adult migration has never actually been followed, however, and no one knows exactly where, at what depth, or how they mate and spawn, nor is it known what then happens to the adults.

Bony fishes also have great importance beyond mere ichthyological curiosity. They are one of the most important protein sources for much of the world's population, particularly in coastal areas. The world's annual marine fish catch, consisting primarily of teleosts, reached approximately 65 million tons in the mid-1960's. It was dominated by a single species, the Peruvian anchoveta (*Engraulis ringens*), then the most abundant harvestable fish in the world. This fishery has collapsed, however, because of a combination of overfishing and changes in the currents off the coast of Peru. There is much to be learned about the proper methods of managing and exploiting fish populations. There is much interest in artificial methods of cultivating fishes, that is, in "aquaculture" (or mariculture, if marine species are involved). Intensive cultivation of such species as salmon, trout, carp, and tilapia has provided an important source of high-quality food in many parts of the world.

Bony fishes have further importance in the enormous sport-fishing industry; angling is one of the most widely practiced outdoor recreational activities in the world. Millions of home aquarists constitute another group of people having keen interest in the biology of bony fishes. Tropical freshwater species from South America, Africa, and Southeast Asia have long been popular in home aquariums. Advances in saltwater aquarium techniques have now also made it possible to maintain the most exotic coral reef fishes together with the invertebrates of their natural habitats.

Despite many advances in scientific knowledge, much remains to be learned about the interrelationships, ecology, behavior, and fishery potential of the world's bony fish species.

Bibliography

Bond, C. E. *Biology of Fishes*. Philadelphia: W. B. Saunders, 1979. Intended as an introduction to the study of fishes for the general reader and for the college student, this text includes a concise summary of bony fish diversity (chapter 7) and ten chapters (8 to 17) on general topics in fish ecology, behavior, and physiology. Illustrated with black and white drawings. Each chapter has a reference list.

Cailliet, G. M., M. S. Love, and A. W. Ebeling. *Fishes: A Field and Laboratory Manual on Their Structure, Identification, and Natural History*. Belmont, Calif.: Wadsworth, 1986. This manual, used in college-level ichthyology courses, is the best source of information on the techniques used in the field and laboratory study of fishes. It is concise, well illustrated, and thoroughly referenced. It spells out, in step-by-step detail, the actual methods used by modern ichthyologists.

Chiasson, Robert B. *Laboratory Anatomy of the Perch*. 3d ed. Dubuque, Iowa: Wm. C. Brown, 1980. The North American yellow perch *Perca fluviatilis* has long served as a "typical bony fish" for college zoology classes. In fact, anatomical structure is highly similar throughout the six or seven thousand perchlike species in the teleost order Perciformes. This short (67-page) dissection guide is an excellent introduction to any of them, and to fish anatomy in general.

Lagler, K. F., J. E. Bardach, R. R. Miller, and D. R. M. Passino. *Ichthyology*. 2d ed. New York: John Wiley & Sons, 1977. This revised edition of a classic textbook is an excellent college-level introduction to the study of fishes, although only one chapter (2) is devoted to discussion of the classification of bony and other fishes. The rest of its fourteen chapters cover fish anatomy, physiology, and other aspects of fish biology.

McClane, A. J. *McClane's Field Guide to Freshwater Fishes of North America*. New York: Henry Holt, 1978. This is probably the best angler's guide to North American freshwater gamefishes available. It is "tackle-box-size," nontechnical, and packed with the kind of information sport fishermen would find most interesting and useful. It is arranged by family and has accurate full-color illustrations and useful glossary.

_____. *McClane's Field Guide to Saltwater Fishes of North America*. New York: Henry Holt, 1978. This is a companion edition to McClane's freshwater fish guide, and it contains similar features. It is a handy, popular guide to the saltwater gamefishes of North American coastal waters. Arranged taxonomically, it includes color illustrations and a glossary. Highly recommended for the saltwater sport fisherman.

Mills, D., and G. Vevers. *The Golden Encyclopedia of Freshwater Tropical Aquarium Fishes*. New York: Golden Press, 1982. This is an attractive popular introduction to tropical freshwater aquarium fishes in two parts. Part 1 is a practical guide to starting and maintaining an aquarium, illustrated with full color drawings and photographs. Part 2 is a detailed guide to two hundred of the most popular and attractive species, illustrated with stunning photographs.

Moyle, P. B., and J. J. Cech. *Fishes: An Introduction to Ichthyology*. 2d ed. Englewood Cliffs, N.J.: Prentice-Hall, 1988. One of the best college-level textbooks of general ichthylology available. It covers all aspects of fish biology and surveys the diversity of bony fishes in eight detailed chapters (16 to 23). Its large, exhaustive

Life Science

bibliography makes it useful to the student of ichthyology who wishes to investigate aspects of fish biology in greater detail.

Pough, F. H., J. B. Heiser, and W. N. McFarland. *Vertebrate Life*. 3d ed. New York: Macmillan, 1989. This large college text, a superlative introduction to vertebrate biology, is revised to incorporate changes in the philosophy and methodology of vertebrate taxonomy. Chapters 1 to 5 provide an excellent general background to vertebrate evolution, and chapter 8 covers the bony fishes in detail.

Whitehead, P. J. *How Fishes Live*. London: Elsevier-Phaidon, 1975. A large-format popular book illustrated with color drawings, maps, and photographs. Suitable for high school readers and useful to any general reader as an introduction to fish biology.

George Dale

Cross-References

Amphibians, 79; Evolution: A Historical Perspective, 903; Jawed Cartilaginous Fishes, 985; Jawless Fishes, 993; Gill, Trachea, and Lung Anatomy, 1212; Higher Invertebrate Animals, 1475; Systematics, 2594.

JAWED CARTILAGINOUS FISHES

Type of life science: Systematics (taxonomy)
Other fields of study: Animal anatomy and zoology

Cartilaginous fishes constitute one of the seven living classes of vertebrates. There are about seven hundred living species of sharks, rays, skates, and ratfishes in this vertebrate group that has ancient origins.

Principal terms
 CARTILAGE: a gristlelike supporting connective tissue that forms the entire skeleton of cartilaginous fishes
 CHONDRICHTHYES: the scientific name for the taxonomic group, or class, in which the jaw-bearing cartilaginous fishes are placed; it includes sharks, rays, skates, and ratfishes
 DEVONIAN: a geological period from about 400 million years ago to about 350 million years ago; during this period, ancestral sharks were abundant and diverse
 PLACOID SCALES: hard, toothlike scales, sometimes called denticles, that are embedded in the skin of most sharks, rays, and skates
 SILURIAN: a geological period from about 440 million years ago to about 400 million years ago; the first jawed fishes appeared during this period
 VERTEBRATES: members of the chordate subphylum Vertebrata; they are characterized by the possession of a vertebral column made of cartilage or bone

Summary of the Phenomenon

The Chondrichthyes, or cartilaginous fishes, constitute a large group of cold-blooded fishlike vertebrates. Like other fishes they are characterized by gills, fins, and a dependence on water as a medium in which to live. Unlike the more primitive jawless fishes (class Agnatha), they possess well-developed jaws; unlike the bony fishes (class Osteichthyes), they possess a skeleton composed entirely of cartilage, although this is often highly calcified (strengthened and hardened by calcium compounds).

Additional features characteristic of cartilaginous fishes include teeth, lack of a swim bladder (the buoyancy organ present in most bony fishes), a spiral valve intestine, internal fertilization, and osmoregulation (salt balance) by means of the nitrogen compound urea. The fossil record for the Chondrichthyes begins in the late Silurian period, over 400 million years ago. They were abundant throughout the next period, the Devonian. Within the class Chondrichthyes are two distinct subclasses, the Elasmo-branchii and the Holocephali; this separation dates back to the Devonian period.

Most living cartilaginous fishes are members of the Elasmo-branchii. This group includes at least six hundred, perhaps seven to eight hundred, living species of sharks (order Selachii) and rays (order Batoidea). The elasmobranchs are characterized by five to seven separate gill openings on each side of the head region; members of this group also usually have placoid scales. Sharks and rays are almost exclusively marine, although there are about ten ray species (the river stingrays) that inhabit only freshwater environments and several other rays and at least one shark species (the bull shark) commonly found in rivers.

Sharks are a diverse group of carnivorous species, ranging in size from the tiny dwarf shark (*Squaliolus laticaudus*), which matures at less than 15 centimeters in length, to the enormous whale shark (*Rhincodon typus*), which reaches 15 meters or more in length and represents the largest fish species of any kind. Curiously, the whale shark and the nearly-as-large basking shark (*Cetorhinus maximus*) are plankton feeders. They capture their tiny food organisms by swimming open-mouthed through the water and straining out the plankton with fine comblike structures in their gills, called gill rakers.

Most sharks, however, have sharp, bladelike teeth, suitable for attacking and feeding on more active prey. The white shark (*Carcharodon carcharias*) is a voracious roving predator that may grow to 12 meters in length. It has been implicated in more fatal shark attacks than any other species.

In addition to well-developed eyes, inner ears, and olfactory (smell) organs, sharks possess a lateral line system, as do most bony fishes. This is a sense organ consisting of a canal beneath the skin, on each side of the body, connected to the surface by numerous pores. It is sensitive to vibrations in the water, giving sharks a sense of "distant touch" that enables them to navigate and hunt their prey in murky water. Another sensory feature of sharks and other elasmobranchs is an electroreception system, consisting of receptors called "ampullae of Lorenzini" on the surface of the snout. Apparently, this system is useful in hunting, since it allows the weak electric fields produced by the muscle contractions of prey species to be detected. It may also function in intraspecific communication (communication with others of the same species), since many elasmobranchs possess electric organs.

Sharks are typically torpedo-shaped and slightly depressed in form—that is, flattened from top to bottom. They swim by means of rhythmic undulations of the body, which are produced by sequential contraction of the myomeres (body-muscle segments). The tile of the shark's pectoral fins (the paired fins toward the front of the body) and heterocercal tail (the upper lobe of the tail fin being larger than the lower lobe), enable it to maintain its relative depth position as it swims forward, despite the fact that the shark lacks a swim bladder. Also improving the buoyancy of sharks are their cartilage skeletons, which are lighter than bone, and their large, oily livers. Some shark livers contain a unique low-density oil called squalene.

Sharks and other cartilaginous marine fishes regulate the concentration of solutes (dissolved substances) in the body in a manner very different from that of the bony fishes, which either retain salt (freshwater bony fishes) or secrete salt (marine bony fishes). Sharks maintain a concentration close to or higher than that of seawater by retaining urea and trimethylamine oxide, two relatively nontoxic nitrogenous waste products.

Reproduction in the sharks and other cartilaginous fishes is characterized by internal fertilization. A pair of intromittent, or copulatory, organs, called claspers are located on the pelvic fins (the paired fins nearer the tail region) of the male. These are used to transfer sperm to the female genital opening. Embryos remain in the body or are released in egg cases, for a long gestation, or development, period. A small number of young either are born alive or hatch from an egg case in active, well-developed form.

Among the more familiar shark species are members of the family Lamnidae. This family includes the dreaded white shark and other "mackerel sharks," such as the shortfin mako (*Isurus oxyrinchus*)—a popular game fish and food fish, but a dangerous species as well. Another family, the Carcharhinidae (requiem sharks), with dozens of species, includes two man-eaters, the tiger shark (*Galeocerdo cuvieri*) and the bull shark (*Carcharhinus leucas*). Bull sharks have been found in rivers and lakes in Central and South America; they have penetrated the Amazon River as far as Peru.

Yet another group of dangerous sharks is the family Sphyrnidae, the hammerheads. These species are distinguished by a laterally expanded head, having the eyes and nasal openings at the ends of the hammerlike extensions. The function of this arrangement is unclear, but it probably aids in detecting and homing in on prey organisms. To students of comparative anatomy, the spiny dogfish (*Squalus acanthias*) is perhaps the most familiar shark, since it is often dissected in the classroom as a typical representative of the lower vertebrates. This worldwide species, inhabiting temperate coastal areas, is also an important food fish in many parts of the world. It commonly appears in England, for example, in "fish and chips."

Most of the more than three hundred living species of the order Batoidea, the rays and skates, are adapted for living on the bottom. In body form they are strongly depressed (flattened), with enlarged pectoral fins extending forward to the head region. Their teeth are usually pavementlike, for crushing their hard-shelled invertebrate prey. Most species give birth to live young, except the skates (family Rajidae), in which the eggs develop in a leathery egg case (the "mermaid's purse" that beach visitors often find in the sand).

Several ray families include members with a venomous spine on the tail, including the Dasyatidae (stingrays), the Potamotrygonidae (river stingrays), and the Myliobatidae (eagle rays). The largest species among rays and skates is the giant manta ray or devilfish (*Manta birostis*), which may attain a width of over 6 meters between the tips of its pectoral fins and a weight in excess of 1,300 kilograms. Like two other cartilaginous fish giants mentioned earlier (the whale shark and basking shark), the giant manta ray is a plankton feeder. It directs plankton into its mouth as it swims by means of large scooplike extensions on its head—the "horns" responsible for the name "devilfish." It then filters out the plankton with its comb-like gill rakers.

Rays and skates swim by means of flapping movements of their winglike pectoral fins. Some species, including eagle rays and manta rays, can make spectacular leaps from the water. Among the more remarkable rays are the electric rays (family Torpedinidae). These sluggish fishes use electrical discharges of up to 200 volts, produced by a pair of disk-shaped electric organs on the sides of the head, to stun their prey and perhaps to repel predators. Another specialized group among the rays is the sawfish family (Pristidae). A sawfish resembles a somewhat flattened shark in body form but has a long, flat, toothed extension (the "saw") on the end of its snout. This is used to slash through a school of prey fish.

The other major subgroup of cartilaginous fishes, the subclass Holocephali, comprises about twenty-five or thirty living marine species, most or all of which are placed in a single family, the Chimaeridae. They have a single gill opening on each side, like the bony fishes, but unlike them have a soft (rather than bony) gill cover. These fishes, commonly called chimaeras or ratfishes (because of their long, slender tails), live and feed on the ocean bottom, usually in deep water. They have pavementlike teeth for crushing their mollusk and crustacean food, and they have a venomous spine on the leading edge of the first dorsal fin (the forwardmost of the unpaired fins on the upper surface of the body) for defensive purposes. Male ratfishes have a fingerlike barbed clasper, of unknown function, on the top of the head, and two pairs of claspers on the ventral (belly) side of the body. At least one pair of these ventral claspers is involved in mating. The female lays eggs in leathery capsules somewhat like skate egg cases.

Methods of Study

The study of sharks, rays, and related species is part of the larger discipline known as fish biology, or ichthyology. This science has its origins in the writings of Aristotle more than twenty-three centuries ago. He was the first to report, for example, that the sex of sharks can be determined by the structure of the pelvic fins, that is, by the presence of claspers in the male. Aristotle also contrived some rather fanciful interpretations of shark anatomy and behavior, as in his explanation for the fact that the shark mouth is on the under side of the head, far back from the tip of the snout, unlike the mouths of most other fish. In his view, this made it difficult for the shark to feed on its prey, requiring it to turn on its back, and thus nature allowed some chance for the poor animals to escape the jaws of this ravenous predator.

Modern study of cartilaginous fishes, like fish biology in general, involves several disciplines. Ichthyology, or systematic ichthyology, is particularly concerned with the naming and classifying of species and higher taxa (taxonomic categories) and determining their interrelationships. Living cartilaginous fishes are probably better known (that is, more of the extant species have been discovered) than living bony fishes, simply because they tend to be larger, more conspicuous, and less secretive. Yet it was not until 1976 that one of the largest shark species, a deep-water filter-feeding species called the megamouth shark (*Megachasma pelagios*), was discovered near Hawaii. There may exist many additional Chondrichthyes species in deep ocean waters and remote coral reef areas.

Chondrichthyes systematics (that is, the classification of the fishes) has undergone many changes and revisions as more has become known about fossil representatives and about the characteristics of the anatomy, biochemistry, and the like, of the living species. Studies of fossil cartilaginous fishes are limited almost entirely to samples of teeth, since these are virtually the only body parts durable enough to be preserved in the fossil record. Nevertheless, there is enough information in the characteristics of the teeth so that knowledge of the interrelationships of fossil species, both among one another and with living species, is quite advanced. It is known, for example, that the enormous hand-sized fossil teeth of *Carcharodon megalodon*, which lived about 20 million years ago, are so similar to the smaller teeth of the white shark (*Carcharodon carcharias*) that they both belong in the genus *Carcharodon*.

Systematic study of modern species requires collection of specimens, generally by means of nets, traps, hooks, and lines, or spearing. Specimens are then preserved in some way and maintained in a museum collection. Entire specimens, if they are relatively small, can be maintained in diluted alcohol after fixation in formalin (formaldehyde solution). Other specimens, especially large ones, are dissected, and only certain parts are preserved, particularly the head skeleton with jaws and teeth. Certain new techniques provide taxonomic information from samples of living tissue. Karyotyping (analysis of the chromosomes), protein analysis (determination of the amino acid sequence), and DNA hybridization (estimation of genetic similarities) are all techniques that can elucidate interrelationships among the Chondrichthyes. Other disciplines concerned with the study of cartilaginous fishes include fisheries biology (the science of management and exploitation of commercially important fish species) and comparative physiology.

Context

Cartilaginous fishes represent an early line in the evolution of vertebrates. Understanding their interrelationships is crucial to an understanding of the ancestry of other fishes and of tetrapods (amphibians, reptiles, birds, and mammals) and thus, ultimately, of humans. Even though humankind's ancestors split from the ancestors of sharks and rays more than 400 million years ago, many anatomical and physiological features are shared. A prime example is the eye, which is extraordinarily similar in all vertebrates. The same system of eye movement, involving six muscles innervated by the same three cranial nerves, has remained unchanged throughout vertebrate evolutionary history. Thus, the study of shark eyes, or any other aspect of shark biology, deepens the understanding of the evolution of higher animals.

Sharks and their relatives are important and interesting in other ways as well. Many species have importance as food, especially in Asia and the South Pacific. Even in the United States, where sharks are considered pests—at best—by most people, shark recipes appear in a few cookbooks, and dishes such as mako steak and shark teriyaki appear on some restaurant menus. A few six-gill and seven-gill shark species are somewhat toxic, but the flesh (excluding the internal organs) of any species with five gill slits (most species do have five gill slits) caught in coastal U.S. waters is edible—except for the Greenland shark, sometimes caught in waters from Cape Cod northward. Even this poisonous species is eaten in Iceland after being prepared in a special way. As human populations around the world continue to grow, shark meat will undoubtedly become more important as a protein source.

Other products derived from sharks include shark liver oil (which was an important vitamin A source before the development of synthetic vitamin A), shark skin (for leather products), and shark cartilage derivatives (used in medicine).

Even though the real risk of shark attack anywhere in the world is statistically very small, sharks have been known to be such brutal killers that interest in preventing shark attacks is widespread. Various chemical shark repellants such as "shark chaser" have been tried. This water-soluble mixture of dye and copper acetate was given to U.S. military personnel during World War II for use if they were stranded in the sea after their ships were sunk or planes downed. It was, however, later shown to have little or no effect on sharks. Other techniques have included the cartridge-loaded "bang-stick," which is probably more dangerous to the untrained user than to a shark. A more promising device is the "shark screen," a floating plastic bag that can be filled with water and entered—masking the odors, sounds, and movements that might attract sharks.

Much remains to be learned about sharks, rays, and other cartilaginous fishes. Studying their ecology, behavior, and evolutionary relationships is important for further understanding of their basic biological nature. It is also essential for maximizing the benefit of commercially important species and minimizing the risk posed by dangerous species.

Bibliography

Budker, Paul. *The Life of Sharks*. New York: Columbia University Press, 1971. A medium-sized, semipopular account of shark biology, translated from the French by Peter J. Whitehead. The taxonomy and bibliography are somewhat dated, but in other respects it is highly interesting and informative. Has drawings and a few black-and-white photographs. Widely considered a classic.

Dingerkus, Guido. *The Shark Watcher's Guide*. Englewood Cliffs, N.J.: Julian Messner, 1985. This short book is intended as a popular introduction to the diversity of shark species, but it is scientifically rigorous and very well illustrated. Very useful for fishermen who might have occasion to seek information about what they have caught.

Ellis, Richard. *The Book of Sharks*. New York: Grosset & Dunlap, 1975. This large-format book is illustrated with the magnificent paintings of Richard Ellis, widely considered the world's premier painter of sharks and whales. The paintings are matched with a concise, highly readable introduction to sharks and shark biology.

An unusual feature is a section of brief biographies, with photographs, of the world's leading shark investigators—a "who's who" of shark research.

Lineaweaver, T. H., and R. H. Backus. *The Natural History of Sharks*. New York: J. B. Lippincott, 1970. This classic account is one of the best popular introductions to sharks. It weaves a story like an extended magazine article, full of anecdotes and historical perspectives, on shark biology and shark-human interactions. Illustrated with drawings and black-and-white photographs. Includes an unusual glossary, giving the origins and meanings of shark scientific names.

McCormick, H. W., T. Allen, and W. Young. *Shadows in the Sea: Sharks, Skates, and Rays*. Baltimore: Johns Hopkins University Press, 1963. This highly readable popular book reads like a history of all man's interactions with sharks. Packed with anecdotes, diary excerpts, and newspaper accounts, it is an encyclopedia of shark information, although the taxonomy and other biological aspects are somewhat out of date.

Moss, S. A. *Sharks: An Introduction for the Amateur Naturalist*. Englewood Cliffs, N.J.: Prentice-Hall, 1984. This introduction to selachians, their diversity, and all aspects of their biology, is a fine popular book on the subject. It is well illustrated and aimed at the general reader.

Moyle, P. B., and J. J. Cech. *Fishes: An Introduction to Ichthyology*. 2d ed. Englewood Cliffs, N.J.: Prentice-Hall, 1988. This college-level text is one of the best such volumes on general ichthyology available. Its exhaustive bibliography runs to fifty-three pages. Its thirty-four chapters deal with all aspects of fish biology, but chapter 15 describes, in detail, the sharks and their relatives. Other aspects of cartilaginous fish biology are scattered throughout the book.

Pough, F. H., J. B. Heiser, and W. N. McFarland. *Vertebrate Life*. 3d ed. New York: Macmillan, 1989. This is a thoroughly revised edition of one of the best undergraduate texts in vertebrate biology, reflecting the extraordinary advances in philosophy and methodology of vertebrate taxonomy. It is a rather large volume, but three of its twenty-four chapters (6, 7, and 8) are a particularly useful account of the origins of cartilaginous and other fishes.

Rosenzweig, L. J. *Anatomy of the Shark*. Dubuque, Iowa: Wm. C. Brown, 1988. This clearly written and well-illustrated text and dissection guide is intended for use in college comparative anatomy classes. It describes shark anatomy, system by system, using the spiny dogfish *Squalus acanthias* as the representative species. Not intended for general reading; it would, however, be useful as a guide to the anatomy of any shark species.

Springer, V. G. and J. P. Gold. *Sharks in Question*. Washington, D.C.: Smithsonian Institution Press, 1989. Written in question-answer format by a leading ichthyologist and a technical writer, this attractive volume is an excellent popular introduction to sharks. It is well illustrated and includes many fine color plates. It has several appendices, a glossary, and a concise and useful bibliography.

George Dale

Cross-References

Amphibians, 79; Evolution: A Historical Perspective, 903; Jawed Bony Fishes, 977; Jawless Fishes, 993; Gill, Trachea, and Lung Anatomy, 1212; Higher Invertebrate Animals, 1475; Systematics, 2594.

JAWLESS FISHES

Type of life science: Systematics (taxonomy)
Other fields of study: Animal anatomy, animal physiology, evolutionary biology, and zoology

Jawless vertebrates, or Agnatha, are represented today by the lamprey and hagfish. Though of little commercial worth, these organisms are of great interest as the survivors of a once flourishing group of Paleozoic vertebrates that include the earliest vertebrates in the fossil record.

Principal terms
AGNATHA: a class of vertebrates that includes all forms in which jaws are not developed; the group to which the earliest vertebrates belong
AMMOCOETE: the larval form of lamprey, which lives in river silts
CLADISTICS: a method of determining relationships in which shared derived (advanced) characters exhibited by the organism are used
CYCLOSTOMES: the modern agnathans, comprising lampreys and hagfish
GNATHOSTOMATA: all vertebrates in which jaws are developed
NASOHYPOPHYSIAL OPENING: an opening in the head of modern agnathans leading to a sac that aids in olfaction
OSTRACODERMS: armored fossil agnathans that flourished during the Paleozoic
PALEOZOIC: time period from 570 to 245 million years ago, which comprises the Cambrian, Ordovician, Silurian, Devonian, Carboniferous, and Permian periods

Summary of the Phenomenon
The vertebrates are normally divided into two groups based on the presence or absence of jaws. The vast majority possess jaws and are termed Gnathostomata; jawless forms are termed Agnatha. The Agnatha are represented today by the lampreys and hagfish, organisms of little economic importance but of great interest to biologists as the sole survivors of an extensive group of Paleozoic (245-570-million-year-old) agnathans, which includes the earliest known vertebrates. The extant forms are often referred to as the cyclostomes, the fossil forms as ostracoderms; however, these do not constitute monophyletic groups (groups including the common ancestor and all descendants), and some fossil Agnatha are closely related to cyclostomes.

Lampreys and hagfish are similar in general appearance despite far-reaching differences in internal organization. Both are elongated fish, without paired fins, that swim with an eel-like motion and reach lengths of 1 meter and weights of up to 1 kilogram. They possess an entirely cartilaginous skeleton; however, the organization of the body conforms to the basic vertebrate pattern. The lamprey has more active life habits and, therefore, has a more developed median fin. The propulsive section of the tail is longer than that of the hagfish. The lamprey's mouth is surrounded by a suckerlike oral disc covered by small teeth on its internal surface. This rasping organ allows the lamprey to attach itself to prey, on which it feeds by rasping away surface tissues and ingesting blood. Above and behind the oral disc is the nasohypophysial opening, which leads into an olfactory pouch and ends blindly in a dilated sac above the anterior gill pouches. Lampreys have seven gill pouches opening through seven gill ports.

In hagfish, the mouth is ventral and overhung by a rostrum, and it contains a dental plate that can be rapidly retracted, enabling the animal to bite off fragments of tissue from the dead and decaying fish on which it feeds. The nasohypophysial duct passes backward below the brain to join the pharynx, and the respiratory current passes along it. Hagfish are quite variable in their number of gill pouches and openings. Pacific hagfish have twelve pouches with separate openings (this number may vary up to fifteen), while Atlantic hagfish have five pouches with one common opening. The eye is vestigial and covered by surface tissue, so it is not normally visible.

There are about thirty-five species of lampreys, and all breed in fresh water and spend the major part of their life cycle in a freshwater larval stage before transformation to an adult stage. The eggs develop into a blind larval form, the ammocoete, which burrows into silt banks and remains for several years filtering microscopic particles from the water. The ammocoete is very unlike the adult, as no suctorial disc is present; a ciliated groove on the floor of the pharynx, together with a tubular endostyle, forms the feeding apparatus. After metamorphosis, three different types of adult lamprey are known: nonparasitic brook lampreys; freshwater parasitic forms; and anadromous forms (living in marine conditions but ascending rivers to spawn). The nonparasitic forms, which constitute about half the known genera, have the mechanisms for parasitic feeding but do not use them. The gonads mature immediately after metamorphosis, the intestine atrophies, and the foregut remains as a solid rod. These forms remain dwarf as they cannot feed, and six to nine months after metamorphosis they reach sexual maturity, spawn, and die.

The parasitic freshwater forms live entirely in river systems, where they feed on fish. The anadromous forms move downstream to the estuary or sea after metamorphosis. There, they feed voraciously and grow rapidly, eventually returning to the river on an upstream spawning migration after one to three years. As in all lampreys, death follows shortly after spawning. In some cases, it appears that populations of originally anadromous lampreys may have become landlocked and are now entirely freshwater. That is what appears to have happened with the lampreys (*Petromyzon marinus*) that now inhabit the Great Lakes. They are capable of causing significant damage to fish populations and almost eradicated trout and whitefish from the Great Lakes between 1950 and 1960, when they peaked in that system, resulting in the collapse of a flourishing fishery.

Hagfish are purely marine fish, in contrast, and as they are benthonic (live on the bottom) and often inhabit deep water, little is known of their reproductive biology beyond the fact that eggs may be laid at any time of year and there appears to be no larval stage. They remain buried in mud during the day, emerging at night to feed. It appears that they normally attack only dead or dying fish, lacking the suction apparatus that makes the lamprey so successful in its attacks on living organisms; however, they will consume small invertebrates if they are available. When feeding, they may show "knotting behavior," during which the flexible body ties into a knot in order to gain a better purchase for the tearing off of food fragments. One characteristic of all twenty species of hagfish is the development of mucus pores along the body. If roughly handled or irritated, these pores produce copious quantities of mucus, resulting in the name "slime eels" for these animals. Neither hagfish nor lampreys are of more than local economic importance. Hagfish are only exploited as human food in one area of Japan; lampreys are fished commercially in the Baltic countries of eastern Europe, where smoked lamprey is valued as a delicacy.

The fossil record of hagfish and lampreys is sparse, presumably because of the lack of an ossified endoskeleton. Both are known only from the Pennsylvanian period (280 million years ago) of Illinois and show close similarity to modern forms. These sediments also include two other agnathans of unknown affinities, indicating a wide diversity of forms of this type. There is, however, an extensive record of armored agnathans (ostracoderms) from rocks of Ordovician to Devonian age (360-470 million years old). These have been divided into two main groups, the Osteostraci and the Heterostraci, together with some smaller groups.

The Osteostraci were a group of fish that lived in the Silurian and Devonian periods (370-425 million years ago) and were characterized by the presence of an armored head-shield, the rest of the body being covered by large bony scales. The large eyes were dorsally placed, and between them were the pineal foramen (an opening for a light-sensitive organ) and the nasohypophysial opening. Located laterally on the head-shield were sensory fields that probably were sensitive to pressure waves in the surrounding water. The ventrally placed mouth and dorsoventrally flattened head indicate that the Osteostraci were benthonic fish, possibly feeding by sucking organic debris or small organisms into the mouth. Paired pectoral fins may have acted to move the animals by rhythmic undulations. Because the head-shield surrounded the brain, a considerable amount of detail of brain structure and cranial nerve pattern has been preserved. It has shown that the general pattern was very similar to that of the lamprey, implying a close relationship.

The Heterostraci were a long-ranging group whose earliest representatives occurred in the Middle Ordovician period (470 million years ago) and represent the first known record of vertebrates. Typical Heterostraci were armored over the anterior part of the body by variable numbers of bony plates and were further characterized by having only one pair of external gill openings. They were common in shallow marine and freshwater environments during the Upper Silurian and Devonian periods (360-425 million years ago) but became extinct at the end of the Devonian. They seem to have been adapted to a variety of modes of life, from benthonic detritus feeding to cropping algae and filter feeding. The Ordovician forms are known from rocks in North and South America and Australia and are united with later Heterostraci by the presence of the same type of acellular bone, aspidin, in the armor. Their exact position is uncertain, however, as they do not appear to have a series of branchial (gill) openings on each side.

Although it is clear that the Osteostraci were closely related to modern lampreys, no relationship has been determined yet between hagfish and any ostracoderm group. The relationship of the fossil and modern agnathans to gnathostomes is also still the subject of considerable debate, though in broad terms it is accepted that lampreys are the sister group of gnathostomes and hagfish the sister group of lampreys and gnathostomes. Much further information is needed before the details of their phylogeny can be elucidated, and continuing work on these organisms will aid understanding of both the origin of vertebrates and the early development of major vertebrate groups.

Methods of Study

Fish are generally excellent subjects for study and for the demonstration of anatomy, physiology, ecology, evolution, and other aspects of science. The detailed anatomy of the cyclostomes has been known for many years, and knowledge in this area is dependent on careful dissection of specimens. General knowledge of the life cycle, ecology, and feeding habits of the modern forms is based on observation either in the natural habitat or in aquariums. As lampreys spend most of their life cycle in fresh water, understanding of their development is fairly complete. Hagfish, however, are marine benthonic fish that move and feed mostly at night, and hence the ability to observe them is somewhat limited and understanding of their life cycle is incomplete. Sophisticated laboratory techniques now make it possible to analyze the biochemistry and physiology of these organisms and compare them to other chordates. Studies have also been made of their swimming methods, using high-speed cameras and electromyography, a technique that allows the tracing of the electrical changes that take place in muscles when they are active.

Fossil Agnatha cannot be studied as completely, because only the hard parts are preserved in the sediments. Techniques for studying these remains have changed very little in the past one hundred years. The bones are removed from the rock by chipping or dissolving the surrounding sediment away. Bone is composed of calcium phosphate and thus will resist some acids that can break down carbonate rocks. The acids most commonly used are acetic acid and formic acid, and the specimen to be dissolved out is often backed with plastic so that it does not disintegrate when the supporting matrix (surrounding sediment) is removed. The bone from these ancient agnathans is often so well-preserved that thin ground sections can be made and viewed through a microscope using transmitted light.

The characters determined by these means are used to determine relationships. Studies on the relationships of the fossil and recent Agnatha have relied in recent years on the methodology termed "phylogenetic systematics," or "cladistics." Cladistics is distinguished from other taxonomic methods (taxonomy is the study of interrelationships) by the fact that it is a rigorous sytem in which only shared advanced characters are used to show relationships. These relationships are expressed as branching diagrams termed cladograms (from the Greek *klados*, "branch"), hence the name cladistics. Although studies using this methodology have improved understanding of the relationship between modern Agnatha and the gnathostomes, the relationships of the fossil forms are still poorly understood.

Context

Modern Agnatha, or cyclostomes, are relatively rare and unimportant organisms, although they are representatives of a group that was important in the early history of vertebrate evolution. For example, hagfish can be a nuisance to fishermen, attacking and destroying bait and even the catch itself. Lampreys, because of their active parasitic mode of life, can be a serious menace to fisheries, as evidenced by the sea lamprey depredations in the Great Lakes. The construction of a canal bypassing Niagara Falls unfortunately allowed lampreys to enter the upper Great Lakes from Lake Ontario, where they had been established. Once in the upper lakes, they underwent a population explosion, probably as a result of the abundance of prey fishes, lack of predators, and suitability of the system for spawning and maintenance of larvae. The establishement of the lamprey resulted in a serious decline of a number of fish species and the collapse of a flourishing commercial fishery that has only been reversed by the establishment of control measures and the use of larvicides.

The fossil Agnatha, or ostracoderms, are generally poorly known as a result of their incomplete preservation. Yet, they do throw some light on the earliest stages of vertebrate evolution, indicating that, as far back as 470 million years ago, humankind's earliest ancestors were small, rather tadpolelike fish with an external armor of bony plates. Although they appear in the fossil record before the earliest jawed vertebrates, or gnathostomes, it appears that the separation into jawed and jawless forms had already occurred. There are many gaps still to be filled, but it is to be hoped that further discoveries will enable humankind to develop a clearer picture of its earliest vertebrate ancestry.

Bibliography

Alexander, R. McNeill. *The Chordates*. 2d ed. Cambridge, England: Cambridge University Press, 1981. This text provides information on Agnatha in the third chapter and describes them in relation to other chordates. It provides an excellent overview of the whole phylum. Suitable for high school and college students.

Bond, C. E. *Biology of Fishes*. Philadelphia: W. B. Saunders, 1979. This text provides a good overview of the modern and fossil Agnatha and their relationship to other fishes. Suitable for high school and college-level students.

Carroll, Robert L. *Vertebrate Paleontology and Evolution*. New York: W. H. Freeman, 1987. This book on vertebrate paleontology is aimed at the college student.

Chapters 2 and 3 deal with the origin of vertebrates and the diversity of jawless forms, but chapter 1 also provides much useful information on evolution and the uses of taxonomy.

Colbert, E. H. *Evolution of the Vertebrates*. 4th ed. New York: John Wiley & Sons, 1990. This volume is not as detailed as Carroll's and is suitable for high school as well as college-level students. The first three chapters on early vertebrates were extensively rewritten and updated for the fourth edition.

Elliott, D. K. "A Reassessment of *Astraspis disiderata*, the Oldest North American Vertebrate." *Science* 237 (July, 1987): 190. This article provides an overview of knowledge of early vertebrates together with a redescription of the earliest North American forms. It contains a rare illustration of a North American Ordovician vertebrate. *Science* is a weekly scientific magazine publishing articles of interest to all branches of the scientific community. Suitable for college-level students.

Gagnier, P. Y. "The Oldest Vertebrate: A 470 Million Year Old Jawless Fish, *Sacabambaspis janvieri*, from the Ordovician of Bolivia." *National Geographic Research* 5 (Spring, 1989): 250. An article on one discovery of early vertebrates, providing good illustrations of the appearance of these animals. This journal provides articles in a variety of scientific disciplines for the general reader as well as the scientist. Suitable for high school and college-level students.

Hardisty, M. W. *Biology of the Cyclostomes*. London: Chapman and Hall, 1979. Almost the only publication that deals only with Agnatha, this text covers all aspects of the biology of the modern forms together with their relationship to the fossil forms. Suitable for high school and college students.

David K. Elliott

Cross-References

Amphibians, 79; Lower Chordates, 439; Evolution: A Historical Perspective, 903; Extinction, 953; Jawed Bony Fishes, 977; Jawed Cartilaginous Fishes, 985; Gill, Trachea, and Lung Anatomy, 1212; Higher Invertebrate Animals, 1475; Systematics, 2594.

•

FLOWER STRUCTURE

Type of life science: Plant anatomy
Other field of study: Botany

*Flowers are organs of sexual reproduction produced by plants called angio-
sperms. Flowers usually contain up to four sets of parts, including sepals, which
protect the immature flower; petals, which attract animal pollinators to the plant;
stamens, which produce pollen; and pistils, which contain ovules and later form
fruits. Flowers from different species vary considerably, and that affects the way
they are pollinated.*

Principal terms

ANGIOSPERM: a plant that produces flowers during its life cycle
CALYX: all the sepals within a flower; usually green and serves to protect
the flower when it is in the immature (bud) stage
COROLLA: all the petals within a flower; usually brightly colored and
serves to attract pollinators to the flower
FRUIT: a ripened, enlarged pistil that contains one or more seeds;
develops after a flower is pollinated
INFLORESCENCE: a cluster of flowers produced by a plant
OVULE: an immature seed; one or more are found in each pistil
PISTIL: the female structure of the flower; consisting of a hollow ovary at
the bottom, which contains one or more ovules, a necklike style
above it, and a stigma at the top that receives pollen
POLLINATION: the process by which pollen is transferred from the anther
to the stigma; can be accomplished by an animal vector or by wind
SEED: an offspring produced by angiosperms after sexual reproduction;
consists of an embryonic plant surrounded by a seed coat; can be
dispersed to new places and can remain dormant during unfavorable
conditions
STAMEN: the male structure of the flower; consists of a hollow,
cylindrical anther, which produces pollen, borne atop a slender
filament

Summary of the Phenomenon

Flowers are organs of sexual reproduction that are produced by plants called
angiosperms. Representative flower-bearing plants include buttercups, roses, dan-
delions, grasses, maples, oaks, lilies, and orchids. There are estimated to be more
than 250,000 different angiosperm species worldwide; however, not all plants produce flowers. Some, such as mosses, ferns, and horsetails, produce tiny balloon-
shaped structures called sporangia that contain numerous tiny, powdery spores.
Others, such as pines, spruces, and hemlocks, produce cones as their organs of

sexual reproduction. These plants are called gymnosperms. Although the spore-producing plants and gymnosperms are important in their own way, they are not nearly as diverse or as ecologically and evolutionarily important as the angiosperms.

Botanists regard flowers as being small, modified shoots bearing modified leaves. In the typical flower, the modified leaves can be grouped into four different sets, based on their appearance and on their function. These sets include the sepals, petals, stamens, and pistils. The sepals and petals are the lowermost set of parts on the shoot and are found toward the sides of the flower. In contrast, the stamens and pistils are at the tip of the shoot and are located at the inside of the flower. While the sepals and petals are easy to see, the stamens and pistils are often obscure, and are visible only when the flower is examined closely. It is also necessary to mention briefly two other parts. One is the pedicel, a stalk that may be long and slender or short and stout on which flowers are frequently borne. The other is the top of the pedicel, called the receptacle, which is the part of the flower to which the other parts are typically attached. Of the four main parts, the sepals are generally the most leaflike, being flattened and green. They are generally attached to the bottom of the receptacle. Sepals function to protect the immature flower, while it is still in the bud stage. Generally, a flower has three to eight sepals, depending on the species. Collectively, the sepals in a flower are called the calyx. Above the sepals are the petals. Although flattened like the sepal, each petal is usually soft and brightly colored, and is therefore not as leaflike. Typical petal colors include white, yellow, pink, blue, and purple, although orange, maroon, and even brown are possible. Petals serve to attract small animals such as insects, hummingbirds, and bats to the flower, thus aiding the reproductive process. Usually, the number of petals in a flower will be the same as the number of sepals. Collectively, the petals in a flower are called the corolla.

The stamens comprise the third set of floral parts, and these are found inside the petals. Each stamen is a small but complex structure. It is composed of a small anther, which may be ball-shaped, egg-shaped, or tubular, and a threadlike filament that connects the anther to the rest of the flower. The anther, in turn, is composed of two or four tiny chambers, within which powdery pollen is produced and stored. The pollen is made up of numerous minute pollen grains, each of which contains the immature sperm of the plant. Thus, stamens function as the male part of the flower and are therefore exceedingly important in sexual reproduction. Each flower may contain from one to dozens of stamens, depending on the species. Botanists use the term "androecium" to refer collectively to all the stamens within a flower.

The final set of parts, found in the center of the flowers, is the pistils. Each pistil is often shaped like a vase, although the shape varies greatly from one species to another. In all cases, the base of the pistil is swollen and hollow; this part is called the ovary. The wall of the ovary is typically green and is called the pericarp. The hollow space in the ovary is called the locule. Although hollow, the inside of the ovary is not empty; instead, there are one or more tiny globular ovules. Each ovule contains an egg nucleus and thus functions as the female structure in sexual reproduction. In addition to the ovary, the pistil is typically composed of two or more parts: the style and the stigma. The style is a slender necklike structure that, when present, is found above the ovary; the stigma is a swollen area at the top of the style. The stigma serves to trap pollen grains and accomplishes that by having minute hairs covered by a sticky, sugary film. While most flowers have only a single pistil, many have several or many pistils, and these are attached to the receptacle. The pistils within a flower are collectively called the gynoecium.

Two important processes occur within a flower: pollination and seed formation. During pollination, the pollen is released from the anther and then carried over to the stigma. There are two major ways for pollen to be transferred: by animal vectors and by wind. Pollination by animals is very well studied. The typical vectors are insects such as bees, wasps, butterflies, moths, beetles, and ants. In addition, hummingbirds and bats also pollinate certain kinds of flowers. These animals visit flowers to obtain food: either the pollen itself or nectar, which is a sugary liquid produced by small glands called nectaries at the base of the flower. The vectors are attracted to flowers by the brightly colored petals and perhaps by an aroma, which arises from oils that are produced by a second set of glands in the flower. When an animal visits a flower, it brushes up against the anthers, which deposit the pollen on the animal's body. Occasionally, the animal transfers the pollen to the stigma of the same flower (self-pollination). More often, the animal makes its way to a second flower, where it deposits the pollen on that flower's stigma (cross-pollination). During wind pollination, the anthers release their pollen, which is then picked up by air currents. Some of the grains are deposited on a stigma. Self- and cross-pollination are also possible when flowers are wind-pollinated.

Whether brought to the stigma by an animal or by the wind, each pollen grain germinates and produces a slender thread of protoplasm that grows downward through the style and into the ovary. This thread, known as a pollen tube, contains the sperm and grows toward an ovule. When it reaches the ovule, the pollen tube deposits its sperm into the ovule. The sperm then fuses with the egg. At this point, fertilization is effected, and the first cell of the new generation is produced. Afterward, the ovule matures to form a seed. At the same time, the surrounding ovary enlarges greatly, becoming a fruit. Thus, fruits are simply ripened ovaries and develop only after a flower is pollinated. In plants grown for their fruits, such as apples, cherries, tomatoes, and peas, the flowers are often termed blossoms.

Since the stamens and pistils are intimately involved in reproduction, botanists refer to these as essential parts. Conversely, the sepals and petals are termed nonessential parts. Yet, they are important parts of the flower and should not be considered any less so. In addition, the sepals and petals are sometimes called the perianth, because they are found on the periphery of the anthers. A complete flower is one that has all four sets of parts. A perfect flower is one that has both androecium and gynoecium, and is thus bisexual. After examining various kinds of flowers, one quickly realizes that many plant species produce flowers that deviate from this idealized format. For example, many flowers do not have sepals and petals that are clearly distinguishable from one another. For example, in some groups, such as certain lilies, the sepals are as brightly colored as the petals. In others, such as magnolias, and some water lilies, each flower produces many perianth parts, and these intergrade from a sepal-like form toward the outside of the flower to a petal-like form toward the inside.

Many flowers lack one or more sets of parts. These are called incomplete flowers. Such flowers are not "mutants" or defective in any way. Instead, they have evolved over many generations to become "simpler." Some incomplete flowers lack one or both sets of perianth parts. Those flowers that have a single set of parts usually have only sepals present. These flowers are termed apetalous. In some instances, such as liverleaf and anemone, the sepals are petal-like. In other instances, such as elm, mulberry, oak, plantain, pigweed, and goosefoot, the sepals remain green and are usually very tiny. Since the perianth of these latter flowers is so small, the flowers are easily overlooked. In some flowers, neither sepals nor petals develop, and these are called naked flowers. Examples of these include birches and willows. Grass flowers are interesting because they are associated with tiny green parts called bracts, which are neither sepals nor petals. The nature of the perianth is related to the type of pollination that a plant has. Flowers that have a well-developed corolla or a calyx made up of petal-like sepals are insect pollinated. Conversely, those flowers that are apetalous with tiny green sepals and those that are naked are wind-pollinated. The latter arrangement makes sense because wind-pollinated flowers would not need to waste their energy making showy flower parts.

Some incomplete flowers lack either the androecium or the gynoecium. These are termed imperfect flowers and are unisexual. There are two categories of imperfect flowers. First, staminate flowers have only stamens and lack pistils, and are therefore male flowers. Second, pistillate flowers have only pistils and lack stamens, and are therefore female flowers. Clearly, imperfect flowers are forced into being cross-pollinated, and that benefits the plant by preventing self-pollination, which can sometimes be harmful. There are two patterns by which unisexual flowers are found on plants of a given species. In the first, both male and female flowers are produced on different parts of the same plant, which is called a monoecious condition and results in bisexual plants. Examples of monoecious species include corn and members of the cucumber family (pumpkins, squashes, watermelons). In the second, male flowers and female flowers are produced on different plants, which is called a dioecious condition and results in some plants being male and others being female. Representative dioecious species include willow, aspen, and staghorn sumac.

A third major way in which flowers differ from one another is based on whether the individual parts are free from one another or are fused together. In the idealized flower, the parts are free from one another to the receptacle; however, such is not the case for many flowers. Many flowers exhibit connation, in which similar parts are fused together above the receptacle. A familiar example is the morning-glory flower, in which the individual petals are fused to form a funnel-shaped corolla tube. In addition, many flowers have sepals that are connate, forming a calyx tube.

The best examples of these include carnations and other plants from the pink family. Many plants have pistils that are actually composed of individual segments, called carpels, fused together, while others, such as the mallow, have stamens that are connate, forming a stamen tube.

In addition to connation, many flowers show adnation, which involves the fusion of different parts. For example, the flowers of phlox plants have the stamens fused to the petals. A more extreme example can be seen in the rose family. Here, the sepals, petals, and stamens are all fused together, forming a cup-shaped structure called a hypanthium. The presence of a hypanthium can be best observed in blossoms of plums and cherries. In those flowers, individual sepals, petals, and stamens are attached to the rim of the hypanthium. Finally, many flowers have a hypanthium that is fused to the wall of the ovary. The result is that the sepals, petals, and stamens emerge from the top of the ovary, a good example being the apple blossom. Flowers of the latter category are said to have an inferior ovary, whereas the others have superior ovaries.

A fourth source of floral variability depends on whether the flowers have a regular or irregular corolla. A regular corolla is one in which all the petals or parts of the corolla are equal in size and shape. The result is that the flower is star-shaped. Examples of flowers with regular corollas include the buttercup, lily, rose, and primrose. Conversely, many flowers have an irregular corolla, in which one or more of the petals is unequal to the others. The result is that the flower is not star-shaped. Examples of irregular flowers include the snapdragon, pea, orchid, and mint. Some irregular flowers have a spur, which is a rounded, cone-shaped, or pointed extension of the corolla and serves to store nectar. Examples include the violet, touch-me-not, snapdragon, Dutchman's breeches, and columbine.

A fifth way in which flowers differ is according to their color. Plant color is determined by special molecules called pigments that occur within the cells of the plant. The most common plant pigment is chlorophyll, which is green. Chlorophyll is involved in photosynthesis and is found mainly in leaves. Chlorophyll, however, is only a minor contributor to flower color, typically found only in sepals and pistils. Instead, the brilliant colors associated with most flowers result from two main categories of pigments: the flavonoids and the carotenoids. Flavonoids include two subcategories: the anthocyanins, which are pink, red, violet, and blue; and the flavonols, which are white, ivory, and yellow. Carotenoids also have two major categories: xanthophylls, which are yellow; and carotenes, which are orange. Interestingly, the way that humans perceive color is often different from the way that other animals perceive flowers. For example, xanthophylls reflect not only yellow but also a deep violet that bees can perceive but that humans cannot. Thus, many flowers that appear yellow to humans are a deep purple to some insect pollinators.

The shape and color of flowers are important because they allow certain pollinators to enter but exclude others. Bowl-shaped flowers are visited by a variety of insects, such as beetles and bees. Irregular flowers are typically pollinated by honeybees and bumblebees, and in some cases the insects fit the flower like a key fits a lock. This highly specific arrangement benefits both partners. Bee flowers are also characterized by being brightly colored—either yellow or blue—and sweet-smelling. Flowers with long spurs are pollinated by long-tongued insects such as moths. Red flowers are pollinated by birds, specifically hummingbirds and butterflies. White flowers are often open during the late evening or at night and are visited by moths. An interesting group of plants have brown or maroon flowers and have an odor of rotting flesh. These "carrion flowers" are pollinated by an array of insects, particularly beetles and flies. The field of pollination biology has received considerable attention from botanists, and while much is known about the fascinating interrelationships between flowers and their pollinators, much more remains to be discovered.

In many plants, such as violets, trilliums, poppies, and lady's-slipper orchids, each flower is produced by itself. More frequently, however, flowers are produced in loose or dense clusters, and these clusters are called inflorescences. There are several different kinds of inflorescences, which are categorized into two broad types. The first type is the determinate inflorescence, in which the flowering stalk is capped by the first flower that opens. The next flower to open must develop from a side-branch that develops from beneath the first flower; the same can be said for all subsequent flowers. The most common determinate inflorescence is called a cyme, and examples include phlox and St. John's-wort.

The indeterminate inflorescence is the second broad type. In this category, all flowers that develop are attached to the side of a single unbranched stalk. The first flowers to open are attached at the bottom of the stalk, while later ones are attached at progressively higher points. There are several kinds of indeterminate inflorescences. One is a raceme, in which each flower is attached by a pedicel, giving the inflorescence the appearance of a bottlebrush. Examples of plants that produce racemes include lupine, mustard, and pokeweed. A spike is a second kind of indeterminate inflorescence. In the spike, the flowers are attached directly to the main stalk, often making it long and thin. Plants that have spikes include cattail, smartweed, and plantain. A catkin is a special kind of spike, produced by certain trees, such as willows, poplars, and birches. In catkins, the flowers are unisexual and all the flowers in each catkin are the same sex. The soft, furry structures produced by the familiar pussy willow when collected in the spring are young male catkins. A fourth kind of indeterminate inflorescence is an umbel, in which the pedicels are attached to the same point on the supportive stalk. Umbels have a flat-topped appearance when viewed from the side and are circular when viewed from the top. Plants that produce umbels include most members of the carrot family, such as Queen Anne's lace, parsnip, and poison hemlock. The last inflorescence discussed is called a head, or capitulum. In a head, the flowers are tightly clustered to form a dense cluster. Plants that produce heads include clover, dogwood, teasel, and buttonbush. It is worth mentioning here that all plants in the aster family, including dandelion, goldenrod, daisy, and sunflower, also produce their flowers in heads. In these plants, however, the individual flowers are very tiny and are called florets. The heads themselves are flowerlike. Thus, in a daisy, the white petal-like structures surrounding the "flower" are really florets, each with a strap-shaped corolla. The yellow material in the center is really composed of several dozen tiny florets, each having a tube-shaped corolla.

The purpose of a flower is to allow pollination to occur. After pollination is finished, the flower begins the process of fruit formation. Fruits are simply ripened ovaries that contain seeds, which are ripened ovules. Each fruit consists of an outer wall, the pericarp, that encloses the seeds. As is true for flowers, there is considerable diversity in the structure of fruits. Botanists recognize two main categories of fruits, depending on the nature of the pericarp. Fleshy fruits have a pericarp that is typically juicy. Dry fruits have a pericarp that is either papery or woody.

The three most common fleshy fruits include drupes, berries, and pomes. A drupe contains a single seed, which is enclosed by a hard, bony, inner layer of the pericarp. Examples of drupes include pitted fruits such as cherries and plums. The pit in these fruit is really the hard inner layer of the pericarp, and the seed is hidden inside. A berry typically has several seeds, and the pericarp is fleshy throughout. Examples of berries include tomatoes and grapes. A pome is a specialized fleshy fruit that forms from a flower with an inferior ovary. Thus, the outer layer of the fruit is really the hypanthium, not the pericarp. Examples of pomes include apples and pears.

The most common dry fruits are follicles, legumes, capsules, achenes, nuts, and samaras. Follicles open up along one side, revealing numerous seeds. An example is a milkweed pod. In contrast, legumes open up along two lines. They are produced by many members of the legume family, such as peas, beans, and peanuts. The capsule opens along three or more lines or by pores at the top of the fruit. Snapdragons and poppies are good examples of plants that produce capsules. Achenes each contain one seed and are typically small, a good example being the sunflower "seed." A nut is similar to an achene, except that the pericarp is hard and woody. Examples of nuts include acorns, walnuts, and hickory nuts. Finally, a samara is a modified achene that has part of the pericarp flattened to form a wing. Examples of plants that produce samaras include maples, ashes, and elms. Fruits are highly evolved structures that function in the dissemination of seeds. Like pollination biology, dispersal of fruits and seeds has been, and continues to be, a well-researched subject.

Methods of Study

The investigation of flower structure is relatively nontechnical, and even nonbotanists can make meaningful observations with a keen eye and an inexpensive magnifying glass. Professional botanists use additional tools to manipulate the flower, including forceps, probes, and scalpels. To see tiny features, botanists use high-power hand lenses in the field; while in the laboratory, they use dissecting microscopes. To investigate flower structure, it is necessary to select plants when they are in the proper season. For many species, this time may be limited to a few weeks during the year. Occasionally, flower structure can be determined when the flowers are in the bud, but to do so requires dissecting the flower with appropriate tools, a good hand lens or dissecting microscope, and considerable patience.

The determination of flower structure is best made in the field because the flower is freshest and in its natural state. There are times, however, in which field determination is not possible. In those cases, the flowers are collected and stored until future study is possible. Once flowers or whole plants are picked, the flower begins to deteriorate by wilting and, sometimes, by losing its color. This deterioration can be delayed in at least two ways. One approach is to place the flowers in a plastic bag containing wetted paper towels and then to tie the bag closed. The flowers can keep for several hours, especially if they are placed in the shade. Alternatively, it is possible to store the flowers indefinitely by placing the plastic bag into a freezer. Once retrieved from the freezer, the flowers thaw and appear fresh. That state usually passes quickly, however, and after about ten minutes the flower turns mushy. A second approach to preserving flowers is by pressing them. To press a flower, one places it between sheets of paper and applies pressure for two to four days. While that can be accomplished by placing the flower between the pages of a book, botanists press flowers within devices called plant presses. A press is made up of cardboard squares, blotting paper, and newspaper stacked together and compressed by wooden frames at both ends and secured with cloth or leather belts. While the flowers are being pressed, they dry out and become flattened. Afterward, the flower can be removed from the press and observed in that state. The flower can also be "revived" by soaking it for a few minutes in a liquid detergent solution.

To study pollination biology of flowers, there are two approaches: the descriptive and the experimental. The descriptive approach involves simply observing flowers and their pollinators. The best way to accomplish that, however, is to spend considerable time in the field watching individual flowers. Observations are then made concerning the identity of the visiting species, the number of visits that individuals make to the flower, the length of time that is spent during each visit, and whether the visitors remove pollen, nectar, or both. Many researchers follow individual pollinators to determine the sequence of flowers that they visit. The experimental approach involves modifying the plant-pollinator system to gain additional insights not available by simply observing pollination under natural conditions. Examples of modifications that are used include placing cloth exclosures over flowers to prevent pollination, removing anthers from flowers, changing the numbers of plants in an inflorescence or the number of plants in an area, or altering the pollinators that are present at the site. Some scientists grow plants so that they contain radioactive elements, which are then incorporated into the pollen. They can then follow the dispersal of pollen to other plants by looking for the "labeled" pollen.

Context

Because flower structure varies considerably from one group of plants to another, and because it does not vary much within each group, flowers are key features that taxonomists use to classify plants. Most technical manuals and nontechnical field guides use floral structure almost exclusively as the basis for plant identification. Therefore, people wishing to identify observed plants must have a good working knowledge of floral structure. Since modern botanists classify plants according to their evolutionary relationships, flower structure is used to provide important clues regarding evolution. For example, most botanists accept that primitive plants had flowers that were regular and had many separate parts that were free from one another. Thus, irregular flowers, those with connation or adnation, or those with one or more sets of parts missing, are evolutionarily advanced. Moreover, since evolution depends on some plants being able to reproduce more successfully than others, botanists study the reproductive aspects of pollination biology intensively.

Flowers are often important because they cause respiratory allergies in many people. Typically, the allergies are caused when people breathe in the pollen of a certain plant species. Allergic symptoms such as sneezing and a runny nose arise when people become sensitive to the proteins in the pollen grains, as a result of a malfunctioning of the immune system. In general, the offending plants are wind-pollinated; animal-pollinated plants do not produce sufficient airborne pollen to be inhaled. Thus, the most noxious allergy-producing plants generally have small flowers that lack petals. In temperate regions of the United States and Canada, there are several groups of wind-pollinated species, and these come into flower at different times of the year. People who suffer symptoms in the middle and late spring are allergic to wind-pollinated trees such as the poplar and the oak. Those who have symptoms in the late spring and early summer are allergic to plants in the grass family. Finally, those who suffer in the late summer and early autumn are most likely allergic to certain weeds such as goosefoot, plantain, and particularly ragweed. It is interesting to note that goldenrod is not really an important allergy-causing plant, simply because the flowers are insect-pollinated.

As mentioned, the odors that are found in many flowers are caused by essential oils that are produced in specialized glands of the petals and other floral parts. Throughout history, people have learned how to extract the odors and convert them into perfumes. Many plants are cultivated for their fragrant oils, including rose, jasmine, lilac, lily of the valley, orange, violet, carnation, and even tobacco. Flowers are also economically important because of their use in floral arrangements and gardens. Typically, the flowers that are grown by florists have been subjected to a high degree of breeding to maximize the size and brilliance of the flowers. The essential structures of the flower (stamens and pistils) are generally not important to florists and may even become lacking or nonfunctional. Such sterile flowers then need to be propagated by vegetative means. Dozens of plant species are cultivated and sold for their flowers. Some of the most important include chrysanthemums, orchids, tulips, pansies, carnations, irises, gladioli, and snapdragons.

Bibliography

Darwin, Charles. *The Different Forms of Flowers on Plants of the Same Species.*

London: John Murray, 1877. A classic work written by perhaps the most influential figure in modern biology. Although the work and the writing style are dated, readers are treated to a detailed account of floral structure of different species, in a way that has stimulated many research projects during the past century.

Jones, Samuel B., and Arlene E. Luchsinger. *Plant Systematics*. 2d ed. New York: McGraw-Hill, 1986. This book provides a fine introduction to the classification and evolution of the seed plants, focusing on the flowering plants. Chapter 8 details methodology for collecting and preserving plants; chapter 10 is devoted to a review of the terminology dealing with variability in vegetative and reproductive structures of the plant.

Meeuse, J. D. *The Story of Pollination.* New York: The Ronald Press, 1961. A brief but fascinating survey of the natural history of pollination biology written for the nonspecialist. Using crisp text and attractive figures, the author leads the reader through a diverse account of some of the more interesting interactions between flowers and their insect pollinators.

Raven, Peter, Ray F. Evert, and Susan E. Eichhorn. *Biology of Plants*. 4th ed. New York: Worth, 1986. An excellent introduction to all phases of modern botanical science, including sections on cell biology, energetics, genetics, diversity, structure, evolution, and ecology. Chapter 18 provides a comprehensive summary of the evolution of seed plants, especially the angiosperms. The presentation of floral structure is excellent, with ample pictures and diagrams. Chapter 29 contains information on the evolution of the flower and includes an outstanding review of the interplay between floral structure and pollinators.

Real, Leslie, ed. *Pollination Biology*. New York: Academic Press, 1983. Although written for advanced-undergraduate and graduate students, this collection of essays prepared by some of the foremost experts in pollination biology will reward the patient reader with a wealth of information about the topic. Additional articles are cited at the end of each chapter, most of which describe the result of original research in pollination biology.

Simpson, Beryl Brintall, and Molly Conner-Orgorzaly. *Economic Botany: Plants in Our World*. New York: McGraw-Hill, 1986. A highly readable and informative account concerning the numerous uses of plants by various societies since the advent of recorded history. Chapters 1 and 2 describe general features of plants and how they vary, with attention paid to floral features and pollination. Chapters 4 to 7 discuss the economic biology of fruits, grains, and legumes. Information on perfumes and cultivated flowers is given in chapters 9 and 18, respectively.

Stern, Kingsley R. *Introductory Plant Biology*. 4th ed. Dubuque, Iowa: Wm. C. Brown, 1988. A fine general text covering all phases of plant science. Chapter 8 details the reproductive structures of the angiosperms, covering floral structure, inflorescences, fruits, and seeds. Attractive illustrations elucidate important points.

Kenneth M. Klemow

Cross-References

FLOWERING REGULATION

Type of life science: Plant physiology
Other fields of study: Botany and genetic regulation in eukaryotes

All angiosperms (flowering plants) flower before they can reproduce. Investigating the regulation of flowering leads to an understanding of how to control the flowering process. Accelerating or inhibiting flowering has significant implications for agriculture and horticulture.

Principal terms

ANTIFLORIGEN: a floral inhibitor produced by the leaves
CIRCADIAN RHYTHM: a regular cycle lasting approximately twenty-four hours; derived from the Latin words "circa" (approximately) and "dies" (a day)
EVOCATION: the arrival of a floral promoter at the shoot apex that leads to various changes before flowering
FLORIGEN: a floral promoter ("flower maker") produced by the leaves
INDUCTION: response in a leaf, triggered by photoperiod, that leads to the production of florigen
PHOTOPERIOD: duration and timing of day and night
PHYTOCHROME: a pigment with two interconvertible forms that can absorb red and far-red light
SHOOT APEX: the growing tip of a plant that produces new leaves and floral structures
VERNALIZATION: exposure to a period of cold is prerequisite for flowering in some species

Summary of the Phenomenon

Control over the time of flowering is essential for the survival of flowering plants (angiosperms). Insect pollinators may be present only at certain times; unless the plant is flowering at that time, pollination and the production of the next generation cannot occur. Embryo and seed development may be successful only under certain climatic conditions. The ability to respond to environmental cues is an essential factor in the regulation of flowering, which is perhaps best viewed as a sequence of developmental processes with many control points. While the basic sequence may be common to all angiosperms, the regulatory steps vary greatly among species. A floral "promoter" is produced by the leaves and translocated to the shoot apex, which results in the evocation and, ultimately, the production of flowers. To analyze control points in this sequence, it is helpful to focus separately on internal signals—environmental signals such as temperature and photoperiod—and the competence of organs to perceive and respond to these signals. An analysis of these factors reveals that the regulation of flowering is a complex process that provides some plants precise control over the time of flowering.

The regulation of flowering requires interactions between the shoot apex and other organs, and thus depends heavily on chemical signals for communication between organs. There is strong evidence for a floral promoter called "florigen" that may be produced in the leaves. The existence of florigen was first proposed by M. Kh. Chailakhyan, a Soviet plant physiologist, in 1937. Florigen is not species- or even genus-specific. Despite more than fifty years of research, it has not been isolated and its chemical nature remains a mystery. Leaves of the same plant can produce floral inhibitors as well as florigen. This was convincingly demonstrated in the tobacco plant in the late 1970's by Anton Lang, Chailakhyan, and I. A. Frolova, who adopted the term "antiflorigen" for the inhibitor. Several genes controlling the production of an inhibitor in pea cotyledons and leaves have been identified in other laboratories. In addition to leaf inhibitors, root inhibitors have been shown to regulate flowering in black currant and tobacco. As with florigen, the chemical nature of all these inhibitors is unknown. Nutrient levels and allocation throughout the plant may also control the time of flowering.

One major role of environmental signals is to control the timing of the production of florigen and antiflorigen. This link between environmental and internal signals has been most clearly established for photoperiod. The role of day length in the regulation of flowering was recognized by 1913. The pervasiveness of photoperiodic control of flowering in numerous species soon became apparent. In the 1930's, W. W. Garner and H. A. Allard found an unusually large tobacco plant growing in the field that failed to flower and named it the Maryland Mammoth. Maryland Mammoth cuttings flowered in the greenhouse in December, and subsequent experimentation demonstrated that flowering would occur only when days were short and nights long. The Maryland Mammoth is an example of a short-day plant. Short-day plants generally flower in the spring or fall when day lengths are shorter; other examples of short-day plants are poinsettias, cocklebur, Japanese morning glory, and chrysanthemums. Plants such as spinach, lettuce, and henbane will flower only if a critical day length is exceeded; they are categorized as long-day plants, and generally flower during long summer days.

Photoperiodic control mechanisms may be more complex as in the case of ivy, a short-and-long-day plant, which requires at least a twelve-hour photoperiod followed by a photoperiod of at least sixteen hours. Still other plants, including sunflower and maize, are day-neutral: They flower independent of photoperiod. By the 1940's, it was established that night length, not day length, is critical in the photoperiodic control of flowering. For example, flowering in short-day Japanese morning glory can be prevented by a brief flash of light during the critical long night. In comparing short-day and long-day plants, it is important to note that the distinguishing factor is not the absolute length of night required; rather, the difference is whether that night length is the minimum (short-day plants) or maximum (long-day plants) dark requirement permitting flowering.

How a plant perceives night length and translates this into the appropriate response in terms of flowering is not fully understood. A pigment known as phytochrome, however, plays a critical role. Phytochrome exists in two forms that are interconvertible. P_r absorbs red light and is converted to P_{fr}, which absorbs far-red light and is subsequently converted back to the P_r form of the pigment. Sunlight contains both red and far-red light and thus an equilibrium between the two forms is achieved. At noon, about 60 percent of the phytochrome is in the P_{fr} form. In the dark, some P_{fr} reverts to P_r and some breaks down. Because of the absence of red light, no new P_{fr} is generated. The relationship between phytochrome and photoperiodic control of flowering has been established using night-break experiments with red and far-red light. (In these experiments, darkness is interrupted by momentary exposure to light.) Flowering in Japanese morning glory, a short-day plant, can be inhibited by a flash of red light (as well as light equivalent to sunlight) in the middle of a long night. Far-red light has no effect. A flash of far-red light following a flash of red negates the inhibitory effect of the red light. In long-day plants, flowering can be induced when the dark period exceeds the critical night length with a red-light night break. Far-red light flashes do not result in flowering. The effect of the red flash can be negated by a subsequent far-red flash. In these experiments, the light flashes alter the relative amounts of P_r and P_{fr}.

How the perception of light by phytochrome is linked to the production of florigen in long-day and short-day plants is not clear. One possibility is that plants measure the amount of P_{fr} present. Flowering in short-day plants would be inhibited by P_{fr} and would not flower until very little or no P_{fr} remained after a long night. To flower, long-day plants would require some minimum level of P_{fr}, which would not be available if the nights were too long.

This explanation is really not viable because P_{fr} vanishes within a few hours after the dark period begins; it is thus unlikely that a plant measures night length by the relative amounts of P_{fr} and P_r. Levels of phytochrome influence an internal biological clock that keeps track of time. The clock establishes a free-running circadian rhythm of about twenty-four hours; this clock needs to be constantly reset to parallel the natural changes in photoperiod as the seasons change. Phytochrome interacts with the clock to synchronize the rhythm with the environment, a prospect that is strengthened by night-break experiments, where the time of the light flash during the night is critical. In the case of the Japanese morning glory, there are times during the night that a red light flash completely inhibits flowering and other times when it has no effect. In these experiments, the phase of the rhythm of the clock defines the nature of the interaction with phytochrome.

Studies on the relationship between flowering and day length have focused on the production of florigen. There is evidence that the production of inhibitors by leaves is also under photoperiodic control. This has been demonstrated for photoperiodic tobacco plants and for some peas. In the case of the pea, the inhibitory effect is most obvious for short days, but lower levels of inhibitor continue to be produced as the days grow longer.

Plants also utilize temperature as an environmental clue to ensure flowering. In some plants, the critical night length depends on the temperature. Assessing two environmental factors provides added protection. Other plants have a vernalization requirement—a chill promotes or is essential for flowering. The control point regulated by vernalization may be different for different species. Vernalization has been shown to affect the sensitivity of leaves to respond to photoperiod. In some plants, only leaves initiated after the shoot apex has been chilled can be induced to produce florigen by the appropriate photoperiod. In other cases, the shoot apex is not competent to respond to florigen until it has been chilled. Clearly, the competence of the leaves and shoot apex to respond to environmental and internal signals is crucial in the regulation of flowering. Pea mutants have been identified that have shoot apexes with differential sensitivity to either florigen or a floral inhibitor. Another pea mutant has an apex that is not competent to initiate flowers, but remains perpetually vegetative. The competence of a day-neutral tobacco apex to respond to florigen or a floral inhibitor changes with age. In another species, the apexes of shoots cannot respond to vernalization early in development; this period of time is considered to be the juvenile phase.

A juvenile phase of development is most common in woody perennials. During this time, flowering cannot occur even under optimal environmental conditions. Phase change to the mature phase occurs gradually, and may be accompanied by changes in leaf morphology and the ability of cuttings to root. The most significant occurrence is that the plant becomes competent to flower.

The above examples illustrate the numerous control points in the development sequence leading to flowering. Flowering is regulated by the integration of environmental cues into an internal sequence of processes that regulate the ability of plant organs to produce and respond to an array of signals. These numerous regulatory switches permit precise control over the time of flowering.

Methods of Study

Most research on flowering has focused on the influence of environmental signals, especially day length. Since the early 1900's, efforts have been devoted to creating controlled environments. The effect of photoperiodicity on flowering in the Maryland Mammoth tobacco plant was evaluated using a box that Allard designed and referred to as "a primitive dog house." Since that time, sophisticated growth chambers have been developed and marketed that allow precise control over day length, temperature, and humidity.

Night break experiments can be conducted with precision in controlled environments with carefully timed light flashes. Using carefully controlled environmental conditions, the precision of environmental regulation of flowering in some plants has been established. The effects of light and temperature have been separated.

Grafting experiments have established that florigen and antiflorigen are substances that are graft-transmissible and can result in floral evocation in shoot apexes of plants of different species and even different orders. Short-day Maryland Mammoth tobacco will flower under long-day conditions when grafted to long-day henbane, even though there is no close evolutionary relationship between the two species. A plant maintained under noninductive conditions can also flower if a photoperiodically induced leaf is grafted to it. Variations in the plant age and genotype have been established by grafting different shoot apexes to compatible stock plants and observing their competency of response of both florigen and floral inhibitors.

Isolating, culturing, and rooting shoot apexes have allowed investigators to assess when they become committed to producing flowers. These experiments have helped establish the sequence leading to the production of flowers. Increasing concentrations of florigen, or decreasing levels of inhibitors, reach the apexes, resulting in evocation. Evocation ends when the apex becomes stably determined to produce a flower; this commitment is seen even when the apex is removed from the signal. Such experiments also provide information on how quickly a signal arrives at the shoot apex. Much has been learned about the regulation of flowering by isolating mutants (especially in the pea) that exhibit abnormal regulation of flowering. In some cases, these mutants arise spontaneously; in other cases, mutations are chemically induced. Using the methods described above, the nature of the mutation can be identified. An understanding of the defect in the mutant provides insight into critical control points in the flowering process.

Biochemical approaches have been taken to isolate florigen. Using different solvents, extracts of plant tissue have been isolated and applied to other plants to test for flower-inducing ability. An extract that induces flowering in other species has been isolated in Chailakhyan's laboratory, but the active component has not yet been identified. Numerous plant hormones have been tested both individually and in combination on different species, but none has been identified as florigen.

Advances in molecular biology are allowing investigators to look for genes that are expressed in leaves in response to an inductive photoperiod. Genes that are active produce messenger ribonucleic acids (RNAs) that are translated into proteins that have a biological function. RNAs that are present after photoperiodic induction (but not before) are isolated from leaves. Using an enzyme called reverse transcriptase, complementary deoxyribonucleic acid (cDNA) copies of the pertinent RNAs can be made. These cDNAs can be radioactively labeled and used as probes for the gene producing the RNA, or even for the RNA itself. The temporal and spatial parameters of the expression of the associated gene can thus be studied by looking for the presence of the RNA with the cDNA probe that will bind to it. Also, the gene could be isolated through other techniques and identified with this probe. Research using these approaches is underway with Japanese morning glory in several laboratories.

Context

Flowering is essential for sexual reproduction in all angiosperms. Complex interactions between many plants and insects have evolved that result in pollination of one species of plant by one or a few species of insects. Precise control over the time of flowering is critical so that the appropriate pollinator will be available. Even for wind-pollinated flowers, environmental conditions must be suitable for embryo and seed development. Flowering too early or too late in the season could have disastrous results on the next generation. The potential to manipulate the flowering process has significant implications for agriculture and horticulture. Commercial growers take advantage of knowledge of photoperiodic control of flowering to have short-day poinsettias flowering at Christmastime. In contrast, short-day chrysanthemums generally flower in the fall, but by lengthening the day or interrupting a long night with a light flash, flowering can be delayed until the spring. For field crops, manipulating photoperiod is not a viable approach. Plant breeders already select for traits affecting flowering time in breeding new varieties. Large-scale farmers, as well as those who grow at home, have the option of choosing varieties of crops, including corn, peas, and tomatoes, that flower early or late in the season. Genetic engineering offers the potential to create unique gene combinations that ultimately could provide even more control over the time of flowering. Alternatively, if a flower-inducing or flower-inhibiting substance were isolated, chemical control of flowering might be possible. Inhibiting flowering would have considerable benefits for forage grasses, where nutritional value would be increased in a leafy hay.

A knowledge of vernalization had significant impact on the wheat crop in Russia early in the twentieth century. Winter wheat had to be sown in the fall to flower the following summer, but much of the seed rotted in the ground, reducing yield. By allowing winter wheat to germinate slightly and then maintaining it at a low temperature ("vernalizing" it), the seed could be planted in the spring and the yield increased. For fruit tree growers, phase change is of considerable interest. If the length of the juvenile phase of an apple tree is reduced by several years, a grower could get a more rapid return on his investment. For tree breeders, this represents a long delay (more than thirty years for some species) and financial investment for species improvement through breeding programs. There are many more possibilities for benefits from the manipulation of the flowering process, and the full potential for control of flowering time remains to be achieved.

Bibliography

Campbell, Neil A. *Biology*. Menlo Park, Calif.: Benjamin/Cummings, 1987. Chapter 35, "Control Systems in Plants," provides clear descriptions of circadian rhythms, photoperiodism, phytochrome, and florigen. Figures in this chapter are especially helpful in elucidating the effect of light on flowering. This is written for introductory-level college students and is also suitable for high school students.

Evans, L. T. *The Induction of Flowering*. Ithaca, N.Y.: Cornell University Press, 1969. The first chapter, "A Short History of the Physiology of Flowering," provides a detailed perspective on the history of research on the regulation of flowering. Original research articles are cited in the bibliography. Although the information in later chapters focusing on specific plants is dated, this chapter will continue to be of value.

Hackett, Wesley P. "Juvenility, Maturation, and Rejuvenation in Woody Plants." *Horticultural Reviews* 7 (1985): 109-155. Hackett provides a wealth of detail at the college level on juvenility and phase change. The phenomenon of phase change is discussed. Several hypotheses concerning the shift from the juvenile to mature phase are evaluated in the light of experimental evidence. Information on the length of the juvenile period in different species is presented.

Key, Joe L., and Lee McIntosh, eds. *Plant Gene Systems and Their Biology.* New York: Alan R. Liss, 1987. Two chapters on flowering may be especially helpful for college-level students. "Perspectives in Flowering Research," by Anton Land, provides insight into research on florigen and antiflorigen as well as molecular approaches to flowering regulation. Daphne Vince-Prue's chapter, "The Induction and Initiation of Flowers," provides more detailed information on the relation between phytochrome and the biological clock. Molecular approaches to studying photoperiodic induction in leaves are also considered. Both chapters are enhanced by clear, informative figures and provide bibliographies of relevant research papers.

Malacinski, George M., and Susan V. Bryant. *Pattern Formation.* New York: Macmillan, 1984. Chapter 16, "Competence, Determination, and Induction in Plant Development," by Carl McDaniel, provides a developmental perspective on the flowering process. It is well illustrated and utilizes numerous specific examples, which strengthen it.

Raven, Peter H., Ray F. Evert, and Susan E. Eichhorn. *Biology of Plants.* 4th ed. New York: Worth, 1986. Chapter 25, "Growth Regulation and Growth Responses," covers much of the same material as the Campbell entry, but in more detail. Specifically, there is more extensive reference to the original experiments.

Sussex, Ian M. "Developmental Programming of the Shoot Meristem." *Cell* 27 (January 27, 1989): 225-229. A brief review of the development of shoot apexes. This places flowering in the context of other shoot-apex activities. The question of shoot-apex programming—specifically, the meristem at the tip of the apex that generates new structures—is addressed. Examples illustrating the value of mutants in understanding shoot-apex development and programming are also included.

Susan R. Singer

Cross-References

Angiosperms, 95; Flower Structure, 999; Fruit Structure, 1038; Germination and Seedling Development, 1205; Leaf-Fall Regulation, 1542; Plant Hormones, 2103; Plant Life Spans, 2110; Plant Tissue Types, 2119; Tropisms and Their Control in Plants, 2669.

FLUID BALANCE

Type of life science: Animal physiology
Other fields of study: Biochemistry and cell biology (cytology)

The regulation of the intake and excretion of salt and water and the distribution of these elements within the body are two of the major requirements of animals. Understanding the mechanisms of fluid balance allows physicians to treat diseases resulting from or causing imbalances.

Principal terms

COLLOIDS: large molecules such as proteins

EQUILIBRIUM: the state in which there is no net change in the concentration of the components of a system, although there will be changes between components back and forth at the same rate

GASTROINTESTINAL TRACT: the organ system through which fluid enters the body

HYDROSTATIC PRESSURE: the force exerted by the equivalent of the weight of the height of a column of water

INTERSTITIAL FLUID: the volume of fluid that occupies the spaces between cells (the interstices) in the body

INTRACELLULAR FLUID: the fluid inside cells

KIDNEYS: the organs that form urine and control the rate of salt and water loss from the body

LYMPHATIC SYSTEM: a system of tubular structures beginning as microscopic closed sacs in the tissues and converging into larger vessels that empty fluids from tissues into veins

MILLIEQUIVALENTS: the chemical concentration of a substance in millimoles multiplied by its valence (charge); a measure of the concentration of charges

PLASMA: the fluid portion of blood in which red blood cells are suspended and which contains dissolved salts and proteins

RENAL: pertaining to the kidneys

SYMPATHETIC NERVES: a division of the autonomic nervous system that responds to a "flight-or-fight" situation

Summary of the Phenomenon

All animals are faced with the problem of maintaining a constant and optimal volume and composition of the fluid compartments in the body. An optimal composition is necessary to provide a chemical environment in which cells can function best. An optimal volume is required to act as a medium through which nutrients are supplied to cells. Maintaining fluid volume and composition is called fluid balance and is the result of the functioning of several organ systems. Fluid balance is created by matching salt and water intake and losses, and by the redistribution of fluid within the body. Fluid is taken into the body through ingestion by the gastrointestinal tract. Fluid is lost from the body through the kidneys, intestine, skin, and lungs. Redistribution in the body takes place between the three major fluid compartments: plasma, interstitial fluid, and intracellular fluid. Movement of fluid among these three compartments depends primarily on osmotic water movement.

The organs that alter intake and excretion also interact with one another so that excretory organs affect intake organs and vice versa. Water balance is achieved when the volume of water entering the body is equal to the volume of water leaving the body. Body water will increase, resulting in a positive water balance, when there is greater water intake than excretion, and conversely, a negative water balance will result when excretion exceeds intake. If there is a decrease in body water or salt for any reason, such as dehydration, blood loss, diarrhea, vomiting, or urine excretion, then water and salt intake are stimulated and excretion will decrease.

The body fluid volumes are separated from one another by certain physical barriers that prevent free diffusion of some components from one compartment to another. The plasma is separated from the interstitial space by the capillary wall. Water and small molecules can diffuse freely between the plasma and the interstitial space, but the larger proteins are retained in the plasma. The cell membrane is the barrier between the interstitial space and the intercellular fluid. The cell membrane prevents diffusion of proteins and sodium between these two compartments. In addition, the cell membrane has ion pumps, which create a higher sodium concentration outside the cells in the interstitial fluid and a higher potassium concentration in the intracellular fluid.

Osmosis is the flow of water across a semipermeable membrane. A semipermeable membrane is permeable to water but not to one or more of the dissolved constituents of the solution on one or both sides of the membrane. A molecule that has restricted diffusion cannot diffuse to the other side of the membrane. Thus, it will not reach the same concentration on both sides at equilibrium. Instead, water will move toward the side of the membrane containing the nondiffusible component in order to reduce its concentration.

The salts of sodium and potassium constitute the largest contributors to the osmotic pressure of the body fluids. Osmotic pressure is a force that pulls water toward a region where there is a higher concentration of particles. Osmotic pressure depends on the total particle concentration. For example, sodium chloride dissociates into sodium and chloride and therefore generates two particles. Water diffuses easily through all the barriers, however, and the osmotic pressure is very nearly the same in all body fluid compartments. Therefore, total osmotic pressure of the body will be determined by the total amount of water and the total amount of sodium and potassium.

The osmotic flow of water is a result of both crystalloid and colloid osmotic pressure. Crystalloid osmotic pressure is caused by small molecules, such as sodium or chloride, that cannot pass a membrane semipermeable to them. Colloid osmotic pressure is caused by large molecules, such as proteins. The two semipermeable membranes that are involved are the capillary wall and the cell membrane. The capillary wall restricts the diffusion of proteins, and the cell membrane restricts the diffusion of sodium and proteins.

There is a related phenomenon, called the Gibbs-Donnan effect, which is associated with the charge on proteins. This effect results in slightly more positive ions (cations) on the side of the membrane containing the proteins and slightly more negative ions (anions) on the opposite side. Most proteins have a net negative charge, and, thus, they are anions. They will attract cations from salts in order to balance the charges and repel anions, thus pulling or pushing salts through the membrane. At the same time, osmotic pressure must be maintained. If proteins and a salt, such as sodium chloride, are placed on one side of a semipermeable membrane and water on the other side, then the salt and water, but not the proteins, will move across the membrane from an area of higher to lower concentration and osmotic pressures. The end result is that there will be more osmotically active particles and more diffusible cations from salts on the side of the membrane that has the proteins and more anions on the opposite side. Water will continue to move by osmosis toward the side of the membrane containing the proteins.

Water has a density of about 1, and therefore 1 gram of weight is nearly equal to the weight of 1 milliliter of water. Grams and milliliters of water can be considered equivalent. Multiplying the weight of a person in grams or kilograms by the percentage of the volume of a body fluid compartment will give the volume of that compartment in milliliters or liters, respectively. For example, an average man weighing 70 kilograms will have a blood volume of 5,600 milliliters (8 percent of body weight).

The normal volumes of the body fluid compartments (expressed as a percentage of body weight) maintained by the body are as follows: Blood volume is about 8 percent, plasma volume 5 percent (about 55 percent of blood volume), interstitial volume 15 percent, and intracellular volume 40 percent of body weight. The plasma and interstitial compartments together are called extracellular fluid. Total body water is the sum of the extracellular and intracellular fluid compartments plus another compartment, called transcellular fluid. Transcellular fluid is a relatively small volume composed of compartments that do not mix quickly with extracellular fluid. Transcellular compartments include the fluid in the bones, joints, eyes, gastrointestinal tract, and some glands, and the cerebrospinal fluid.

Fluid intake is controlled by the nervous system through the mechanism of thirst. Thirst is stimulated when there is an increase in osmotic pressure of the body fluids. Nerves in a brain structure called the hypothalamus are stimulated by increased osmotic pressure and drive an animal to drink. In addition, these nerves stimulate the release of a hormone called antidiuretic hormone (ADH) that causes the kidneys to retain water in the body by reducing water losses in the urine. The reverse occurs (thirst is repressed and kidney output increased) when there is more than an optimal level of water in the body.

Salt content in the body is controlled, in part, through the rate of sodium and potassium excretion by the kidneys. The kidneys can increase or decrease the rate of salt excretion. Salt retention is increased when there is a decrease in the plasma or blood volume or an increase in potassium concentration in the plasma. Sodium excretion is controlled, in part, through the secretion of a hormone, aldosterone, from the adrenal cortex. Aldosterone causes the kidneys to retain salt in the body. Aldosterone secretion is increased by two mechanisms. First, the secretion of another hormone, renin, by the kidneys is increased when there is a decrease in blood flow through the kidneys. Renin, in turn, splits a plasma protein called angiotensinogen into hormones called angiotensins that then stimulate aldosterone secretion. Angiotensin also increases ADH secretion. Second, increased plasma potassium concentration acts directly on the adrenal cortex to stimulate aldosterone secretion.

Decreased kidney blood flow is an important stimulus to salt and water retention in the body through several mechanisms. As mentioned above, the secretion of renin and subsequent formation of angiotensin is one mechanism. Angiotensin also stimulates thirst by acting on certain regions of the brain; it also decreases renal (kidney) blood flow. Decreased renal blood flow, of itself, reduces the excretion of salt and water in the urine by reducing the amounts presented to the kidneys for excretion. Renal blood flow is also decreased by sympathetic nerve stimulation. Sympathetic nerves fire when blood pressure decreases, and, thus, this factor will also control salt and water excretion by the body. Sympathetic nerve stimulation also directly stimulates the kidneys to retain more salt and water in the body. In turn, this action restores blood pressure.

The kidneys are especially important because they are the only organs that can completely restore the normal body fluid volumes. Other mechanisms restore disturbances only part of the way back to normal. Also, these other mechanisms adapt to the altered conditions after a period of time and thus can no longer sense that a disturbance is still present. The kidneys are responsible for long-term regulation of fluid balance. There are also receptors, however, which sense the blood volume of the circulation. These are located primarily in the atria of the heart and the larger veins. These volume receptors decrease water and salt excretion and increase thirst when blood volume decreases.

Water losses from the body also occur from the skin and lungs. These are primarily evaporative losses of water. Sweating is another mechanism for water loss and also causes relatively more water than salt loss. A small amount of salt and water is also lost from the gastrointestinal tract in the feces. Water loss by these routes is generally not controlled by the same mechanisms that control fluid balance, though fluid balance must also compensate for these losses.

While the body is adjusting the intake and excretion of salt and water, there is a redistribution of fluid within the body. Osmotic adjustments shift water among the plasma, interstitial fluid, and intracellular fluid compartments. Plasma volume is regulated to maintain the circulation. Interstitial fluid is regulated to maintain a small diffusion distance between the blood and the cells so that nutrients can diffuse over this distance in a short time. Fluid movement across the capillary wall is called bulk flow when it is driven by pressures. A distinction is made between bulk flow and another mechanism of movement, diffusion. Diffusion is a movement of individual molecules driven by random motion down a concentration gradient. Bulk flow is the movement of a volume of fluid driven in the direction of high to low pressures. These pressures can be osmotic or hydrostatic.

There are two pressures that force fluid movement across capillary walls: colloid osmotic and hydrostatic. There are colloid osmotic (also called oncotic) and hydrostatic pressures in both the blood plasma and the interstitial fluid compartments. These forces are called Starling forces after their discoverer, Ernest Henry Starling. The hydrostatic pressure in the plasma forces fluid out of the plasma and into the interstitial space. The colloid osmotic pressure in the plasma pulls fluid out of the interstitial space back into the plasma. Interstitial colloid osmotic pressure pulls fluid from the plasma. In most tissues, the interstitial hydrostatic pressure is negative (below atmospheric) and thus pulls fluid out of the plasma. When tissue pressure is positive, fluid is forced out of the interstitial space into the plasma.

Normally, the average blood (hydrostatic) pressure in a capillary is about 25 millimeters of mercury but can vary somewhat among tissues. The colloid osmotic pressure of the plasma proteins is also about 25 millimeters of mercury and thus equals the average capillary pressure. The tissue colloid and hydrostatic pressures are relatively small and variable from one tissue to the next. Normally, the four forces are balanced so that relatively little fluid is lost into the tissues. The small amount that is lost is returned to the circulation in the lymph.

There are conditions in which the Starling forces become out of balance and fluid is lost from the plasma into the tissues or is pulled from the tissues into the plasma. Many of these conditions revolve around decreased plasma volume, which can occur following hemorrhage, dehydration, and excess fluid loss from the kidneys, skin, or gastrointestinal tract. When plasma or blood volume decreases, blood pressure also falls, because there is less blood pumped by the heart and less blood to fill up the blood vessels. Capillary blood pressure then falls below plasma colloid osmotic pressure. Colloid osmotic pressure, being now greater than blood pressure, begins to pull fluid from the interstitial space and into the plasma. Plasma volume then increases and blood pressure returns toward normal. The reverse occurs if blood pressure increases. Starling forces thus tend to regulate blood pressure by regulating plasma volume.

Normally, there is a proportional change in plasma and interstitial volume because of the adjustments created by Starling forces. When the plasma volume becomes excessively expanded, however, the interstitial space then takes up any extra fluid because blood pressure increases and plasma colloids become diluted to the point that the Starling forces now favor continual fluid losses into the interstitial space. The accumulation of fluid in the interstitial space is called edema. Starling forces also act to adjust absorption from the intestine and excretion by the kidney to match the requirements of the body. Any situation in which the Starling forces pull fluid into the plasma from the interstitial space will also pull fluid from the kidney and intestine. Thus, salt and water absorption will increase and excretion will decrease.

The presence of very high concentrations of proteins in cells also tends to draw fluid into cells through the high intracellular colloid osmotic pressure. The cell combats the tendency to swell by two mechanisms: pumping sodium out of the cell into the interstitial fluid compartment and regulating the loss of potassium through channels in the cell membrane. There is a protein in cell membranes called the sodium pump. This pump requires adenosine triphosphate as an energy source and transports three sodiums out of the cell in exchange for two potassiums into the cell. This pump works all the time, and water follows the sodium out of the cell. The loss of water from the cell tends to counteract the entry of water from intracellular proteins. In addition, there are channels or pores in the cell membrane that allow potassium or other ions to pass through the cell membrane. These pores are opened when the cell membranes are stretched by even very small amounts as the cell swells. When potassium leaves, it pulls water with it, and the cell shrinks back toward a normal volume. In addition, there may be pumps, other than the sodium pump, which move potassium into the cell when it shrinks. Because potassium and its associated negative ions are the major contributors to the intracellular osmotic pressure, the volume of the cell will be determined by the amounts of these ions. Water will follow the potassium into the cell until there is the same osmotic pressure in the cells and the interstitial fluid.

Methods of Study

The main technique for determining fluid balance within the body requires measuring the volumes and ionic composition of the different fluid compartments. These are not directly accessible to measurements, however, so what is measured is a quantity called the volume of distribution. A known amount of a substance, which is restricted to one of the compartments, is injected into the body, and its concentration in the plasma measured after it has equilibrated in its compartment. Usually, the substance is tagged with a radioactive tracer so that the injected substance can be distinguished from the amount of the substance that was already present in the body.

Measurement of the volume of distribution can be illustrated by the following example: If 100 milligrams of a substance is dissolved in a beaker containing 1,000 milliliters of water, then the final concentration will be 0.1 milligram per milliliter. If one did not know the volume in the beaker, one could take a sample of the solution, measure the concentration of the substance, and calculate the volume. Dividing the amount of the substance added by the final concentration will equal the volume of distribution. Measurement of the body fluid compartments requires using a substance that is restricted only, or at least primarily, to a specific compartment.

Radioactive sodium and potassium can be used to measure the amounts of these ions in the body. Radioactive water can be used to measure total body water.

Radioactive colloids or red blood cells can be used to measure plasma or blood volume. Radioactive chloride or sucrose, a sugar restricted to the extracellular space, can be used to measure extracellular fluid volume. Interstitial fluid volume can be calculated by subtracting plasma volume from extracellular fluid volume. Intracellular volume can be calculated by subtracting extracellular fluid volume from total body water.

Context

Fluid balance is relatively easily distributed in many disease states because of the large number of organs and factors involved in its regulation. The complexity of fluid balance, the large number of organ systems involved, and the interdependency of the organs and their functions makes diagnosis of the causes of fluid balance dysfunctions extremely difficult. In many cases, the attempt of the body to compensate for one problem causes others, which makes these diseases especially difficult to treat or diagnose.

There are a number of situations in which there is a loss of body water. Depending on the source of the loss, there may be problems associated with the specific salts that are lost along with the water. Diarrhea causes water and potassium losses because the contents of the large intestine are relatively high in potassium. Cells will gradually lose potassium and water to replace the plasma potassium and water that is lost from the body. Thus, both extracellular and intracellular fluid will be lost. Sweating will cause a relatively greater loss of water than salts. The plasma volume will be reduced, and the plasma salts will become more concentrated and pull water from the cells by osmosis. As a result, in both the above cases, the volume receptors will stimulate drinking and the reduced blood pressure will cause retention of fluid in the body until the losses are replaced.

Congestive heart failure is a case in which there is fluid retention in the body even though there is excess extracellular fluid. When the heart is too weak to pump adequate amounts of blood, the blood accumulates in the veins leading to the heart. This situation increases the hydrostatic blood pressure in the capillaries and causes edema. Hence, there is an accumulation of extracellular fluid. It might be expected that the kidneys would begin to excrete more salt and water. Yet, the sympathetic nervous system is stimulated because of the reduced arterial blood pressure, and the kidneys respond by retaining salt and water. That increases the blood pressure but makes the edema worse.

Bibliography

Ganong, William F. *Review of Medical Physiology.* East Norwalk, Conn.: Appleton & Lange, 1989. An advanced text but with well-illustrated and concise explanations of physiological phenomena. Numerous chapters provide descriptions and mechanisms of the organs and forces affecting fluid balance. The text is useful because the topics are presented in small sections and subsections. Well indexed for locating information.

Guyton, Arthur C. *Human Physiology and Mechanisms of Disease*. Philadelphia: W. B. Saunders, 1982. An intermediate-level animal physiology text by a world expert on fluid balance. Several general and specific chapters devoted specifically to fluid balance and regulatory mechanisms. Well written and verbally oriented.

_____. *Textbook of Medical Physiology*. Philadelphia: W. B. Saunders, 1986. An advanced-level, medically oriented physiology text. Fluid balance is an area of Guyton's expertise, and, indeed, he has carried out much of the research in this area. Extensive discussion of clinical aspects of fluid balance.

Rhoades, Rodney, and Richard Pflanzer. *Human Physiology*. Philadelphia: Saunders College Publishing, 1989. A very current and well-written intermediate-level animal physiology text. Excellent illustrations; clear, direct, and pertinent writing.

Soloman, Eldra, Richard Schmidt, and Peter Adragna. *Human Anatomy & Physiology*. Philadelphia: Saunders College Publishing, 1990. This introductory text has excellent diagrams and pictures of structures as well as clearly written text. Index.

Sullivan, Lawrence, and Jared Grantham. *Physiology of the Kidney*. Philadelphia: Lea & Febiger, 1982. A paperback devoted to the functions of the kidney and body fluid regulation. Includes the kidney cells, basic processes governing water flow, and functions of the kidney. Covers many details in a clear and readable manner.

Tortora, Gerard J., and Nicholas Anagnostakos. *Principles of Anatomy and Physiology*. 3d ed. New York: Harper & Row, 1981. An introductory-level text with medically oriented examples. Glossaries of medical terms, prefixes and suffixes, and normal values for medical tests make this a useful book.

David Mailman

Cross-References

Blood Circuits, 248; Blood Pressure, 270; Circulatory Systems of Invertebrates, 476; Circulatory Systems of Vertebrates, 483; Diffusion in Circulation, 621; Endocrinology of the Adrenal Glands, 800; Kidneys and Other Excretory Structures, 1514; The Lymphatic System's Function, 1619; Osmoregulation, 2015; Water Retention and Excretion, 2709.

FLUORESCENT ANTIBODY STAINING
OF CYTOSKELETAL ELEMENTS

Type of life science: Cell biology (cytology)
Other fields of study: Biochemistry, immunology, and molecular biology

Each cell has an internal cytoskeleton that supports it and helps it move and change shape. It is possible to make antibodies that attach to the proteins that make up the cytoskeleton. The location of these antibodies, and therefore of the cytoskeleton in a cell, can be visualized by chemically fastening to each antibody a light-emitting molecule that can be observed through a microscope.

Principal terms
ANTIBODY: a special type of protein made by the immune system when it is exposed to a foreign molecule (antigen); it fastens tightly to the foreign molecule and thus provides a defense against invading organisms and unhealthy substances
ANTIGEN: a substance that stimulates the immune system to produce specifically designed antibodies that then stick to the antigen tightly but do not stick to any other molecules
CELL: the structural and functional unit of living organisms, basically a fluid-filled bag that contains genes, energy-producing structures, and other components needed to carry out the functions of life; the human body is made up of several trillion cells
CYTOPLASM: the contents of a cell, including everything but the nucleus (which contains the chromosomes and genes); it essentially consists of a salty liquid in which the various specialized structures of the cell are suspended
CYTOSKELETON: a meshwork of three different kinds of strandlike proteins inside a cell; it serves functions similar to the human skeleton, such as support and movement
ELECTRON MICROSCOPE: an ultra-high-power microscope that uses electron beams instead of visible light to produce its enlarging effect; it can magnify up to several hundred thousand times
FLUORESCENCE: the emission of light by a substance in response to intense stimulation by light of another wavelength; materials that "glow in the dark" can be such substances
FLUORESCENCE MICROSCOPE: a special kind of light microscope, in which a light beam of a particular wavelength is passed through a specimen; this light excites fluorescent dyes in the specimen, and the observer sees only the light emitted by the fluorescent dyes
LIGHT MICROSCOPE: the standard microscope, in which glass lenses are used to magnify an image up to about one thousand times

Summary of the Methodology

Fluorescent antibody staining is a sophisticated and extremely precise technique for visualizing the location of the cytoskeleton within a cell. The methodology makes use of a combination of several types of techniques.

Cells contain collections of distinct, fiber-forming proteins that can arrange themselves into a scaffolding within a cell. This cytoskeleton can be characterized if the cells are first ground up and if the molecules are then isolated, in the process disrupting the interactions and specific arrangements of the parts of the cell. The properties of the cytoskeleton depend upon its precise three-dimensional architecture within the intact cell. Thus, it is also important that the researcher use methods designed to analyze the intact cytoskeleton inside whole cells.

Various kinds of microscopy techniques have been applied with some success to understanding the architecture of the cytoskeleton. The fibers of the cytoskeleton are far too small to be seen using an ordinary light microscope. They can, however, be observed using electron microscopy, which provides much higher magnifications. Electron microscopy was used first to show that cells contain cytoskeletal fibers; however, a cell must be treated harshly to prepare it for electron microscopy, which may change its structure in unknown ways. Furthermore, electron microscopy allows the researcher to observe only a tiny portion of the cell at a time, so it is difficult to visualize the bigger picture of how the fibers are arranged within the whole cell.

Ideally, one should be able to visualize an entire, intact cell all at once, in such a way that the natural arrangement of the cytoskeletal proteins can be readily observed. An entire cell can be seen with the light microscope, but because the cytoskeletal fibers are too small to see in this way, they must be tagged or marked to make them more visible. Fluorescent antibody staining is used for this purpose.

If a foreign protein is injected into a mammal (usually a rabbit or goat), the animal's immune system will sense that the protein is foreign and will produce antibodies that help defend the animal against the invading substance. Proteins of one species (for example, mice or humans) will be sensed as foreign in a different species (for example, rabbits or goats). This so-called immune reaction can be utilized to produce antibodies that interact very specifically with each of the different proteins of the cytoskeleton. A purified solution of a cytoskeletal protein is injected into the circulatory system of a host of a different species. After several injections at weekly intervals, the host will have produced antibodies that interact specifically with the injected antigen, this is, the cytoskeletal protein. The specific antibody protein can then be purified from blood samples of the host animal.

If the antibody is applied to cells that contain the original cytoskeletal antigen protein, the antibody molecules will adhere very tightly to the antigen but not to other molecules in the cell. If a way to mark or tag the antibody could be devised, so that it was visible in the light microscope, the distribution of the marked antibody would indicate where in the cell the antigen protein is located. Several different kinds of substances have been used as visual tags on antibodies. The most popular method is to fasten a fluorescent dye on the antibody. The most commonly used dyes are rhodamine (for red fluorescence) and fluorescein (for greenish-yellow fluorescence). When such a fluorescent antibody is then added to cells, it can be located using a special fluorescence microscope.

Although this procedure works reasonably well, it can be improved by amplifying the signal—that is, devising a method to add more than one molecule of fluorescent dye to each anticytoskeleton antibody molecule, which will increase the amount of fluorescent light emitted. The brighter light is much easier to see. This can be done using the so-called secondary-antibody procedure. A "secondary antibody" must be prepared using the first antibody (against the cytoskeletal protein) as antigen. This time, the secondary antibody is made fluorescent. The cytoskeletal proteins are then tagged in two steps: First, the primary antibody is added to cells, then the fluorescent secondary antibody is added. Because of the nature of the secondary antibody, numerous molecules of it can adhere to each molecule of primary antibody. In this way, many fluorescent molecules can be attached to each molecule of primary antibody. The result is that the researcher can now see strikingly beautiful images in the fluorescence microscope: brilliantly colored glowing strands of the cytoskeleton, arranged in various patterns depending on what is happening inside the cell.

Applications of the Method

Cells require an internal system of fibers in order to maintain and change their shape. The fibers serve other functions as well—for example, as rails along which substances shuttle from one part of the cell to another. Fluorescent antibody techniques allow scientists to observe exactly how various fiber types are oriented within the cell. This technique has greatly increased knowledge of how the cytoskeleton does its jobs. It is also among the most aesthetically beautiful of all the procedures used by cell biologists.

The cytoskeleton is composed of three different kinds of fibers, each with different, specialized functions. Microfilaments are the smallest (6 nanometers in diameter). They are made up of a protein similar to the actin protein in muscle. It is thus not surprising that microfilaments participate in cell movement and shape changes. They usually are found in bundles just inside the surface of the cell, where they are best situated to help the cell change shape. Intermediate filaments are somewhat larger. Unlike microfilaments, they seem to serve as passive scaffolding elements within the cell. They typically form an interlaced meshwork in the cytoplasm. The proteins that make up these fibers are subtly different in different kinds of cells; the significance of such variation is not clear. The largest fibers are called microtubules (25 nanometers in diameter). They are hollow spirals of protein building blocks. The microtubules have important, specialized roles in particular regions of cells and at certain times in a cell's life. For example, they help move the chromosomes around during division of one cell into two. They are important components of both cilia and flagella—whiplike structures on the surfaces of some cells that serve as oars to help them swim about or to move substances along their surfaces. (The air passages of the lungs are lined with cells covered with cilia, and they help move dust particles and other debris away from the delicate lung surfaces.)

Fluorescent antibody techniques have helped scientists learn that microfilaments and microtubules are dynamic fibers, which grow and shrink as necessary. (Intermediate fibers are more stable.) They can be assembled or disassembled, like Tinkertoys or a set of blocks. The building blocks can be moved from one part of a cell to another quite rapidly if required. Within a few seconds, the distribution of fibers can change dramatically within a living cell. This phenomenon occurs, for example, if a moving cell encounters an obstacle and changes direction. Under certain conditions, microtubule proteins can be added to one end of a microtubule at the same time that they are removed from the opposite end. The result is that the microtubule appears to "move" toward the growing end. This process has been likened to the movement of the tread on a Caterpillar-type tractor.

Cytoskeletal fibers are complex, sophisticated, dynamic structures. Many kinds of protein make up each fiber, perhaps as many as several hundred. In addition to proteins, whose primary role is to construct the filament itself, there are proteins associated with each fiber type whose role is to make the decisions about when, where, and how fast to assemble or disassemble the filaments. If the structural proteins are the girders of a building, the associated proteins are like construction workers, engineers, and supervisors, who decide how the girders should be assembled and assist in the construction itself, guiding the girders to the proper place.

Our understanding of life processes is often limited by our ingenuity in developing procedures that will help answer important questions. Fluorescent antibody techniques have helped cell biologists leap ahead in their understanding of the structure and function of the cellular cytoskeleton.

Context

A cell is a highly complex structure with many subcomponents that must work together smoothly if each cell is to carry out its function properly. The cytoskeleton is an inconspicuous but important player on the team. As scientists have learned more about the cytoskeleton, it has become increasingly obvious that this apparatus is necessary for a wide variety of behaviors of cells. Fluorescent antibody techniques have revealed much about the activities of the cytoskeleton.

Perhaps the most straightforward function of the cytoskeleton is for cell support. It provides a scaffolding that gives each cell a distinctive three-dimensional shape; without such support every cell would be shaped like a fried egg. Equally important, however, is the role of the cytoskeleton in cell movement and change in cell shape. The various cytoskeletal fibers can be rearranged, dissolved, and reconstructed at new locations when need be. The cytoskeleton is also a key component of some highly specialized cell structures, such as cilia and flagella.

The first cell function to be definitely attributed to the cell's cytoskeleton was cell division. This process is an elaborate, highly choreographed minuet in which one fiber type (microtubules) moves two sets of chromosomes (the structures that carry the genetic information) apart from one another, and another fiber type (microfilaments) squeezes the cell in two between the chromosome sets. The result is two cells where there was only one, and each has a complete set of genes. How are the activities of the two kinds of fibers coordinated in both time and space, so that this elegant process occurs properly? It is now understood that changing concentrations of calcium atoms inside cells help to coordinate the actions of the several fiber types. Fluorescent antibody staining has revealed that the chromosome-moving microtubules change in length during movement and that they generate a force sufficient to drag the chromosomes through the cell.

Any number of human diseases involve problems with cytoskeletal functions. Cancer is essentially uncontrolled cell multiplication, and the cytoskeleton is a key element in the multiplication process. On the other hand, during aging and senescence, cell replication slows down, and the cytoskeleton is again altered. Cytoskeletal filaments participate in growth and function of nerves, and problems with the nerve's cytoskeleton can lead to malfunctioning of the nerves. In Alzheimer's disease, for example, fibers accumulate in an abnormal pattern in specific areas of the brain.

Bibliography

Becker, Wayne M. *The World of the Cell*. Menlo Park, Calif.: Benjamin/Cummings, 1989. This is a textbook for a beginning-level college course in cell biology. Because it is written in an unusually straightforward manner, however, an interested nonscientist should be able to learn from it about all aspects of cell biology. The use of fluorescent antibodies is described in chapter 10, "Membranes: Their Structure and Chemistry." The diagrams are particularly good. Each chapter has a list of suggested further readings, both general and specific.

Bershadsky, Alexander D., and Juri M. Vasiliev. *Cytoskeleton*. Cellular Organelle Series. New York: Plenum Press, 1988. A comprehensive summary of the cytoskeleton, providing the reader with some insight into the complexity of the cytoskeleton. Emphasis is on concepts rather than on details of experiments; thus, the main themes should be accessible to those with a solid background in high school or college chemistry and biology. Includes many excellent photographs and helpful drawings.

Hood, Leroy E., Irving L. Weissman, and William B. Wood. *Immunology*. Menlo Park, Calif.: Benjamin/Cummings, 1978. A wide-ranging introduction to the complicated topic of how the immune system works. It is superbly done and has become a standard textbook in college courses. It is likely to be challenging to those without a background in biochemistry, but there is much excellent information that can be extracted nevertheless. The arrangement of the book is unusual and helpful; each chapter is divided into "Essential Concepts," an appendix that typically discusses relevant experimental techniques, "Selected Bibliography," and problems followed by answers. This format allows the reader to focus on the subtopics of interest, and then test her/his understanding. Chapter 2 covers the immunological aspects presented in the current article.

Kennedy, Ronald C., John L. Melnick, and Gordon R. Dreesman. "Anti-Idiotypes and Immunity." *Scientific American* 255 (July, 1986): 48-56. This article explains how antibodies made against other antibodies in animals help to adjust the immune response and make it more effective. This should help the reader understand the "second-antibody" procedure, which can be manipulated to increase understanding of how the immune system works and to provide therapeutic advantages.

McIntosh, James R., and Keith L. McDonald. "The Mitotic Spindle." *Scientific American* 261 (July, 1989): 48-56. On the basis of work described by Mazia, McIntosh, and other researchers developed more refined analyses of the role of microtubules and other fibers in cell division. McIntosh is not only a superb and clever scientist, his writing lucidly explains his results in understandable fashion. This article is particularly recommended for its spectacular color photographs of fluorescent antibody staining of the cytoskeleton. No one can see these and not be awed by the beauty and complexity of the living cell.

Mazia, Daniel. "How Cells Divide." *Scientific American* 201 (September, 1961): 93-107. A classic summary of early studies on how the cytoskeleton contributes to cell division. Mazia was a pioneer in studies of microtubule function and became famous for his research in this area. He is also a superb writer who can make the concepts not only understandable but exciting as well. Although outdated in some details, the information is still basically accurate, and well explained.

Starr, Cecie, and Ralph Taggart. *Biology: The Unity and Diversity of Life*. Belmont, Calif.: Wadsworth, 1989. A superb biology text designed for college-level freshmen. It is particularly good at explaining the structure of cells and how they work. Chapter 30, on immunity, is a straightforward, basic introduction to how the immune system is constructed and how antibodies are produced in response to antigens. The section on the cytoskeleton in chapter 5 has several good immunofluorescence photographs, drawings of the structure of each fiber type, photographs of cilia on a single-cell animal, and other useful information—all compacted into a few pages.

Tonegawa, Susumu. "The Molecules of the Immune System." *Scientific American* 253 (October, 1985): 122-131. Tonegawa won the Nobel Prize for his insights into how the immune system works. The production of antibodies in response to antigens involves a totally unexpected shuffling around of pieces of genes to make new kinds of antibody genes. In this way, relatively few antibody genes can code for an enormous number of antibody proteins. This article is a clear and readable summary of these highly complicated events.

Weber, Klaus, and Mary Osborn. "The Molecules of the Cell Matrix." *Scientific American* 253 (October, 1985): 110-120. An excellent review of various aspects of the cytoskeleton, by two of the best writers in this area. The immunofluorescence procedure is described. The article contains truly spectacular photographs of cells with their cytoskeletal elements stained by using immunofluorescent antibody procedures. Highly recommended.

Howard L. Hosick

Cross-References

Antibodies, 112; Cilia, Flagella, Basal Bodies, and Centrioles, 470; The Cytoskeleton, 582; Electron Microscopy, 744; The Immune Response, 1384; Immunization, 1392; The Mitotic Spindle Apparatus, 1760; Flagellar and Ciliary Motion, 1797.

THE FOREBRAIN

Type of life science: Neurobiology
Other fields of study: Animal anatomy and animal physiology

The forebrain—the seat of consciousness—is the highest and most advanced level of the nervous system and is found to varying extents in all vertebrates. It processes information, plans, remembers, and abstracts information.

Principal terms

ASSOCIATION CORTEX: the portion of the cerebral cortex that carries on higher level information processing and provides the mind with the power to understand

BASAL GANGLIA: a large group of neurons buried deep within the parietal lobes of the cerebrum and considered part of the extrapyramidal system that controls complex learned activities

BROCA'S AREA: found in the lower frontal lobe of the dominant hemisphere and controls the output of speech

CEREBRUM: the highest level of the central nervous system physically and functionally; includes cerebral cortices and the basal ganglia

CORPUS CALLOSUM: a large band of myelinated fibers that connects the left and right cerebral cortices

CORTICAL LAYERS: a series of six distinct histological layers in the cerebral cortex which also serve different functions such as input functions, output functions, or associative functions

DIENCEPHALON: embryologically part of the forebrain but functionally part of the brainstem and includes the thalamus and hypothalamus

EXTRAPYRAMIDAL SYSTEM: an output system that reproduces complex learned movements with a minimum of involvement of the conscious cortex

HYPOTHALAMUS: part of the diencephalon and brainstem and functions as master of the autonomic nervous system

LIMBIC SYSTEM: that part of the central nervous system associated with emotions and drives; the "older" brain which is covered by the cerebral cortex

PYRAMIDAL SYSTEM: an efferent system originating in the pyramidal cells of the cortex and dealing with discrete volitional movements

THALAMUS: part of the diencephalon that processes and relays sensory experience to the cortex and also coordinates the outflow of information

WERNICKE'S AREA: includes parts of the parietal and temporal lobes associated with language understanding

Summary of the Phenomenon

The central nervous system is the first system to appear in embryonic development, and fortunately so, considering its complexity and the number of cells it contains (100 billion). The central portion of the embryonic disk's outer layer (the ectoderm) is triggered to begin producing the neuroblasts (immature neurons) of the nervous system in the third week of development. Genes are turned on for the production of unique proteins and factors that guide growth. Neuroblasts will be guided by recognition molecules on the cell surfaces of their neighbors, by the amount of cell contact, and by a cell's position in the inner cell mass of the embryo, as well as by electrical field gradients in this mass.

The neuroblasts multiply and grow, forming the neural tube in the first month of life. Pioneer neurons from the marginal layer of this tube will blaze a trail to specific targets that others will follow later. The first signs of a forebrain occur when the rostral (nose) end of the neural tube has formed three bulbous structures with demarcations that allow separation of the brain into its first three components: forebrain, midbrain, and hindbrain. The greatest growth occurs (ten thousand cells a second) at the rostral end and will continue until birth, when the brain will contain all the neurons that it will ever contain. Flexions, or bends, and later, the folds (gyri) of the cerebral cortex develop. One flexion demarcates the two divisions of the forebrain: the telencephalon and the diencephalon. The telencephalon will completely overgrow the diencephalon, forming the cerebral hemispheres. The diencephalon will become the uppermost portion of the brainstem, which contains the thalamus and hypothalamus. The thalamus routes information to the cerebral cortex; the hypothalamus monitors and controls vital functions via the autonomic nervous system (ANS). Other cells from the neural tube, called glial cells, have important supporting roles. They nourish, protect, insulate, and buffer the neuronal environment. Cells that will give rise to peripheral sensory nerve ganglia are pinched off from the dorsal (back) part of the tube (the neural crest). Nerve cells that control muscle activation, the lower motoneurons, will come from cells in the ventral (front) portion of the neural tube.

The forebrain is a layered structure. The newest layer (neocortex) is the outermost layer, just under the dura mater of the skull; the middle layer is older (archicortex) and contains the limbic system, which governs drives and emotions. The deepest layer is the brainstem, which controls the vital functions, such as circulation and respiration. Deep inside the cerebral hemispheres, and closely associated with the brainstem but part of the forebrain, are the basal ganglia, which control (and possibly remember) complex learned movements. Together with portions of the brainstem and the cerebellum, they form the extrapyramidal system (a system outside of the pyramidal tracts) which assesses, predicts, and remembers body position in three dimensional space. The pyramidal tracts deal with the simpler, more focused volitional movements under the direct control of the conscious cortex.

The brain's surface appears gray because the outer layer lacks myelin, which is white. This layer has the nerve cell bodies and synapses (connections), that process information, store it, and retrieve it while the white matter is simply a conduit for nerve impulses called action potentials (APs). The average mature brain weighs three pounds, but can range from two to five pounds. This weight includes the tracts, the blood supply system, four ventricles containing cerebral spinal fluid, as well as billions of nonneuronal supportive cells.

The cerebral cortex is anatomically divided into four lobes: frontal, parietal, temporal, and occipital. The frontal lobes contain smell, memory, emotions, planning, and motor abilities; the parietal lobes contain body sensations, position sense (kinesthesia), memory and past associations, and language interpretation; the temporal lobes containing hearing, sound interpretation, memory, facial recognition, and emotions; the occipital lobes contain visual processing and visual memory. The cortex can also be divided into major functional areas designated as primary sensory areas, primary motor areas, and association areas.

Sensations are produced when primary sensory areas are stimulated. Movement is produced when the primary motor areas are stimulated. The most fascinating areas of the cortex are the secondary and tertiary association areas, where information is integrated and abstracted. Some of the secondary areas also have topographical maps of the body surface, and the speculation is that "interpretation" of the sensory experience occurs here, as compared to merely "feeling" the sensation. These higher functions do not recognize neat anatomical boundaries, although, generally speaking, motor functions are located more anteriorly and sensory functions more posteriorly, while the processing areas lie between them. These are subdivided according to processing levels—secondary and tertiary associations areas at the least. The information from each sense first goes to the thalamus, followed by distribution to the primary sensory areas, secondary association areas, and tertiary areas, where consciousness and the confluence of all input reside. These are closely associated with the language areas in the dominant hemisphere. Memories probably reside in all the lobes, but they first must be processed in the hippocampus and amygdala of the temporal lobes before becoming permanent.

The overall left-right symmetry of the body extends to the brain, which has distinct left and right cerebral hemispheres. They are connected at the brainstem via commissures, the major one being the corpus callosum, the minor ones being the anterior and posterior commissures. Both halves share information through these connections. The appearance of symmetry is superficial because, upon close inspection, the pattern of gyri and sulci are unique to each brain. The amount of functional asymmetry increases as one proceeds to higher levels. It is this lateralization of function that results in cerebral dominance. Usually the left hemisphere is dominant in humans and expresses itself as a tendency to favor the right side. In individuals with a severed corpus callosum (a treatment for some severe forms of epilepsy), the two halves function independently, which can produce internal conflicts and ambiguous responses—for example, response written with the right hand versus one written with the left hand. In these patients there is evidence for the existence of two spheres of consciousness. Language may be distributed differently between people whose left hand predominates over the right one, for example, or between men and women. Mathematical abilities, visual-spatial abilities, and verbal abilities may be assigned different amounts of space within different hemispheres. Amazingly, the localization of these functions can redistribute or relocate after injury or surgery. Removal of, or damage to, parts of the primary areas produces obvious and localized deficits, which are more likely to be permanent. Removal or loss of parts of association areas may escape notice because of a built-in redundancy and because of the plasticity of the brain. An adjacent area may compensate, or the equivalent area on the opposite side may be used, even though that particular function had never previously been controlled by that area. There is speculation that the cortical area associated with consciousness can also relocate in certain cases.

Methods of Study

To study the brain, researchers use a number of methods, depending upon the questions being asked. At the biochemical level, there are enzyme, neurotransmitter and receptor assays that can be used to determine the localization of, and amounts of, these three types of molecules. These assays are done on either homogenized samples of tissue or on slices. Transmitter levels and receptor binding utilize radioactively labeled transmitter analogs. Also, tagged monoclonal antibodies (radioactive, fluorescent, or ferritin-labeled) derived from cultured hybridized white blood cells that have come into contact with these molecules can reveal their effects at specific sites.

The electrical activity of the brain can be measured using metal electrodes (such as platinum-iridium) that are placed on the surface of the brain. These record extracellular electrical fields from hundreds of neurons closest to the electrode, and this system is referred to as an electrocorticogram (ECG). One can also record brain cell activity using disk electrodes placed on the scalp. This is called an electroencephalogram (EEG). In general, the EEG is not as sensitive as the ECG. Stimulation studies can be performed during surgery to reveal what a particular part of the brain does by observing the subject, or in some cases, querying the subject during the stimulation.

To ascertain the rate of metabolism of a given area of the brain, one can use a system called positron emission topography (PET). This measures the amount of radioactive glucose absorbed by the neurons as a correlate of energy usage. A special helmet with an array of radioactivity sensors feeds coordinates into a computer, which produces a color-coded image that maps the deoxyglucose accumulation.

One can also do either computerized axial tomography (CAT) scans of the brain, producing essentially a three-dimensional X ray of the brain, or magnetic resonance imaging (MRI) of the brain. These techniques provide physical-anatomical information, but not functional information.

Much can also be learned about the brain following an injury to the brain. When a localized lesion is correlated with a particular deficit, this can provide evidence for the role of a particular area of the brain. Good medical records, which include both pathological and behavioral changes, are important.

Context

The forebrain is the source of motivation, decisions, analysis, and thought. It is the ultimate destination of all sensory experiences. Mental health is dependent upon a delicate balance and complex interaction of many forebrain components. In addition to the interaction between levels and groups of neurons, there is a cooperation between the left and right hemispheres, each processing the information in a different way, the left being more analytical and logical, and the right more creative and intuitive. Language is processed differently by the two sides. The former is concerned with the exact meaning of the words, while the latter is associated with the context and tone of the words. One side is usually dominant. Individuals can vary in the distribution of the language centers as well as in their preferred way of receiving input, such as visual versus auditory.

The forebrain is a marvel when it is healthy and a tragedy when it is not. Accidents, infections, strokes, drugs, and genetics can cause the forebrain to malfunction. Some people have a predisposition for certain conditions, such as depression, schizophrenia, and Huntington's disease, that have known neurotransmitter imbalances associated with them. In some diseases, the symptoms can be treated by supplying the missing substance or inhibiting the excess substance. In cases of excess of excitability, such as epilepsy, the behavior can be diminished with a drug that is a membrane stabilizer. Another example is Parkinson's disease, which is associated with aging, trauma, and infections. It is possible to reduce the tremors in Parkinson's disease using a drug called L-DOPA, which raises the level of the neurotransmitter dopamine in the brain stem. On the other hand, it is possible to increase the activity of the brain with other drugs such as caffeine or amphetamines. There is some evidence that memory in older people can be improved by drugs that raise the acetylcholine level.

Addiction to opiate drugs is based on a physical entity in the brain called the opiate receptor protein. It stimulates pleasure centers in the limbic system and inhibits pain. A large number of pain killers work by enhancing the action of an endogenous opiate called endorphin (the term means "the morphine within"). The more that is known about particular pathways, neurotransmitters, and receptors, the more specifically neurological illnesses can be treated.

Bibliography

Andreasen, Nancy. *The Broken Brain*. New York: Harper & Row, 1985. An excellent paperback with a table of contents. Covers the history of psychiatry as well as basic neuroscience. Discusses the physiology of the brain and the recent knowledge about brain chemistry. Written by a practicing psychiatrist.

Bloom, Floyd, and Arlyne Lazerson. *Brain, Mind, and Behavior*. 2d ed. New York: W. H. Freeman, 1988. Specifically designed for the nonmajor, and easy to understand. Material was extracted from the Public Broadcasting Service series *Nova* and expanded into a book. Its coverage is broad for its size and therefore less detailed. It has a wealth of color illustrations that are detailed.

The Brain. San Francisco: W. H. Freeman, 1979. A collection of papers from the *Scientific American* by authorities in neurobiology. It is written for the educated nonspecialist and is well illustrated. It covers neurobiology from the level of the cell to that of high-level information processing.

The Brain: Mystery of Matter and Mind. New York: Torstar, 1984. A well-illustrated book covering the functioning of neurons, parts of the brain, and mental illness. An excellent introduction for the high school student.

Changeux, Jean-Pierre. *Neuronal Man: The Biology of the Mind.* New York: Pantheon, 1985. The author's research has covered the gamut from enzymes and receptors at synapses to learning and neural networks. It provides a good historical basis and covers the field of neurobiology from the neuron to the consciousness. Recent neurogenetics is discussed also.

Diamond, Marion, Arnold Scheibel, and Lawrence Elson. *The Human Brain Coloring Book.* New York: Harper & Row, 1985. More than a coloring book with excellent illustrations, it also discusses pathways and major functions. Written for the undergraduate, it is rife with vivid analogies.

Gillig, Richard, and Robin Brightwell. *The Human Brain.* New York: Facts on File, 1982. An excellent first book to read about the brain. It is very easy to understand and flows in a storylike fashion. Excellent pictures and photography.

Kolb, Bryan, and Ian Whishaw. *Fundamentals of Human Neuropsychology.* 3d ed. New York: W. H. Freeman, 1990. An excellent text for an upper-level undergraduate neurophysiology course or first-year graduate course. It is well-written and easy to understand in spite of the complexity of the material it covers. It has a text that flows without the interruptions of referencing. There are, however, excellent references in the back of the book, as well as a glossary.

Springer, Sally, and Georg Deutsch. *Left Brain Right Brain.* New York: W. H. Freeman, 1985. A small paperback that does a good job covering the functions of different parts of the brain. It focuses on the lateralization of function. Brief descriptions of the necessary neuroanatomy and excellent clincal examples are provided. A good supplementary text in neuroscience or physiological psychology.

Thompson, Richard F. *The Brain: An Introduction to Neuroscience.* New York: W. H. Freeman, 1985. An excellent introduction to neurobiology in paperback form covering the nervous system from neuron to behavior. Thorough enough to serve as an introductory text. Contains good "suggested readings."

William D. Niemi

Cross-References

Afferent and Efferent Neurons, 35; Electrical Activity of the Brain, 292; Central and Peripheral Nervous System Functions, 404; Commissures and Split-Brain Patients, 520; Emotions, 765; The Hindbrain and Midbrain, 1291; Learning, 1548; Memory, 1683; Neural Receptors, 1904; Neurotransmitters, 1936; The Reticular Activating System, 2390.

FRUIT STRUCTURE

Type of life science: Plant anatomy
Other field of study: Botany

Fruits are seed-bearing organs produced by plants called angiosperms and are formed when the pistils of flowers ripen after pollination. Some plants produce fleshy fruits that are typically dispersed when eaten by animals. Others produce dry fruits, and these have various means of dispersing their seeds.

Principal terms

ANGIOSPERM: a plant that produces flowers during its life cycle

DRY FRUIT: a fruit with a nonfleshy pericarp; representative types include follicles, legumes, capsules, achenes, nuts, caryopses, and samaras

FLESHY FRUIT: a fruit with a moist, juicy pericarp; representative types include drupes, berries, pomes, hesperidia, and pepos

FRUIT: a ripened, enlarged pistil that contains one or more seeds; it develops after a flower is pollinated

LOCULE: the hollow space(s) within the fruit, technically between the pericarp and the seeds

OVULE: an immature seed; one or more are found in each pistil

PERICARP: the outer wall of the fruit, it develops from the ovary wall and can be either fleshy or dry

PISTIL: the female structure of the flower, consisting of a hollow ovary at the bottom, which contains one or more ovules, a necklike style above it, and a stigma at the top that receives pollen

POLLINATION: the process by which pollen is transferred from the anther to the stigma; pollination can be accomplished by an animal vector or by wind

SEED: an offspring produced by angiosperms after sexual reproduction; consists of an embryonic plant surrounded by a seed coat and can be dispersed to new places and remain dormant during unfavorable conditions

Summary of the Phenomenon

When most people think of a fruit, the image that typically comes to mind is of a juicy, edible object such as an apple, orange, or banana. To botanists, however, the definition of a fruit is much broader and encompasses many other plant-derived structures that bear little resemblance to the fruits that one buys in a supermarket.

Technically, a fruit is a seed-containing reproductive organ produced by angiosperms (flowering plants). To understand fruits, it is important to understand the structure of a flower, which is a complex organ that enables sexual reproduction to occur. Each flower contains up to four sets of parts: the calyx, the corolla, the stamens, and the pistil. The calyx is composed of leaflike sepals that protect the immature flower when it is in the bud stage. The corolla is composed of petals that are often brightly colored and serve to attract pollinators such as butterflies and bees. The stamens are the male parts of the flower and produce a powdery substance called pollen. Finally, the pistil is a vase-shaped, tubular, or spherical structure at the center of the flower, and it functions as its female organ. The base of the pistil is a swollen structure called an ovary, which is hollow and contains one or more minute, beadlike structures called ovules. The flower's primary purpose is served when the pistil receives pollen from a stamen of another flower. A sperm nucleus originating from the pollen grain makes its way to an egg nucleus within the tiny ovule. Fertilization occurs, producing a new embryonic plant within that ovule. As that embryonic plant develops, the ovule turns into a seed. At the same time, the petals, the stamens, and often the sepals fall from the flower, leaving the pistil. That pistil also begins to enlarge and forms a fruit.

In essence, a fruit is an enlarged pistil that develops after a flower is pollinated. That relationship should be clear to anyone who has grown tomatoes or apples. Those plants produce blossoms, which are really the flowers. After a period of time, the peripheral parts of the blossom fall away, leaving the immature fruit. The fruit subsequently enlarges and then ripens to form the edible tomato or apple, which contains seeds.

Almost all fruits have a general structure that consists of an outer layer called the pericarp. The pericarp, in turn, encloses the seed or seeds. Usually, there is a space between the seed and the pericarp. That space is called a locule. A pumpkin gives a good illustration of the pericarp (the orange rind), the locule (the hollow space within), and the seeds that are inside.

When one examines many different species of flowering plants, it becomes clear that there are many different kinds of fruits. Some, such as cherries, tomatoes, and apples, have fleshy, juicy pericarps. Others, such as peanuts, milkweed pods, and acorns, have dry pericarps. The variability in fruits represents different strategies for dispersing the seed.

In some plants, the seeds are dispersed while still enclosed within the fruit. Seeds that are contained within fleshy fruits are often dispersed by animals that eat the fruit. In that case, the seed typically passes through the digestive system and is defecated by the animal. Animals also carry other fruits that have barbs or hooks that catch on to their fur. Still other fruits, such as those of maple and ash, have wings for wind dispersal. A few others, such as the coconut palm and many sedges, have fruits that float and are dispersed by water. Many other plants produce fruits that disperse their seeds while the fruits are still attached to the parent plant. In most instances, the fruit merely opens and the seeds drop onto the ground. Some plants, such as witch hazel and the touch-me-not, produce fruits that open explosively and can disperse their fruits great distances.

Botanists have developed a classification of fruits that is based primarily on the nature of the pericarp. In this classification, fruits are categorized into two groups:

fleshy and dry. Fleshy fruits, in turn, are classified into several types, including drupes, berries, pomes, hesperidia, and pepos. Dry fruits are also subdivided into several categories, including follicles, legumes, capsules, achenes, nuts, samaras, and caryopses. These are described as follows.

The three most common fleshy fruits include drupes, berries, and pomes. A drupe is a fleshy fruit that contains a single seed surrounded by a hard, bony inner wall of the pericarp (called the endocarp). The middle and outer walls of the pericarp (called the mesocarp and exocarp, respectively) are juicy and often sweet. Drupes include all the pitted fruits, such as cherries, plums, peaches and olives. The pit in these fruits is really the hard inner layer of the pericarp, and the seed is hidden inside. A berry typically has several seeds, and the pericarp is fleshy throughout. Familiar examples include tomatoes, eggplants, and grapes. A pome is a fleshy fruit that has a thick layer of accessory tissue immediately surrounding the pericarp. The accessory tissue is generally juicy, sweet, and often edible. Representative pomes include apples and pears. Two other fleshy fruits, the hesperidium and the pepo, are characterized by a leathery rind. The hesperidium, also known as a citrus fruit, has a rind rich in aromatic oils, surrounding a juicy pericarp that has a sugary, acidic sap. Representative hesperidia include oranges, grapefruits, lemons, and limes. The pepo has a smooth, fleshy pericarp and normally contains many seeds. Examples include pumpkins, cucumbers, cantaloupes, and squash.

The most common dry fruits are follicles, legumes, capsules, achenes, nuts, samaras, and caryopses. Follicles open up along one side, revealing numerous seeds. An example is a milkweed pod. In contrast, legumes open up along two lines. They are produced by many members of the legume family, such as peas, beans, and peanuts. The capsule opens along three or more lines or by pores at the top of the fruit. Snapdragons and poppies are good examples of plants that produce capsules. Achenes each contain one seed and are typically rather small. A good example is a sunflower "seed." A nut is similar to an achene, except that the pericarp is hard and woody. Representative nuts include acorns, hazelnuts, and hickory nuts. A samara is a modified achene that has part of the pericarp flattened to form a wing. Examples of plants that produce samaras include maples, ashes, and elms. Finally, a caryopsis is a single-seeded fruit whose seed coat is fused to the pericarp. Caryopses are produced only by plants in the grass family and include the familiar grains wheat, corn, rice, and oats.

The fruits listed above commonly fall under the category of "simple fruits." In other words, they are identifiable as individual structures. Other plants produce fruits in dense clusters, and these are termed either "aggregate fruits" or "multiple fruits." Aggregate fruits are produced by a single flower that has numerous pistils. One example is a raspberry, which is an aggregate of berries. Another is the strawberry, which is an aggregate of tiny black achenes inserted on the surface of a juicy, red receptacle. In contrast, multiple fruits are produced by clusters of small flowers, each of which produces a single fruit. Representative multiple fruits include mulberries, figs, and pineapples.

For many years, botanists have studied three important questions related to the development and physiology of fruits: What causes a fruit to develop from a flower? What causes a fruit to ripen? and What regulates the timing of fruit-drop from the parent plant?

The first question is interesting only when one realizes that, in nature, fruits develop only after the flower is effectively pollinated. If pollination does not occur, the entire flower shrivels up and no fruit is formed. Fruit development is apparently stimulated when the developing seeds produce substances called hormones that diffuse to the pericarp, causing it to enlarge. Two hormones are particularly implicated in fruit formation: auxin and gibberellin. Many fruit growers routinely spray their plants with auxin to induce the formation of seedless, or "parthenocarpic," fruits.

Fruit ripening is an important process that must occur properly in order for the seeds to be effectively dispersed. In fleshy fruits, such as tomatoes, cherries, apples, oranges, and bananas, fruit ripening involves several important changes in the pericarp that make the fruit more visible and palatable to a potential animal disperser. Perhaps the most visible change relates to the color of the fruit. Immature fruits are green, because of the presence of the pigment chlorophyll in the cells of the outer layer. Potential dispersers fail to notice the immature fruit, because it blends in with the surrounding leaves. As fruits ripen, the chlorophyll breaks down, and other colors, such as orange, yellow, red, or blue, become evident. Those colors are the result of pigments that either are present in the unripe fruit and masked by the chlorophyll or develop as the fruit ripens. Upon ripening, the brightly colored fruit attracts the attention of the disperser. The texture and chemical composition of the pericarp also change as the fruit ripens. Most fruits soften as they ripen, a result of the degradation of the cell walls in the pericarp. At the same time, starches or oils in the pericarp are chemically transformed into simple sugars such as fructose. That change causes the fruit to become better-tasting and more digestible, and thus more attractive to a hungry animal.

The physiology of fruit ripening has been well studied. Some fruits, such as grapes, citrus fruits, and strawberries, ripen gradually. Others, such as tomatoes, apples, and pears, exhibit a transitional event called "climacteric," which is marked by a dramatic increase in the rate at which oxygen is absorbed by the fruit, followed by a rapid change in the color and physical nature of the pericarp. Studies of climacteric fruit have shown that the onset of ripening can be delayed by storing the fruit in low temperatures or in an atmosphere devoid of oxygen. On the other hand, climacteric can be induced by exposing the fruit to ethylene, which is another plant hormone. Interestingly, ethylene is produced by ripening fruits, and thus a ripe fruit promotes the development of any unripe fruits with which it may be placed in contact.

Finally, many plants drop their fruits at some point after they become ripened. Botanists use the term "abscission" to refer to the dropping process. Fruit abscission, like leaf abscission, occurs when a layer of cells at the base of the pedicel become weakened. Studies have shown that abscission is influenced by two hormones: ethylene and auxin. Ethylene promotes abscission of fruits in many plant species, such as cherries, blueberries, and blackberries. Auxin, on the other hand, has effects that vary depending on the dose: Low concentrations promote fruit retention, while high doses cause fruits to drop.

Methods of Study

Studies of fruits examine both their structure and their development. The investigation of fruit structure is relatively straightforward and involves looking at both the whole-fruit (morphological) and tissue-level (anatomical) features. Morphological investigations are done by simply observing the external features and, after appropriate dissections, the internal features. Studies of fruit morphology frequently seek to assess the changes that occur in a developing fruit. Some scientists record changes in the developing fruit by time-lapse photography. That technique involves setting up a camera next to the developing fruit and repeatedly taking a picture after a specific time interval passes (for example, once every thirty minutes).

Many scientists also examine the anatomy of fruits to learn more about features associated with both the pericarp and the developing seeds. Such tissue-level observations require the use of microscopes, of which there are three general types: light, scanning-electron, and transmission-electron. In each case, the cells must be fixed and dried to stabilize them. When light and transmission electron microscopy are used, the tissues must also be embedded, sliced into thin sections, and stained (to allow certain structures to become more visible).

Fixation is typically accomplished by soaking the fruit tissue in a fixing solution, such as formalin acetic alcohol (FAA), which is a mixture of 90 percent ethyl alcohol, 5 percent formalin, and 5 percent glacial acetic acid, for twenty-four to seventy-two hours. Sometimes, a solution of 5 percent glutaraldehyde in 0.2 molar phosphate buffer is often used, followed by a brief (one- to two-hour) "postfixation" with 1-2 percent osmium tetroxide. Fixed tissues are then dehydrated by immersion in a drying agent such as butyl alcohol or acetone. Dehydrated plant tissues that are to be sliced into thin sections must be embedded with molten paraffin or a similar plastic material to make them more stable. Next, the tissues are sectioned either by hand (using a razor blade) or by an instrument called a microtome.

Sectioned fruit tissues are stained using various aniline dyes, such as safranin, fast green, and toluidine blue. These stains cause various substances in the cells to turn a specific color. For example, suberin, cutin, and lignin turn red, while cellulose turns blue-green. The advantage is that some tissues are rich in lignin, cutin, and suberin, while other tissues have mainly cellulose. Osmium tetroxide, lead citrate, and uranyl acetate are effective stains for transmission electron microscopy. Material that is viewed by scanning electron microscopy does not need to be embedded and sliced. Instead, bits of whole, dehydrated material are placed on an aluminum stub that acts as a holder, then coated with a gold-palladium mixture that is detectable by the electron beam.

The factors that affect fruit formation and development are also widely studied. When fruits fail to form on a plant, inadequate pollination is sometimes seen as a cause. To test that idea, a sample of flowers is pollinated by hand, and subsequent fruit development is noted by carefully watching the plant for one or two weeks. If fruits do develop, then pollination was indeed limiting.

Many studies seek to understand the degree to which various plant hormones (such as auxin, gibberellin, and ethylene) cause fruits to develop from unpollinated flowers. To study this, scientists spray flowers with each of the hormones in question and follow the flowers over time to determine the degree of fruit set. Sometimes the concentration of hormone is varied from plant to plant. Also, scientists often combine hormones in various ratios to determine the degree to which they interact.

Many studies also seek to understand the role of physical environmental factors, such as temperature, moisture, light, atmospheric gases, and soil nutrients, on fruit production and maturation. To assess these factors, scientists typically expose different groups of plants to a range of conditions, in the field, in a greenhouse, or in a growth chamber. Various characteristics of the fruits, including their size, shape, color, and the number of enclosed seeds, are then recorded. Statistical tests are typically used when analyzing the results.

Context

Fruits are important parts of our diets. As mentioned, most people think of a fruit as a sweet-tasting structure produced by a plant, usually eaten for dessert. That definition is overly restrictive; many of the "vegetables" that people put into their salads, such as cucumbers, tomatoes, snap beans, and green peppers, are also fruits. True vegetables are derived from other plant structures: leaves (lettuce), buds (brussels sprouts), bulbs (onions), stems (asparagus), tubers (white potatoes), flower buds (broccoli), and roots (carrots). Simply put, if it contains any seeds, it is a fruit.

Almost all fruits that are important in the human diet come from cultivated plants rather than wild ones. Such cultivated plants were derived from wild ancestors hundreds or thousands of years ago. As these plants were being cultivated, they were subjected to intensive selection by people to make them easier to grow, to produce larger, better-tasting fruit, and to increase their resistance to disease. During the cultivation process, many species were hybridized to produce new varieties. Others underwent polyploidy, which is a type of mutation that involves a doubling in the number of chromosomes per cell and often results in larger and more vigorous plants. Some, such as the banana and the pineapple, developed seedless varieties that can be propagated only vegetatively.

Edible fruits can be classified according to their general structure (drupes, berries, pomes, and legumes, for example), taxonomically by plant family, or according to the region in which it originates. Many edible fruits are grown in the tropical areas, such as Central America, Africa, the West Indies, and Southeast Asia. While some, such as the mango, guava, breadfruit, carambola, and passion fruit, may be unfamiliar to people in North American and Europe, others are very familiar. Bananas are widely grown in Latin America, although they are native to eastern Asia and Australia. They are nutritious and rich in carbohydrates and the element potassium. Pineapples are so named because Christopher Columbus thought that they resembled pinecones. Each pineapple is actually a multiple fruit formed by the fusion of about one hundred ovaries around a central core. Coconuts are the drupes of a certain species of palm tree. Normally, most people see only the bony endocarp of the coconut; the mesocarp is discarded prior to marketing. The white and liquid material inside the coconut seed is called the endosperm. The flavoring agent vanilla is derived from the capsule of an orchid native to Central America.

Other fruits are grown in the subtropical areas such as the Middle East, southern Europe, and the southern United States. Middle Eastern fruits include figs, which are fleshy multiple fruits that are pollinated by wasps; dates, which are the fruits of the date palm; and pomegranates, which have juicy red seeds. Citrus fruits are juicy hesperidia that are produced by woody plants in the rue family. Their juice is typically sweet, yet acidic and rich in vitamin C. The most popular citrus fruits include oranges, grapefruits, lemons, limes, and tangerines. Members of the squash family are native to subtropical areas of both the Old World and the New World. Some, like the cucumber, pumpkin, and squash, have little sugar in their pericarps and are eaten as vegetables. Others, such as the cantaloupe, watermelon, and honeydew, have a high sugar content and are delicious warm-weather treats. Several plants in the nightshade family produce berries that are cultivated in subtropical and temperate regions worldwide. These include the tomato, green pepper, and egg-plant. Interestingly, until the early 1800's, tomatoes were thought to be poisonous and edible only by werewolves.

Many fruits are cultivated mainly in temperate regions, which are characterized by cold winters. Perhaps the greatest diversity of edible fruit-bearing species in temperate regions is found in the rose family. Some members of this family, such as apples and pears, produce sweet-tasting pomes. Others are pit-containing drupes, including cherries, plums, apricots, and peaches. Still others, such as strawberries, blackberries, and raspberries, produce aggregate fruits. The heath family contains blueberries and cranberries, and these are generally limited to regions with acid soils. Grapes are produced by vine-forming plants belonging to the grape family. Grapes are eaten fresh, dried to make raisins, processed to make jellies and juice, and fermented to make wine. Members of the bean family produce nitrogen-rich fruits called legumes. Widely cultivated legumes include peas, beans, peanuts, soy-beans, and lentils. The entire fruit is eaten in some (such as snap beans), while in others (lima beans and peanuts) only the seeds are eaten. Several temperate tree species are cultivated for their nuts and nutlike fruits, including walnuts, pecans, fil-berts, chestnuts, pistachios, and almonds.

Besides being used for food, several fruits are cultivated for other products. The tropical fruit papaya is used to produce the enzyme papain, which is used as a meat tenderizer and to clean contact lenses. The poppy capsule contains a white milky latex that contains psychoactive substances such as morphine. The outer husk of a coconut produces a fiber called coir, which is used to make rope and floor mats.

Bibliography

Benson, Lyman. *Plant Classification.* 2d ed. Lexington, Mass.: D. C. Heath, 1979. This textbook contains a wealth of detailed information about the science of vascular plant taxonomy. Although much of the book is rather advanced, the first several chapters explain general principles of plant morphology in a way that high school students and college freshmen can easily understand. Chapter 8 focuses on fruits and seeds, describing the major types. The accompanying digrams are outstanding.

Jones, Samuel B., and Arlene E. Luchsinger. *Plant Systematics.* 2d ed. New York: McGraw-Hill, 1986. This book provides a fine introduction to the classification and evolution of the seed plants, focusing on the flowering plants. Chapter 10 is devoted to a review of the terminology dealing with variability in vegetative and reproductive structures of the plant and includes a well-illustrated summary of the various kinds of fruits. Chapter 14 gives a detailed synopsis of the major plant families and includes a description of the fruit types in each.

Kaufmann, Peter B. *Plants: Their Biology and Importance.* New York: Harper & Row, 1989. This book was written to introduce nonbiology students to the basic biology and economic aspects of plants. Chapter 25 includes an outline of the types of fruits found in flowering plants, complete with diagrams. The effect of hormones on fruit initiation is reviewed in chapter 26. Fruits of economic importance are reviewed in chapter 30.

Langenheim, Jean H., and Kenneth V. Thimann. *Botany: Plant Biology and Its Relation to Human Affairs.* New York: John Wiley & Sons, 1982. This book gives a lucid account of all phases of botany, with emphasis on how plants have been used by people through the ages. Chapter 18 describes the basic and economic biology of fruits, including a discusion of fruit classification, the physiology of ripening, and a species-by-species account of the chief temperate and tropical fruits.

Nadakavukaren, Mathew, and Derek McCracken. *Botany: An Introduction to Plant Biology.* St. Paul, Minn.: West, 1985. This well-illustrated basic botany text provides a fine orientation to the important principles of plant science for those at the high school or college level. An interesting feature is that new terms are concisely defined in a space at the margin of the text. Fruit structure, classification, and dispersal mechanisms are reviewed in chapter 21.

Raven, Peter, Ray F. Evert, and Susan E. Eichhorn. *Biology of Plants.* 4th ed. New York: Worth, 1986. An excellent introduction to all phases of modern botanical science, including sections on cell biology, energetics, genetics, diversity, structure, evolution, and ecology. Chapter 24 gives an authoritative review of the role that various hormones play in fruit set and ripening. The diversity of fruits is reviewed in chapter 29.

Simpson, Beryl Brintall, and Molly Conner-Ogorzaly. *Economic Botany: Plants in Our World*. New York: McGraw-Hill, 1986. A highly readable and informative account concerning the numerous uses of plants by various societies since the advent of recorded history. The book is copiously illustrated throughout, with photographs and line drawings. Chapters 4 and 5 provide an excellent account of fruits and nuts from temperate and tropical regions. Legumes are covered in chapter 7.

Kenneth M. Klemow

Cross-References

Angiosperms, 95; Flower Structure, 999; Flowering Regulation, 1010; Plant Hormones, 2103; Sexual Reproduction in Plants, 2326; Seeds, 2452.

FUNGI

Type of life science: Systematics (taxonomy)
Other field of study: Microbiology

The classification of the fungi has rapidly changed as new information about them has been obtained. The kingdom fungi is classified into three divisions: the "slime molds," the motile-celled fungi, and the nonmotile-celled fungi.

Principal terms

ASEXUAL REPRODUCTION: reproduction not involving the fusion of two cells; cell division, budding, fragmentation, and the production of certain spores are examples

EUKARYOTIC: having a complex, membranous cell construction with distinct nucleus, mitochondria, and other organelles

FLAGELLUM (*pl*. FLAGELLA): a hairlike cell appendage that propels a motile cell; fungal flagella are of two types: "whiplash" and "tinsel"

MYCOLOGY: the study of fungi

MYCOSIS (*pl*. MYCOSES): any disease caused by a fungus

PATHOGEN: any organism capable of causing a disease

PROKARYOTIC: having a relatively simple cell construction with few membranous organelles

SEXUAL REPRODUCTION: reproduction involving the fusion of two cells, called gametes, and the subsequent development of the next generation from that fusion

SPORE: a small (often unicellular) unit of dispersal comparable to a seed but not containing an embryo

Summary of the Phenomenon

Approximately eighty thousand species of fungi have been described by mycologists. They are worldwide in distribution and occur in almost all habitats, especially in the soil. The fungi are a complex group of organisms with several characteristics in common. They are eukaryotic (their cellular construction is complex). They are heterotrophic (they obtain energy from outside their bodies by acting as decayers or parasites). Their cells do not contain chlorophyll. They usually have filamentous bodies, often forming a mesh known as the mycelium. Their bodies are usually multicellular; their cells have walls made of chitin and other complex carbohydrates. They reproduce by spores, which may be formed sexually or asexually.

Opinion about the proper taxonomic classification of the fungi varies widely among biologists. Well into the twentieth century, they were classifed as members of the plant kingdom (Plantae), and they do have certain plantlike characteristics, notably cell walls. Some fungi so closely resemble certain algae that they have been called "algal fungi" (the phylum Mastigomycota). Most biologists have recognized that the fungi are not as closely related to plants as they are to animals, however, and that these organisms may be descendants of unicellular animal-like ancestors. For these and other reasons, the fungi are separated into one kingdom among five. The other four kingdoms are: Plantae, Animalia, Protista (the eukaryotic unicellular organisms), and Monera (the prokaryotic unicells, bacteria). The kingdom fungi (or Myceteae) is further classified into three divisions.

Division Gymnomycota ("naked fungi"), the slime molds, are soil inhabitants that differ from other fungi in two ways: Their body parts (except for spores) lack cell walls, and they feed by phagocytosis, the engulfing of food particles by the amoebalike cell or fungal body. The slime molds are of no significance to humans except for their role as soil decomposers and as laboratory models for the study of certain developmental processes. Representative genera of slime molds are *Dictyostelium* and *Physarum*. Of all the fungal groups, the slime molds have had the most varied taxonomic history. Studies of the motile cells have caused a majority of biologists to consider them as members of the animal kingdom. They are included here because of their long history of being classified as fungi and because most of the biologists who study them are mycologists. The division was formerly called the Myxomycetes.

Division Mastigomycota ("flagella fungi") is a group that forms motile spores with either one or two flagella; many are aquatic. They are classified into two subdivisions. Haplomastigomycotina ("one-flagellum fungi") are fungi that have motile cells with a single flagellum. Included here are the unicellular chytrids of aquatic habitats. Representative genera are *Chytriomyces* and *Allomyces*. Diplomastigomycotina ("two-flagella fungi") are often referred to as the "water molds" and have motile cells with two flagella. Most are filamentous. Several are pathogens of crop plants: *Phytophthora infestans* causes potato blight, and *Plasmopara* is the pathogen of downy mildew, which affects grapes. This phylm was formerly called the Phycomycetes ("algal fungi").

Division Amastigomycota ("no-flagellum fungi") includes most of the familiar fungi and is characterized by the lack of motile cells. There are four subdivisions. The Zygomycotina ("yoke fungi," a reference to the special spore produced by these fungi, the zygospore) reproduce sexually by means of copulation. The external appearance of the two genders is identical, however; the only sex differences are biochemical. Representative genera are the black bread mold (*Rhizopus*) and the fly fungus (*Entomophthora muscae*), which is a parasite of insects.

The Ascomycotina ("sac fungi") is one of the largest groups of fungi. They bear their spores in a special sac known as the ascus. There are usually eight spores per ascus. In many species, the asci are localized in a spore-bearing surface known as the hymenium. Asexual spores called conidia are also important in their reproduction. The sac fungi are one of the fungal groups most significant to humans. Some are edible, others are important in the manufacture of valuable products, and still others cause various diseases of plants and animals. Yeasts, one of the few unicellular fungal groups, include valuable food sources and fermenters of sugars in the manufacture of wine, beer, and bread. A representative yeast species is *Saccharo-*

myces cerevisieae, the common baker's or brewer's yeast. Certain important molds are also included in this group. *Aspergillus* and *Penicillium* are common molds of food that are frequently seen on refrigerator leftovers and moldy fruit. *Penicillium* is also the source of the valuable antibiotic penicillin and is responsible for the ripening of several varieties of cheese, such as Roquefort and certain blue cheeses. Many diseases of plants are caused by sac fungi. Chestnut blight, caused by *Endothia parasitica*, brought the American chestnut to the verge of extinction during the first half of the twentieth century. Dutch elm disease is caused by *Ophiostoma ulmi*. Ergot of several grain crops is caused by infection by *Claviceps purpurea*. In addition to being a serious crop pathogen, this fungus causes a poisoning called ergotism when the infected grains are eaten by cattle or when bread baked from infected grains is eaten by humans. Symptoms include convulsions, hallucinations, spontaneous abortion, blindness, gangrene of the limbs, and even death. Some of the most highly prized edible fungi are also members of the sac fungi group: the morels (*Morchella*) and the truffles (*Tuber*) are considered to be gourmet items.

The Basidiomycotina ("club fungi") bear their sexual spores on the outer surface of a unique clubshaped structure called the basidium. There are usually four spores per basidium. Mushrooms are the best-known club fungi. Many of these are edible; the common field mushroom is *Agaricus*. Poisonous or inedible mushrooms are sometimes referred to as toadstools; unfortunately, there are no reliable means of distinguishing edible and poisonous mushrooms on sight. Some of the most poisonous mushrooms are the death cups or destroying angels, well-named members of the genus *Amanita*. Other, less familiar, club fungi are the puffballs, pore fungi, stinkhorns, jelly fungi, rusts, and smuts. The last two groups are important pathogens of plants. Wheat rust (caused by *Puccinia*) and corn smut (caused by *Ustilago*) are examples of two significant plant diseases.

The Deuteromycotina ("other fungi") are also known as the imperfect fungi; in this context, the term "imperfect" means "asexual." Sexual stages of the life cycle or sexual spores have not been observed in these fungi. Since the fungi are classified on the basis of the characteristics of their sexual stages, especially by their methods of bearing sexual spores, the imperfect fungi cannot be placed in any of the natural categories. There are two possible explanations for this odd taxonomic situation. One explanation is that the sexual stages of these fungi do not exist—that they disappeared during the evolution of the group. Another explanation is that the sexual stage exists but that it is only formed rarely, under special conditions that have not been observed by mycologists. Laboratory cultivation of many imperfect fungi has resulted in the formation of the sexual spores and the realization that these organisms are almost always classifiable as sac fungi (or, rarely, as club fungi).

When this happens, the species is reassigned to the appropriate category. An example of this reclassification is the case of the fungi that cause ringworm, a skin disease. Two genera are involved, *Trichophyton* and *Microsporum*. Both were once classified as Deuteromycetes, because their sexual stages had never been observed. Sexual stages were observed later, however, and the organisms were reclassified as

Ascomycetes. The Deuteromycotina include many important fungi. Some are pathogens of plants, animals, and humans. Histoplasmosis, cryptococcosis, candidiasis, and athletes' foot are a few of the human diseases caused by members of the imperfect fungi. Many people are allergic to various molds; the molds are almost always members of this group. The Deuteromycotina are thus a completely artificial category—a taxonomic "holding pen" for organisms whose peculiar life cycles make them impossible (sometimes only temporarily) to classify using the usual criteria.

Methods of Study

Ancient man knew and classified the larger fungi, mostly mushrooms, according to a simple system: They were either edible or poisonous. The smaller fungi were not placed into any classification system until the end of the sixteenth century, about one hundred years after the invention of the microscope. Since the classification of the larger fungal groups depends upon observations of their microscopic spores and spore-bearing structures, the microscope has been the chief instrument in the identification and classification of fungi for at least two hundred years. The details of the spore-bearing structures of the Gymnomycota, Mastigomycota, and Amastigomycota were once the criteria for the entire classification and still remain important. The size, shape, number, arrangement, and color of spores and sporangia are a few of the observed characteristics. Some spore characteristics may be observed without microscopy: The color of mushroom spores in large quantities is an important characteristic in their identification. A "spore print" is obtained by cutting off the cap of a gilled mushroom, placing the cap on a sheet of paper, covering it with a jar, and leaving it overnight in order for the spores to fall onto the surface of the paper, where they accumulate to form a spore print of characteristic color and design.

Life-cycle patterns are also significant in the classification of fungi. Some life cycles are relatively simple and involve a well-studied pattern of alternation between a conspicuous asexual phase and a less easily observed sexual stage. Other life cycles are extremely complex and may involve the infestation of at least two alternate hosts during the life of the fungal parasite. One of the most complex life cycles is that of *Puccinia graminis*, the wheat rust, which alternates between barberry and grain hosts and has different morphological characteristics on each host species. Control of such parasites has not only involved the use of the usual fungicides but also the elimination of the alternate host—in this case, the barberry. The parasite is unable to complete its life cycle without the presence of the barberry in the vicinity of the wheat.

Biochemical characteristics are also used in fungal classification, particularly at the level of the species or subspecies. Yeasts, especially, exist in a multitude of biochemically and genetically variable strains. This information is valuable to the brewing and baking industries. There is a constant search for new yeast mutants that will improve the products of these industries.

The invention of the electron microscope and its application to mycology have resulted in many insights into fungal relationships. Electron microscopy has enabled mycologists to examine the nature of the flagellated spores of fungi, and this has been one of the pieces of information that has resulted in the reclassification by some taxonomists of the slime molds and the Mastigomycota into the animal kingdom. The number and types of flagella are especially important in the classification of the Mastigomycota. Haplomastigomycotina have a single flagellum; the group is further classified into classes partially on the basis of whether the flagellum is of the "whiplash" type (sheathed along its length with the end unsheathed) or "tinsel" type (having hairlike protrusions along its length, resembling Christmas tree tinsel). Zoospores of the Diplomastigomycotina are biflagellate, having flagella of both types.

Context

The taxonomy of the fungi is similar to that of the other four kingdoms in that it serves two purposes. Because of the sheer number of species and the complexity of the group, the classification system serves as a convenient way to place each kind of fungus into a category. Thus, the classification system is a method of bringing order to a complex situation. The system enables mycologists to communicate effectively and with precision about their subjects. Second, the aim of all classification systems is to include related organisms in their categories. Such a classification system is referred to as "natural" (as opposed to an artificial system in which the organisms are classified without regard to their relationships and which may be composed of groups with unrelated members). For example, older classifications of the plant kindgom that included the fungi are now considered to be artificial classifications because the fungi are no longer considered to be close relatives of the plants. The modern system of placing the fungi in a separate kingdom is considered to be more natural and reflective of current ideas about the evolution of the group. The shifting of the slime molds and (by some authors) the Mastigomycota to the animal kingdom is another example of the changes made in the classification system as knowledge of the fungi increases.

When the slime molds and Mastigomycota are excluded from the kingdom and only the Amastigomycota are considered to be fungi, they may be considered a natural group with common evolutionary origins. The ancestry of these fungi, however, remains in doubt. Organisms similar to the red algae and the nonflagellated green algae ("Gamophyta," according to biologist Lynn Margulis) are possible ancestors.

Communication about the fungi and knowledge of their evolutionary relationships is important because of the significance of these organisms. The fungi are important decomposers of organic matter and therefore play important roles in the cycling of minerals within natural systems. The fertility of soil is maintained, in part, by fungal decomposition activities. Many fungi are directly useful to humans as foods (for example, mushrooms and yeasts) or indirectly useful as processors of materials in the production of valuable products such as cheese, bread, organic chemicals, and alcoholic beverages. The search for the development of new strains of molds and yeasts is an important aspect of mycology. Because of their simplicity, ease of cultivation, rapid growth, and distinctive characteristics, some fungi have been intensively used as laboratory subjects in the study of genetics and developmental biology. One species of Ascomycotina, *Neurospora crassa*, has been aptly called the "fungus fruit fly," a reference to its importance as a genetic research subject.

Some fungi cause effects harmful to humans. Because of their decomposition activities, many are responsible for the destruction of valuable products such as food, clothing, paper, and wood. Many species are pathogens of plants, animals, and humans, causing mycoses of varying severities, ranging from minor ailments such as athlete's foot to fatal diseases such as cryptococcosis. On the other hand, the pathogenic characteristics of certain fungi may be used by humans as a form of biological control of certain other species considered to be pests. Such a system has been intensively investigated for the control of mosquitoes by *Coelomomyces*, a member of the Haplomastigomycotina that infects the larval stage of the insects.

Bibliography

Alexopoulos, Constantine J., and C. W. Mims. *Introductory Mycology.* 3d ed. New York: John Wiley & Sons, 1979. This advanced college-level textbook has been considered the most authoritative and complete coverage of the fungi. Well-written, with complex vocabulary. Illustrated with line drawings and photographs. There are further references at the end of each chapter and a complete glossary.

Bessey, Ernst A. *Morphology and Taxonomy of Fungi.* Philadelphia: Blakiston, 1950. Bessey's work is the most advanced of the references listed here. Its chief value is its intricate detail and its many references to the older literature of mycology. Contains some useful keys for the identification of the major groups of fungi. No glossary for the complex vocabulary.

Bold, Harold C., Constantine J. Alexopoulos, and Theodore Delevoryas. *Morphology of Plants and Fungi.* 5th ed. New York: Harper & Row, 1987. This is a popular college-level textbook that is also suitable for advanced high school science students. Previous editions were entitled *Morphology of Plants*; the expanded title is a reflection of the changing taxonomy of the fungi. Covers both the plant and fungus kingdoms. Fungi are covered in chapters 28-35. Excellent glossary; illustrated with line drawings and photographs.

Christensen, Clyde M. *The Molds and Man: An Introduction To the Fungi.* 3d ed. Minneapolis: University of Minnesota Press, 1965. This is a nontechnical account of the impact of the fungi on humans for the "layman and beginner." Written in an enjoyable style, it includes chapters on fungal parasites and pathogens, food spoilage, and industrial processes. There is a useful chapter on experiments with fungi suitable for biology students. The last chapter is a slightly outdated but easily understood summary of the fungal classification. Illustrated with a few photographs.

Hawker, Lillian E. *Fungi*. London: Hutchinson, 1966. This is a concise (216-page) summary of the fungi and their characteristics, written at an elementary college level. It is a useful reference for its viewpoint on fungal evolution and on the relationships of the fungi to other organisms. Illustrations are limited to a few diagrammatic line drawings. No glossary.

Kavaler, Lucy. *Mushrooms, Molds, and Miracles*. New York: John Day, 1965. This entertaining book was published in both hardcover and paperback versions. It received high praise from reviewers for its witty style and readability for the general public. There is an excellent discussion of the reasons for separating the fungi into a kingdom. Similar to the book by Christensen, but less technical and more enjoyable to read. No illustrations, but there is a useful bibliography.

Margulis, Lynn, and Karlene V. Schwartz. *Five Kingdoms: An Illustrated Guide to the Phyla of Life on Earth*. 2d ed. New York: W. H. Freeman, 1988. Ninety-one phyla of the five kingdoms are described and illustrated with line drawings and photographs. This is an advanced high school to college-level book about systematics by one of America's most eminent evolutionary biologists. There are some interesting differences between Margulis' classification and the one presented in this article. For example, she places the slime molds and the motile-celled fungi in the animal kingdom and considers the fungi to be represented only by the nonmotile species.

P. E. Bostick

Cross-References

Algae, 50; Gymnosperms, 1247; Microbial Diseases, 1714; Microbiology: Scope and Methodology, 1729; Applied Microbiology, 1737; Monera and Viruses, 1768; Lower Plants, 2127; Protista, 2281; Pterophyta, 2294; Asexual Reproduction in Plants, 2318; Sexual Reproduction in Plants, 2326; Systematics, 2594.

THE GAIA HYPOTHESIS

Types of life science: Ecology and the origin of life (paleontology)
Other fields of study: Biophysics and evolutionary biology

The Gaia hypothesis is a radical model of the earth as an organic entity that creates and maintains the conditions for its own survival and for the existence of all other forms of life inhabiting it.

Principal terms

CHLOROFLUOROCARBONS (CFCs): industrial chemicals used as a
    propellant in spray cans, in foam blowers, and refrigeration
FEEDBACK: a sensor, organ, or probe that can activate certain
    mechanisms of response
HOMEOSTASIS: a system of control and feedback that ensures stability
    and consistency of living organisms in a changing environment
OZONE: a poisonous and explosive gas that filters out ultraviolet
    radiation; it is found at trace levels in the stratosphere
STRATOSPHERE: the upper atmosphere between 11 and 64 kilometers
    above the earth
ULTRAVIOLET RADIATION: a component of sunlight that contains high
    energy

Summary of the Phenomenon

In 1969, at a scientific meeting on the origin of life on earth, British scientist James E. Lovelock presented his Gaia hypothesis. Responses came from only two members of the audience, and few could have predicted that, within two decades, the hypothesis would command the attention of an international audience and that extensive research would support continuing work on the hypothesis. The idea behind Lovelock's hypothesis is both simple and radical: The earth is not simply an inorganic mass on which life is sustained, but a complex living entity that maintains the exact requirements for life through the atmosphere, oceans, and soil. Lovelock gave the entity in this hypothesis the name "Gaia," derived from the ancient Greek word for Mother Earth. What troubled many scientists was the idea that the earth—Gaia—actively controls a set of constant living conditions, as though Gaia herself were alive instead of merely supporting life.

The scientific term for this mechanism is "homeostasis," a system of chemical controls and feedback cycles that maintain an equilibrium. The term was invented shortly after World War I by American physiologist Walter Cannon. Homeostasis was used to describe living organisms, such as cells, that are able to create a stable and constant chemical balance in a changing environment. Consequently, organisms can live under changing and different conditions while preserving their internal chemistry. In order to maintain such stability, a feedback mechanism is required to adjust chemical balance as conditions change. One simple feedback mechanism is an oven's thermostat, which maintains a pre-set temperature; it turns the heat on when the oven cools, and turns it off when the oven becomes too hot.

Whether it is operating within a single cell or upon an entire plant, the process of homeostasis tends to work more successfully with intricate, interdependent cycles rather than separate, isolated ones. In 1979, through an exploration of the complex chemical cycles of the earth, Lovelock expanded his Gaia hypothesis in a book entitled *Gaia: A New Look at Life on Earth*. As a hypothesis, Lovelock was able to examine the consequences of his idea and present its compatibility with a number of other possible theories. Presented as a theory, however, it would require a detailed description of the experimental tests that would ensure its validity. Since then, several components of the Gaia hypothesis have been assembled to the extent that this idea may be the key to planetary ecology.

The story of Gaia began some fifteen years earlier, when Lovelock was invited by the National Aeronautics and Space Administration (NASA) to participate in the Viking exploration of Mars. Working over a period of a year with American microbiologist Lynn Margulis, Lovelock developed test probes that could detect signs of life on Mars. Lovelock and Margulis came to the conclusion that the Martian atmosphere lacked the necessary chemical gases that would indicate signs of life. The by-products of life on earth include oxygen from green plants, methane from microbes in the soil and oceans, and ammonia from animals; without life, there would only be traces of such gases. Indeed, the Viking probe found Mars lifeless. Consequently, it may not be necessary to send intricate and expensive machinery to Mars, because observations from the earth could be sufficient.

Lovelock and Margulis were not content with the prediction of lifeless condition on Mars, but went on to suggest that earth is not merely a collection of chemical compounds and gases, but is actively involved with life itself. Lovelock uses the example of the fur of a cat or the shell of snails to show that while these are not living entities, they protect the organism against hostile environments. Similarly, the balance of gases in the atmosphere and the amount of salt in the ocean provide a friendly environment for life. The complex cycles of life on earth provided the homeostatic controls on the environment, and that environment enables life to flourish throughout the planet. The debate on whether the earth is an inorganic home of life, or is actively engaged in the process of life, centers on the source of energy for all living entities, the sun.

According to the current theory of astronomy, 4 billion years ago, when the first living organisms began to appear on earth, the sun produced 25 to 30 percent less heat than it does today. Yet fossil evidence indicates that surface temperature of the earlier period was similar to temperatures today. The earlier earth should have been much cooler and hence hostile to life. In 1972, Carl Sagan and George Mullen suggested a solution to what had been called the "faint early sun paradox." They proposed an extensive greenhouse effect produced by the presence of methane and ammonia that would have trapped the heat of the sun. Although the concentration of these gases need not have been large to produce the initial greenhouse condition, ammonia and methane are extremely active gases and would soon be depleted from the atmosphere. This proposal needs some additional replacement mechanism for it to work. The greenhouse concept was attractive enough to produce alternative hypotheses. It was known that the planet Venus, with its extensive greenhouse, produced temperatures high enough to melt lead. Mars, with an insignificant greenhouse, was almost too cold to support life.

Several scientists supported an alternative gas, carbon dioxide, and thought that early volcanic action could serve as the source of the gas in the atmosphere. Yet this created a second problem: What mechanism would reduce the amount of carbon dioxide as the earth warmed to its present level? Lovelock and Margulis accepted the premise that carbon dioxide created the initial greenhouse effect but believed that biological organisms removed much of the initial gas and continue to regulate the amount of the gas today. For evidence of the homeostatic mechanism, Lovelock and Margulis point to recent research on phytoplanktons. These tiny aquatic organisms act like plants in their ability to photosynthesize by taking carbon dioxide out of water and incorporating it into their bodies. When they die, they sink to the bottom of oceans and the carbon is locked into rock formations such as limestone. On land, the carbon dioxide absorbed by plants becomes incorporated into the soil or washed into the ocean when the plants die. One problem with this scenario concerns the question of what happened during the first 3 billion years before plankton came along as carbon dioxide extractors. As yet there exists no answer.

In all, Lovelock raised four serious questions in planetary evolution. The idea for Gaia came from the improbability of the present proportions and kinds of gases in the atmosphere and the salt content of the oceans. Almost a century ago, Ludwig Boltzmann redefined the second law of thermodynamics to define entropy as the probability of certain molecular distributions. Another way of stating this theory is that molecules tend to lose energy and move to a state of greater equilibrium. A lifeless steady-state earth would be vastly different from its present condition. For example, both Mars and Venus are closer to a steady-state condition than the earth is. A comparison of the atmospheres of these planets shows great differences in the levels of carbon dioxide and other gases. On the earth, only 0.03 percent of the atmosphere consists of carbon dioxide, while on Mars and Venus the levels approximate 98 percent. The atmosphere of the earth consists of 79 percent nitrogen and 21 percent oxygen; the corresponding figures for both Mars and Venus are only 1.9 percent for nitrogen and barely measurable trace amounts of oxygen. Similar projections can be made for the salinity of the earth's oceans, with a current value of 3.5 percent and a theoretical value of 13 percent in equilibrium. Some mechanism must control the earth's environment to explain this unlikely distribution of chemicals and gases.

Life requires a range and level of temperature for its existence. A theory of temperature control needs to address a time span of more than 4 billion years and describe the nature of a mechanism that sustains the required temperature for life.

There was little attention paid to this subject when Lovelock first proposed his Gaia hypothesis. Since then, more emphasis has been placed on this area, some of which is described above.

A third concern raised by Lovelock was the composition of the atmosphere. Until the advent of space research in the second half of the twentieth century, much of research was focused on the surface of the planet rather than above or below it. For example, the oxygen content of the atmosphere is about 21 percent. While this concentration sustains life, somewhat higher or lower values would work equally well. Each 1 percent increase in oxygen content, however, increases the dangers of fire through lightning by 70 percent. At the level of 25 percent oxygen concentration, much of the planet's vegetation, including damp tropical rain forests, would be destroyed by fire. The traces of other gases, such as carbon dioxide, methene, nitrous oxide, ammonia, and sulfur gases are also critical to life on earth. For example, methane may act as a regulator of oxygen and ensure that the concentration of oxygen does not reach a general conflagration level.

The oceans also serve as an environment for life and a mechanism for homeostasis. The role of plankton as described above may serve as one means of balancing carbon dioxide in the atmosphere. The stability of the salt content of the oceans remains unexplained. It has been accepted by convention that rain and rivers wash salt to the oceans. Calculations have shown that, by this method, the current salinity level of 3.4 percent can be arrived at in 80 million years. Clearly, over billions of years, oceans should have reached far higher levels of salt. With salt levels of 6 percent, however, life in the oceans would no longer be possible: The process of osmosis, which allows the flow of liquids through the membranes of organic cells from lower concentrations of salt to higher concentrations, would cause disruption of the cells. If the oceans contained more salt, living creatures would shrivel up and die.

In 1988, the American Geophysical Union Chapman Conference highlighted the Gaia hypothesis. For one week in San Diego, California, a heated debate occurred between those in favor of a living planetary system of controls and those who advocated inorganic mechanisms. Despite this inconclusive debate, the Gaia hypothesis has already produced a significant step toward an understanding of the evolution of planetary environments.

Methods of Study

The Gaia hypothesis is an idea that incorporates a number of known facts in biology, biochemistry, the evolution of planets, meteorology, and other allied sciences. It presents an interesting scientific possibility for our planet. In order for Gaia to have the status of a theory, it needs to offer models for temperature control for the atmosphere, the evolution of gases in the atmosphere, and stability of saline content in the oceans. These control mechanisms need to be exact. They must contain detailed descriptions in chemical, physical, and mathematical terms. Although the phytoplankton cycle is well established, its function as a feedback mechanism for carbon dioxide levels is open to debate. One reason can be placed on the vagueness of the principal term homeostasis. Since the 1920's when Cannon first used the term, there exists no known method of quantifying this term on the organic level, much less than on the planetary one.

One direction for research may be found in the feedback mechanism. During the early 1970's, Lovelock began to estimate the amount of chlorofluorocarbons (CFCs) in the atmosphere and use the level as a tag or label for the presence of other gases. CFCs are industrial chemicals used to pressurize aerosol containers and cool refrigeration units. Lovelock attempted to estimate the amount of CFCs released into the atmosphere by determining the number of aerosol cans manufactured per year. Because of the dangers of CFCs to the ozone layer in the stratosphere, recent techniques used to measure the levels of both CFCs and ozone include the use of high-altitude balloons at the Antarctic and airplanes. A decade later, this initial research led Lovelock to explore the nature of aerosols as small particles suspended in the air. Working with Robert Charlson and Meinrat Andreae, they found a feedback link in the atmosphere in the form of an obscure sulfur cycle that involves the gas dimethyl sulfide (DMS), which is produced by phytoplankton in the ocean. It turns out that DMS causes cloud condensation and thus controls the amount of radiation reflected from the cloud cover, which implies a new mechanism to control climate patterns. To test this pattern over long periods of time, ice core samples were taken from Antarctica. The analysis of sulfide concentration suggests a twenty-three-thousand-year cycle. If the earth were significantly warmer, this would trigger feedback by plankton to decrease cloud cover and cool the climate.

Context

The Gaia hypothesis produced extensive debates within the scientific community, and there is no indication that the issues raised during the San Diego meeting in 1988 are close to resolution. Outside scientific circles, Gaia has also produced a significant following. For environmentalists, it provides further evidence of the unity of life on earth and indicates how pollution, deforestation, and overpopulation can ultimately destroy the delicate balance of nature. On the other side, the apologists for polluters and the advocates of industrial growth point to the self-correcting nature of the planet. Thus, after a severe oil spill, one side can argue that damage to wild life can never be reversed, while the other side can point to the restorative process of the ocean.

Any indication of the amount of control life exerts over our planet can bring international attention to two potential ecological disasters: climatic change resulting from a runaway greenhouse effect and depletion of the ozone layer. Because of significant dependency on carbon-based fuels such as gasoline and coal, the proportion of carbon dioxide in the air has increased. Several possible scenarios project the warming of the earth's climate in the future and indeed some suggest that this has already occurred. Others, using similar data, have argued that a gradual cooling of the earth's climate would occur. In either case, life cannot be sustained easily outside the range between 0 degrees Celsius, the freezing point of water, and 40.5 degrees Celsius. Other disasters that might follow an abnormal greenhouse effect include the melting of the polar icecaps, resulting in general flooding of all coastal regions; radical alteration of current climatic patterns; and the release of further carbon dioxide from the soil to create a supergreenhouse that would extinguish all life.

The depletion of ozone gas in the stratosphere can also produce a major ecological disaster. A thin ozone layer protects biological organisms from harmful ultraviolet radiation from the sun. The penetration of such high-energy radiation can produce, among other effects, a greater number of mutations and an increase in the incidence of cancer. In the mid-1980's, a large ozone hole was discovered over Antarctica as a result of CFC interaction with ozone. There is an active attempt to ban future use of CFCs and to replace them with less reactive chemicals, but worldwide agreement on limiting the use of CFCs remains elusive. Even though it is not possible to render a final judgement on the validity of the Gaia hypothesis, the idea that a mere level of 0.03 percent carbon dioxide and trace levels of ozone gas can produce such dramatic effects is an important contribution to science and human society.

Bibliography

Hutchinson, G. Evelyn. "The Biosphere." *Scientific American* 223 (September, 1970): 64-74. This article describes how the thin surface of living matter on earth is sustained by energy and chemical cycles. There are useful graphs and scales that depict the existence of life in time and space. Hutchinson also speculates on the origins of these cycles.

Lovelock, James E. *The Ages of Gaia: A Biography of Our Living Earth*. New York: Norton, 1988. Based on Lovelock's earlier work, this book opens an even larger vista on the concept of life controlling the earth and providing suitable conditions for life. This book describes the evolution of homeostatic controls over billions of years together with recent research on the subject.

_____. *Gaia: A New Look at Life on Earth*. Oxford, England: Oxford University Press, 1979. This short and highly readable book contains all the relevant arguments on the Gaia hypothesis. Lovelock believes that science can be written with a minimum of technical terms and jargon. Also, there is an ample glossary, and later editions of the book add little to the original edition.

Oort, Abraham H. "The Energy Cycle of the Earth." *Scientific American* 223 (September, 1970): 54-63. The article describes the distribution of solar energy as it is absorbed by the earth and then redirected back into space. The result is a clearer understanding of the annual cycle of the earth's climate. Although the article contains some technical terms, they do not detract from the overall understanding of the text.

Press, Frank, and Raymond Sivers. *Earth*. San Francisco: W. H. Freeman, 1982. This is a textbook that provides the conventional account of the geological and geochemical evolution of earth. It is worthwhile reading this established point of view that the earth is inorganic and merely contributes materials to life, since Lovelock argues against it.

Rambler, Mitchell B., Lynn Margulis, and Rene Fester, eds. *Global Ecology: Towards a Science of the Biosphere*. San Diego, Calif.: Academic Press, 1989. The articles in this collection vary in their accessibility for the general reader, but are nevertheless a valuable source. In particular, the contribution of Margulis is important not only for her initial contribution to the Gaia concept, but also for her work on cell evolution, which is consistent with a view of an interdependent world.

Schneider, Stephen H. *Global Warming*. San Francisco: Sierra Club Books, 1989. This book covers worldwide climate change and its consequences. Although it contains a number of technical terms, they can be understood in context. The book does not require a background in the subject. Chapter 4 covers the Gaia hypothesis, but it should not be used as a substitute for the Lovelock book.

Victor W. Chen

Cross-References

Bioethics: Ecological Decisions, 171; The Biosphere, Biomes, and Habitats, 210; The Greenhouse Effect, 1225; The Definition of Life, 1564; The Origin of Life, 1572; Life's Effect on Earth, 1589; The Nitrogen and Phosphorus Cycles, 1951; The Water Cycle, 2695.

GAMETOGENESIS

Types of life science: Developmental biology (embryology) and genetics
Other field of study: Cell biology (cytology)

Gametogenesis is the process of sex cell formation. It includes the events that lead to a reduction in chromosome number so that the sex cells will have one-half the chromosomes that are found in normal body cells.

Principal terms

DIPLOID: the number of chromosomes or the amount of genetic material normally found in the nucleus of body cells; this number is constant for a particular species of animal

GAMETE: a sex cell; the egg or ovum in the female and the sperm in the male

HAPLOID: one-half of the diploid number; the number of chromosomes or the amount of genetic material found in a gamete

MEIOSIS: reduction division of the genetic material in the nucleus to the haploid condition; it is the process used by animal cells to form the gametes

OOGENESIS: gamete formation in the female; it occurs in the female gonads, or ovaries

SPERMATOGENESIS: gamete formation in the male; it occurs in the male gonads, or testes

SPERMIOGENESIS: the structural and functional changes of a spermatid that lead to the formation of a mature sperm cell

Summary of the Phenomenon

Sexual reproduction is the predominant mode of reproduction in animals. Sexual reproduction involves the production of gametes: the eggs and sperm. In most animals, these gametes are produced in specialized organs called gonads (ovaries and testes). The sex cells in most animals are separate—that is, each individual animal contains either testes or ovaries, but not both. Such animals are said to be dioecious. In dioecious animals, the sex cells from two different individuals (one male and one female) will fuse together in a process known as fertilization to form the offspring. The advantage of sexual reproduction seems to be in its potential to produce variability in the gametes and therefore in the new organism.

Gametes are highly specialized cells that are adapted for reproduction. These egg and sperm cells develop by a process of gametogenesis, or gamete formation. Sperm cells are relatively small cells that are specialized for motility (movement); egg cells are larger, nonmotile cells that, in many species, contain considerable amounts of stored materials that are used in the early development of the zygote (fertilized egg).

In animals, gametogenesis consists of two major events. One involves the structural and functional changes in the formation of the gamete. The other involves the process of meiosis. Animal body cells normally contain the diploid amount of genetic material. Each species of animal has a characteristic diploid number that remains the same from generation to generation. Because fertilization involves the fusion of the egg and the sperm, bringing together each cell's set of genetic material, some mechanism must reduce the amount of genetic information in the gamete, or it would double every generation. Meiosis is a special nuclear division whereby the genetic material is reassorted and reduced to form haploid cells. Therefore, gametes are haploid, and gamete fusion during fertilization reestablishes the diploid content in the zygote.

Sperm are highly motile cells that have reduced much of their cellular contents and are little more than a nucleus. Sperm are produced in the testes from a population of stem cells called spermatogonia. Spermatogonia are large diploid cells that reproduce by an equal division process called meiosis. Spermatogenesis is the process by which these relatively unspecialized diploid cells will become haploid cells; it is a continuous process that occurs throughout the sexually mature male's life. When a spermatogonium is ready to become sperm, it will stop dividing mitotically, enlarge, and begin the reduction division process of meiosis. These enlarged committed cells are known as primary spermatocytes. Primary spermatocytes, then, are large diploid cells that begin to divide meiotically.

The first step in the division process involves each primary spermatocyte dividing to form two secondary spermatocytes. Each secondary spermatocyte continues to divide, and each forms two spermatids. These spermatids are haploid cells. For each primary spermatocyte that undergoes spermatogenesis, four spermatids are formed. The spermatids are fairly ordinary cells; they must go through a process that will form them into functional sperm. The transformation process of a spermatid into a sperm is called spermiogenesis and involves several changes within the cell. The genetic material present in the nucleus begins to condense, while much of the cytoplasm and its subcellular structures are lost. The major exception to this latter event is the retention of mitochondria, cytoplasmic structures involved in energy production. The mature sperm has three main structural subdivisions: the head, the neck (or midpiece), and the tail. All are contained within the cell's membrane. The oval head has two main parts, the haploid nucleus and the acrosome. The acrosome comes in various shapes but generally forms a cap over the sperm nucleus. The acrosome functions differently in various animals, but generally its functions are associated with the fertilization process (union and subsequent fusion of egg nucleus and sperm nucleus). Acrosomes contain powerful digestive enzymes (organic substances that speed the breakdown of specific structures and substances) that allow the sperm to reach the egg's membrane. The midpiece of the sperm contains numerous mitochondria, which provide the energy for the sperm's movement. The tail, which has the same general organization as flagella or cilia (subcellular structures used for locomotion or movement of materials), uses a whiplike action to propel the sperm forward during locomotion. The structural changes that occur during spermiogenesis are meant to streamline and pare down the sperm cell for action of a special sort and of a limited duration. The sperm's function is to "swim" to the egg, to fuse with the egg's surface, and to introduce its haploid nculeus into the egg's interior.

The female gamete, the egg or ovum, is produced by a process known as oogenesis. This process occurs in the female gonads, the ovaries. At first glance, oogenesis and spermatogenesis appear to be very similar, but there are some striking differences. The major similarity is that both processes form gametes, which contain genetic material that has been reduced to the haploid condition. To understand oogenesis, one must consider that its goal is to produce a cell that is capable of development. The mature egg in all animal cells is large in comparison with other cells, particularly with the sperm. There are two important features of the egg that must be considered: the presence of a blueprint for development and the means to construct an embryo from that blueprint. In other words, the egg must be programmed and packaged during oogenesis. The programming refers to the information that somehow is coded within the structure of the egg. This information includes the genetic material as well as the cytoplasmic information. Together the nucleus and cytoplasm provide the egg with the potential to transform a relatively simple cell into a complex preadult form. Since it is within the egg that this transformation occurs, the programming must be within the organization of the egg, and the directions for development must be within that organization. The packaging refers to the presence of all the material necessary to build embryonic structures, to nourish this developing embryo, and to provide its energy until it can obtain nourishment on its own.

As happens in spermatogenesis, the potential eggs are formed from unspecialized stem cells, in this case called oogonia. Oogonia contain the diploid amount of genetic material and divide by the process of mitosis. At some point in their life, oogonia stop dividing mitotically, enlarge, and prepare to become eggs—that is, they begin meiosis. The cell that begins this reduction division process is called the primary oocyte. Each primary oocyte divides into two cells—one large cell, the secondary oocyte, and a very small cell, the first polar body. The secondary oocyte continues the final reduction phase of meiosis and forms two cells, one large one (the ovum) and one very small one (the second polar body). The first and second polar bodies are nonfunctional by-products of meiosis. The one functional cell, the mature egg, contains most of the cytoplasm of the primary oocyte and one-half of its genetic material. In many animals (primarily the vertebrates), all oogonia present in the ovaries enter meiosis at the same time; the initial events of oogenesis are synchronous within the animal. For example, in the human female, all oogonia have entered the first phase of meiosis by birth, and no reserve oogonia remain in her body. Oogenesis in humans and many other animals is not a continuous process, as is spermatogenesis in the male. Rather, the primary oocytes in the first stages of reduction division may remain inactivated for a long time—in some cases, for several decades. Therefore, in female animals with this format of oogenesis, a primary oocyte population is maintained, and eggs will mature as they are needed.

Thus far it appears that the egg's formation differs from the sperm's in three ways. First, in many female animals, there is a limited number of primary oocytes capable of going on to form eggs; second, this egg formation is not necessarily a continuous process; third, one primary oocyte yields one mature egg at the end of meiosis. Although these are three very important differences, there are other distinctly egg events that deal with the developmental programming and the packaging of materials in this potential gamete.

Little is known about the egg's storage of developmental directions or the actual programming of information, but developmental and molecular biologists are beginning to elucidate events that occur during oogenesis that are concerned with function of the egg. One such event, fairly widespread among the animal kingdom, is the formation of so-called lampbrush chromosomes during oogenesis. The chromosome's backbone unravels at many sites so that regions, composed of specific genes, loop outward from the backbone. These loops give the chromosome its distinctive lampbrushlike appearance. Large amounts of a nucleic acid known as messenger ribonucleic acid (mRNA) are being made on each loop. This mRNA is then processed and sent into the developing eggs's cytoplasm, where most of it will be stored for use during early development. After fertilization, these maternal (egg-derived) mRNAs can be used to make specific proteins necessary for the embryo.

Another event present in some developing eggs is the mass production of another type of RNA known as ribosomal RNA (rRNA). Most of this rRNA will also be stored until fertilization. After fertilization, these rRNA particles will help form cytoplasmic structures called ribosomes (the sites of protein synthesis). In addition to these egg products, many animal eggs must become filled with yolk. Yolk is the general term that covers the major storage of material in the egg.

Because the maternal proteins (yolk and other protein components) and nucleic acids (various RNAs) form the bulk of the egg cytoplasm, they have profound influences on the development of the embryo. In particular, the positions of maternal mRNAs, ribosomes, and proteins affect the organization of the embryo. It is evident, then, that the maternal genetic information and the arrangement of the products of this information provide crucial developmental information that will control much of the course of embryonic development. Therefore, the egg contributes considerably more than a haploid nucleus to the zygote.

Methods of Study

There are several approaches to the study of gametogenesis. Early biologists employed cytological techniques (methods of preparing cells for the study of their structure and function) and microscopy to study gamete formation. These early studies were, in fact, observations of the actual events themselves. Although these early descriptive approaches gave much information about the cells involved at each stage of gamete formation, they did not provide any information about the control mechanisms for this process. Biochemical studies have contributed to the understanding of certain regulatory substances and how they function in gametogenesis. By enhancing or inhibiting the presence of these regulatory substances in the organism, investigators have been able to elucidate many of the normal events of gametogenesis and utilize this information to address problems of contraception and infertility.

Beginning at puberty, the hormones (substances released from endocrine glands, generally functioning to regulate specific body activity) of the hypothalamus, the pituitary gland, and the gonads interact to establish and regulate gametogenesis in the organism. Gonadotropin-releasing hormone (GnRH) from the hypothalamus stimulates the release of follicle-stimulating hormone (FSH) and luteinizing hormone (LH) from the anterior portion of the pituitary gland. All three of these hormones are necessary for spermatogenesis and oogenesis.

Surgical removal of the mammalian pituitary gland (hypophysectomy) in the male leads to degeneration of the testes. Testicular function can be restored in these hypophysectomized animals by administering the hormones FSH and LH. These studies suggest that FSH and LH are necessary for normal functioning of the testes. LH appears to stimulate the release of testosterone (male hormone) by certain cells (Leydig cells) of the testes. Both testosterone and FSH are necessary for spermatogenesis, but the exact role that each of these hormones plays in male sexual physiology has yet to be determined.

Oogenesis in the female has been the subject of intense investigation. By understanding the normal events of the ovarian cycle (a monthly cycle that results in the formation of a fertilizable gamete and its release from the ovary), investigators can develop methods to correct some of the problems in female sexual functioning. Once a month, from puberty to menopause, one primary oocyte present in the woman's ovaries is activated to continue the process of gamete formation. The events that occur each month are part of the ovarian cycle. Release of GnRH from the hypothalamus at the beginning of each monthly cycle stimulates the anterior portion of the pituitary gland to release FSH. FSH, in turn, affects the ovaries: It stimulates a primary oocyte to mature to the point that it can be released from the ovary, as a secondary oocyte, and it causes certain cells (follicle cells) in the ovary to produce estrogens, female hormones. High estrogen levels will cause the pituitary to inhibit FSH release, a negative feedback mechanism, and stimulate LH release. These estrogen-mediated events occur at approximately the middle of the ovarian cycle. LH also affects the ovaries. LH, however, is responsible for ovulation (the release of the oocyte from the ovaries) and for the formation of a cellular structure called the corpus luteum. LH also stimulates the corpus luteum to produce progesterone, another female hormone. Eventually, high levels of progesterone will inhibit LH release from the pituitary gland, and the cycle begins anew.

Context

Scientific and technological advances have made it possible to deal with reproductive events in striking ways. Two particular areas are contraception and infertility.

Reproductive research concerning problems of fertility made great strides in the 1970's and 1980's. In vitro fertilization, first accomplished in England in 1978, is now being done throughout the world. The procedure involves the removal of mature follicles from a woman's ovary. Each follicle contains the female gamete. Fertilization then takes place in a Petri dish in the laboratory. After several mitotic divisions of the zygote (fertilized egg) have occurred, the young embryo is introduced into a receptive uterus. From there, development is permitted to proceed normally. The procedure is difficult and costly, and only about one in six attempts is successful. Actually, these odds are fairly close to the success rate of natural fertilization and subsequent development. Women who have occluded (obstructed) Fallopian tubes (the tubes that catch the released gamete from the ovary and transport it to the uterus) are candidates for in vitro fertilization.

A second technique developed for women having trouble conceiving is gamete intrafallopian transfer (GIFT), introduced in the United States in 1984. In this technique, mature follicles are once again removed from the ovaries. The gametes are then placed in the presence of mature sperm; then, both the egg and sperm are introduced into the Fallopian tube for fertilization to take place in its natural site. Fertilization and development are allowed to proceed normally. Women having Fallopian tubes that are opened but lack fimbriae (projections at the ends of the tubes necessary to catch the egg as it is released from the ovary) are good candidates for GIFT. A major disadvantage of GIFT is that it is an intrusive technique: The woman must be placed under general anesthesia, and the abdominal cavity must be opened. Ways to eliminate this disadvantage are being investigated.

Another area of investigation is that of male contraception. Male chemical contraceptives have proved to be quite elusive, whereas female chemical contraceptives—birth-control pills—have been available for some time. There are several types, but all are either estrogens or progesterone or a combination of both. Testosterone, the male hormone, will block the release of certain hormones from the pituitary gland that stimulate gamete production in the male. Testosterone itself, however, also stimulates spermatogenesis. Therefore, it is not an effective contraceptive. Estrogens (female hormones) are effective in the male, but they inhibit libido and may be feminizing. One prospect for male oral contraception is a substance called gossypal. Gossypal, a chemical extracted from cotton seeds, appears to block spermatogenesis. It seems to be highly effective, and its effects appear to be reversible. There are some problems with this drug, however, that present themselves as possible serious side effects. At high dosages, gossypal can induce malnutrition, diarrhea, circulatory problems, and even heart failure. Even at lower concentrations, male subjects have experienced some negative side effects. Much more research is necessary before the drug might be made available to the general male population.

Bibliography

Epel, D. "The Program of Fertilization." *Scientific American* 237 (November, 1977): 128-140. A summary of the events of fertilization and an excellent account of the fascinating world of the egg and the sperm. This article is written for the college-level reader with some background in general biology. It explains the events that occur after the formation of the gametes.

Lenhoff, Howard. *Conception to Birth*. Dubuque, Iowa: Kendall/Hunt, 1989. A nonscience student text that begins with human reproduction, proceeds to human genetics, then considers human development through birth. The sections on human reproduction and cell reproduction are thorough and will provide the reader with additional information about cell division and formation of human gametes.

Mader, Sylvia S. *Human Reproductive Biology*. Dubuque, Iowa: Wm. C. Brown, 1980. A good, short, nontechnical account of reproduction. The text presents the biological material in an easy, approachable fashion. In addition to giving the reader insight into human gametogenesis, it stresses hormonal cycles and human coital events.

Rugh, Roberts, and Landrum B. Shettles. *From Conception to Birth: The Drama of Life's Beginnings*. New York: Harper & Row, 1971. A book written for the general audience; no scientific background is necessary. Although much of the book deals with the actual events of development, the first two chapters do cover gametogenesis. Effectively illustrated with photographs of human embryos and fetuses. An excellent overview of human development for the concerned individual.

Sadler, R. M. *The Reproduction of Vertebrates*. New York: Academic Press, 1973. A survey of reproductive patterns and mechanisms of reproductive control in the major vertebrate groups. Useful to the student who wants a comparative presentation of all aspects of reproductive events.

Sher, Geoffrey, Virginia A. Marriage, and Jean Stoess. *From Infertility to In Vitro Fertilization*. New York: McGraw-Hill, 1988. An account for the general reader of the technical aspects as well as the emotional considerations concerning in vitro fertilization. In addition, the text presents a survey of the various procedures that can help deal with fertility problems. Excellent reading for individuals considering these procedures.

Stine, Gerald J. *The New Human Genetics*. Dubuque, Iowa: Wm. C. Brown, 1988. A college-level text directed toward the nonscience major. It is well organized and illustrated. Presents aspects of molecular genetics and Mendelian genetics. The chapters of particular interest to those interested in gametogenesis are 1 and 2. Covers the cellular basis of heredity (mitosis and meiosis) and human reproduction (oogenesis and spermatogenesis).

Swanson, Harold D. *Human Reproduction Biology and Social Change*. New York: Oxford University Press, 1974. The text assumes that the reader has a basic understanding of high school biology. Takes many biological events, such as the ovarian-menstrual cycle and meiotic recombination, and presents them in a very readable manner with limited technical terms.

Geri Seitchik

Cross-References

GAS EXCHANGE IN ANIMALS

Type of life science: Animal physiology
Other fields of study: Biochemistry, biophysics, and cell biology (cytology)

Gas exchange refers to the processes used by animals to take up oxygen and eliminate carbon dioxide. These processes are the basis for understanding how animals breathe, particularly in diverse conditions.

Principal terms

DIFFUSION: the passive movement of a gas across a membrane from a region of high pressure to one of low pressure

EPITHELIUM: a thin layer of cells that lines a body surface, such as the lining of the lungs or the intestines

PARTIAL PRESSURE: that part of the atmospheric pressure caused by only a single gas of many in a mixture; it is determined by how much of the gas is present in the mixture

PERMEABILITY: the tendency, in this case of a membrane, to permit the movement of a gas across that membrane

RESPIRATORY MEDIUM: the water or air that contains the oxygen used by an animal to carry out biochemical reactions

VENTILATION: the movement of the respiratory medium to and across the site of gas exchange

Summary of the Phenomenon

Gas exchange is the uptake of oxygen and the loss (or elimination or excretion) of carbon dioxide. It refers to two major steps in the overall oxygen consumption (or carbon dioxide excretion) by the whole animal. These two steps are the movement of the respiratory medium (containing oxygen) past the site of gas exchange, known as ventilation, and the diffusion of oxygen across the gas-exchange surface into the animal. The final step in diffusion of oxygen into an animal always involves diffusion from a liquid into a liquid, even in air breathers. Both ventilation and diffusion depend on the design of the structures as well as the way in which the systems and structures work. The additional steps in the whole respiratory system are the internal counterparts to ventilation and diffusion. These are perfusion, or blood flow, and diffusion from the blood to the tissues.

Basically, gas exchange takes place at a respiratory surface where the source of oxygen, the respiratory medium, is brought into contact with the surface. Oxygen diffuses into the animal, carbon dioxide diffuses out, and the spent or used respiratory medium is removed. The movement of the respiratory medium is termed ventilation. Once oxygen is in the animal, it is transported to the site of oxygen utilization, the tissues. Carbon dioxide, on the other hand, must be transported from the tissues to the site of gas exchange for excretion in gaseous form.

Animals have three basic types of gas-exchange organs: skin, invaginations (inpocketings of the epithelium), and evaginations (outpocketings of the epithelium). All three show modifications to improve the conditions of gas exchange. Skin always permits gas exchange unless it is coated with some material that limits diffusion. The skin of a snake or a turtle is so coated and permits very little gas exchange. The skin of a worm or an octopus, on the other hand, is quite thin and permits gas exchange quite freely. Invaginations of the external epithelium are basically what lungs and insect trachaea are, but in a highly modified condition. Evaginations of the skin are represented by the gills of aquatic animals; even when inside a cavity, as are fish and crab gills, they are still evaginations.

There is only one way that animals take up oxygen from the external medium, regardless of whether that medium is air or water. Gas must passively diffuse across the membrane that separates the animal from its environment. That membrane is a type of tissue called epithelium and is similar in nature and structure to the tissue that lines other body surfaces. The different types of epithelia are classified according to their locations and functions; those lining gills, lungs, and certain other organs of gas exchange are all known as respiratory epithelia. The respiratory epithelium not only separates the internal and external fluids but also represents a barrier to the movement of materials such as gas.

Diffusion of a gas across a membrane occurs according to the laws of physics. The driving force for gas diffusion is the difference in the partial pressure of the gas across the membrane. A high external partial pressure and low internal partial pressure will provide a large difference and will enhance diffusion. Oxygen makes up 20.9 percent of the air, so that 20.9 percent of the atmospheric pressure at sea level (14.72 pounds per square inch) is attributable to oxygen (3.08 pounds per square inch). At higher altitudes, atmospheric pressure and partial pressure of oxygen are reduced.

The other factors that determine the diffusion of a gas are the thickness of the membrane across which it diffuses, the membrane's total surface area, and the nature or composition of the membrane. Obviously, a thick membrane will retard diffusion of gas because the gas must move across a greater distance. The distance the gas must diffuse is known as the diffusion distance. Additionally, the total surface area of the membrane available for diffusion has a direct effect on the rate of diffusion from one place to another. The greater the surface area, the greater the quantity of gas that can diffuse in a given time. Finally, the composition of the membrane is of critical importance in determining the diffusion of a gas. The nature of the membrane is referred to as the permeability of the membrane to the gas in question. The greater the permeability, the more easily gas diffuses. A membrane with a layer of minerals (calcium, for example) on the cells will not be as permeable as one without such a layer.

A very important point to note is that gases diffuse according to the difference in the partial pressure of the gas and not according to the concentration of the gas in the liquid. Several scientists have proved this by constructing artificial systems with two dissimilar fluids separated by a membrane. The movement of oxygen is always from high partial pressure to low and not from a high concentration to low. The reason is that pressure is a measure of molecular energy, but concentration of a gas in a liquid depends on the amount of that gas that can dissolve in the liquid—its solubility.

All gas exchange occurs across a fluid-fluid boundary—that is, from one liquid to another—even in air breathers. The explanation for this is that all respiratory epithelia are moist and are kept so by the cells that line the surface. If the surface were to dry out, the permeability to gases (and other materials) would be substantially reduced. Thus, in air breathers, oxygen must first dissolve in the thin fluid layer lining the surface before diffusion across the epithelium takes place.

Organs of gas exchange work as do radiators, except that a gas is exchanged instead of heat. In this system, there are two liquids, one the source and the other the sink for the transferred material, the gas. The source is the external supply, and the sink is the blood or other internal fluid. Both fluids are contained in vessels or tubes that channel and direct it, with a thin layer of epithelium between the two. In the most efficient transfer systems, both the source and the sink flow, and they flow in opposite directions. If they did not flow, then the two fluids would simply come to an equilibrium, with oxygen partial pressure the same in both of the fluids. By moving in opposite directions, each is renewed, and the difference between them is always maximized. This type of exchange system is a "countercurrent system," because the two fluids flow in opposite directions. The most efficient of the gas-exchange organs function this way.

Two other types of gas-exchange systems are based on fluids flowing in directions other than perfectly opposite to each other. Birds have a respiratory system in which blood and air do not flow in opposite directions; rather, the blood flows perpendicularly to the direction of the air flow. This is referred to as crosscurrent flow. While not as efficient as countercurrent flow, it provides for an acceptably high level of efficiency. A system in which the respiratory medium is not channeled, but the blood is instead in vessels, is known as a mixed volume system. The mammalian lung functions in this way; the air is pumped into sacs that are lined with tiny blood vessels, but the air does not flow.

Ventilation of gas-exchange organs is accomplished by a pumping mechanism that brings the respiratory medium to and across the gas-exchange surface. Both water and air breathers use ventilatory pumps, but water breathers must move a much heavier and denser medium than air breathers. Pumping mechanisms may be located at the inflowing end of the system or at the outflowing end. The former are positive pressure pumps that push respiratory medium, and the latter are negative pressure pumps that pull respiratory medium into the cavity. Negative pressure is used in mammalian lungs, insect trachaea, and crab gills, while positive pressure is used in some fish that push water from the mouth into the gill chamber.

There are two basic patterns of flow of the respiratory medium through gas-exchange organs: one-way and tidal. One-way flow is found in fish, crabs, clams, and a number of other aquatic animals. Interestingly enough, the bird respiratory system also uses one-way flow. In one-way flow systems, the medium is always moving and passes over the gas exchange surface only once. In tidal-flow systems, the respiratory medium moves in and out (like the tide) through the same passages and tubes. The mammalian and insect respiratory systems both utilize tidal ventilation. The respiratory medium is not always moving, and when it is exhaled, there is some amount remaining in the cavity. The remaining respiratory medium will contain more carbon dioxide and less oxygen than fresh respiratory medium, with which it will mix upon inhalation.

Methods of Study

The total amount of oxygen used by an animal is a gross measure of gas exchange known as oxygen uptake or oxygen consumption. Its counterpart for carbon dioxide is carbon dioxide excretion. Oxygen uptake is expressed as the amount of oxygen used per minute per kilogram of animal mass. Carbon dioxide excretion is expressed in the same terms. In theory, oxygen uptake and carbon dioxide excretion will be numerically the same, but in live animals there are several circumstances that cause the two to differ. Measurement of both rates is accomplished in similar ways. One method is the use of a respirometer and involves placing an animal in a sealed container and measuring the rate at which oxygen is depleted or carbon dioxide produced by an animal. Alternatively, respiratory medium, either air or water, is pumped through the respirometer and the oxygen or carbon dioxide measured in the inflowing and outflowing medium; the difference will be the amount used by the animal. The flow rate of the air or water must also be known for the calculations. The use of a respirometer is preferable but may not be practical for large animals, such as a horse.

In the case of animals too large to use a respirometer, oxygen uptake or carbon dioxide excretion is determined by measuring the rate of flow of the respiratory medium through the gas exchange organ and measuring the oxygen in the inspired and expired air or water. The result is the ventilation rate and the oxygen extraction, the product of which is the oxygen consumption rate. This measurement is straightforward in animals with one opening for inspired and another for expired respiratory medium, such as a fish or a crab. In humans, however, there are complications that make the measurements more difficult. Still, it is possible to measure the flow of air in and out of a lung and to collect at least some of the gas and measure either the oxygen or carbon dioxide in that air.

There is an additional advantage to the latter technique, measuring ventilation and the oxygen in the water or air. That advantage is that another measure of gas exchange is provided in these measurements. The difference between the amount of oxygen in inspired and expired water or air is the extraction (the amount taken out) and assesses the efficiency of the gas exchange organ. The efficiency is usually given as the percentage of oxygen taken out of the respiratory medium (the amount removed divided by the amount in inspired air or water). There are numerous factors that affect extraction, and measuring the efficiency provides one piece of information.

Studies of gas exchange encompass all levels of organization of animals, from the cellular to the whole animal. One of the most important levels concerns the structure of the organ and the parts of the organ. For this, it is necessary to see the spatial relationships among the parts, measure distances and areas, and count structures. The surface area, the volume, the number of structures or substructures, and the diffusion distances must all be measured. The results describe the morphology and morphometrics of the organ. Both whole, intact animals, and preserved specimens are used to make these measurements. The techniques are those used in surgery and dissection, and the results are critical to an understanding of the basic function of the respiratory organ. The electron microscope has been a powerful tool in this regard, permitting the accurate measurement of cellular-level distances, such as the diffusion distance.

Measuring the partial pressure difference between the inside and outside of the animal is critical because of the role that this pressure difference has in gas exchange. Partial pressure of oxygen may be measured in two ways: in the intact animal or in a sample removed from the animal and injected into an instrument. The instrument most commonly used for measuring oxygen or carbon dioxide partial pressure is an electrode that changes electrical output when oxygen diffuses across an artificial membrane into a salt solution. Some of these electrons have been miniaturized and are only 4 millimeters across, and they will fit in a syringe needle. Still, it is difficult to use one of these in an intact mammal. The other way to measure partial pressure of oxygen or carbon dioxide on either side of the respiratory epithelium is to withdraw a sample of the air or water on the outside or the blood from the vessels on the inside. This procedure may be routine (in animals such as fish and crabs) or somewhat difficult (as in a mammal). A small tube is threaded into the lung to withdraw the air sample.

The movement of the respiratory medium, ventilation, is an important measure in determining the rate at which oxygen is brought to the respiratory surface. The blood flow (perfusion) on the inside is the counterpart to ventilation and is equally important. Ventilation can be measured either indirectly (meaning it is calculated) or directly. Indirect determinations require measuring other functions and then calculating ventilation based on known equations. If the rate of oxygen uptake and the extraction are measured, for example, then ventilation can be calculated.

Direct measures of ventilation use an electronic sensing device to determine the flow of water or air at the site of intake or outflow of respiratory medium on the animal. A human subject can simply breathe into such an electronic or mechanical device. Nonhuman mammals are more difficult and frequently require indirect techniques.

Direct measures may be the flow rate of the respiratory medium, the frequency of breathing, the hydrostatic pressure in the respiratory chamber, or a change in shape and size of the respiratory chamber. Any of these measures can be used to monitor routine respiratory function, but all are needed to assess gas exchange completely and accurately.

It is also necessary to know the general pattern of water or air movement at the respiratory surface. To do so often requires some invasive technique and the use of an indicator, such as a dye in the respiratory medium. The movement of the medium can then be visualized to determine the pattern. In some animals, video cameras can be used to photograph flow patterns of dyed medium, particularly water.

Context

Gas exchange is studied by researchers and health practitioners both to assess basic function and to determine the source and nature of limitations of the systems of the body. These two areas may seem quite different at first; one is applied research, and the other is considered basic research. Both, however, have the same bases and use the same equations and principles. Only the animals or conditions differ. Nonhuman animals are sometimes used as models for examining processes related to health care. This model systems approach is common throughout biology, but especially so in medicine.

One of the clinical applications, or contexts, in which gas exchange is studied is in respiratory distress or pulmonary (lung) disease. In these cases, the respiratory epithelium may become inflamed and thickened. This will increase the diffusion distance and retard, or limit, oxygen uptake and carbon dioxide release at the lung. Secretion of mucus by a respiratory epithelium may have a similar result for the same reasons. Mucus secretion occurs in several diseases and also takes place in fish gills when irritated by noxious chemicals in the water.

Gas exchange is also studied in diverse animals to understand evolutionary trends and pressures. Animals that live at high altitudes, for example, are constantly faced with low oxygen pressure in the air, and therefore some adjustment must be made by the animal. Scientists study the respiratory systems of these animals to determine if one of the other factors that affects gas exchange, such as diffusion distance or total surface area, is altered to compensate for the lower pressure difference.

All animals have similar basic physiological needs, including a need for oxygen to fuel the conversion of food materials into energy and other substances. Many animals have unique or specific forms or structures enabling them to survive in a particular habitat. Some of these forms affect the respiratory system—as in the differences between the respiratory surface in land animals compared with similar species that live in water. Scientists have compared the gas-exchange systems in aquatic and terrestrial species to learn more about evolutionary processes.

Bibliography

Comroe, Julius H. "The Lung." *Scientific American* 214 (February, 1966): 56-68. Explains the basic mechanism of lung function, including illustrations and applications to humans. Similar in nature to the medical text by the same author, but written for the reader with no background in biology. Includes material on the control of ventilation.

_____. *Physiology of Respiration.* 2d ed. Chicago: Year Book Medical Publishers, 1974. Chapters 2, "Alveolar Ventilation," and 12, "Pulmonary Gas Diffusion," give some basic material on gas exchange as it applies specifically to humans. Although a medical text, it does not presume as much background as many college texts. The explanation is the strong point, along with applications.

Dejours, Pierre, ed. *Principles of Comparative Respiratory Physiology.* 2d ed. New York: Elsevier, 1981. An excellent book for professionals and for those who have mastered other readings in the field. Chapters 3-6 explain the basics. Dejours gives the whole story, from basic concepts to more complex research, but the primary focus is clearly on the latter. He presents such a strong foundation that the information is not overwhelming. Uses equations freely and provides complete documentation for the graphs he has drawn from other scientists' work.

Hill, R. W., and G. A. Wyse. *Animal Physiology.* New York: Harper & Row, 1989. Chapter 11, "Principles of Diffusion and Dissolution of Gases," and chapter 12, "Exchange of Oxygen and Carbon Dioxide 1," provide a relatively complete discussion of the topic of gas exchange from first principles to application. The illustrations are of very high quality, and the explanations are neither too complex nor filled with jargon; they are understandable to entering college students. Additional readings are listed.

Klystra, J. A. "Experiments in Water Breathing." *Scientific American* 219 (August, 1968): 66-74. The real positive in this article is the illustration and accompanying explanation that compares gills and lungs, water and air breathing. Discusses the basis for function of both. The application is also interesting.

Rahn, H., A. Ar, and C. V. Paganelli. "How Bird Eggs Breathe." *Scientific American* 240 (February, 1979): 46-55. This application of basic diffusional-based gas exchange provides the fundamental concepts and an example of how these concepts are used to understand evolutionary processes.

Raven, P. H., and G. B. Johnson. *Biology.* 2d ed. St. Louis: Times Mirror/Mosby, 1989. Chapter 50, "Respiration," is not very long but has good illustrations and simple explanations of gas exchange. Others on various animal groups do provide additional comparative information in one text. Written at the introductory college level.

Warren, J. V. "The Physiology of the Giraffe." *Scientific American* 231 (November, 1974): 96-105. This article is a good application of comparative respiratory function to an interesting evolutionary animal. Also includes circulatory adaptations.

Peter L. deFur

Cross-References

Animal Cell Types, 105; Blood Circuits, 248; Breathing Regulation, 300; Cellular Membrane Specializations, 388; Diffusion in Circulation, 621; Gill, Trachea, and Lung Anatomy, 1212; Hemocyanins, Hemoglobins, and Myoglobins, 1277; Respiration Adaptation to Low Oxygen, 2369; Respiration in Birds, 2383.

GAS EXCHANGE IN PLANTS

Type of life science: Plant physiology
Other fields of study: Biochemistry, biophysics, and cell biology (cytology)

Gas exchange is the process by which water vapor and oxygen are released from the leaf surface of a plant and carbon dioxide is allowed to enter. The uptake of carbon dioxide is especially crucial to the survival of the plant; an understanding of gas exchange could lead to improved plant production in the future.

Principal terms

DIFFUSION: the movement of particles down a concentration gradient from an area of high concentration to an area of low concentration

FLACCID: the limp condition that results when water no longer moves into plant cells

OSMOSIS: the diffusion of water across a semipermeable membrane

OSMOTIC POTENTIAL: a measure of the tendency for a solution to take up water when separated from pure water by a semipermeable membrane

PALISADE PARENCHYMA: a region of the leaf composed of somewhat uniform rows of tightly packed thin-walled cells

PH: a term referring to the degree of acidity or alkalinity, based on the hydrogen ion concentration

SPONGY PARENCHYMA: a region of leaf composed of rather loosely arranged thin-walled cells with numerous air spaces

TRANSPIRATION: a term referring to the loss of water as it evaporates from the leaf surface through specialized pores called stomata (*sing.* stomate)

TURGOR: the pressure exerted within a cell caused by the continued uptake of water

XYLEM: a tissue composed of dead cells that conducts water from plant roots to the shoot

Summary of the Phenomenon

All living organisms continually produce gases via metabolic and cellular activities, and the vast majority of living things are in one way or another in intimate contact with a gaseous medium. In most instances, therefore, there is ample opportunity for all organisms to exchange gases with the environment. Gas exchange in plants primarily refers to the process whereby gaseous water vapor and oxygen are released from the leaf and carbon dioxide is allowed to diffuse into the vegetative tissues.

The general conception of the contributions of both plants and animals to the gaseous composition of the atmosphere is that as animals respire, oxygen is consumed and carbon dioxide is released, whereas plants use carbon dioxide and produce oxygen during photosynthesis. In actuality, however, the gaseous balance in plants is much more complex than this, because plant cells conduct both respiration and photosynthesis. Plants respire in much the same way as animals. During this respiration, oxygen is used to oxidize carbohydrates, and carbon dioxide and water are produced as waste products. The photosynthesis process requires an input of carbon dioxide and water. These two reactants are used to produce carbohydrates, and oxygen is released as a waste product. Under normal conditions, photosynthesis rates are higher than respiration rates; thus, there is a net increase in oxygen production, accompanied by a net increase in the usage of carbon dioxide. The overall impression, then, is that plants use carbon dioxide and produce oxygen.

The gases move into and out of the plants through specialized openings located along the surface of the leaf. These openings, called stomata, are of optimum size, shape, and distribution for the efficient diffusion of gases. Each stomate is surrounded by two specialized structures called guard cells. These two cells are attached together at each end of both cells. The lateral edges of the two cells are not attached to each other, but, when flaccid, the sides of the guard cells do touch each other and effectively close the stomate. Specialized structural components prevent the guard cells from increasing in diameter as expansion occurs. Hence, when guard cells take up water, expansion takes place only along the longitudinal axis. Since the ends of the cells are connected to each other, the expanding of the cells forces the sides apart and results in the opening of the stomate.

The opening of the stomata is dependent on the movement of water into guard cells. The water initially comes from the soil. The water enters the root by osmotic processes, then moves across the root and into the xylem tissues, which transport it up the stem to the leaves. From the xylem in the leaves, the water moves into the palisade and spongy parenchyma cells, which make up the bulk of the leaf tissue. The water then moves into the subsidiary cells that immediately surround the guard cells.

When the leaf is exposed to light, the process of photosynthesis begins. As the photosynthetic reactions proceed in the guard cells, the residual carbon dioxide is converted to carbohydrates. The disappearance of carbon dioxide from the guard cell cytosol results in an increase in the cellular pH. As the pH rises, the activity of the enzymes that convert starch and sugars to organic acids increases. The higher concentration of organic acids results in a higher concentration of hydrogen ions. The hydrogen ions of the guard cells are then exchanged for potassium ions in the subsidiary cells. This increased concentration of potassium, combined with the higher levels of organic acids, lowers the osmotic potential of the guard cells, and, since water moves from regions of high osmotic potential to regions of lower osmotic potential, water will move from the subsidiary cells into the guard cells. This movement of water increases the turgor (inner pressure) of the guard cells and causes them to swell. Thus, the stomata open.

Once the stomata open, the intracellular free space around both the palisade and spongy parenchymas is put into continuous contact with the outside atmosphere. As the water within the parenchyma cells moves across the cellular membranes, it evaporates into the free space and diffuses through the stomata into the atmosphere. Oxygen produced during photosynthesis exits the plant in much the same manner as the water vapor. Carbon dioxide, however, follows the reverse path. It enters through the open stomata and diffuses through the free space and across cell membranes into the parenchyma tissues. In each case, the gas involved moves down a concentration or pressure gradient. The pressure of water vapor and oxygen is higher inside the leaf free space than in the atmosphere, whereas the partial pressure of carbon dioxide is greater in the atmosphere than within the free space. Thus, the impetus is for the former two gases to move out of the plant and for the latter to enter it.

This exchange will take place as long as the stomata remain open and the pressure gradient is in the right direction. As a general rule, stomata close in the dark. Without an input of solar energy, the light-mediated reactions of photosynthesis stop. In the absence of these reactions, the carbon dioxide level increases; as a result, the pH decreases. The lower pH activates the enzymatic conversion of organic acids to sugars and starch. This causes the potassium ions to move from the guard cells into the subsidiary cells. As a result, the osmotic potential of the guard cells is raised, the water moves out, the cells become flaccid, and the stomata close.

Environmental conditions can also affect stomatal openings. Drought conditions, which induce water stress, can affect gas exchange because the lack of water moving through the plant causes the guard cells to lose turgor and the stomata to close. When the temperature becomes too warm, stomata also tend to close. In some instances, the higher temperature causes water to transpire more rapidly, which leads to water stress. Insufficient water moving through the plant causes the guard cells to lose turgor and the stomata to close. In other cases, the increase in temperature causes an increase in cellular respiration that, in turn, increases carbon dioxide levels. Internal high carbon dioxide concentrations both reverse the carbon dioxide pressure gradient and cause the stomata to close. The percent of relative humidity can drastically affect the rate of water evaporating from the leaf surface. As the humidity increases, the higher water content of the air decreases the rate of water loss from the leaf because the water pressure gradient no longer favors evaporation from the leaf surface. The amount of solar radiation can also influence gas exchange. As the amount of light increases, the stomata open faster and wider, resulting in a more rapid rate of gas exchange. Wind currents will also increase gas exchange rates: As the wind blows across the leaf, it carries water vapor away and, in a sense, reduces the humidity at the leaf surface. Because of this lower humidity, the water evaporates from the leaf surface more rapidly.

Methods of Study

Because the opening of stomata is critical to gas exchange of any kind, the study of gas exchange must include a study of transpiration rates. Methods for measuring this movement of water through the plant range from the fairly simple to the very complicated. Transpiration measurements can be as simple as weighing a well-watered potted plant on a very sensitive balance. Very little of the water absorbed by the plant actually contributes to growth. Hence, after a given time interval, virtually all loss of weight from the potted plant will be attributable to transpiration. Note that this method, however, is based on the assumption that transpiration from a potted plant is the same as transpiration under field conditions. A somewhat easier approach is to remove a leaf from a plant and immediately measure the decrease in weight that will occur because of water loss. Another method is to construct a potometer. This means to attach a leaf or a stem with several leaves to a small-diameter glass tube; as the leaves transpire, water that can be measured will be pulled up the tube. Again, the assumption is that a part of a plant will transpire at the same rate as an entire plant under field conditions. One of the most accurate (and most complex) methods of measuring transpiration and overall gas exchange is to enclose one or more plants in a clear plastic tent. The temperature as well as the water vapor and carbon dioxide content of the air entering and exiting the tent can be monitored. Both photosynthesis and respiration rates can be calculated from these measurements.

Measurement of the exchange rates of oxygen and carbon dioxide is useful in determining certain aspects of cellular metabolism. For example, the ratio between carbon dioxide released and the amount of oxygen consumed (referred to as the respiratory quotient, or RQ) is indicative of the food being burned by cells for energy. A value of 1.0 indicates that carbohydrates are being utilized, while a value of around 0.7 suggests that fats are being consumed. These measurements have traditionally been done with some sort of manometric device. Manometers measure changes in gas volumes. The plant tissues are placed in sealed containers connected to manometers; the carbon dioxide in some of the samples can be selectively absorbed, and the volume of both oxygen and carbon dioxide can then be calculated. These values can be used to calculate the respiratory quotient. Modern instrumental analysis using carbon dioxide and oxygen analyzers have replaced many of the manometric techniques. These instruments not only provide even more accurate measurements, but also are portable and thus lend themselves to a broad range of both field and laboratory applications.

Cytological studies are also important in studying gas exchange. Cytology refers to the study of cell structure and function and often involves differentially staining parts of the cell, which can then be studied under the microscope. Electron microscopy techniques and cytologic staining and fixing methods are necessary to investigate visually the structural changes that take place during stomatal opening.

Context

The exchange of gases between living plants and the atmosphere is critical to the survival of all living organisms. Without the release of the oxygen produced during photosynthesis, the atmosphere would contain very little of this necessary gas. As a result, all the organisms that require oxygen could not exist, because, for all practical purposes, photosynthesis is the only source of atmospheric molecular oxygen. Furthermore, the vast majority of organisms on this planet depend on the organic materials supplied by plants. The carbon dioxide taken from the atmosphere is photosynthetically fixed into the more complex carbon molecules that eventually serve as food not only for the plants but also for all those organisms that consume plants. The amount of carbon dioxide fixed in this fashion is tremendous. Although the amount varies among plants and from place to place throughout the world, it is estimated that an average of approximately 191 million metric tons of carbon dioxide is fixed daily. This means that about 466 million metric tons of organic dry matter is photosynthetically produced each day of the year.

The flux of oxygen out of and carbon dioxide into the plant is possible only because of the opening of the stomata. The stomatal mechanism is dependent on the flow of water through the plant, and the amount of water that passes through the plant in order to keep the stomata open is rather amazing. Studies have shown that for every kilogram of grain (such as corn) produced, as much as 600 kilograms of water will transpire through the stomata. This represents tremendous water loss and raises a very interesting question: What is the selective advantage of transpiration? In other words, why did plants evolve such a wasteful mechanism?

The most logical explanation is that water loss by transpiration is the price plants pay to absorb carbon dioxide, essential to the life of the plant. The stomatal mechanism evolved to supply this need, and the disadvantageous aspect of transpiration also resulted. There is the additional possibility that transpiration may serve some purpose beyond opening the stomata. Some mineral ions move from the roots to the shoots more easily in the transpiration stream. Perhaps this movement of mineral nutrients is an essential component of transpiration. Plant cell growth appears to be partially dependent on the existence of turgor pressure within the cell. Hence, the transpirational flow of water through the plant could supply the turgidity necessary for plant cell growth. Transpiration may also serve the same purpose in plants that perspiration does in humans—that is, to cool the leaf surface. The evaporation of water, combined with wind currents at the leaf surface, can help reduce high leaf temperatures caused by such factors as solar radiation and high air temperature.

Gas exchange and transpiration in plants are very dynamic and interrelated processes. A thorough knowledge of both processes and of the interaction between them could one day lead to increasing maximum crop production while decreasing the amount of water required for the process.

Bibliography

Aylor, Donald E., Jean-Yves Parlange, and A. D. Krikorian. "Stomatal Mechanics." *American Journal of Botany* 60 (1973): 163-171. An excellent technical paper that discusses the various parameters associated with the opening and closing of stomata. Complex technical articles are cited in the bibliography.
Campbell, Neil. *Biology.* 2d ed. Menlo Park, Calif.: Benjamin/Cummings, 1990. An

introductory college-level textbook for science majors. Chapter 32, "Transport in Plants," provides a clear, concise, and somewhat detailed description of water movement through plants. The well-written text, combined with superb graphics, furnishes the reader with a clear understanding of transpiration. List of suggested readings at the end of the chapter. Glossary.

Curtis, Helena, and N. Sue Barnes. *Biology*. 5th ed. New York: Worth, 1989. An introductory college-level textbook for science majors. Chapter 31, "Transport Process in Plants," provides an excellent discussion of stomatal action. Very readable text and well-done graphics make the process understandable even for the novice. List of suggested readings at the end of the chapter. Glossary.

Mansfield, T. A., and W. J. Davies. "Mechanisms for Leaf Control of Gas Exchange." *Bioscience* 35 (March, 1985) 158-164. A somewhat complex yet excellent article that discusses the function of stomata. Complex technical articles are cited in the bibliography.

Raven, P. H., P. F. Evert, and S. E. Eichorn. *Biology of Plants*. 4th ed. New York: Worth, 1986. An introductory college-level textbook for science students. Chapter 23, "The Shoot: Primary Structure and Development," provides an excellent discussion of leaf structure. The profusely illustrated text furnishes an excellent pictorial study of stomatal arrangement within the leaf. Glossary.

Salisbury, Frank B., and Cleon Ross. *Plant Physiology*. 3d ed. Belmont, Calif.: Wadsworth, 1985. An intermediate college-level textbook for science students. Chapter 3, "The Photosynthesis—Transpiration Compromise," gives an in-depth view of the physiological role of gas exchange. An excellent explanation of the process is provided in text and graphics. Contains detailed bibliography for each chapter.

Schulze, E. D., R. H. Robichaux, J. Grace, P. W. Rundel, and J. R. Ehleringer. "Plant Water Balance." *Bioscience* 37 (January, 1987): 30-37. Discusses the various evolutionary adaptions that plants have made to keep water loss at a minimum. Complex technical articles are cited in the bibliography.

Stern, K. R. *Introductory Plant Biology*. Dubuque, Iowa: Wm. C. Brown, 1988. An introductory college-level textbook for science or nonscience students. Chapter 9, "Water in Plants: Soils," provides a very good general discussion of the control of transpiration. Very readable text applicable to the nonscience student. Suggested readings at the end of each chapter. Glossary.

D. R. Gossett

Cross-References

Gas Exchange in Animals, 1069; The Greenhouse Effect, 1225; Life's Effect on Earth, 1589; Liquid Transport Systems in Plants, 1613; Osmosis, Free Diffusion, and Facilitated Diffusion, 2022; Photorespiration, 2059; Root Uptake Systems, 2430; The Water Cycle, 2695.

GEL ELECTROPHORESIS AND BLOTTING

Type of life science: Genetics
Other fields of study: Biochemistry and molecular biology

Gel electrophoresis and blotting provide a rapid method for the separation and purification of biological molecules. The techniques also form part of the methods used to identify and sequence genes, which have revolutionized the life sciences.

Principal terms

BLOTTING: a method for retrieving a band or spot of molecules from an electrophoretic gel

CHARGE DENSITY: the number of charges per unit of surface area on a molecule

GEL ELECTROPHORESIS: a method for separating molecules by their relative abilities to move through a gellike medium in response to an imposed electric charge

NORTHERN BLOT: a blotting technique that removes RNA molecules from electrophoretic gels

ONE-DIMENSIONAL GEL ELECTROPHORESIS: separation of molecules in a single dimension or direction using a single tube or slab gel

SLAB GEL: an electrophoretic gel cast in the form of a flat sheet between glass plates

SOUTHERN BLOT: a blotting technique that removes DNA molecules from electrophoretic gels

TUBE GEL: an electrophoretic gel cast in the form of a cylinder in a glass or plastic tube

TWO-DIMENSIONAL GEL ELECTROPHORESIS: separation of molecules in two dimensions or directions using two successive gels

WESTERN BLOT: a blotting technique that removes protein molecules from electrophoretic gels

Summary of the Methodology

Many types of investigations in genetics, biochemistry, molecular and cell biology, and other fields require the separation and purification of molecules or the determination of molecular weight. Gel electrophoresis is widely used for these purposes because the technique uses relatively inexpensive equipment and is easy to learn and apply. The method allows rapid and precise separation of molecules ranging in size from short polypeptide and nucleic acid chains to large proteins. A group of techniques collectively known as "blotting" provides a ready means for the collection and identification of molecules separated by gel electrophoresis.

The gel electrophoresis apparatus uses an electrical field to move molecules through a viscous, gellike medium. Variations in the rate at which different molecules move through the gel provide the means for their precise and sensitive separation. The gels used in the apparatus are cast as a cylinder encased in a glass or plastic tube, or as a slab sandwiched between flat glass or plastic plates. For the separation of proteins, gels are usually cast from a plastic, polyacrylamide; for the separation of nucleic acids, gels are cast from agarose, a complex carbohydrate molecule extracted from seaweed. The gel takes the form of a molecular network with openings not much larger than the molecules being separated. The smaller passages in the polyacrylamide gel network are the correct size for the movement of proteins but are too small for the successful separation of nucleic acid molecules, for which the larger openings in the agarose network are ideal.

A tube or slab gel is placed in the electrophoresis apparatus, held in its glass or plastic cast so that its ends are immersed in separate salt solutions. The salt solutions, by virtue of their ion content, are able to conduct electricity. The positive electrode of a power source is placed in the salt solution at one end of the gel, and the negative electrode in the solution at the opposite end. When the power is turned on, a current flows from one electrode through the gel to the other electrode. A solution of charged molecules placed in the gel will move toward the positive or negative end of the gel in response to attraction or repulsion by the + or − electrodes—negatively charged molecules toward the + end of the gel, and positively charged molecules toward the − end. Assuming that the current applied to the gel is held constant, the rate or speed at which different molecules move depends on the interaction of three factors: molecular size, molecular shape, and a characteristic known as charge density.

Molecules migrate through the gel according to their ability to thread through the openings in the gel network. Larger molecules, therefore, thread through the openings more slowly, since they encounter more resistance to their passage, and smaller molecules pass through the openings more rapidly. Molecular shape has a similar effect on the rate of migration. Molecules with compact, spherical shapes move through the gel openings most rapidly; those with more extended elliptical or fibrillar forms become entangled in the gel network to a greater extent and move more slowly. The greater the difference in shape from a compact, spherical form, the more slowly the molecule moves through the gel. The third factor affecting the rate of movement, charge density, refers to the number of positive or negative charges per unit of surface area on a molecule. The higher the charge density, the more rapidly a molecule tends to move toward the end of the gel with opposite charge, subject to the restrictions of size and shape. Uncharged molecules will not migrate toward either electrode, and therefore remain stationary in the gel. The charge density of many biological molecules, particularly proteins, varies according to the degree of acidity (pH) of the solution containing them. For this reason, the pH of the solutions used in the gel electrophoresis apparatus must be closely controlled by the addition of buffers, which compensate for local changes in acidity and maintain the pH at a constant value that is selected by the investigator.

In operation of the gel electrophoresis apparatus, a mixture of the molecules to be separated is carefully placed in a layer at one end of the gel. Usually, this is accomplished by taking up a solution of the molecules in a hypodermic syringe and slowly releasing the molecules from the needle onto the top of the gel. A dye is often added to the solution to make it visible and allow the formation of the layer to be observed. Slab gels are wide enough to allow several samples to be placed at separate locations along the top of the gel and run simultaneously. After the molecules to be separated are layered on the gel, the solutions at the ends of the gel are then connected to the power source, with the electrodes placed so that the charge at the bottom of the gel is opposite that of the molecules of interest.

When the apparatus is turned on, the layered molecules move downward through the gel in response to the attractive charge. Because the relative rates at which individual molecular types move downward depends on their size, shape, and charge density, the different molecules gradually separate into a series of distinct bands moving at different rates through the gel. The bands containing the smallest molecules with the highest charge density and most compact shape move most rapidly and are spaced toward the bottom of the gel. Bands with larger molecules of lower charge density and less compact form are retarded and are spaced proportionally toward the top of the gel. In order to prevent the fastest moving bands from running off the gel, a dye molecule expected to move slightly faster than the smallest molecule of interest is mixed with the solution initially layered on the gel. The apparatus is turned off as the band containing the dye molecule, readily recognized because of its color, reaches the bottom of the gel.

Once separated, the bands of molecules are made visible or identified in various ways. Frequently, if the separated molecules are proteins or other molecules that take up colored dyes, the gels are stained with one of the dyes to reveal the positions of the bands. The proteins in individual bands may also be identified by radioactive labels or reaction with antibodies. Bands containing nucleic acids are identified by radioactive labels, or by reacting them with ethidium bromide, which emits visible light (fluoresces) when the bands are exposed to ultraviolet light. Under the ultraviolet light, which is invisible, the bands glow brightly and are easily recognized.

Individual bands are separated for further analysis by slicing the gels into sections, or by blotting. Blots are made by pressing slab gels against a piece of filter paper, selected or treated so that it is able to bind and immobilize the proteins or nucleic acids contained in the bands. For nucleic acids, a piece of filter paper containing a salt solution is placed on one side of the gel. A piece of nitrocellulose filter paper, on which the blot is to be formed, is placed on the other side, backed up by several sheets of dry filter paper; nitrocellulose is used because it can directly bind deoxyribonucleic acid (DNA). As the salt solution is drawn through the gel to the dry filter paper, it carries the molecules in the bands into the nitrocellulose paper, where the band is deposited as a blot. A blot of DNA bands produced in this way is called a "Southern" blot, after E. M. Southern, the investigator who originated the blotting technique for use with DNA. Essentially the same technique used to isolate ribonucleic acid (RNA) instead of DNA bands is called a "Northern" blot. Once the nucleic acid molecules are isolated in the blots, they can be identified or analyzed by a variety of techniques. The sample in a single blot can be isolated for chemical analysis simply by cutting the blot from the paper.

A more extensive modification is used to form blots of protein bands. A slab gel containing protein bands is placed on a piece of nitrocellulose filter paper and sandwiched between additional pieces of filter paper and two perforated plastic plates. Current is then applied across the plates. The current drives the proteins from the gel onto the nitrocellulose paper, producing the pattern of blots corresponding to the bands. A protein blot formed in this way is called a "Western" blot.

Applications of the Method

Gel electrophoresis is routinely used to separate crude mixtures of proteins or nucleic acids extracted from the cells into highly pure, individual samples. Because molecular size affects the rate at which molecules move through electrophoretic gels, the positions of the bands along the gel are often used to estimate relative molecular weight. The estimation is most accurate if the shape and charge density of the molecules under study is uniform. Nucleic acids satisfy this requirement nicely because each nucleotide in a nucleic acid chain carries a single negative charge. A mixture of DNA or RNA molecules therefore separates into distinct bands, primarily according to molecular weight, with the bands containing the smallest molecules located closest to the bottom of the gel. The method is sensitive enough to place nucleic acid molecules differing in molecular weight by the equivalent of only one nucleotide in separate bands.

The molecular weights of proteins are more difficult to determine by gel electrophoresis because proteins vary so widely in shape and charge density that these factors, rather than molecular size, are usually the primary determiners of the rate of migration. In order to increase the accuracy of molecular weight estimations, proteins are often reacted with a chemical that eliminates or reduces the effects of differences in shape and charge density. The chemical used for this purpose, sodium dodecyl sulfate (SDS), is a detergent that carries a negative charge. SDS attaches to the portions of protein molecules that contain hydrophobic amino acids, that is, amino acids that are more readily soluble in oily than in watery solutions. Because most proteins contain roughly similar numbers of hydrophobic amino acids, they bind approximately equivalent quantities of SDS. Many more SDS molecules are usually bound than the number of + or − charges naturally present on the protein, so that the natural charge of the protein is completely obscured. The coating of SDS gives the proteins a negative charge, in a density that is relatively uniform from one protein to another. As a result, native charge differences are eliminated as a source of variation in the rate of migration of proteins through electrophoretic gels.

The SDS coat also causes most proteins to unfold or unwind into an extended random shape, with a length that primarily reflects the length of the amino acid chain. The unfolding is promoted by the addition of mercaptoethanol to the solution, which breaks internal linkages (disulfide bonds) that hold many proteins in their native three-dimensional form. The treatment eliminates most of the differences in the rate of migration of proteins attributable to variations in native shape. With differences in native shape and charge density eliminated, the SDS-coated proteins migrate primarily according to differences in the length of their amino acid chains, which directly reflect their molecular weight.

Molecular weights are usually estimated by mixing several proteins of known molecular weight bracketing the proteins being separated by gel electrophoresis. After the proteins have been separated by the gel, the distance between the bands is measured and plotted in a graph against the logarithm of molecular weight (using the logarithm of the molecular weight transforms the plot into a straight line). The knowns allow the scale of the log plot to be fixed and allow a reasonably accurate estimate to be made of the molecular weights of the unknowns. Molecular weights determined in this way are frequently designated M_r, indicating that the figure given is an estimate made relative to a known molecular weight used as a standard.

The ability of gel electrophoresis to separate nucleic acid molecules that differ in length by only a single nucleotide forms the basis for several methods used to sequence DNA. Copies of a DNA sequence are broken by chemical techniques into fragments of different lengths that end in a particular base. The fragments are then separated according to length by gel electrophoresis, with longer fragments located toward the top of the gel. Because the base at the end of each fragment can be identified, the sequence of the DNA molecule used to make the fragments can be read directly from the bottom to the top of the gel.

Running electrophoretic gels through a single gel, by the methods described up to this point, is termed "one-dimensional" because the proteins are separated into bands along a single direction. One-dimensional gel electrophoresis is sometimes unable to separate proteins into distinct bands, particularly if the mixture contains a large number of proteins of closely similar size and shape. This problem is successfully circumvented by a variation of the method known as two-dimensional (2D) gel electrophoresis. In the 2D technique, a mixture of proteins is first run in native form, without exposure to SDS, in a tube gel containing ampholytes. Ampholytes are chainlike molecules containing different numbers of positive and negative charges. The individual ampholyte molecules migrate according to charge in the gel, sorting out into an even gradient with the most negative located toward the + end of the tube and the most positive toward the − end. Each protein added to the gel migrates until it reaches a level at which the charges carried by the ampholytes exactly balance and neutralize its native charges. At this point, the protein becomes uncharged and remains in position because it is not attracted to either the + or − end of the gel. Eventually all the proteins reach levels at which their charges are neutralized and they remain as stationary bands. Concentration of the proteins into stationary bands by this method is called isoelectric focusing. The tube gel containing the focused bands is the first dimension; in mixtures containing large numbers of different proteins, many of the bands in the tube gel are likely to contain more than one protein.

The tube gel is then removed from the apparatus and soaked in a solution containing SDS and mercaptoethanol. The soak unwinds the proteins in the bands and gives them a uniformly negative charge coat. The tube gel is then placed on its side along the top of a slab gel. Current is applied so that the bottom of the slab gel is given a positive charge, causing the SDS-coated proteins to move from the bands in the tube gel into the slab. As they move, the proteins from each band of the tube gel separate into distinct groups according to molecular size. The migration produces a series of spots of proteins in the slab gel, distributed downward in straight rows originating from the bands in the tube gel. This distribution is the second dimension. The second dimension separates most or all the proteins of the sample into distinct and different spots. This happens because it is unlikely that different proteins focused into the same band in the first dimension because of an identical number of + and − charges will also have identical molecular weights. Applications of the 2D gel technique have allowed all the proteins of an entire bacterial cell or embryo to be separated into distinct and separate spots. The method is sensitive enough to produce separate bands or spots from proteins that are identical except for the presence or absence of a single phosphate group.

Context

Gel electrophoresis has become the primary method used in the life sciences to separate and purify proteins and nucleic acids. The method was developed partly as a solution to problems inherent in separating molecules by spinning them in a centrifuge. As molecules become smaller, the speeds required to spin them down become higher, and centrifugation times are greatly lengthened, often to a matter of days or even weeks. The centrifuges required for this precise and demanding work are so expensive that many institutions simply cannot afford them. The electrophoresis offers a simple alternative, using inexpensive equipment, that is able to separate the smallest molecules in a matter of hours. The method revolutionized the study of protein and nucleic acid molecules and paved the way for many of the most significant discoveries of cell and molecular biology.

This method is often the first step used in identifying the protein components present in biological structures. Once separated and identified, usually by number designating their relative molecular weight, the proteins can be subjected to physical and biochemical tests designed to reveal their structure and function. The identity, structure, and function of many cellular proteins have been worked out in this way.

Gel electrophoresis has also provided a means to follow modifications made to proteins as a part of regulatory mechanisms acting in the cell. The ability of gel electrophoresis to separate two versions of a protein differing only in the presence or absence of a phosphate group, for example, has revealed that the activity of many proteins is controlled by phosphorylation and has permitted both the active and inactive forms to be separately identified and purified.

More significant than any of these applications, however, has been the use of electrophoretic gels as a means for the rapid sequencing of DNA molecules.

Sequencing DNA molecules on electrophoretic gels is much more rapid than previous methods, which involved a laborious chemical analysis of fragments of nucleotide chains in complex procedures that literally required years to accomplish for even relatively short molecules. The gel techniques have reduced sequencing relatively short molecules to a matter of hours, and made feasible projects such as the sequencing of the entire human DNA complement. Many individual genes have now been sequenced, and the sequence differences between mutated and normal forms of genes have been identified. The control sequences responsible for turning genes on and off have also been located by the sequencing methods. Once the coding portion of a gene is sequenced, it is a relatively simple matter to deduce the amino sequence of the protein encoded in the gene. The ready availability of gene and protein sequences has been of incalculable value to research in the life sciences and is one of the most significant factors underlying the molecular revolution in biology and medicine.

The relative ease of sequencing normal and defective genes and proteins has also paved the way for genetic engineering—replacing defective genes with normal ones or adding desirable genes to domestic plants or animals. The development of these techniques will undoubtedly lead to further revolutions in medicine and agriculture, including the possible cure of hereditary defects that have plagued the human population since its beginnings.

Bibliography

Alberts, Bruce, Dennis Bray, Julian Lewis, Martin Raff, Keith Roberts, and James D. Watson. *Molecular Biology of the Cell*. 2d ed. New York: Garland, 1989. Chapter 4, "How Cells are Studied," includes a description of the gel electrophoresis technique and many of its modifications, including its use in the analysis and sequencing of nucleic acids. The text is clearly written at the college level and is illustrated by numerous diagrams and photographs.

Andrews, A. T. *Electrophoresis*. 2d ed. Oxford, England: Clarendon Press, 1986. A technical but readable book that provides a description of the development, theory, and practice of gel electrophoresis. Extensive diagrams are included that illustrate the principles discussed in the text.

Darnell, James, Harvey Lodish, and David Baltimore. *Molecular Cell Biology*. New York: Scientific American Books, 1986. Chapter 7, "Tools of Molecular Cell Biology," provides an excellent description of gel electrophoresis (pages 232-234), Southern and Northern blotting (pages 243-245), and DNA sequencing techniques (pages 246-248). Many highly illustrative diagrams and photographs are included.

Karp, Gerald. *Cell Biology*. 2d ed. New York: McGraw-Hill, 1979. Pages 179-180 and 840-843 describe the gel electrophoresis technique, including both one- and two-dimensional gel electrophoresis. The text, written at the college level, includes diagrams of the apparatus and its operation and photographs of gels.

Sanger, Frederick. "Determinating of Nucleotide Sequences in DNA." *Science* 214

(1981): 1205-1210. A technical but easily understood article describing the development of techniques using electrophoretic gels to sequence DNA, written by a scientist that developed one of the two methods now in use.

Watson, J. D., J. Tooze, and D. T. Kurtz. *Recombinant DNA: A Short Course*. New York: W. H. Freeman, 1983. A clearly and simply written book that is a basic textbook as well as providing a description of methods used in molecular biology. DNA sequencing is described on pages 61-63, and blotting techniques on pages 83-84. Many informative diagrams are included.

Stephen L. Wolfe

Cross-References

Autoradiography and Subcellular Fractionation of Radioactive Tracer Molecules, 148; Cloning to Produce Recombinant DNA, 505; DNA Sequencing, 698; Gene Therapy, 1128; Genes and Nucleic Acids, 1134; The Genetic Code, 1148; Nucleic Acid Structure, 1987; Proteins, 2272; Subcellular Fractionation Using Centrifugation, 2552.

GENE AMPLIFICATION AND DELETION

Type of life science: Genetic regulation in eukaryotes
Other fields of study: Genetics and molecular biology

Some specialized cells and tissues show amplification of specific genes or whole chromosomes, while others lose certain genes in their development. These unusual changes in genetic material may provide glimpses into how evolution works.

Principal terms

DELETION: the removal of a portion of a gene or chromosome, usually through unequal crossing over in meiosis, or the removal of a portion of the germ line genome of a species through chromosome fragmentation in somatic cells

DOMAIN: a compact, folded part of the structure of a protein molecule that is usually stable structurally if separated from the rest of the protein

ENDOREDUPLICATION: multiple duplications of chromosomes that remain within the same cell in parallel association with one another; best known from larval salivary gland chromosomes of the fruit fly *Drosophila*

EXON: a sequence of DNA base pairs that is expressed in the protein encoded for by the gene; each exon frequently codes for a separate domain in the protein

FRAGMENTATION: the breakdown of chromosomes into pieces either to get rid of some of the genome's DNA or to produce nucleolar organizing regions

GENE AMPLIFICATION: differential replication of a particular gene or genes while the rest of the chromosome remains unreplicated; best known through oocyte rDNA replication in amphibians and insects

INTRON: a sequence of DNA base pairs that is not expressed in the protein encoded for by the gene

MULTIGENE FAMILY: a group of homologous genes with similar functions, apparently arising as a result of duplication of a gene and subsequent mutation of duplicated genes

POLYTENE CHROMOSOME: a chromosome that has up to thousands of replicated copies of the same chromosome that have stayed associated with one another in the same cell; most widely known from the salivary gland chromosomes in *Drosophila* (fruit flies)

SUPERGENE FAMILY: a set of multigene families and associated single genes that are related in their DNA sequences but not necessarily in function

TANDEM GENE DUPLICATION: duplication of a gene so that the two copies are located with one right after the other on the same chromosome; it occurs because of unequal crossing over in meiosis

Summary of the Phenomenon

The central hypothesis of developmental genetics says that cell differentiation occurs without loss or alteration of the genetic material in the cells. Thus, even though a neuron, a muscle cell, and a skin cell of a human look very different and carry out separate functions, they all contain the same genetic information, with different genes being expressed in the various kinds of cells.

While in most cases genetic information seems to remain constant throughout differentiation, exceptions to the theory of genetic constancy have been found in numerous animal tissues. Examples of chromosome endoreduplication, gene amplification, deletion of genetic information, and specific rearrangement of genetic information have been found. In many cases, these changes have been seen in somatic cells — cells of the body that are not involved in the formation of the next generation of organisms. In some instances, it can be shown that genes with similar or different functions have the same nucleotide base sequences. This indicates that they are derived from a single "parent gene" that was duplicated and that subsequently changed and developed into different genes. These duplicated genes can apparently act as the raw material for the evolution of the species.

Examination of larval tissues of certain insects, such as fruit flies, shows massive endoreduplication of each chromosome into polytene chromosomes, in which the chromosomes have divided many times without an accompanying division of the cells. The resultant chromosomes may have a thousand or more copies of the deoxyribonucleic acid (DNA) lined up parallel to one another. They are large enough to be seen easily in a microscope, and the chromosome banding patterns are closely similar in all the different larval tissues that have such chromosomes. It is interesting that the polytene chromosomes are found in terminal tissues, which die off as the larval insect goes through metamorphosis to become an adult. The cells that will become adult tissues do not form polytene chromosomes, but apparently keep a single copy of the DNA in each chromosome.

In some organisms there are hundreds or thousands of copies of the same genes in the cells of certain tissues, with the same sequence of nucleotide bases appearing in each copy. This seems to indicate that there is some sort of mechanism that picks one gene from this multigene family and copies it many times to replace possible mutations that may arise in the normal course of replication of genetic information. Even mutations that would be silent and have no effect are eliminated in this way. An example of this kind of duplication and amplification of a multigene family is seen in the genes for production of ribosomal ribonucleic acid (rRNA), particularly in some amphibian oocytes. The rRNA is needed for the formation of ribosomes, the cellular factories for protein synthesis, during the production of the egg cell. Since many proteins must be made for storage in the egg, many ribosomes are needed in a very short period of time. Although there are already multiple copies of the genes for rRNA in the genome, there are not enough for this production process. The solution to the immediate need is to amplify the genes for rRNA even further, until there may be fifty thousand copies of the same gene. This amplification also occurs in the rRNA genes needed in the formation of the chorion (eggshell) membrane in the eggs of some insects. It occurs as well in some protozoa, such as *Paramecium*, when some genes in the micronucleus are amplified to make a macronucleus that will control the metabolic needs of this very complex single-celled organism.

In other cases, certain tissues make multiple copies of the same gene from a single copy that was present in the zygote. Cells which are producing vast quantities of a single particular protein in a short period of time may do this through selective amplification of the gene for that protein. Gene amplification can also be artificially induced in response to environmental stress, as in cells grown in culture with the metabolic poison methotrexate. Those cells that continue to live and reproduce in the presence of the poison already had extra sets of genes for dihydrofolate reductase (DHFR). Duplication of this particular gene can occur once in every thousand cells and is selected for by the poison. This artificial induction of amplified genes can be applied in a stepwise fashion, by increasing the amount of methotrexate, to raise the number of DHFR genes from one per haploid genome to as many as a thousand copies of the gene. These extra gene sets can be stable, if they are present on the normal (but lengthened) chromosomes, or unstable, if they are present as tiny "double minute chromosomes"—genetic material with no centromere and so no guarantee of being passed to the next generation of cells in mitosis.

The deletion of genetic information from somatic cells also occurs in some species. A nematode (roundworm) studied at the beginning of the twentieth century has two chromosomes per haploid set (so a diploid cell has four chromosomes) in the germ line. These cells will eventually produce the eggs and sperm in the worm. When the fertilized ovum goes through its first cleavage division, one pole of the embryo keeps the germ line chromosomes, while the other pole begins to lose genetic information. The ends of the chromosomes at the second pole fragment to form dozens of tiny pieces that are lost in later cell divisions. These cells become the somatic cells, the body cells that carry on the metabolic processes of the worm. Only the cells that are part of the germ line (that will form the next generation) maintain all the genetic information of the species. This process of chromatin loss is called chromosome diminution, since the chromosomes are diminished in size by the fragmentation and loss of their ends.

A small fly called a midge also eliminates much of its chromatin in most of its cells. Most of its cell nuclei lose thirty-two of their forty original chromosomes in embryonic cell divisions shortly after fertilization. Two nuclei at one pole of the embryo retain all their chromosomes and become the source of the germ line cells. The other cells lose chromosomes. As in the nematode, the eliminated chromatin contains genes that specify the production of the germ cells and are not needed by the somatic cells.

Methods of Study

The idea that all cells in a multicellular organism contain the same basic complement of genetic information has several lines of argument to support it. Banding patterns in cells of different tissues in various kinds of organisms remain constant throughout development, with no loss of bands. DNA extracted from different tissues of the same organism show the same number of gene copies, so genes are not lost in tissue differentiation. Embryological studies have shown that cell nuclei or whole cells may remain totipotent despite being many cell generations away from the zygote, the original fertilized ovum from which all other cells of the organism develop.

Early studies of embryological development showed the loss of chromosomes by fragmentation in the nematode. This was visible in the early 1900's by light microscopy. Similar studies using light microscopy showed the presence of polytene chromosomes in fruit fly larvae and the loss of chromosomes in the embryo of the midge.

More modern biochemical methods have been used to show the presence of single or multiple copies of the DNA of a particular gene in different tissues. One method used is nucleic acid hybridization, in which radioactive RNA is made and used to bind to single-stranded DNA of a cell to show the presence of the gene that codes for the RNA. This can show the amplification of a particular gene for which the RNA is known. Gene cloning is another modern technique that allows the purification and amplification of a specific region of DNA. This can be used to provide the RNA for use in nucleic acid hybridization. The Southern blotting technique of attaching DNA to a nitrocellulose (blotting paper) filter is also used to determine if a gene is located in a cell and how many copies there are. The Northern blotting technique does the same with RNA and can be used to show when a gene is being used in development.

Techniques of growing cells in tissue culture are important in the study of gene amplification and deletion. Cells grown in culture with methotrexate have been mentioned, and the stepwise addition of more poison will allow the development of cells that have greatly amplified genes for DHFR, produced through artificial selection for survival. Cells of the immune system are grown in tissue culture for studies of the genetic changes that produce antibodies and T cells with different recombinations of genes. Multigene and supergene families have also been determined from cells grown in culture.

Context

Probably the most important aspect of the phenomena of the amplification and deletion of genetic information in a few organisms is that it points up the fact that, in most cases, genes are not changed as cells develop into their mature and differentiated forms. The "exceptions prove the rule" that the genome usually remains the same and it is only through the selective activation of genes that cell differences generally occur. Examination of the process of differentiation in developmental biology has brought to light many unusual ways of dealing with genetic information, from the need to duplicate chromosomes, amplify genes, or delete genes to the need to move genes around and modify the genome in certain cells. In most cases, the changes only occur in somatic cells, and the germ line cells are left as they were. In the amplification of genes, this usually occurs only in tissues that need a specific product in large quantities in a short time. Deletion of genes is a very uncommon occurrence.

The duplication of genes is important in the evolution of species, since the formation of a second copy of a gene allows the gene to keep its original function while the second copy is free to change and perhaps develop another function. This is seen in the formation of multigene families and supergene families of multiple copies from the same precursor gene that may have either the same or different functions. The process of gene amplification over evolutionary time may explain the presence of these gene families, groups of similar genes that are related to one another by their nucleotide base sequence but are not identical. These gene families tend to cluster in the same area of one or more chromosomes, arranged in tandem (head-to-tail) sequences that may be separated by stretches of spacer DNA. Such gene families probably are produced by tandem gene duplication, a process that seems to occur fairly frequently in all cells during DNA replication and recombination. If the duplication provides the organism with no selective advantage, it will tend to become lost. Once a gene has been duplicated, however, the extra copy is now available to mutate to perform a new function. The family of globin genes that are involved in hemoglobin production in vertebrates seems to have developed in this way. If the mutations that occur provide a new or better (or at least different) alternative function for the gene, it will be advantageous to the species, and natural selection will favor keeping both copies of the gene.

Similarly, introns and exons seen within eukaryotic genes may be the result of replications of gene segments that are then free to evolve through the accumulation of changes in the base sequence. Exons seem to be the information for production of individual domains of proteins, and they may be shuffled around to produce new combinations that result in new proteins that can serve different functions. An example is the presence of apparently the same exons in the receptor for low-density lipoprotein (LDL) and in epidermal growth factor (EGF). These molecules have very different functions, but at least a portion of the molecule is the same in each case. The development of the various antibody classes in vertebrates also seems to have occurred through duplication or amplification of exons that then produced slightly different proteins with different functions. The supergene family involved with the immune system is one of the most important groups of genes in the organism.

In addition to amplification and deletion of genetic material, an important reshuffling of genes occurs in the immune system. The movement and deletion of certain genes provides a reorganization of the genome. This allows the generation of a wide variety and specificity of antibodies and T cells that can respond to antigens of different types. This is another aspect of changing the genetic content of somatic cells that does not fit completely with the idea that all cells of an organism have the same genetic complement.

Alteration of the genome also occurs in some yeasts and parasitic protozoa. The mating type of yeast changes between two possible types through movement of the mating-type genes from one location to another. The protozoan that causes African sleeping sickness changes its genome to produce a different cell-surface antigenic type in order to avoid detection and elimination by the immune system of its host. The genome is amazing in its complexity and versatility.

Bibliography

Alberts, Bruce, Dennis Bray, Julian Lewis, Martin Raff, Keith Roberts, and James D. Watson. *Molecular Biology of the Cell*. 2d ed. New York: Garland, 1989. This upper-level textbook is well-organized, well-written, and very informative. While covering technical material in detail, it is not overwhelming. Chapter 15, "Germ Cells and Fertilization," and chapter 16, "Cellular Mechanisms of Development," cover topics of gene amplification and deletion. Numerous references are given at the end of each chapter.

Avers, Charlotte J. *Molecular Cell Biology*. Menlo Park, Calif.: Benjamin/ Cummings, 1986. This introductory text is geared to sophomore college students with some background in chemistry and biology, but it is clearly written and easily understandable. Gene amplification is covered in chapter 14, "Regulation of Gene Expression," and duplication of genes in evolution is covered in chapter 18, "Cellular and Molecular Evolution." Numerous references are supplied at the end of each chapter.

_____. *Process and Pattern in Evolution*. New York: Oxford University Press, 1989. This textbook on evolution may be read by the informed layman as well as by the college student. It covers the nature of split genes in chapter 4, "Some Evolutionary Themes in the Living World," and exon shuffling and genomic alterations in chapter 5, "Genetic Diversity." Each chapter has numerous references and additional readings.

Darnell, James, Harvey Lodish, and David Baltimore. *Molecular Cell Biology*. New York: Scientific American Books, 1986. This is an upper-level textbook that provides well-written detailed coverage of amplified genes in chapter 9, "RNA Synthesis and Processing in Eukaryotes," of development in chapter 22, "Development of Cell Specificity," and of evolution in chapter 25, "Evolution of Cells." Along with excellent illustrations, it provides very thorough information on the methods used in research in this area. A long list of references appears at the end of each chapter.

Gilbert, Scott F. *Developmental Biology*. 2d ed. Sunderland, Mass.: Sinauer Associates, 1988. An excellent college text on embryology and development in animals, this book provides material on amplification and deletion in several locations. Chapters 9 and 10 discuss genomic equivalence and differential gene expression at the embryological and molecular levels. Techniques are particularly stressed. Other chapters contain mention of these topics as well. Chapter 22, "The Saga of the Germ Line," discusses the differences between somatic and germ cells. Literature is cited at the end of each chapter.

Pritchard, D. J. *Foundations of Developmental Genetics*. London: Taylor & Francis, 1986. Topics of interest in this British book are covered in chapter 3, "Embryonic Induction," chapter 7, "Unstable Differentiation," chapter 9, "RNA," and chapter 15, "An Epigenetic Theory of Evolution." The text contains numerous illustrations and an extensive bibliography at the end of each chapter.

Stryer, Lubert. *Biochemistry*. 3d ed. New York: W. H. Freeman, 1988. Gene duplication is covered very briefly in chapter 5, "Flow of Genetic Information," then more thoroughly later in chapter 33, "Eukaryotic Chromosomes and Gene Expression." Selected readings appear at the end of each chapter.

Watson, James D., Nancy H. Hopkins, Jeffery W. Roberts, Joan A. Steitz, and Alan M. Weiner. *Molecular Biology of the Gene*. 4th ed. Menlo Park, Calif.: Benjamin/Cummings, 1987. The first volume of this two-volume set covers eukaryotic chromosomes in chapters 20 and 21. The second volume contains chapter 22, "The Molecular Biology of Development," and chapter 23, "The Generation of Immunological Specificity," which cover information discussed in this article. The text is very thorough and may be difficult to follow for some readers. Emphasis is placed on the experimental evidence for currently accepted theories of gene action, so some areas are quite technical. Numerous references to original research articles are listed.

Jean S. Helgeson

Cross-References

DNA's Molecular Structure, 706; Eukaryotic Post-transcriptional Control, 880; Positive and Negative Eukaryotic Transcriptional Control, 895; Genes and Nucleic Acids, 1134; The Genetic Code, 1148; Nucleic Acid Structure, 1987; Prokaryotic Transcriptional Control: Attenuation, 2227; Negative Prokaryotic Transcriptional Control, 2234; Positive Prokaryotic Transcriptional Control, 2242; Translation of Messenger RNA to Form Protein, 2647.

GENE FLOW

Type of life science: Evolutionary biology
Other fields of study: Anthropology, ecology, and genetics

In biology, "migration" refers to the movement of a member or many members of a species of animal or plant from one geographic location to another. If other members of the same species interbreed with the migrating species, either along the way or in the new location, an exchange of genes occurs. Biologists call this exchange "gene flow" and consider it to be fundamental to the evolutionary process.

Principal terms
ALLELE: one of a group of genes that occurs alternately at a given locus
DEME: a local population of closely related living organisms
FOSSIL: a remnant, impression, or trace of an animal or plant of a past geologic age that has been preserved in the earth's crust
GENE POOL: the whole body of genes in an interbreeding population that includes each gene at a certain frequency in relation to other genes
MUTATION: a relatively permanent change in hereditary material involving either a physical change in chromosome relations or a biochemical change in the codons that make up genes
POPULATION: a grouping of interacting individuals of the same species
SPECIATION: the process whereby some members of a species become incapable of breeding with the majority and thus form a new species
SPECIES: a category of biological classification ranking immediately below the genus or subgenus, comprising related organisms or populations capable of interbreeding

Summary of the Phenomenon

Prior to the nineteenth century, religious dogmatism retarded the activities of most scientists investigating the origins and nature of life by insisting on the immutability of species created by God. Despite mounting fossil evidence that many species of flora and fauna that once inhabited the earth had disappeared and that many extant species could not be found in the fossil record, pre-nineteenth century naturalists could find no viable explanation (other than divine intervention) for the disappearance of life-forms and their replacement by other forms. Then, in 1859, Charles Darwin published his epochal *On the Origin of Species*, which proposed the theory that all contemporary life-forms have evolved from simpler forms through a process he called "natural selection."

Many individuals before Darwin had proposed theories of evolution, but Darwin's became the first to be widely accepted by the scientific community. His success resulted from the careful and objective presentation of an overwhelming amount of evidence showing that species can and do change, and his concurrent promulgation of a convincing explanation of the mechanism that produces that change—natural selection. Since Darwin, scientists have modified and added new concepts to his theory, especially concerning the ways in which species change (evolve) over time. One of those new concepts, which was only dimly understood in Darwin's lifetime, is the importance of genetics in evolution, especially the concepts of migration and gene flow.

Genes are elements within the germ plasm of a living organism that control the transmission of a hereditary characteristic by specifying the structure of a particular protein or by controlling the function of other genetic material. Within any breeding population of a species, the exchange of genes is constant among its members, ensuring genetic homogeneity. If a new gene or combination of genes appears in the population, it is rapidly dispersed among all members of the population through inbreeding. New alleles may be introduced into the gene pool of a breeding population (thus contributing to the evolution of that species) in two ways: mutation and migration. Gene flow is integral to both processes.

A mutation is the appearance of a new gene or the almost total alteration of an old one. The exact causes of mutations are not completely understood, but scientists have demonstrated that they can be caused by radiation. Mutations occur constantly in every generation of every species. Most of them, however, are either minor or detrimental to the survival of the individual and thus are of little consequence. A very few mutations may prove valuable to the survival of a species and are spread to all of its members by migration and gene flow.

When immigrants from one population interbreed with members of another, an exchange of genes between the populations ensues. If the exchange is recurrent, biologists call it "gene flow." In nature, gene flow occurs on a more or less regular basis between demes, geographically isolated populations, races, and even closely related species. Gene flow is more common among the adjacent demes of one species. The amount of migration between such demes is high, thus ensuring that their gene pools will be similar. This sort of gene flow contributes little to the evolutionary process, since it does little to alter gene frequencies or to contribute to variation within the species. Much more significant for the evolutionary process is gene flow between two populations of a species that have not interbred for a prolonged period of time.

Populations of a species separated by geographical barriers often develop very dissimilar gene combinations through the process of natural selection. In isolated populations, dissimilar alleles become fixed or are present in much different frequencies. When circumstances do permit gene flow to occur between two such populations, it results in the breakdown of gene complexes and the alteration of allele frequencies, thereby reducing genetic differences in both. The degree of this homogenization process depends on the continuation of interbreeding between members of the two populations over extended periods of time.

The migration of a few individuals from one breeding population to another may, in some instances, also be a significant source of genetic variation in the host population. Such migration becomes more important in the evolutionary process in direct proportion to the differences in gene frequencies—for example, the differences between sharply differentiated races or distinct species. Biologists call interbreeding between members of separate species or distinct races "hybridization." Hybridization usually does not lead to gene exchange or gene flow, because hybrids are not often well adapted for survival and because most are sterile. Nevertheless, hybrids are occasionally able to breed (and produce fertile offspring) with members of one or sometimes both the parent species, resulting in the exchange of a few genes or blocks of genes between two distinct species. Biologists refer to this process as "introgressive hybridization." Usually, few genes are exchanged between species in this process, and it might be more properly referred to as "gene trickle" rather than gene flow.

Introgressive hybridization may, however, add new genes and new gene combinations, or even whole chromosomes, to the genetic architecture of some species. It may thus play a role in the evolutionary process, especially in plants. Introgression requires the production of hybrids, a rare occurrence among highly differentiated animal species. Among closely related plant species, however, hybridization is common. Areas where hybridization takes place are known as contact zones or hybrid zones. These zones exist where populations overlap; in some cases of hybridization, the line between what constitutes different species and what constitutes different populations of the same species becomes difficult to draw. The significance of introgression and hybrid zones in the evolutionary process remains an area of some contention among life scientists.

Biologists often explain, at least in part, the poorly understood phenomenon of speciation through migration and gene flow—or rather, by a lack thereof. If some members of a species become geographically isolated from the rest of the species, migration and gene flow cease. The isolated population will not share in any mutations, favorable or unfavorable, nor will any mutations that occur among its own members be transmitted to the general population of the species. Over long periods of time, this genetic isolation will result in the isolated population becoming so genetically different from the parent species that its members can no longer produce fertile progeny should one of them breed with a member of the parent population. The isolated members will have become a new species, and the differences between them and the parent species will continue to grow as more ages pass. Scientists, beginning with Darwin himself, have demonstrated that this sort of speciation has occurred on the various islands of the world's oceans and seas.

Methods of Study

Scientists from many disciplines are currently studying migration and gene flow in a variety of ways. For decades, ornithologists and marine biologists have been placing identifying tags or markers on members of different species of birds, fishes, and marine mammals to determine the range of their migratory habits in order to understand the role of migration and subsequent gene flow in the biology of their subjects. These studies have led, and will continue to lead, to important discoveries. Most studies of migration and gene flow, however, relate to human beings.

Many physical anthropologists study ancient migrations of human populations to understand the evolution of *Homo sapiens* more fully. Through exhaustive examinations of fossil hominids, scientists are slowly untangling the complex origins of our species and its slow climb from subhuman beginnings, evidently in Africa. Researchers are investigating the dispersal of human blood groups in a further effort to understand past migrations. Other scientists are attempting to evaluate the effect of migration on the spread of agriculture and technology, two of the foundation blocks of the modern world. Some anthropologists are trying to ascertain the role of migration and gene flow in the origin of the various races of humankind and in the enormous variation among individual members of our species. Scientists involved in these studies assign primary roles in evolution to migration and gene flow. Medical researchers and epidemiologists are also seeking to understand human migration patterns in order to control the spread of communicable diseases. These and many other inquiries into migration and gene flow will continue to yield valuable information in the years ahead.

Many of the important discoveries concerning the role of gene flow in the evolution of life come from the continuing study of the nature of genes. A gene, in cooperation with such molecules as transfer ribonucleic acid (tRNA) and related enzymes, controls the nature of an organism by specifying amino acid sequences in specific functional proteins. In recent decades, scientists have discovered that what they previously believed to be single pure enzymes are actually groups of closely related enzymes, which they have named "isoenzymes" or "isozymes." Current theory holds that isozymes can serve the needs of a cell or of an entire organism more efficiently and over a wider range of environmental extremes than can a single enzyme. Biologists theorize that isozymes developed through gene flow between populations from climatic extremes and enhance the possibility of adaptation among members of the species when the occasion arises. The combination and recombination of isozymes passed from parent to offspring are apparently determined by DNA. Investigation into the role of DNA in evolution is one of the most promising avenues to an understanding of the nature of life.

Context

Further research into migration and gene flow promises to provide information indispensable to the attempt to unravel the mysteries of life. Coupled with the concept of mutation, gene flow is a crucial component of evolution. Gene flow may provide valuable information regarding genetic engineering. Future generations may be spared hereditary disease, mental deficiency, and a host of other undesirable inheritable traits.

Another potentially beneficial offshoot of research into migration and gene flow is the prevention of epidemic disease. Human migration of individuals and groups has contributed significantly to most of the major epidemics of history. The infamous Black Death, the plague that devastated Europe during the fourteenth century, traveled along the trade routes between India and the Mediterranean seaports, eventually killing between one-fourth and one-third of the people of Western Europe within a few decades. Western Europeans later brought a multitude of diseases with them to the Americas in the sixteenth century, which decimated the native populations. Diseases such as smallpox had as much to do with the virtual eradication of the Indian populations of North America as did the rapaciousness of the European colonists. The spread of AIDS in the late twentieth century has also been greatly affected by human migration patterns.

Ironically, migration and gene flow may also account for solutions to disease-related problems. A case in point is a malaria-resistant gene that apparently appeared through mutation in southeast Asia several thousand years ago. Because of the relative genetic isolation of that area, the gene has been slow to spread and is absent in many of the human populations in areas of high malarial infestation. The data concerning the malaria-resistant gene present an argument for the potential benefits of human genetic engineering, regardless of the moral and philosophical issues raised by that concept.

A classic example of the importance of understanding migration and gene flow in the animal kingdom is the spread of the so-called killer bees. In the 1950's, a species of ill-tempered African bee was accidentally released in South America. The African bees mated with the more docile wild bees in the area; through migration and gene flow, they transmitted their violent propensity to attack anything approaching their nests. As the African genes slowly migrated northward, they proved to be dominant. Although biologists knew enough about migration and gene flow to predict the approximate date of the arrival of the "berserker" gene in the United States, their efforts to forestall it were unsuccessful. Some humans and many domestic and wild animals have been stung to death by angry bees. The African gene is expected to have a detrimental effect on the honey and beeswax industries as well as on important pollenization enterprises.

A fuller understanding of migration and gene flow is an important piece in the puzzle of evolution and life itself. Most humans wonder who they are and what their place and purpose in the universe might be. Understanding the evolutionary process may provide part of the answer to those most fundamental questions, and understanding migration and gene flow will help unravel evolution's mysteries.

Bibliography

Ammerman, A. J., and L. L. Cavalli-Sforza. *The Neolithic Transition and the Genetics of Populations in Europe*. Princeton, N.J.: Princeton University Press, 1984. This book is rather technical in its language, but it presents a thoughtful discussion of the influence of migration and gene flow on the Neolithic revolution and the complex workings of gene flow on human evolution.

Clegg, E. J., and J. P. Garlick, eds. *Disease and Urbanization*. Atlantic Highlands, N.J.: Humanities Press, 1981. Clegg and Garlick's book contains a number of articles dealing with the nature and results of urban-rural migration, with special reference to its role in causing and transmitting diseases. Most of the articles do use some technical language.

Crow, J. F., and Motoo Kimura. *An Introduction to Population Genetics*. New York: Harper & Row, 1970. An excellent starting place for those whose knowledge of migration and gene flow and their influence on evolution is limited and who wish to learn more about the subject. The book is relatively free of the technical jargon that can make some biological texts difficult for the nonbiologist.

Endler, John A. *Geographic Variation, Speciation, and Clines*. Princeton, N.J.: Princeton University Press, 1977. Endler's book is valuable primarily because of an excellent chapter on gene flow and its influence on the evolutionary process. Endler sees evolution as a very slow and gradual process in which gene flow and small mutations cause massive change over long periods of time.

Mascie-Taylor, C. G. N., and G. W. Lasker, eds. *Biological Aspects of Human Migration*. Cambridge, England: Cambridge University Press, 1988. The articles in this book present a precise summary of knowledge concerning the study of migration and gene flow in contemporary and ancient human populations and their impact on human evolution. Many of the articles contain some jargon, but they are well worth reading.

Mourant, A. E. *The Distribution of Human Blood Groups*. Oxford: Blackwell, 1954. This is the most comprehensive work available on the influence of migration and gene flow on the distribution of blood groups in contemporary human populations. The language is often technical, but the implications of blood groups for understanding the dynamics of evolution are thoroughly examined.

Raup, D. M., and D. Jablonski, eds. *Patterns and Processes in the History of Life*. New York: Springer-Verlag, 1986. Raup and Jablonski's book is a compilation of articles from the Dahlem workshop, "Patterns and Processes in the History of Life," held in Berlin in 1985. The articles in the book discuss the evidence concerning the role of migration and gene flow in the evolutionary process. Thought-provoking.

Smith, Fred H., and Frank Spencer, eds. *The Origins of Modern Humans: A World Survey of the Fossil Evidence*. New York: A. R. Liss, 1984. The most comprehensive work available on the fossil evidence for migration and gene flow among ancient hominid populations and their influence on human evolution.

Paul Madden

Cross-References

The Biosphere, Biomes, and Habitats, 210; Demographics, 597; Ecological Niches, 729; Ecological Principles, 736; Evolution: A Historical Perspective, 903; Punctuated Equilibrium versus Continuous Evolution, 926; The Hardy-Weinberg Law of Genetic Equilibrium, 1262; Speciation and the Species Concept, 2521.

GENE MUTATION AND REPAIR

Types of life science: Genetics and molecular biology
Other field of study: Biochemistry

Gene mutations are changes in the nucleotide sequence of the DNA molecule caused by environmental conditions or by cellular mistakes. Some mutations can damage cells and threaten life itself. Cells possess enzymes that can correct certain mutations, however, thereby reducing their effects upon the organism.

Principal terms

AUXOTROPH: a mutant organism that needs a particular nutritional ingredient in its diet for proper growth

DEFICIENCY: the removal of a large section of a chromosome resulting in the loss of genes that encode essential cell proteins

DUPLICATION: the addition of a large block of genes to a chromosome, often an exact replica of another section of the same chromosome

FRAMESHIFT: a mutation within a gene in which a nucleotide base pair is added or deleted, causing the amino acid reading frame to be changed

MISSENSE: a mutation within a gene in which an incorrect nucleotide base pair is inserted, causing a single incorrect amino acid in the encoded protein

MUTAGEN: a substance that produces mutations in deoxyribonucleic acid (DNA), including physical factors such as X rays and chemicals such as benzene

NONDISJUNCTION: the failure of paired chromosomes to separate during meiosis, resulting in an extra or missing chromosome per cell in the affected individual

PHOTOREACTIVATION: a process in both prokaryotic and eukaryotic cells by which certain enzymes repair mutations in DNA when exposed to visible light

REVERSION: a reverse mutation that negates a gene mutation, thereby returning the gene to its normal, or "wild-type," state

TRANSLOCATION: the movement of a large block of genes from one chromosome to another chromosome

Summary of the Phenomenon

A gene mutation is a change in the nucleotide sequence of deoxyribonucleic acid (DNA), the genetic material in all living organisms. The DNA molecule consists of two parallel polynucleotide chains, each chain consisting of millions of nucleotides. Each nucleotide consists of a phosphate, a sugar, and one of four nitrogenous bases:

adenine (A), guanine (G), cytosine (C), and thymine (T). A nucleotide on one DNA chain pairs with a complementary nucleotide on the second DNA chain. A nucleotide bearing the nitrogenous base adenine always pairs with a nucleotide bearing thymine. Similarly, a cytosine nucleotide always pairs with a guanine nucleotide.

A DNA molecule can have hundreds of millions of consecutive nucleotide pairs, thus making DNA an enormous molecule. Coupled with protein support, this enormous DNA molecule is called a chromosome. A small region of a chromosome, consisting of approximately a few thousand nucleotide base pairs, is called a gene. The order of nucleotide base pairs in a gene determines its information content— that is, its genetic code. The enzyme RNA polymerase reads the nucleotide base sequence of a gene in order to manufacture a complementary ribonucleic acid (RNA) molecule.

RNA is much like DNA, except that it is a single polynucleotide chain and uses the nitrogenous base uracil (U) instead of thymine. The multienzyme ribosome reads the RNA base sequence to manufacture a specific protein. Proteins accelerate chemical reactions and provide structure within living cells. A protein is a long chain of amino acids, with each amino acid being encoded by every group of three consecutive nucleotide bases (called a codon) on RNA. Therefore, the cell uses the inherited DNA molecule, or gene, as information to produce RNA, which is used as information to produce a long chain of amino acids called a protein. Therefore, a gene (DNA) encodes RNA, which encodes protein. A mutation is a change in the nucleotide sequence of DNA for a given gene. Thus, a change in a gene's nucleotide sequence will lead to a change in the corresponding RNA nucleotide sequence, which will lead to a change in the protein's amino acid sequence.

The change in the protein's amino acid sequence may affect how the protein functions in the cell, depending upon whether the affected amino acids are critical for proper functioning of the protein. Even if the affected amino acids completely disable the protein, however, that particular protein may not necessarily be critical for the cell's survival. Consequently, many mutations do not seriously affect cell functions.

Nevertheless, a mutation that affects a critical amino acid of an essential protein can seriously damage or kill the cell, thereby crippling or killing the entire organism. Mutations cause various human genetic diseases, including cystic fibrosis, sickle-cell anemia, Tay-Sachs disease, Huntington's chorea, and a host of cancers.

Conversely, some mutations are beneficial, conferring distinct advantages upon the affected individual. In fact, every minute characteristic of every living organism is the result of mutation. The first living cell arose on Earth approximately 3.8 billion years ago; subsequently, it divided and eventually gave rise to billions of different species by the process of evolution—gradual changes in organisms over time caused by mutations that are passed along to the organisms' descendants. Evolution occurs by mutation and the environmental selection for favorable mutations, that is, those that help organisms to survive better. All humans are the products of billions of mutations accumulated by living cells. The uniqueness of each person is attributable to mutations affecting such things as hair color and height.

Environmental substances called mutagens cause mutations. These substances include chemicals such as benzene, 5-bromouracil, ethers, and hydrogen peroxide. Chemicals mutate DNA either by inserting themselves in place of a nucleotide or by preventing nucleotide base pairs (such as A-T, G-C) from pairing properly. The net result is misreading of the DNA by RNA polymerase, causing an errored RNA polynucleotide chain and subsequently an errored protein having one or many incorrect amino acids.

Mutagens also include high-frequency, low-wavelength radiations such as ultraviolet light, X rays, gamma rays, and cosmic radiation. The earth's atmospheric ozone layer shields life from most of these radiations, which originate from stars such as the Sun. These radiations, however, are present on Earth from various natural and man-made sources. Radiation can change the structure of DNA nucleotides, fuse nucleotides together, add nucleotides, or delete nucleotides. The result is mispairing of the DNA chains, thus changing the corresponding RNA and the amino acids of the encoded protein.

Mutagens can cause point mutations and chromosomal rearrangements. Point mutations include both missense and frameshift mutations. Missense mutations involve a single base change in the gene's nucleotide sequence, resulting in an incorrect RNA base, resulting in an incorrect amino acid for the encoded protein. Frameshift mutations involve shifts in the reading sequence of the DNA nucleotide bases. A famous frameshift mutation is the thymine dimer, in which ultraviolet radiation fuses two consecutive thymines together. When RNA polymerase reads the DNA to make an RNA, it will see the thymine dimer (TT) as one base, resulting in an RNA which is one base short. Because every three consecutive bases in an RNA constitute a codon encoding an amino acid, this mutation would then cause the codons to be shifted by one base position, causing all further amino acids to be incorrectly added to the protein. The result is the synthesis of dysfunctional protein.

Cells can repair certain mutations, especially thymine dimers, by two chemical processes: photoreactivation and excision repair. In photoreactivation, a light-sensitive enzyme removes the thymine-thymine fusion when the cell is exposed to visible light, thus leaving the thymines unattached and allowing correct reading for making the corresponding RNA and protein. Excision repair occurs when the DNA chain bearing the thymine dimer is broken by an enzyme called an endonuclease. A second enzyme, called an exonuclease, digests the DNA piece containing the thymine dimer. A third enzyme, DNA polymerase, rebuilds the digested DNA chain correctly. This correction mechanism does not require light.

Besides mutations occurring because of environmental conditions, such as chemicals and radiation, some mutations naturally occur; these mutations may result from mistakes in DNA replications, RNA transcription, and the like. These naturally occurring mutations are called spontaneous mutations. Whether mutations are spontaneous or environmentally induced, they tend to concentrate in particular locations, termed hot spots, on the DNA molecule.

Occasionally, a reverse mutation, or reversion, occurs in a mutant gene at the exact site of the original mutation, thereby restoring the correct DNA sequence as well as the correct RNA and protein sequences. Suppression, which is very much like reversion, occurs when a second mutation happens in a mutant gene at a point other than the original mutation. The suppression mutation restores the DNA, RNA, and protein sequences enough to ensure proper protein function.

The accumulation of mutations in an individual over time may be responsible for the aging process, according to a major theory proposed by Leslie Orgel of the Salk Institute. Some aging research is focusing on cellular enzymes such as superoxide dismutase, which attacks chemical mutagens known as free radicals. While mutations may contribute to aging, they also have other effects upon the individual, ranging from minor conditions (such as freckles) to major ones (cancer). Mutagens that cause cancer are called carcinogens. Hereditary mutations in humans, such as physical traits (eye color, for example) as well as serious defects (cystic fibrosis), are transmitted to offspring and later descendants through the reproductive cells (sperm and egg).

Chromosomal rearrangements usually occur during meiosis, the process by which chromosomes are evenly distributed into the reproductive cells (sperm or egg). Rearrangement types include nondisjunction, translocation, inversion, deficiency, and duplication.

Nondisjunction occurs when chromosome pairs fail to separate during meiosis. Consequently, either the sperm or the egg may have an extra copy of a chromosome or may be missing a chromosome. When a sperm fertilizes an egg in such a situation, the resulting first cell, or zygote, and all cells that will make up the future individual will have either one or three copies of a particular chromosome type, whereas normal individuals have two copies of each type per cell. If the affected individual survives to birth (many do not), he or she usually has many physical disabilities (such as heart problems, stunted growth, low intelligence) and a shortened life span. The best-known human nondisjunction is Down syndrome, also called trisomy 21 because affected individuals have three copies of chromosome number twenty-one per cell. Down syndrome occurs because of nondisjunction of chromosome number twenty-one in the egg.

A translocation involves the breakage and movement of a chromosome segment from its normal chromosome to a different chromosome. Control of the genes on this segment is affected during the transfer, resulting in a variety of conditions. Some leukemias and a form of Down syndrome are caused by translocations. A chromosome inversion involves the breakage of a chromosome segment, followed by reinsertion of the segment into the chromosome backwards. A chromosomal deficiency is the loss of a region of a chromosome, and therefore a loss of the genes located on that region. A chromosomal duplication is a doubling of a chromosome region, thus doubling the genes of that region. All these rearrangements can affect gene expression and thereby drastically affect the cell and the organism.

Methods of Study

The study of mutations involves both classical and molecular techniques. Point mutations are studied using visible traits, nutritional mutations, and DNA sequencing. Chromosomal rearrangements are identified by karyotyping an individual's chromosomes. Mutagens are identified using the Ames Mutagenicity Test.

For point mutations affecting single genes, one can begin with visible traits that an organism may possess that are different from wild-type, or normal, individuals. Gregor Mendel, the father of genetics, used this approach with garden peas during his discovery of inheritable traits. Beginning in the 1920's, various researchers began mutagenizing organisms with radiation and chemicals. Thomas Hunt Morgan mutated the fruit fly *Drosophila melanogaster*, obtaining a variety of visible mutations, including white eyes and vestigial wings. Thousands of visible mutations have since been cataloged for *Drosophila*. Geneticists studying humans use visible characteristics of individuals to detect possible mutations and chromosome abnormalities.

The identification of nutritional and biochemical mutations in fungi, plants, and animals has been an extensive avenue of research. For example, the human disorder alkaptonuria is caused by a mutation in the gene that encodes the enzyme homogentisic acid oxidase. Alkaptonuric individuals cannot make this enzyme, resulting in a buildup of homogentisic acid in their bodies, which can cause arthritic symptoms and blackish urine.

With modern molecular techniques, if a gene has been cloned and its DNA nucleotide sequence has been determined, then its mutant gene can also be cloned and DNA-sequenced. The mutant nucleotide sequence can then be compared to the wild-type nucleotide sequence. Any base changes can be identified, so that the exact source of the mutation can be understood.

Chromosomal rearrangements can be identified by karyotyping, a process by which cells are removed from an individual, followed by the isolation, staining, and observation of the chromosomes microscopically. For this technique, blood cells are obtained from adults and children. Sloughed-off amniotic cells from a fetus can be drawn from the mother's womb by the process of amniocentesis. The chromosomes can then be examined for the presence of any abnormalities.

Potential mutagenic substances can be identified by the Ames Mutagenicity Test, named for its developer, Bruce Ames of the University of California at Berkeley. The test uses mutant strains of the bacterium *Salmonella typhimurium*. Suspected chemical mutagens are applied to the minimum food on which mutant bacteria are placed. If the bacteria start growing on the mutant food, then reverse mutations have occurred, evidently caused by the chemical. The rationale behind the Ames test is that if a chemical can cause a reverse mutation, it can also cause a forward, or initial, mutation. In either case, the chemical is designated a mutagen.

Context

Understanding mutation and repair is of considerable importance for a number of reasons: their applications to health care, environmental concerns, their use in the discovery of gene structure and regulation, and their role in evolution. In health care, mutations are the cause of numerous diseases and defects, including hemophilia, deafness, and cystic fibrosis. Many of these disorders are untreatable. Progress in gene cloning and the development of tissue-specific cloning vectors for delivering the cloned gene to appropriate tissues may one day be very effective in helping or even curing these individuals.

Understanding natural processes of mutation repair (photoreactivation and excision repair) can be important for developing molecules or diets that enhance the repair process. Certain nutrients (such as vitamins C and E and selenium) have been implicated in contributing to the activities of certain mutagen-destroying enzymes, such as glutathione peroxidase and superoxide dismutase.

Mutation is of considerable environmental concern because of the human use of radioactive substances, hazardous chemicals, and chlorofluorocarbons that are depleting the earth's atmospheric ozone layer. Humans are exposed to radiation from a variety of sources, including television, smoke detectors, X rays, and nuclear power plants. Hundreds of chemicals encountered every day are mutagenic, including household chemicals, asbestos, and pesticides. The dangers are further enlarged by the careless disposal of hazardous and radioactive wastes, which eventually may contaminate the groundwater that humans drink as well as enter animal food chains. Atmospheric ozone depletion will increase penetration of ultraviolet light, contributing to an increase in skin cancers (including the fatal malignant melanoma) as well as to severe damage to animals and plants.

While mutagens have obvious dangers, they can also be valuable medical and scientific tools. Chemotherapy and radiation therapy each rely upon the use of mutagens to kill cancer cells. Cancer cells are more sensitive to chemical toxins and radiation than are normal cells, although both cell types are killed during these treatments.

Mutations are also used to study evolutionary patterns: that is, how closely related various species are to one another. Specific proteins can be obtained from different species, followed by comparisons of their respective amino acid sequences. Two closely related species, such as humans and chimpanzees, should have very similar amino acid sequences for a particular protein that they share. Distantly related species, such as humans and frogs, should have numerous amino acid differences between them for the same protein. Similar comparisons can be made using DNA sequences for particular genes. These studies add to the understanding of the process of mutation and selection for these mutations (evolution) over millions of years.

Bibliography

Goodenough, Ursula. *Genetics*. 2d ed. New York: Holt, Rinehart and Winston, 1978. A beginning undergraduate genetics text, this book provides excellent coverage of genetics, including molecular genetics. It also maintains the importance of classical genetics experiments. The text cites extensive experimental evidence, with references, and covers a variety of different species. Chapter 6, "Mutation and Repair," is comprehensive, well written, and illuminating.

Klug, William S., and Michael R. Cummings. *Concepts of Genetics*. Westerville, Ohio: Charles E. Merrill, 1983. A strong undergraduate genetics textbook, profusely illustrated. Clearly written, it places a strong emphasis on human genetics. Chapter 12, "Variations in Chromosome Number and Arrangement," and chapter 13, "Mutation and Mutagenesis," are thorough discussions of mutations and their causes.

Lewin, Benjamin. *Genes II*. New York: John Wiley & Sons, 1985. As a sequel to *Genes*, this advanced undergraduate/graduate level textbook is a comprehensive yet very readable summary of advances in molecular biology. Lewin, editor of the prestigious journal *Cell*, has complete command of important breakthroughs in genetics and cell biology. Chapter 3, "Mutations Change the Sequence of DNA," chapter 33, "Systems That Safeguard DNA," and several gene regulation chapters are clearly written with excellent illustrations.

Raven, Peter H., and George B. Johnson. *Biology*. 2d ed. St. Louis: Times Mirror/ Mosby, 1989. This fine textbook is for beginning biology majors. It is very clearly written and understandable to the layperson. The book is packed with information, along with beautiful photographs and illustrations. Chapter 16, "Mutation," is a clear, concise introduction to the topic.

Starr, Cecie, and Ralph Taggart. *Biology: The Unity and Diversity of Life*. 5th ed. Belmont, Calif.: Wadsworth, 1989. This is a popular beginning biology textbook for undergraduate science and nonscience majors. It is well written and provides excellent illustrations and photographs. Chapter 14, "Human Genetics," and chapter 16, "Protein Synthesis," provide a very understandable discussion of mutation without technical details.

Stryer, Lubert. *Biochemistry*. 2d ed. San Francisco: W. H. Freeman, 1981. Stryer's *Biochemistry* is a classic undergraduate textbook. It is extremely well written and has outstanding illustrations. Chapter 26, "The Genetic Code and Gene-Protein Relations," and chapter 31, "Gene Rearrangements: Recombination, Transposition, and Cloning," are more in-depth studies of mutation, causes of mutation, and repair mechanisms.

Swanson, Carl P., Timothy Merz, and William J. Young. *Cytogenetics: The Chromosome in Division, Inheritance, and Evolution*. 2d ed. Englewood Cliffs, N.J.: Prentice-Hall, 1981. *Cytogenetics* is an advanced undergraduate/graduate-level survey of chromosome structure, evolution, and abnormalities. The subject matter of the text covers a wide range of species. Chromosome abnormalities from many species, including humans, are covered. Numerous references are cited.

Wallace, Robert A., Jack L. King, and Gerald P. Sanders. *Biosphere: The Realm of Life*. 2d ed. Glenview, Ill.: Scott, Foresman, 1988. An excellent introductory biology textbook for both science and nonscience majors. It is clearly written and comprehensive in its coverage, although it is not too detailed for the layperson. Chapter 15, "DNA in Action," provides an outstanding discussion of gene regulation and the effects of mutation on gene expression.

Zubay, Geoffrey. *Biochemistry*. Reading, Mass.: Addison-Wesley, 1983. As a graduate biochemistry textbook, this work is very detailed. The subject matter covered is extensive, and the accompanying illustrations are simply outstanding. Chapter 20, "DNA Metabolism," discusses gene structure and the effects of mutagenesis.

David Wason Hollar, Jr.

Cross-References

DNA Replication, 692; DNA Sequencing, 698; DNA's Molecular Structure, 706; Eukaryotic Post-transcriptional Control, 880; Positive and Negative Eukaryotic Transcriptional Control, 895; Genes and Nucleic Acids, 1134; Genes and Polypeptide Chains, 1141; The Genetic Code, 1148; Deciphering the Genetic Code, 1155; Protein Synthesis: Locational Specificity and Targeting, 2266; Transcription of DNA to Form RNA, 2632; Translation of Messenger RNA to Form Protein, 2647.

EUKARYOTIC GENE REGULATION

Type of life science: Genetic regulation in eukaryotes
Other fields of study: Biochemistry, genetics, and molecular biology

Gene regulation is concerned with the mechanisms by which genes are turned "on" or "off"—that is, how they are controlled. Eukaryotic gene regulation appears to be quite different from prokaryotic gene regulation, partly because of cellular characteristics unique to eukaryotes.

Principal terms

EUKARYOTE: an organism with a true nucleus bounded by a membrane; animals, plants, fungi, and protozoans are all eukaryotes

HISTONE: a type of protein that is basic (positively charged) and is found exclusively in eukaryotic chromosomes

NUCLEOSOME: a chromosomal structure consisting of a length of deoxyribonucleic acid (DNA) wrapped around four pairs of histone proteins

OPERON: a set of adjacent structural genes plus a sequence of regulatory DNA that controls the transcription of the structural genes

PROKARYOTE: an organism lacking a well-defined nucleus and nuclear membrane; bacteria are prokaryotes

PROMOTER: a sequence of DNA found adjacent to structural genes that controls the transcription of those genes

RIBONUCLEIC ACID (RNA): a molecule made of a single strand of nucleotides whose order is determined by a sequence of DNA

STRUCTURAL GENE: a sequence of DNA that contains the information to make a structural component (usually a protein) needed by a cell

TRANSCRIPTION: the process by which RNA is formed using DNA as a blueprint; it requires the enzyme RNA polymerase

TRANSLATION: the process by which a protein is formed following the information contained in a molecule of messenger RNA (mRNA)

Summary of the Phenomenon

Gene regulation is the process by which the synthesis of gene products is controlled. The ability to turn genes "on" and "off" is especially important in eukaryotes. Many eukaryotes, including humans, are multicellular, with many specialized cells. It would be a waste of energy for a muscle cell to produce proteins for hair or for skin cell to produce hemoglobin, needed only in red blood cells. Since every cell in an organism contains the same genetic information, there must be a way to use only the information needed by one particular cell at a particular time. How this control works is part of the study of molecular biology.

The process of going from the information contained in the genetic material to a final product involves many steps and is sometimes known as the "central dogma of molecular biology." This phrase was invented by Francis Crick, who, along with James Watson, discovered the structure of DNA. According to the central dogma, information in coded form in the DNA is copied to a molecule of ribonucleic acid (RNA) by the process of transcription. One type of RNA, called messenger RNA (mRNA), contains information used in protein synthesis, specifying the actual sequence of amino acids in a process called translation. The protein thus synthesized may undergo further modifications before it is used. If the final products are to be rRNA or tRNA molecules, the translation step is bypassed. For many years, the phenomenon of gene regulation in prokaryotes was studied in the hope that it would give insight into the same process in eukaryotes. In prokaryotes (for example, bacteria), regulation mostly takes place at the level of transcription.

One of the most thoroughly studied prokaryotic systems is the regulation of the enzyme needed by bacteria to digest lactose, a disaccharide. Many bacteria are also able to produce beta galactosidase, an enzyme that breaks lactose into two simple sugars, glucose and galactose. This enzyme is usually produced only when lactose is available to the cell. This makes sense in terms of cell energetics: Time and energy will not be wasted making the enzyme unless there is something for that enzyme to act upon.

The structural gene for beta galactosidase is found on the bacterial chromosome adjacent to two other genes involved more indirectly in the utilization of lactose. All three genes are transcribed together when lactose is present; none is transcribed when lactose is absent. This regulation is accomplished by a regulatory sequence of DNA called the promoter. The structural genes plus their promoter make up an operon. A promoter region is found just before the beginning of the first structural gene. The promoter includes two subdivisions; the first acts as a binding site for the RNA polymerase enzyme that carries out transcription. The second subdivision, called the operator, can act to prevent transcription. In the absence of lactose, a protein called a repressor normally binds to the operator region. This protein acts as a physical roadblock, preventing the RNA polymerase from reaching the first structural gene and beginning transcription. When lactose is present, it binds to the repressor molecule, causing it to change shape and lose the ability to bind to the operator region. Without an active repressor, the RNA polymerase can reach past the operator to begin transcription.

When scientists turned their attention to the more complex problem of gene regulation in eukaryotes, they immediately found many differences. At the level of transcription, regulatory sequences of DNA (promoters) control individual genes in eukaryotes. Unlike prokaryotes, however, structural genes tend not to be clustered, so operons, as such, do not exist. Additional sequences, called enhancer elements, encourage transcription independent of their distance from the controlled gene. These are thought to exist in all eukaryotes and some viruses, but not in bacteria.

The physical structure of DNA may also play a role in gene regulation. The DNA molecule described by Watson and Crick is a double-stranded, right-handed helix containing ten nucleotide pairs for every complete turn of the strands. This structure is now called the B form, or B-DNA, and is the pattern typically found in cells. Some years later it was discovered that DNA can exist in different forms, two of which have been named A-DNA and Z-DNA. A-DNA depends on conditions of low humidity to form, so it probably does not exist naturally. Z-DNA is a form in which the DNA twists in a left-handed direction and contains twelve nucleotide pairs per turn. Z-DNA has been found in eukaryotic cells, and some theories suggest that the ability of stretches of DNA to assume this form may play a role in gene regulation.

DNA molecules contain four different bases: adenine (A), guanine (G), thymine (T), and cytosine (C). When new DNA is synthesized by a eukaryotic cell, some of these bases are immediately modified by specialized enzymes. The addition of a methyl group to the fifth carbon of a cytosine creates a new base called 5-methylcytosine. The DNA of most eukaryotes contains some amount of 5-methylcytosine, but experiments have shown that the relative amount of 5-methylcytosine is lower in genes that are transcriptionally active. Methylation cannot be the only method of "turning off" genes, however, because only trace amounts of 5-methylcytosine have been found in some eukaryotes, especially many invertebrates.

In cells, DNA does not exist as an isolated molecule but is packaged in structures called chromosomes. A typical bacterial chromosome, such as found in *Escherichia coli*, is a circular piece of DNA that includes about a thousand nucleotide pairs. Some proteins may be associated with this chromosome to support and protect the DNA. While most prokaryotes have only one chromosome, eukaryotes have several, which usually occur in pairs. Eukaryotic chromosomes are linear, rather than circular, and include many proteins. The proteins found in a eukaryotic chromosome are of two types, histones and nonhistones, which play important structural and regulatory roles.

There are five main types of histones associated with eukaryotic DNA. All are small and basic (positively charged), which help them bind to the acidic (negatively charged) DNA. Four of the histones, which are very similar in sequence in all eukaryotes, complex in pairs to form a core around which part of the DNA strand winds. This histone package, with associated DNA, constitutes the structure called a nucleosome. The fifth histone is associated with stretches of DNA between individual nucleosomes. Because histones are so uniform from cell to cell and species to species, their role in gene regulation is not thought to be very specialized. DNase I is an enzyme that digests DNA not contained in nucleosomes. It is known that DNA that contains transcriptionally active genes is more sensitive to DNase I. This suggests that histones may play a negative role in preventing transcription of certain genes.

There are hundreds of different types of nonhistone proteins, and the type and distribution of these tend to vary greatly from cell to cell. Experimental evidence from many sources strongly suggests that at least some of these proteins play a role in starting or preventing transcription of some genes. Some nonhistone proteins may control genes through their interactions with hormones. Hormones are organic molecules produced in small amounts by an organism to act as chemical messengers. In animals, steroid hormones are thought to play an especially important role in gene regulation. Steroid hormones travel through the bloodstream to arrive at the surface of a target cell, where they bind to specific protein receptors on the surface of the cell. A hormone-receptor complex is formed, which then crosses the nuclear membrane and binds to the chromosomes. These complexes may recognize certain sequences of DNA, such as enhancer elements, and influence transcription directly. Other theories suggest that the hormone-receptor complexes interact first with certain nonhistone proteins, which then act to affect transcription of particular genes.

The majority of control mechanisms studied in eukaryotes act at the level of transcription. Other levels of control are believed to exist, but they are not as well understood. For example, in order for a protein to be formed, an mRNA must leave the nucleus, where it was transcribed, and reach a ribosome in the cytoplasm, where it can be translated. The nuclear membrane may act as a point of control, although the means by which the flow of different RNA molecules may be affected has not yet been discovered.

Even before an mRNA leaves the nucleus, it typically undergoes a step called processing. Eukaryotic genes often contain long regions of nonamino acid coding sequences. These sequences are called introns, or intervening sequences, and they must be removed from the mRNA transcript before protein synthesis can occur. During processing, introns are removed (leaving only coding sequences called exons), and additional modifications are usually made to both ends of the mRNA molecule that are apparently useful in the process of translation.

Once an mRNA has entered the cytoplasm, how long the mRNA molecule survives reflects another level of regulation. While rRNAs and tRNAs are very stable, mRNAs may last for months or only minutes. The longer an mRNA survives, the more often it can be transcribed. Even when an mRNA is present, however, it will not necessarily be transcribed. Ribosomes may exert control at the level of translation, avoiding certain or all mRNA molecules. This is seen in some unfertilized eggs in which many mRNAs are stored. The rate of translation is very low until fertilization triggers a dramatic increase in protein synthesis.

Methods of Study

Nearly every technique known to geneticists and molecular biologists has been used to understand the mechanisms of gene regulation better. Early work in this area included microscopic studies of chromosomes. Stains that react with DNA reveal chromosomal regions with different staining patterns. Densely staining regions of a chromosome, called heterochromatin, seem to be tightly compacted and genetically inactive. More lightly staining regions are called euchromatin and contain most of the active genes.

Other chromosome structures related to gene activity have been discovered microscopically. Some tissues of the larvae of various species of flies (including the fruit fly, *Drosophila melanogaster*) contain giant chromosomes called polytene chromosomes. Certain regions of these chromosomes swell or "puff" at times that correlate with certain developmental events.

Experiments have verified that these puffs represent areas of active transcription. By adding radioactive ("labeled") uracil to cells, researchers can follow the formation of RNA. Uracil is found only in RNA; it replaces the base thymine, found in DNA. High amounts of labeled RNA can be seen around chromosome puffs by using a technique called autoradiography. In autoradiography, photographic film is placed over a slide on which chromosomes and labeled RNA have been fixed. The energy emitted by the radioactive element exposes the film the same way that light does. After several days in the dark, the film is developed, and areas of high radioactivity (areas where RNA is being made) appear as dark spots.

A technique known as "footprinting" allows scientists to identify proteins that have the ability to recognize and bind specific sequences of DNA and that are presumably involved in gene regulation. In one procedure, DNA is mixed with the protein to be tested. After a period of incubation, the mixture is treated with a nuclease that breaks down DNA chains not sheltered by the bound protein. The protein can then be broken down with a protease and the remaining DNA examined and sequenced.

In mammals, the effect of hormones on gene activity is studied in cells kept in culture. In small sterile plates, cells from different types of tissue can be grown under controlled conditions. If cells in culture are treated with radioactive hormone, the amount of hormone that binds to cell receptors can be measured using an instrument called a liquid scintillation counter. After unbound hormone is gently washed off, cells are concentrated, dried, and placed in a vial with a special mixture of organic solvents called a "cocktail." Some molecules in this mixture react to radioactivity by giving off pulses of light (scintillating). These emissions of light are picked up by photosensitive tubes in the liquid scintillation counter. The tubes convert light energy to electrical energy, which is then measured, scaled, and recorded.

Finally, the more classical genetic techniques have also proved essential to the study of gene regulation. Chemicals and X rays can be used to induce mutations, or changes in the DNA sequence. Studying the effects of these changes on different genes is what led to the discovery of promoter and enhancer regions. The sequence of these regions was also shown to be critical, since overly extensive mutation of short, critical sequences, often called "boxes," prevents transcription of the structural gene.

Context

Genetic regulation is essential to the development of higher organisms; without the ability to start and stop synthesis of certain molecules, every cell in an organism would be identical. A human baby starts as a single cell; as that cell divides and becomes many, whole sets of genes are turned on and off, and cells become specialized. The very fact that the process of gene regulation is more complex in eukaryotes than in prokaryotes allows for a more responsive, more "fine-tuned" control of genes.

One example of the role of gene regulation in development is the determination of the sex of an individual. In humans, maleness is determined by a gene or genes linked to the Y chromosome. Occasionally, however, an individual with one X and one Y chromosome will develop as female. This phenomenon, called testicular feminization, is associated with a mutation to a gene on the X chromosome, which prevents the sex organs from reacting to the presence of male hormones. Medical geneticists are interested in gene regulation to understand not only sex determination but also the thousands of birth defects that occur every year.

The complexity of gene regulation is of great concern to scientists studying cancer cells. Cancer cells differ from normal cells in many ways, including altered shapes, rapid growth, and production of new surface proteins. All these changes reflect an alteration in gene regulation; how these changes come about is of primary interest. One line of research concentrates on a group of genes called oncogenes, which can cause cancer, perhaps by making products that turn other sets of genes on or off at the wrong time. If the initiation of the cancer process is understood, it may be possible to halt or reverse the changes associated with it.

Knowledge of how genes are regulated is also important to those studying the phenomenon of aging. Normal animal cells are capable of undergoing only a limited number of cycles of cell division in cell culture. For example, cells taken from a human adult will divide fewer times than cells taken from an infant. Some genetic diseases, such as progeria, cause premature aging, and cells taken from individuals with symptoms of such a disease will divide very few times. It is thought that cell division must be genetically regulated in some way, and by understanding this process it might be possible to moderate the symptoms associated with aging or even to extend life spans past the present limits.

Another example of specialized gene regulation is seen in the immune system. The immune system of vertebrates provides the main defense against diseases caused by bacteria, viruses, and fungi. One of the major weapons of the immune system is the antibody, a protein that recognizes foreign cells by the shapes and molecules on their surfaces. Geneticists are particularly interested in the role of gene regulation in antibody production. Such knowledge can help in treating diseases of the immune system such as acquired immune deficiency syndrome (AIDS).

Bibliography

Gehring, W. J. "The Molecular Basis of Development." *Scientific American* 253 (October, 1985): 152B-162. This article concentrates on the genetic regulation of the events of development in the geneticist's favorite organism, *Drosophila melanogaster*, the fruit fly. The discussion is at a senior college level, but the illustrations and diagrams are practically self-explanatory.

Kornberg, Roger D., and Aaron Klug. "The Nucleosome." *Scientific American* 244 (February, 1981): 52-64. As the title suggests, this article reviews the structure and function of the nucleosome in eukaryotic chromosomes. The figures and photographs are outstanding and have been reproduced in many texts.

O'Malley, Bert W., and W. T. Schrader. "The Receptors of the Steroid Hormones." *Scientific American* 234 (February, 1976): 32-43. While some of the information in this review article is out-of-date, this is a generally helpful introduction to a very important topic in gene regulation.

Rothwell, Norman. *Understanding Genetics*. 4th ed. New York: Oxford University Press, 1988. This edition of a popular intermediate-level college text has references at the end of every chapter and an expanded glossary. Chapter 17, "Control Mechanisms and Differentiation," contains a particularly thorough discussion of gene regulation. Chapter 18 is also valuable for its coverage of modern techniques of molecular genetics.

Russell, Peter. *Genetics*. 2d ed. Glenview, Ill.: Scott, Foresman, 1990. Particularly well written, with many touches of humor, this intermediate-level college textbook contains a helpful bibliography for each chapter following an extensive glossary. Regulation of gene expression in eukaryotes is discussed in chapter 21. Other relevant chapters include 8 and 9, which cover the structure and organization of DNA, RNA, and chromosomes from a genetic perspective.

Sheeler, Phillip, and Don Bianchi. *Cell and Molecular Biology*. 3d ed. New York: John Wiley & Sons, 1987. This book is a useful reference, written for intermediate-level college students. Chapter 1 reviews cell structures of prokaryotes and eukaryotes; chapter 7 discusses DNA and RNA structure. Chapters 12-14 cover modern tools of molecular biology, including autoradiography and liquid scintillation counters. Chapter 20 reviews the organization of the nucleus and chromosomes.

Suzuki, David, Antony Griffiths, Jeffrey Miller, and Richard Lewontin. *An Introduction to Genetic Analysis*. 4th ed. New York: W. H. Freeman, 1989. This is a popular intermediate-level college text with excellent diagrams and a useful selection of recommended readings at the end of the book. Gene regulation in prokaryotes and eukaryotes is discussed in chapter 16, and the importance of gene regulation in development is covered in chapter 21. The structure of DNA and chromosomes is reviewed in chapters 11 and 13.

Wolfe, S. L. *Introduction to Cell Biology*. Belmont, Calif.: Wadsworth, 1983. This brief text integrates cell structure, biochemistry, and physiology at a level appropriate for a college freshman or sophomore. While gene regulation is not featured, this book is a valuable introduction to cell structure (chapter 1) and to the process of transcription and translation (chapters 9 and 10).

Lisa A. Lambert

Cross-References

PROKARYOTIC GENE REGULATION

Type of life science: Gene regulation in prokaryotes
Other fields of study: Biochemistry, genetics, and molecular biology

Genetic control mechanisms in bacteria have been intensively studied and are well understood. Needed proteins are turned on and unneeded ones turned off by regulation of the genes that code for them, making bacteria very efficient and successful.

Principal terms

ATTENUATION: a mechanism of operon control that is regulated by allowing transcription to begin but terminating the transcription process before the structural genes are reached and transcribed by RNA polymerase

COREPRESSOR: a molecule that binds with the repressor protein, causing it to become capable of binding to the operator gene site, thus repressing the production of the operon's structural gene products

INDUCIBLE ENZYMES: enzymes whose production is controlled so that they are only synthesized when the substrate molecule on which they operate is present in the cell's environment; examples are the lactose operon products

OPERATOR: one of the genes at the beginning of an operon; if a repressor protein is bound to it, products of the structural genes in the operon will not be made because the promoter is blocked so RNA polymerase cannot initiate transcription

OPERON: a coordinated set of regulatory and structural genes, most of which are clustered together on the DNA molecule, which act together to perform a particular cell function

PROMOTER: a regulator gene located next to the operator, often overlapping the operator; the site at which the RNA polymerase molecule binds to the DNA molecule to begin transcription of the operon

REGULATORY GENES: genes that regulate the production of proteins from structural genes; they include the operator gene, the repressor gene, and the promoter gene

REPRESSIBLE ENZYMES: enzymes whose production is controlled so that they are synthesized only when the metabolite that they produce is in very low concentration within the cell; examples are the tryptophan operon products

REPRESSOR PROTEIN: protein, produced by a repressor gene, that interacts with the operator site to turn off the expression of structural genes; may require a corepressor to function

STRUCTURAL GENES: genes for the production of proteins, the last part of an operon group; a mutation in one of these genes would change the structure of the protein

Summary of the Phenomenon

The earliest mechanisms of genetic regulation to be discovered were in the bacterium *Escherichia coli*, commonly known as *E. coli*. The first of these was the lactose operon, which is concerned with the breakdown of lactose, the disaccharide sugar in milk.

An operon is a set of genes that work together to regulate the production of enzymes needed by a prokaryotic cell at some times but not at others. An *E. coli* bacterium has only about a thirty-minute life span and must use its resources in the most efficient manner possible to allow it to compete successfully against other bacteria. It would be very useful for a bacterium to have the ability to digest lactose if the cell were in an environment with milk available, but it would be unreasonable for all bacteria continually to produce the enzymes that allow the digestion of lactose, especially if they had no access to milk. This problem is solved by locating the structural genes for enzymes that are needed to deal with lactose in a group on the bacterial chromosome and by adding regulatory genes to make a complete functional set that can be turned on or off as needed.

The lactose operon contains three structural genes that produce the enzymes needed to deal with lactose. It also contains regulatory genes, located in front of the structural genes. One regulatory gene, called the promoter, is the site of ribonucleic acid (RNA) polymerase binding to the deoxyribonucleic acid (DNA). RNA polymerase is the enzyme that copies the information in the DNA into a messenger RNA (mRNA) molecule, which is then used to provide information to make a protein molecule, such as an enzyme. If the RNA polymerase can bind to the promoter of the lactose operon, it can then move down the DNA molecule and make mRNA from the structural genes. This process is called transcription. A second regulatory gene, located between the promoter and the structural genes, is the operator. It can also bind a protein, but in this case it binds a repressor protein, which stops the function of the operon. The repressor protein is made by a third regulatory gene, the repressor gene, which is located at a distance from the rest of the operon on the DNA molecule. The repressor gene continually makes a small amount of repressor protein. If there is no lactose in the bacterium's environment, the repressor protein binds to the operator gene and blocks the binding of RNA polymerase to the promoter gene. Thus, if the enzymes are not needed, the cell turns off the operon and does not waste its raw materials and energy in making them.

If the cell has access to lactose in its environment, the operon is turned on rather than off. As lactose enters the cell, it binds with the repressor protein molecules that are always being made from the repressor gene. The repressor protein-lactose complex cannot bind to the operator gene. The operator is free, so the promoter gene is not blocked either. RNA polymerase can then bind to the promoter and begin transcription, leading to the production of the enzymes specified by the three structural genes. Since the gene products are only made when needed (they are induced by the presence of their substrate), they are inducible enzymes, and the lactose operon is an inducible operon.

Another kind of regulation is exemplified by the tryptophan operon, involved in the production of the amino acid tryptophan. This operon has five structural genes that produce enzymes that operate sequentially to make the tryptophan molecule if it is not present in the immediate environment. It is a repressible operon, with repressible enzymes, since the presence of tryptophan keeps the cell from making more. The regulatory genes again are the promoter and the operator, located just before the structural genes, and a repressor gene, located at a distance from the other genes on the DNA molecule. Again, the repressor gene continually makes repressor protein, but the free protein does not attach to the operator gene. It can only attach there if it has a corepressor molecule bound to it. That corepressor is the tryptophan molecule. When there is no repressor bound to the operator, the promoter is free, RNA polymerase binds and transcribes the enzymes, and tryptophan is produced. If there is enough tryptophan in the cell, some will bind to the repressor protein, and the repressor-corepressor complex becomes capable of binding to the operator. The bound complex blocks binding of RNA polymerase to the promoter, and the synthesis of tryptophan is turned off. The cell thus has the ability to regulate the production of necessary protein components, so that if it has the amino acid supplied in its environment, the cell can use its raw materials and energy on some other product.

The features of the operons discussed so far are examples of negative control, in which the repressor protein binds to the operon to turn off transcription of the operon's structural genes. Other regulation is done by positive control, in which a protein binds to DNA and stimulates transcription of the associated structural genes. The features of the lactose operon examined earlier are the negative control aspects, but there are also positive control aspects for this operon. A positive regulatory gene, called the catabolite activator protein (CAP) binding site, is located immediately before the promoter gene in the lactose operon. It binds to the CAP molecule, which increases the rate of binding of the RNA polymerase to the promoter when the promoter site is available. The CAP molecule can only bind to its CAP binding site if it has cyclic adenosine $3^1,5^L$-monophosphate (cAMP), a molecule related to adenosine triphosphate (ATP), attached to it. Levels of cAMP rise in the cell when glucose is in short supply. Glucose is the first substrate for cellular respiration, the process from which the cell makes ATP to be used in many energy-requiring activities. If glucose is already present, the cell uses it in preference to breaking down lactose or other sugars to produce the simpler sugar glucose. Thus, if lactose and glucose are both present, the lactose operon is not repressed, but it is also not accelerated in its production of the enzymes to break down lactose. The level of enzyme production remains relatively low, since the promoter gene is not very strong in its binding of RNA polymerase. If lactose is present, but glucose is not, the cAMP levels rise, cAMP binds to the CAP molecule, and the complex binds to the CAP binding site. That accelerates the binding of RNA polymerase, increasing production of lactose-breaking enzymes and giving the cell more simple sugars to use.

These gene controls all operate at the level of the initiation of transcription, binding the RNA polymerase so it can start making mRNA. Attenuation is another aspect of prokaryotic gene regulation that involves detaching the RNA polymerase molecule from the DNA before it reaches the structural genes. This process leads to premature termination of transcription, so that the mRNA needed to produce the structural proteins is not made. Attenuation is seen in the tryptophan operon and in others that produce enzymes for making amino acids. There is a leader sequence in the tryptophan operon, located between the promoter and operator genes on one side, and the five structural genes on the other side. Transcription begins at the start of the leader sequence, which contains a regulatory site for attenuation. When tryptophan levels are high enough in the cell, a portion of the leader sequence, called the attenuator, forms a loop in the DNA that causes the RNA polymerase to stop transcription and drop off the DNA. That happens about 85 percent of the time that transcription of the operon begins. In the other 15 percent of transcription starts, there is not sufficient tryptophan to make the DNA loop, and a different loop forms that allows the RNA polymerase to continue transcription, thus producing the enzymes to make tryptophan. Operating together with the negative repressor controls in the tryptophan operon, attenuation fine-tunes the cell's ability to determine if more enzymes to make tryptophan should be produced. Some operons appear to have only attenuation control, including those that produce the amino acids histidine, leucine, and threonine.

Methods of Study

Research at the Pasteur Institute in Paris led to the discovery in 1961 of the lactose operon in *E. coli* by François Jacob and Jacques Monod, who received the Nobel Prize in Physiology or Medicine in 1965, along with Andrè Lwoff. Beginning in the early 1940's, they did a detailed genetic analysis of the system of lactose metabolism in these bacteria. They knew that an inducer could increase the cell's level of enzymes that broke down lactose by one thousand-fold over the levels present without the inducer. The inducer did not have to be lactose, the normal metabolic substrate of the induced enzymes and the usual inducer, but could also be a nonmetabolizable molecule similar to lactose. Use of this kind of inducer rather than lactose made it easier to study the system.

Jacob and Monod added radioactively labeled amino acids to bacterial cells before or after addition of the inducer molecule and followed their incorporation into proteins at short times after the additions. They found that the cell produced lactose-specific enzymes within three minutes of the addition of inducer and stopped making the enzymes immediately after the inducer was removed. They also found that an enzyme (permease) that allowed the cell to import lactose was induced at the same time as the enzyme (beta-galactosidase) that breaks down lactose, along with another enzyme (transacetylase) whose function is still not known. These coordinately controlled enzymes are the products of the three structural genes of the lactose operon.

Through studies of mutations, the scientists found that the genes for these enzymes were linked together on the DNA molecule, and they also found other genes close to the structural genes that controlled their expression. A mutation in the operator gene could make the three structural genes continually produce their proteins. This mutation interfered with binding of some cytoplasmic agent, which kept the system from being regulated by the presence or absence of the inducer. A cell produced by such a mutation is called a constitutive mutant, since the products are made continually (constitutively) in an unregulated fashion.

Jacob and Monod examined mutants in the operator and structural genes and compared synthesis of the enzymes in cells that were haploid (having one DNA strand) and heterozygous diploid (having two DNA strands that are genetically different). In this way, they recognized the sequential and regulatory nature of the genes, which they called an operon. They found that a mutation at a distance from the operon also could produce a constitutive mutant. This mutant was the repressor gene, and the mutation kept it from making the cytoplasmic agent (which turned out to be the repressor protein) that would normally turn off the lactose operon in the absence of lactose. While they did not find the repressor protein, they recognized that it must exist.

The identification of the repressor protein and its connection with the operator gene was made by W. Gilbert and B. Müller-Hill in 1966. They purified the repressor protein that was attached to a labeled inducer. Once they had the protein, they bound it to DNA, digested away all the unbound DNA around it, separated the protein from the operator gene, and determined the base sequence of the DNA molecule fragment. Each of the mutants in the operator could be shown to be a change from the normal sequence they had thus determined. A similar procedure of binding the CAP-cAMP complex to DNA, digesting unbound DNA away, and looking at the protected DNA sequence was later used to determine the location and sequence of the CAP binding site in the lactose operon.

Attenuation control was recognized after the discovery of the repressor controls of many different operons. It had been thought that all bacterial operons worked in the fashion of having inducible or repressible enzymes, but no repressors could be found for the operons making histidine and a few other amino acids. C. Yanofsky studied deletion mutants of *E. coli* and found that deletions in an area near, but distinct from, the operator and promoter genes caused an increase in the production of enzymes in the tryptophan operon. This finding revealed the presence of the leader sequence and the attenuator site within it, which was incomplete in the deletion mutants and so could not regulate the termination of transcription of the operon. Sequencing of the DNA bases in the area led to the discovery of the two looped areas of DNA that are alternative structures formed with lower and higher tryptophan concentrations.

All the methods used in this field of study are biochemical or genetic or both. Many studies involve the production of mutants that lack the ability to make the structural gene products, that make the products in greater quantities than usual when induced, or that make the products continually regardless of whether they are induced. Biochemical assays with radioactive tracers led to the recognition of products and gene sites, and sequencing of the DNA bases led to the understanding of deletions and loops and their effects.

Context

The mechanisms of gene regulation are different in bacteria, which are prokaryotic cells, and in the eukaryotic cells of multicellular organisms. The simpler systems of bacteria were studied first, and much of what is known about gene regulation at the molecular level concerns bacteria. In the early 1960's, Jacob and Monod investigated the fact that enzymes appeared in bacteria only in the presence of their substrates, a phenomenon that researchers had noted since the 1800's. It was thought that enzymes or their precursors adapted to the substrate, changing form to change function when a new function was needed. Jacob and Monod showed that it was really a system of gene control that operated here: There was not a change in the individual enzymes, but the production of new enzymes from genetic information that was turned on by the addition of substrate. This conclusion led scientists to a new understanding of the genetics of bacterial enzyme control, and the use of *E. coli* as a standard research organism has brought about a continual expansion of this understanding.

It is important to realize that the mechanisms uncovered in bacteria are not the same as the mechanisms that operate in the eukaryotic cells of multicellular organisms such as plants, animals, and fungi. Bacteria are highly adapted to a very short life span and to the efficient use of their resources. About 4,000 genes are present in an *E. coli* cell, but most of them are not active at any one time. The ability to turn genes on and off as the conditions of the environment dictate is one of the characteristics that make bacteria so successful and widespread.

Bacteria are small, prokaryotic cells, without a nucleus and with only one chromosome of naked DNA, unlike the larger eukaryotic cells, which have a nucleus, many organelles, and multiple chromosomes of DNA with associated histone proteins. Bacteria do not have to interact with other cells or carry in them all the genes to make many kinds of tissues, as cells of multicellular organisms do. The cells of a human, for example, are thought to carry as many as 100,000 different genes, and they are the same in every cell, from bone to skin to muscle. It is not surprising to think that the control mechanisms in such very different cells would also be very different.

It was, however, a surprise to researchers to find that there is no structure such as an operon in a eukaryotic cell. Much more complex systems of regulation operate in the eukaryote than in the prokaryote. It is important to continue the investigation of the mechanisms of gene control in prokaryotes, though, since these investigations have been so basic in the understanding of the processes of molecular genetics and the biochemistry of all organisms. For example, it would not be possible to have achieved the results of modern genetic engineering, such as human insulin production in bacterial cells, if scientists did not understand the genetic regulation mechanisms of both the bacterial cell and the human cell that provides the DNA for the human insulin production.

Bibliography

Alberts, Bruce, Dennis Bray, Julian Lewis, Martin Raff, Keith Roberts, and James D. Watson. *Molecular Biology of the Cell.* 2d ed. New York: Garland, 1989. This upper-level textbook is well organized, well written, very informative, and up-to-date. While covering technical material in detail, it is not overwhelming. In chapter 10, "Control of Gene Expression," the authors give very clear explanations of experimental results and current theories of how this process works. Many diagrams accompany the information in the text, and numerous references are given at the end of the chapter.

Avers, Charlotte J. *Molecular Cell Biology.* 2d ed. Menlo Park, Calif.: Benjamin/ Cummings, 1986. This introductory text is geared for sophomore college students with some background in chemistry and biology, but it is clearly written and easily understandable. Prokaryotic and eukaryotic genes are both covered in chapter 14, "Regulation of Gene Expression." The presentation is very concise and contains much information in a relatively short discussion. Numerous references are supplied at the end of the chapter.

Curtis, Helena, and N. Sue Barnes. *Biology.* 5th ed. New York: Worth, 1989. This book is a widely used freshman biology text, and covers bacterial gene regulation clearly and simply in chapter 16, "The Molecular Genetics of Prokaryotes and Viruses." Excellent diagrams help the beginning reader to grasp the concepts being presented. No references.

Darnell, James, Harvey Lodish, and David Baltimore. *Molecular Cell Biology.* New York: Scientific American Books, 1986. An upper-level textbook that provides well-written, detailed coverage of prokaryotic gene control in chapter 8, "RNA Synthesis and Gene Control in Prokaryotes." Along with excellent illustrations, it provides very complete information on the methods used in research in this area. A long list of references appears at the end of the chapter.

Klug, William S., and Michael R. Cummings. *Concepts of Genetics.* 2d ed. Glenview, Ill.: Scott, Foresman, 1986. Bacterial genetics is the main focus of chapter 21, "Genetic Regulation," in this excellent general genetics college text. An overview of prokaryotic gene regulation is followed by discussion of the lactose and tryptophan gene systems, then by regulation in eukaryotic cells. Numerous references include mostly research reports.

Lewin, Benjamin. *Genes.* 3d ed. New York: John Wiley & Sons, 1987. This upper-level college text covers, in great detail, bacterial gene regulation in chapter 9, "RNA Polymerase-Promoter Interactions Control Initiation," chapter 10, "A Panoply of Operons: The Lactose Paradigm and Others," and chapter 11, "Control at Termination: Attenuation and Antitermination." Coverage of the topic is much more complete than in most other references but assumes background knowledge that beginning students will not have. Multiple references are listed with each chapter.

Prescott, Lansing M., John P. Harley, and Donald A. Klein. *Microbiology.* Dubuque, Iowa: Wm. C. Brown, 1990. This biology majors' textbook provides a brief but in-depth look at the mechanisms of prokaryotic gene control in chapter 11, "Metabolism: The Regulation of Enzyme Activity and Synthesis." A historical look at the discovery of bacterial gene control is included, along with numerous references.

Stryer, Lubert. *Biochemistry.* 3d ed. New York: W. H. Freeman, 1988. One of the best college biochemistry books to be found. It covers bacterial gene controls in chapter 32, "Control of Gene Expression in Prokaryotes." There is very thorough coverage of the transcriptional level controls and of the biochemistry of all the steps along the way. Many diagrams show the binding of regulatory proteins to the DNA molecule. Selected readings are at the end of the chapter.

Suzuki, David T., Anthony J. F. Griffiths, Jeffrey H. Miller, and Richard C. Lewontin. *An Introduction to Genetic Analysis.* 4th ed. New York: W. H. Freeman, 1989. An upper-level genetics text that concentrates on problem-solving, this book discusses both prokaryotic and eukaryotic gene regulation in chapter 16, "Control of Gene Expression." The arabinose operon is discussed in addition to the lactose and tryptophan operons, and the lambda bacteriophage and eukaryotic systems are also explored. Problems are given and answered at the end of the chapter, and references are listed at the end of the book.

Villee, Claude A., Eldra P. Solomon, Charles E. Martin, Diana W. Martin, Linda R. Berg, and P. William Davis. *Biology.* 2d ed. Philadelphia: Saunders College Publishing, 1989. While written for freshman biology students, this text has a very thorough presentation of the mechanisms of bacterial gene regulation in chapter 14, "Gene Regulation." Diagrams help to explain the lactose and tryptophan operons, as well as positive regulation of the lactose operon.

Weaver, Robert F., and Philip W. Hedrick. *Genetics.* Dubuque, Iowa: Wm. C. Brown, 1989. This college textbook takes a very biochemically oriented view in its approach to the study of genetics. Chapter 8, "Transcriptions and Its Control in Prokaryotes," covers the various aspects of bacterial transcription and gene expression through the control mechanisms that operate on transcription, including the lactose operon's positive and negative controls, and negative control and attenuation in the tryptophan operon. Problems with answers are included, but no references.

Jean S. Helgeson

Cross-References

DNA Bending in Regulation, 679; DNA Sequencing, 698; Eukaryotic Post-transcriptional Control, 880; The Genetic Code, 1148; Prokaryotic Transcriptional Control: Attenuation, 2227; Negative Prokaryotic Transcriptional Control, 2234; Positive Prokaryotic Transcriptional Control, 2242; Transcription of DNA to Form RNA, 2632; Transposable Elements, 2654.

GENE THERAPY

Types of life science: Bioethics and molecular biology
Other fields of study: Biochemistry, evolutionary biology, and genetics

Genetic diseases are not treated at the source of the affliction, the gene. Treatment is generally aimed at symptoms or secondary defects. Gene therapy can be defined as the insertion of a specific gene into an organism to achieve a therapeutic objective.

Principal terms

GENE TRANSFER: a process or method by which a gene is moved from one cell into another

GENOME: the sum of the entire genetic information of an organism

GERM CELL: a reproductive cell (an ovum or sperm)

SOMATIC CELL: all the cells of the body of an organism other than germ cells

STEM CELL: a precursor cell that differentiates into a variety of different cell types

VIRAL VECTOR: a virus that is used as a vehicle to carry a gene into a cell or a specific location

Summary of the Methodology

Gene therapy is based on the assumption that definitive treatment for genetic disorders should be possible by directing treatment to the site of the defect itself, namely, the mutant or abnormal gene, rather than treatment of symptoms of the disease alone or other secondary effects of the mutant gene products.

Genes are the structures that encode all the traits and functions that are passed on from generation to generation. The information for all these traits is contained in a long chainlike two-stranded molecule known as deoxyribonucleic acid (DNA), which, in turn, is made up of four molecules called bases. The total human genome, as represented in the genetic content of every single human cell, consists of approximately 2-3 billion of these four bases, arranged in only forty-six separate long strings called chromosomes, each tens or hundreds of millions of bases long. The genes are the storehouses of information for proteins and must first be copied into another nucleic acid called messenger ribonucleic acid (mRNA). The gene is therefore the original blueprint, the RNA is a copy in a slightly changed form, and the protein is the final product.

Mistakes in the genetic information are called mutations and represent errors or changes in the sequence of the bases. Therefore, errors in the DNA lead to defective functioning of the protein products. If the protein is vital to the normal function of an organ, such a change may also lead to disease. Genetic diseases may be broadly classified as falling into three categories: single gene disorders, multiple gene diseases, and chromosomal disorders. The single gene disorders are individually rare, but collectively they represent a significant body of diseases because there are so many of them. It is this group of disorders that are best studied and may be ideal target diseases for gene therapy. Examples of such disorders are sickle-cell anemia and thalassemia, both serious and potentially life-threatening disorders involving the beta-globin gene that result in defective beta-globin protein, an important component of the oxygen-carrying, life-sustaining hemoglobin molecule in human blood. Disorders resulting from multiple gene abnormalities and chromosomal disorders are complex and not directly amenable to gene therapy.

The therapy for most human genetic disorders is generally aimed at symptoms or secondary defects because therapy directed at the genetic defect itself is impossible. Therefore, the therapy of most genetic disorders is ineffective and inadequate. Two of the most important severe human genetic disorders of blood formation, namely, sickle-cell anemia and thalassemia, are treated almost exclusively with symptomatic therapies such as blood transfusions. Therefore, treatment involves replacing the missing product, not the correction of the defect responsible for this failure to produce the blood component. Another genetic disorder, cystic fibrosis, which is characterized by a tendency to chronic lung infections, is treated by antibiotics, not by correcting the underlying defect that is responsible for the symptoms of the disorder. With increasing knowledge of the genetic defects, and the inadequacy of the standard therapy of these diseases, it is desirable to try direct correction of the defect in some human diseases either by replacing missing or defective genes or by directly modifying existing ones to bring about a permanent genetic "cure."

A maneuver by which genes are inserted into germ cells (for example, fertilized eggs) would permit the transferred gene to pass on to subsequent generations; this process is called germ line therapy. Because of the biologic complexity involved in such a method, and the profound ethical considerations raised by such genetic manipulation, germ line therapy is not contemplated in humans. Gene transfer into cells that cannot pass on the new gene to subsequent generations (somatic cells) is called somatic gene therapy, and most research is directed toward this form of gene therapy.

Before genes can be inserted into humans with genetic diseases, several prerequisites must be met. The disease must be serious enough to warrant gene therapy, because despite knowledge of the molecular basis of the disease one cannot always predict the severity of the disease, and genetic diseases vary widely in their severity. Second, the particular target gene must be isolated, and the portions of the DNA that regulate its function must be defined. Third, the correct target cell or tissue must be identified, and efficient and safe methods must be developed to introduce the new gene into the target cells. Finally, there must be definite evidence from animal experiments that the inserted gene functions adequately and produces no deleterious effect in its new environment and that the cell that receives the new gene has a normal life span.

Broadly, gene therapy involves four steps. Isolation of the desired gene would be the first step. This step has been made feasible by recombinant DNA technology that uses procedures for isolating genes from large pieces of DNA. The isolated gene would then have to be transferred into cells, which can be accomplished by several physicochemical means or by using a particular virus known as a retrovirus as a vehicle, or vector, for transfer of genetic material into the cell. Once in the cell, the gene would have to be directed to the appropriate chromosomal location, and once inside the cell, the activity of the gene would have to be regulated appropriately so that it functions sufficiently and at the appropriate time in its new position. These latter two steps are complex and less understood and are the focus of ongoing research.

Applications of the Method

Isolation of the desired gene as a first step toward gene therapy is accomplished by standard recombinant DNA technology. Genes can be isolated from so-called complementary DNA libraries, which are collections of copies of all the mRNAs, that is, the expressed genes in any given tissue. Synthetic, small pieces of DNA can be used as hooks or probes for identifying and isolating the appropriate genes from these libraries. These methods have led to the isolation of genes from various kinds of organisms, including viruses, bacteria, yeast, algae, plants, and humans and other mammals. A limiting step, however, is that knowledge of the regions that control the expression of genes is still primitive.

Once a gene is isolated, it would have to be transferred into cells. There are four general methods used to accomplish this transfer. The first and main method is fusion. A gene can be put into a "bag" that can then be fused to the target cell. The bag can be a whole cell, a fat globule called a liposome, or a red cell. The second method includes the use of chemicals, such as calcium phosphate, that have been used in gene transfer. The third possibility is the use of physical methods: For example, genes can be physically injected into the cell using microinjection techniques, or they can be passively transferred across membranes that have been exposed briefly to rapid pulses of high-voltage current, a technique called electrophoration. These methods, however, have been generally thought to be inefficient forms of achieving gene transfer. The fourth method is the use of viral vectors. Viruses used as vehicles that carry the gene are capable of infecting virtually every cell in the target population and can efficiently deliver the gene to the target cells. The most useful and popular viral vectors for the efficient introduction of foreign genes into target cells are retroviruses. These viruses carry an important unique enzyme called reverse transcriptase. This enzyme can make a DNA copy from a piece of RNA. These viruses can infect cells and, making use of this enzyme, integrate portions of the viral genome into the host cell genome. Then, foreign genes packaged into these viruses can be transferred into a target cell by infecting the target cell with the virus.

Once in the cell, the possibility of putting a new gene into the appropriate chromosomal location rather than anywhere on the chromosome at random is marginal. It has only been accomplished in yeast cells, and the reason for the inability to insert genes into the correct position in mammalian cells is unclear. The aberrant chromosomal location does not necessarily interfere with the ability of the cell to express the new gene, and the recipient cells can bring new genes under the regulation of the usual cell mechanisms.

Once inserted into the target cell chromosome, even if it is inserted randomly in a wrong position, there is evidence that suggests that the gene is being expressed, that is, copies of it in the form of RNA can be identified. There is insufficient knowledge about the regulation of these transferred genes at their new site. There may be multiple sites on a chromosome that influence the newly inserted gene and control its function appropriately. Overall, the newly added genes do seem to function and even are controlled at least partly by normal cell regulatory mechanisms.

In order to use gene therapy for human genetic diseases, research has focused on approaches that achieve gene transfer into target diseased cells harvested from the patient and then reimplant these genetically modified cells into the patient. The target organ for the implantation must be the site of relevant disease, easily accessible, manipulatable in the test tube or in the laboratory, susceptible to genetic modification methods, and, ideally, contain cells that are able to perpetuate a genetic correction, such as stem cells. If only mature cells carry the new gene, the newly introduced gene function will be lost as the cells mature and die. Finally, it should be possible to reimplant genetically modified cells into the patient in a functional and stable form. Mammalian bone marrow satisfies all these criteria, and it has been one of the most attractive organs for early studies on gene therapy. Based on several animal studies, a genetic approach to the treatment of human bone marrow diseases has been proposed. One example of such a disease is thalassemia; therapeutic procedures would involve complete eradication of all the patient's abnormal bone marrow and the reinfusion of bone marrow that has cells that contain the new normal beta-globin gene inserted into them by viral vectors. This procedure is called bone marrow transplantation.

There are other genetic diseases in which the symptoms and manifestations of the disease are a result of abnormalities of the bone marrow and blood cells, although the basic defect affects the gene in all cells universally. An example is a disease caused by adenosine deaminase deficiency (ADA), which causes severe abnormalities in some blood cells, leading to immune deficiency. Bone marrow transplantation is useful for treating affected children because it restores immune competence, without which they invariably die. In practice, marrow from a normal, healthy matched donor is implanted, and immune competence is reestablished without correction of the ADA-deficiency in other tissue cells. These results suggest that the same objective can be achieved by infusion of the patient's own bone marrow cells into which the normal ADA gene has been inserted. All studies thus far have been in animal models; more knowledge will have to be acquired regarding the regulation of the gene that is transferred and the safety of using viral vectors will have to be demonstrated before bone marrow transplantation for gene transfer becomes a new option for therapy of some genetic diseases.

Context

The most obvious human genetic diseases that are candidates for potential gene therapy are those in which a single known gene does not function properly. Single gene defects are important because they account for a high health-care burden. That condition results from the fact that they are chronic and often appear at birth, and may require therapy with expensive special diets or blood products. In addition, there is the personal problemfaced by the family burdened with a handicapped child. There are more than 100 million people in the world who carry the abnormal gene for the potentially lethal blood disorders sickle-cell anemia and thalassemia, and approximately 200,000 children die each year from this single set of gene defects. It is now possible to detect some single gene defects in the fetus during the first two months of pregnancy and offer the parents an abortion. Most communities accept this alternative as being better than having a severely handicapped child. There may be some families who refuse abortion, however, or who do not come for diagnosis in time. Also, there are a range of single-gene defects that result in diseases that require much attention but are not so handicapping that the families regard abortion as acceptable. Therefore, there is an identifiable need for gene therapy.

Disease models that have been studied include several diseases in which the bone marrow has been studied as a target organ for gene therapy. Genetic diseases that involve the brain and the nervous system have been studied as potential models for gene therapy using viral vectors that specifically infect nerve cells.

Human cancer is associated with several genetic aberrations, and gene therapy may be feasible for some types of cancer. One example is the cancer of the eye called retinoblastoma. The cancer cells from this tumor lack a gene that in normal cells is thought to control normal cell growth—the so-called tumor-suppressing gene. Gene therapy in animal models has successfully reinserted this gene, resulting in inhibition of tumor growth. Similar studies with other suppressor-gene defects will be important to establish this general approach to therapy.

Nongenetic diseases may also be treated by gene transfer. Infectious diseases such as acquired immune deficiency syndrome (AIDS) result from the infectious agent's genes; an understanding of those genes and their functions will suggest new targets for therapy.

Despite the documented medical need, and the powerful technology available, prospects for gene therapy in humans remain controversial. One of the concerns is the ethical problems in relation to human experimentation. The prospects for gene therapy do not seem to pose any new ethical problems in relation to well-established codes of conducting human experiments. Because of the irreversible nature of this therapy, however, more care than usual must be exercised in the design of the experiments, and scientific rigor should be considered an ethical requirement for work in this field. Other ethical considerations are directed at concerns that genetic manipulation threatens the very concept of what it is to be human and may interfere with the natural development of the human species. Before gene therapy can be effectively performed in humans, more knowledge will have to be gained about the structure and function of normal and abnormal genes and their regulation. It must be proved that it is safe and effective before it is applied in practice. In the words of Theodore Friedmann, a leading scientist in the field, the alteration of mutant genes by gene transfer that corrects the manifestations of a disease represents the conversion of the swords of pathology into the plowshares of therapy.

Bibliography

Friedmann, Theodore. *Gene Therapy: Fact and Fiction*. Cold Spring Harbor, N.Y.: Cold Spring Harbor Laboratory, 1983. This book summarizes the proceedings of a conference on gene therapy attended by the world's leading authorities on gene therapy and molecular biology. It is specifically aimed at a lay audience and covers all aspects of gene therapy in simple and dramatically lucid language. The 124-page book has an excellent glossary to supplement a well-written text.

_____. "Progress Toward Human Gene Therapy." *Science* 244 (June 16, 1989): 1275-1281. This state-of-the-art review highlights the various applications of gene therapy. It reviews all aspects of the methodology, using a simple diagram to explain gene therapy. A brief review of the ethical considerations is also presented, and there are more than a hundred references.

Lehn, P. M. "Gene Therapy Using Bone Marrow Transplantation." *Bone Marrow Transplantation* 1 (1989): 243-258. This article is a state-of-the-art review of the use of bone marrow transplantation in gene therapy. It is a well-written article that provides great detail regarding the use of viral vectors for gene transfer and uses three simple figures to explain the process. The potential applications of gene therapy are reviewed with particular emphasis on the bone marrow as a target organ. A list of sixty-six references supplements the text.

Weatherall, D. J. "Gene Therapy." *British Medical Journal* 298 (March, 1989): 691-693. A brief review of the subject succinctly summarizes the prospects for gene therapy. Methodology as well as applications are reviewed, and this article is aimed at an audience with a basic background in molecular biology. Twenty pertinent references are provided.

Williamson, Bob. "Gene Therapy." *Nature* 298 (July, 1982): 416-418. This article is meant for a broad audience, and hence the review contains simple language. The main focus of the article is to provide the background information on the need for gene therapy, highlight the potential problems, and review the ethical considerations. The actual description of the methods involved is very briefly outlined. A short list of seven pertinent references is provided.

Anand Karnad

Cross-References

GENES AND NUCLEIC ACIDS

Type of life science: Molecular biology
Other fields of study: Biochemistry, developmental biology (embryology), evolutionary biology, genetics, and microbiology

Genes, the basic hereditary units of all living cells and of viruses, are composed of molecules of DNA, within which is encoded the information necessary for RNA molecules to transcribe and translate the genetic message into the proteins of all living cells. DNA and RNA are macromolecules of nucleic acid that respectively constitute and express genetic messages.

Principal terms

AMINO ACID: one of the twenty types of organic molecules that combine linearly to form proteins during translation

ANTICODON: a group of three nucleotides at one loop-end of a transfer RNA molecule that pairs with a reciprocal three-nucleotide codon of a messenger RNA

CODON: a group of three nucleotides on a messenger RNA that recognizes and pairs with reciprocal nucleotides of the transfer RNA's anticodon

DEOXYRIBONUCLEIC ACID (DNA): a double-stranded, helical macromolecule composed of H-bonded pairs of purines (double ring nitrogen bases) and pyrimidines (single ring nitrogen bases)

NUCLEIC ACID: a macromolecule composed of many nucleotides joined by linkages through adjacent nitrogen base-sugar-phosphate covalent (strong, shared) chemical bonds

NUCLEOTIDE: a molecule composed of a nitrogen base (purine or pyrimidine) covalently bonded to a pentose sugar at its #1 carbon and at the sugar's #5 carbon to a phosphate group

PURINE: an organic base molecule with a double ring structure composed of carbon and nitrogen atoms with attached $-NH_2$ (amino), $=O$ (oxygen), or $-H$ (hydrogen) groups

PYRIMIDINE: an organic base with a single ring structure of carbon and nitrogen atoms with attached $-NH_2$, $-H$, $=O$, or $-CH_3$ groups

REPLICATION: precise duplication of a macromolecule

RIBONUCLEIC ACID (RNA): a single-stranded nucleic acid composed of purine nucleotides (adenine or guanine) and pyrimidine nucleotides (uracil or cytosine)

Summary of the Phenomenon

Nucleic acids were discovered in the mid-nineteenth century, but their role as genetic material was not substantiated until the mid-twentieth century. Many individuals contributed clues which led to the recognition that "genes are nucleic acid," but primary credit is given to James D. Watson and Francis H. C. Crick for explaining the molecular basis of deoxyribonucleic acid (DNA) in what came to be known as the central dogma of molecular genetics. Though newer revelations have caused minor revisions of the dogma, it remains the established basis for both the structural and functional aspects of the gene and molecular biology generally.

To be a prime candidate for genetic material, a molecule must possess stability sufficient to avoid excessive spontaneous change/mutation, replication mechanisms which ensure that the copy of the genetic material is precisely like that of the original from which it was copied, and capability for translation into the protein structures—including enzymes—which are the means by which gene expression is achieved in living cells.

One of the first questions asked by persons studying DNA as a likely genetic material was, how does a complicated molecule like DNA duplicate itself? If each cell in an organism or each single-celled organism in a population is to contain identical genetic information, the duplication process must guarantee that the product of molecular replication is identical to that of the original molecule. There is excellent evidence that this is accomplished by concurrent enzymatic separation of the purine-pyrimidine nucleotide pairs along the DNA molecule by breaking of the hydrogen bonds between them, permitting the two strands of the double helix of nucleotides to separate into two single strands at the point of replication. Each nucleotide then acquires new complementary nucleotides to reestablish the identical double helix structure of the initial DNA. This process is semiconservative, since it retains the linear integrity of the sugar-phosphate linkages and because the nucleotides are neither fully dispersed nor fully conserved while serving as a pattern or template for formation of the new DNA molecule. Furthermore, the specific enzymes that direct separation of the helical strands and synthesis of the new DNA have been identified sufficiently to permit experimental synthesis of a "gene" in vitro, to transcribe this gene, and to translate it into the genetic message coded for in the de novo gene.

The genetic message is determined by a coding system in which the sequence of nucleotides ultimately is translated into the amino acid sequence (primary structure) of proteins (enzymes and structural protein molecules), which expresses the genetic message of hereditary traits in living cells of all organisms. While not completely universal, this code is so widely prevalent as to be accepted as part of the central dogma.

Genetic information is analogous to a language system in which the "alphabet" consists of four letters: the first four letters of the nucleotides adenine, cytosine, guanine, and thymine for DNA, with uracil replacing thymine in ribonucleic acid (RNA), which is used in transcription and translation of the gene. All "words" are three letters long (triplet code). The DNA is used as a template for synthesis of three classes of RNA (messenger RNA, transfer RNA, and ribosomal RNA) necessary for transcription and translation of a "message" that determines a gene product/

protein. RNA is copied—starting from a specific promoter site—from a single DNA strand. Single strands of messenger RNA (mRNA) codons (mRNA being triplets of RNA nucleotides) are synthesized until a termination site occurs on the DNA; the mRNA then moves to and resides on the ribosomes, to which transfer RNA (tRNA) brings the specific amino acids needed for translation of the nucleic acid message into the amino acid/polypeptide message. tRNA is relatively shorter than either mRNA or rRNA, is coiled back upon itself to form a hairpin- or clover-leaf-shaped structure which is able to attach specific amino acids at one of its single-strand ends, and has an "anticodon" in a closed-loop that is reciprocal for the triplet of nucleotides in the codon of the mRNA. For example, the mRNA codon UUU attracts the tRNA carrying the amino acid phenylalanine and having the anticodon AAA.

Ribosomes consist of two different sizes of subunits, both made of structural protein and ribosomal RNA (rRNA), which forms two binding sites, the aminoacyl (A) site and the peptidyl (P) site. The near-universality of the code is accompanied by several peculiarities. First of all, because there are four nucleotides in the code, there are 4^3, or sixty-four, possible genetic words in the "dictionary" of DNA. Only twenty words (amino acids), however, are necessary for the messages, one for each different amino acid, and it is known that two or more DNA code words can specify mRNAs, each of which will attract the appropriate tRNA with the specific amino acid to be added to the polypeptide chain formed during translation. This "redundancy" in the code permits some "wobble effect" in the coding process so that if the first two bases are correct, the remaining third base may utilize one or another of the other three possible nucleotides and still specify the correct message. This "safety factor" in the code is presumed to have evolutionary significance in permitting some changes in nucleic acids without major influence on important protein structures.

The central dogma of molecular genetics as presently modified asserts that in most circumstances DNA constitutes the nucleotide sequence of the genetic molecule, which is transcribed into the nucleotide sequence of mRNA, which, in turn, is translated with the assistance of tRNA and rRNA into the amino acid sequence of polypeptides, which are incorporated into protein structures of gene expression. The modifications of the dogma are necessary to meet the few exceptions that occur, and especially to accommodate the fact that there are enzymes, such as reverse transcriptase in the Rous sarcoma virus, that preferentially use RNA as a template for assembly of DNA, a reversal of the usual tenets of the central dogma. Despite these amendments, the central dogma as envisioned by Crick remains valid for DNA as the nearly universal genetic material: Genes *are* nucleic acid.

Methods of Study

Early chemical studies of nucleic acids were conducted by the Swiss physician Frederick Miescher, who described "nuclein" (now known to include nucleic acids and proteins). The firm connection between nucleic acids and hereditary material did not, however, occur until about 1944, when O. T. Avery, C. M. Macleod, and M. McCarty found DNA to be the substance inducing transformation of pneumococcal bacteria. At about the same time, Alfred Mirsky and Hans Ris found that the amount of DNA in sperm nuclei (which have only one set of chromosomes) was precisely one-half the amount present in body cells (having two sets of chromosomes, one set from each parent). Erwin Chargaff and his associates in 1952 showed that the ratio of adenine to thymine in degraded DNA is one to one, and so is the cytosine to guanine ratio, but the amount of adenine plus thymine is not necessarily equal to the amount of guanine plus cytosine and varies greatly in different sources of DNA.

Watson and Crick, studying X-ray crystallographs of DNA (prepared in another laboratory by Maurice Wilkins and Rosalind Franklin) and building models of sticks and copper wire with uncanny insight, came up with a molecular structure for D.N.A. (deoxyribose nucleic acid), which "caught the imagination of geneticists as few other ideas ever did." Their publication in 1953 of specific aspects of this model and its self-replicating capacities fueled the revolution which came to be called the central dogma of molecular genetics. They fully recognized that the two helical chains were wound around the same axis, the "phosphate diester groups joining beta-D-ribofuranose residues with 3', 5' linkages" and with the chains running in opposite directions: "The two chains are held together by the purine and pyrimidine bases . . . joined together in pairs" by hydrogen bonds. They recognized that the purines and pyrimidines must occur in pairs to fill the space between the side chains appropriately, and they repeated the previous assertion of Chargaff that adenine (A) always pairs with thymine (T), and guanine (G) with cytosine (C), the reason being that A and T tend to form only two hydrogen bonds in their usual form, while G and C tend to form three hydrogen bonds in their usual form.

The years immediately following saw many applications of radioisotope technology, biochemistry, biophysics, and molecular separation technologies, including chromatography, electrophoresis, density-gradient centrifugation, and ultimately nucleic acid and protein sequencing, all of which made possible the fleshing-out of the theory-become-dogma. In 1958, M. Meselson and Stahl showed evidence (from studies of density gradient centrifugation of homogenates from bacteria synthesizing new DNA in the presence of nucleotides with heavy nitrogen) that semiconservative replication of DNA occurred, and was consistent with the Watson and Crick DNA model; M. W. Nirenberg and J. H. Matthaei reported in 1961 the dependence of cell-free protein synthesis upon naturally occurring or synthetic polyRNAs, and by 1977 Hap Khorana and his group ultimately synthesized a bacteriophage gene — the entire gene, its promoter, and terminator regions consisted of a total of 207 nucleotide pairs — without relying on a natural DNA template. Literally hundreds of small pieces of the jigsaw puzzle that ultimately became the central dogma were contributed by many scientists in many different laboratories, but those mentioned above represent the more important breakthroughs that made the detailed aspects more complete. There will no doubt be many additional contributions arising from future research, but it is unlikely that the dogma will be significantly modified, because of the overwhelming support it has received to date.

Context

Nucleic acid molecules are the genetic material; individual genetic differences in all living organisms, including humans, result from differences in the structure of their individual DNA makeup. Blood types, hair color, eye color, height, and virtually all other individual human traits can be traced to the proteins specified by genetic information encoded in DNA, transcribed into mRNA, and translated into protein structure with the assistance of tRNA and rRNA. Knowing the molecular structure of DNA and its genetic expression in proteins has permitted a much better understanding of the molecular basis for genetic evolution, genetic manipulation via genetic engineering, and the application of the molecular basis for and treatment of genetic diseases in human beings and other organisms.

It is known that mutations of genetic material occur as a result of changes in the nucleotides of the DNA or RNA. Mistakes are thus seen as "language errors" in the genetic sentence that cause mutant protein molecules to form, resulting in a change of expression of a genetic trait. For example, one medically important gene mutation, sickle-cell hemoglobin in humans, results from the substitution of a single amino acid (valine for glutamic acid) encoding the sixth amino acid from the end of the beta chain of hemoglobin. Individuals receiving the sickle-cell gene from two asymptomatic parents (but carriers of the recessive sickle trait) have a one-fourth probability of having the disease known as sickle-cell anemia, in which altered hemoglobin molecules change the erythrocyte to a sickle-shaped cell, which is associated with insufficient oxygen transport in the circulatory system.

Similar explanations are known for Tay Sachs disease, insulin-dependent diabetes, phenylketonuria, and many other diseases of humans that may ultimately be treated by using the knowledge of and products formed by application of the central dogma of molecular genetics in an integrated, coherent system of knowledge which connects all molecular phenomena of genetic structure and function with nucleic acid structure and function. For example, human insulin and an important human growth hormone are produced by genetically engineered bacteria that use specific human DNA genes spliced into the DNA of the bacteria, which are then grown in large quantities to produce the desired human insulin and growth hormone, each now available at a greatly reduced cost.

While most mutations are detrimental to the organism possessing them, some confer better adaptability for the specific genetic characteristic which they determine; thus, mutation of genes furnishes the genetic raw materials and variability upon which natural selection and evolution are based. Moreover, the use of new and engineered genes in plant and animal breeding programs promises new and exciting frontiers for even greater agricultural and pharmacological productivity, as well as more effective treatment against pathogens of both humans and domesticated animals.

Bibliography

Campbell, Neil. *Biology.* 2d ed. Menlo Park, Calif.: Benjamin/Cummings, 1990. This textbook clearly presents structural and functional features of nucleic acids, transcription, and translation, as well as related topics of gene mutation and the genetic code. Clearly labeled diagrams are helpful to the nontechnical reader. Suggested further readings, glossary, and index are present. College level, but can be useful to the high school student as well as the general reader.

Darnell, James. "RNA." *Scientific American* 253 (October, 1985): 68-78. Describes RNA in its role between gene and protein. Outlines differences between RNA and DNA and their important functional and structural significance and complexities. The relationship between genes and gene products is well illustrated with diagrams.

Darnell, James, Harvey Lodish, and David Baltimore. *Molecular Cell Biology.* New York: Scientific American Books, 1986. Chapter 4 gives excellent details of synthesis of proteins and nucleic acids. It has good illustrations, clear explanations of the experimental basis of the roles assigned to the different major molecules and structures of the cell. Dimensional diagrams are helpful to conceptualize the information, and the detailed bibliography is excellent. College level.

Raven, Peter H., and George B. Johnson. *Biology.* 2d ed. St. Louis: Times Mirror/Mosby, 1989. This voluminous college textbook features multicolored diagrams and clear explanations of various structural and functional aspects of nucleic acids, transcription, and translation, as well as gene mutation, the genetic code, and evolution. Study questions (and answers), further readings, glossary, and index. College level, but the intrepid high school student or general reader will also benefit from the well-written coverage.

Watson, James. *The Double Helix.* New York: New American Library, 1969. A fascinating best-seller by James Watson, a Nobel Prize winner and one of the founders of the central dogma of molecular biology. A personal account (with many personal insights) of the race for determining the structural and functional aspects of DNA and its implications for molecular biology.

Watson, J. D., and F. H. C. Crick. "Molecular Structure of Nucleic Acids: A Structure for Deoxyribose Nucleic Acid." *Nature* 171 (1953): 737-738. This is the remarkably lucid two-page account of Watson and Crick's published concept of the DNA molecule, based on previous work by Chargaff and on unpublished X-ray crystallographic patterns from the laboratory of Maurice Wilkins and Rosalind Franklin. The hypothetical structure suggested here for a self-reproducing molecule "caught the imagination of geneticists as few other ideas ever did," according to James Peters in his foreword to the reprinted copy of the article in *Classic Papers in Genetics* (Englewood Cliffs, N.J.: Prentice-Hall, 1959).

Donald M. Huffman

Cross-References

DNA's Molecular Structure, 706; Eukaryotic Gene Organization, 871; Genes and Polypeptide Chains, 1141; The Genetic Code, 1148; Deciphering the Genetic Code, 1155; Genetics: A Historical Perspective, 1177; Nucleic Acid Structure, 1987.

GENES AND POLYPEPTIDE CHAINS

Type of life science: Molecular biology
Other fields of study: Biochemistry and genetics

Genes are sequences of nucleotides in DNA chains in the nuclei of cells in higher animals. The sequence of organic bases in these nucleotides contains information in code form that is transferred through RNA to polypeptide (protein) synthesis sites outside the nucleus. In this way the genetic material, DNA, forms the organism by directing the construction of its enzymes and other proteins.

Principal terms

CHROMOSOME: a structure in the nucleus of cells of higher plants and animals that contains the genetic material DNA, with associated proteins

CODON: a sequence of three bases in the RNA that conveys genetic information from chromosome DNA to the site of protein (polypeptide) synthesis in the cell; each codon specifies an amino acid in the final protein

DEOXYRIBONUCLEIC ACID (DNA): a very long-chain molecule in the cell nucleus that holds genetic information in the form of sequences of bases in the connected units (nucleotides) that make up the DNA molecule

EXON: an active portion of a gene, containing genetic information that gives the sequence of amino acids in a particular protein

GENE: a sequence of nucleotides in a DNA molecule that gives (through its sequence of bases) the order of amino acids in a polypeptide, or protein, synthesized in the cell

INTRON: an inactive portion of a gene that contains no usable information leading to protein synthesis

NUCLEOTIDE: the small unit that, linked head-to-tail with other nucleotides, makes up DNA and RNA molecules; each nucleotide contains a sugar and a phosphate group, which together form the links of the chain molecule, plus an organic base that conveys genetic information

POLYPEPTIDE: a chain-type molecule in which the individual links are amino acids, numbering from a few to more than a thousand; also called a protein

PROTEIN: properly, a polypeptide containing fifty or more amino acids, but "protein" is often used interchangeably with "polypeptide"

RIBONUCLEIC ACID (RNA): a long-chain molecule of different types that serves a number of functions in assembling a finished protein; types include messenger RNA, transfer RNA, and ribosomal RNA

RIBOSOME: a structure outside the nucleus, composed of RNA molecules and enzymes (protein molecules), that is the site of protein synthesis

Summary of the Phenomenon

When the relation between genes and proteins was first established in the 1940's, the molecular nature of the gene material was not understood. It was known only that some structure contained in the chromosome caused the cell to synthesize a particular protein. This knowledge was summed up in the phrase, "one gene, one enzyme." Later it became clear that genes dictate the synthesis of all body proteins, not only enzymes in a particular cell, and the slogan changed to "one gene, one polypeptide chain." Even the expanded formulation has proven vastly too simple, however, and what is known about DNA, genes, and proteins can no longer be contained in a single statement of this type. A series of statements is needed to give even an outline of the relationship among these essential genetic structures.

Genes are portions of the nucleic acid molecule deoxyribonucleic acid (DNA), found in cell nuclei in higher animals. DNA is a very long-chain molecule with no side chains or branches. The links of the DNA chain are units called nucleotides, each of which contains a sugar molecule (deoxyribose) and a phosphate group that form the actual chain and an organic base (a nitrogen-containing organic molecule) that attaches to the sugar and projects from the chain. A DNA molecule can contain from a million to a billion or more nucleotides.

Four bases are found in DNA: adenine (A), cytosine (C), guanine (G), and thymine (T). Because of their size, shape, and polarity, the bases in one DNA molecule form selective attractions to those in another, leading to stable attachments between particular pairs of bases. The pairs that form attachments are adenine and thymine (A-T) and cytosine and guanine (C-G). These are the attachments that hold together two complementary strands of DNA in the well-known double helix configuration.

A gene is a part of one strand only. A gene consists of a sequence of a few hundred to a few thousand nucleotides in a DNA molecule. This means that a unique order exists for a few hundred to a few thousand bases in the gene. Given the size of a DNA molecule, it is clear that it has room for many such sequences; each DNA molecule contains many genes.

The gene relates to a protein in a specific way. The protein, like DNA, is a long, unbranched chain molecule, with the difference that the links in the protein chain are amino acids instead of nucleotides. Twenty different amino acids are found in proteins. The sequence of these amino acids in the protein is dictated by the sequence of bases in the nucleotides of the gene. Four bases cannot be related to twenty amino acids on a one-to-one basis; rather, the sequence of bases in the gene is divided into three-base "words," each of which indicates a particular amino acid in the finished protein. Other code words indicate the beginning and end of the gene, so that the protein-building mechanism knows where to start and stop.

The information thus contained in the gene is not used directly to synthesize a protein molecule. Rather, it is copied to an intermediate molecule of ribonucleic acid (RNA), a chain molecule like DNA but much shorter. The mechanism of copying is the pairing of bases: The RNA copy of the gene contains bases in a sequence complementary to that in the parent DNA, somewhat like a photographic negative. The three-base sequences in this "messenger" RNA (mRNA) are the codons that actually cause particular amino acids to be selected and linked in series to form the polypeptide (protein) molecule. This linkage takes place outside the cell nucleus (therefore, away from the parent DNA) at subcellular structures called ribosomes.

A gene leads to a polypeptide (or protein), but neither directly nor inevitably. First of all, in higher organisms all the DNA (hence all the genes) responsible for every protein in the body is present in the nucleus of each cell in the body. The cells of the body are of different types, and the differences are both structural and functional. Yet both structure and function are dictated by proteins—structural proteins such as those of bones, tendons, and skin, and enzymes that catalyze all body functions. The question is how a particular cell can make only those proteins it needs when it has the genes to make all proteins. The answer lies in a set of reactions that activate only the necessary genes for a given cell, leaving the others dormant.

Second, a gene is not necessarily a simple sequence of a certain number of bases coding for one-third as many amino acids. The gene also contains bases outside the code sequence to show where it begins and ends; more confusingly, the gene can contain sequences that are not part of the protein-forming information at all. A gene, that is, contains active sequences called exons and inactive sequences called introns; the introns can be from a small part to more than half of the chunk of DNA chain that is termed a gene. Moreover, some introns actually do contain genes— that is, they are base sequences that are inactive to a gene in which the intron is nothing but an intron, but they contain an active portion that is another, different gene. All this information raises a set of questions about how the protein-forming mechanism makes sense of this complex template. The answers to these questions concern the mechanism by which the gene's information is transferred from the DNA chain to an intermediary chain called RNA, thence to the growing protein molecule. Introns can be snipped out at a number of points in this sequence.

Finally, the original "one gene, one enzyme" pronouncement is sometimes inaccurate in the strictest sense—that is, more than one protein can be attributed to a particular gene. Again, more questions are raised, this time about how a gene's base code can be used in different ways; the answers involve different kinds of intricate regulatory reactions. Nevertheless, the central fact is that a gene is clearly and (in general) unambiguously linked to a particular polypeptide or protein that an organism requires for its function or structure.

Methods of Study

Three major problems have been investigated in the relation of genes to proteins:

confirmation that the DNA of a gene passes its message in three-base codons through mRNA to a protein molecule; identification of the start- and stop-signals that allow only the gene material to be copied from DNA to the intermediate RNA; and identification of the devices by which intron material is removed from the RNA to produce a final template for protein synthesis.

The three-base code was the first of these problems to yield to research. Biochemist Marshall Nirenberg constructed a synthetic RNA containing only one base, uracil (U), a base that occupies the same positions in RNA as thymine does in DNA. He then made an artificial protein-synthesis mixture containing ribosomes, amino acids and their carrier molecules, protein-building enzymes, and his one-base RNA. This mixture produced a polypeptide (protein) containing only the amino acid phenylalanine. Thus, the three-base sequence UUU is the RNA code (that is, the codon) for phenylalanine. Since the bases in RNA are complementary to those in DNA (that is, they are in a kind of photographic negative and positive relationship to each other), this means that the base sequence AAA (three adenines) is the DNA coding unit that dictates the presence of a phenylalanine unit in the finished protein. Other one-base RNA's revealed that AAA is the codon for lysine, CCC for proline, and GGG for glycine; the corresponding DNA sequences are TTT, GGG, and CCC. As chemists learned to control the laboratory synthesis of RNA molecules, all combinations of repeating three-base units were tried, and a complete table of RNA codons now exists.

Constructing the RNA codon table had an unexpected spinoff: Three of the sixty-four codons were found to indicate not a particular amino acid but a "stop" command in protein synthesis. This solved half of the problem of how genes are turned on and off. The other half is much more complex. It appears that the "start" sequences are always present at the beginning of genes, but they are wrapped in an inhibitory enzyme that prevents the gene information from being transferred to an RNA molecule. Various chemicals (usually specific to the protein that the cell needs) can initiate the unwrapping process to make an RNA and ultimately a protein molecule. Research has concentrated on identifying these chemicals by including them in protein-synthesis mixtures to see whether any synthesis takes place.

Identifying the chemicals that cause removal of introns from RNA copies of gene material has followed much the same "see whether it works" pattern, but the problem is very complex. Some workers have identified a group of compounds that act in concert; they called it a "spliceosome." The function of this structure (if it is a discrete structure) is exactly what the name implies: to remove introns and then splice the exons together into a finished template for protein synthesis. Much work remains before this process is fully understood.

Context

The relation between genes and polypeptides (proteins) is the pivot point of genetics, developmental biology, reproduction, and evolution, and it also has a bearing on many more remote areas of biology. Proteins, in the form of enzymes, direct literally every aspect of growth, function, and reproduction in all organisms from bacteria to higher plants and animals. Enzymes catalyze the synthesis of all structural and metabolic materials, whether protein, lipid, carbohydrate, or nucleic acid, or molecules containing more than one of these types. Enzymes even direct the operation of other enzymes, allowing different cells and tissues to be constructed from the same raw materials, often by the same reactions. Thus, enzymes help create individuals that differ from one another both within and among species. Enzymes, since they are proteins, are formed according to patterns contained in genes that are parts of the DNA molecules central to this whole process.

New organisms are able to develop from a single cell because that cell contains all the DNA—hence, all the genes—that the new individual needs to grow to its characteristic shape and function. If the single cell comes from a single parent, the offspring will be identical to the parent, because its entire array of genes is identical. If the single cell comes from two parents, as a fertilized ovum, the traits of the offspring will be an amalgam of those of the parents, because each parent has contributed some DNA, hence some genes. This is the process of sexual reproduction, which keeps the "gene pool" of a species distributed so that the loss of an individual rarely means the loss of an entire set of genes.

Evolutionary change is related to the gene-protein axis in two ways. First, an individual may simply inherit an unusually favorable set of genes from its parents, allowing it better to compete for territory, food, and mating. Second, if an individual's gene material is altered (by radiation or other molecular accident), different proteins can result, thereby producing an individual different from the parents. If the difference is favorable and breeds true, it can give a competitive edge to further offspring of that individual. In either case, the competitive edge brings about the evolutionary selection that, over time, has produced the adaptability and enormous diversity of species that currently exist.

When gene material is inserted into normal cells by viruses, wrong proteins can be produced that are required by the virus but damaging to the cell. This results in the viral infection of diseases from the common cold to acquired immune deficiency syndrome (AIDS) and certain kinds of cancer. The infection can be eliminated only when the body's immune system eliminates the source—the virus and its alien genetic material. If this cannot be done quickly enough, permanent damage or death can occur.

Bibliography

Baum, Stuart J., and Charles W. J. Scaife. *Chemistry: A Life Science Approach.* New York: Macmillan, 1975. Introductory-level discussion of biochemistry. Chapter 27, "The Nucleic Acids," gives information on the relation of DNA to protein synthesis. The book has the advantage of containing background material in both general and organic chemistry. A more recent treatment, also by Baum, is *Introduction to Organic and Biological Chemistry.* 4th ed. New York: Macmillan, 1987.

Bronk, J. Ramsey. *Chemical Biology*. New York: Macmillan, 1973. The elementary material in this older textbook is sound, with later discovery updating it rather than making it obsolete. Moreover, the quality of the explanation is very high. The relevant chapters are 5, "Nucleic Acids and Heredity," and 16, "Control of Protein Synthesis."

Darnell, James E., Jr. "RNA." *Scientific American* 253 (October, 1985): 68-78. Describes the function of RNA as the intermediary between the gene and the protein. Several types of RNA serve in this function; they are described in detail.

Doolittle, Russell F. "Proteins." *Scientific American* 253 (October, 1985): 88-99. Discusses the relation of DNA and proteins, including interesting information on how amino acid sequence is related to base sequence in the laboratory. Much information on protein structure and function in enzymes.

Felsenfeld, Gary. "DNA." *Scientific American* 253 (October, 1985): 58-67. Describes structure of DNA, principally, but also discusses (with illustrations) how genes are turned on by removal of repressor molecules that prevent their information from being passed on to intermediate RNA molecules. This article, together with the preceding two and seven others, is contained in a single issue of *Scientific American* under the collective title "The Molecules of Life."

Holliday, Robin. "A Different Kind of Inheritance." *Scientific American* 260 (June, 1989): 60-73. A somewhat speculative article about the methods by which genes are turned on and off during development of the mature organism to allow it to grow into its characteristic form and function by directing different cells to assume different activities.

Monmaney, Terence. "Complex Window on Life's Most Basic Molecules." *Smithsonian* 16 (July, 1985): 114-119. Excellent color illustrations, with accompanying text, of computer-generated structures of DNA, RNA, and other important biological molecules.

Ptashne, Mark. "How Gene Activators Work." *Scientific American* 260 (January, 1989): 40-47. Brief but highly informative discussion, by a researcher in the field, about advances in understanding how genes are activated to direct protein synthesis: what types of compounds (and in some cases, what specific compounds) remove repressor molecules and how repression operates. Excellent diagrams.

Steitz, Joan Argetsinger. "'Snurps.'" *Scientific American* 258 (June, 1988): 56-63. The word of the title is an acronym for "Small NUclear RibonucleoProteins," the molecules that remove intron sequences from the RNA that carries gene information to the ribosomes. The author describes her work that shows how these molecules form a "spliceosome" that carries out intron removal to leave a usable copy of gene information for protein synthesis.

Stryer, Lubert. *Biochemistry*. 3d ed. New York: W. H. Freeman, 1988. A college-level text that assumes extensive knowledge of organic chemistry, this book gives the full and detailed picture of the gene-to-protein relationship and synthesis. The most relevant chapters are 5, "Flow of Genetic Information"; 29, "RNA Synthesis and Splicing"; 30, "Protein Synthesis"; and 33-34, "Gene Expression in Procaryotes and Eucaryotes." Pertinent information is found in other chapters as well.

White, Ray, and C. Thomas Caskey. "The Human as an Experimental System in Molecular Genetics." *Science* 240 (June 10, 1988): 1483-1488. Techniques of gene-mapping—establishing the sites of genes on DNA molecules—in the human genetic material. Technical and somewhat difficult, but filled with information.

Robert M. Hawthorne, Jr.

Cross-References

DNA's Molecular Structure, 706; Eukaryotic Gene Organization, 871; Genes and Nucleic Acids, 1134; The Genetic Code, 1148; Nucleic Acid Structure, 1987; Proteins, 2272; Transcription of DNA to Form RNA, 2632; Translation of Messenger RNA to Form Protein, 2647.

THE GENETIC CODE

Type of life science: Molecular biology
Other fields of study: Biochemistry and genetics

The genetic code is the "language" of three-letter code words in RNA molecules that specifies the exact nature of every protein made by living organisms. Deciphering the genetic code has led to understanding the genetic basis for many diseases and how mutations occur.

Principal terms

AMINO ACID: any of twenty different small organic molecules that are polymerized to proteins by the translation process

ANTICODON: a sequence of three bases in a transfer RNA (tRNA) molecule that pairs with a particular codon in a messenger RNA (mRNA) molecule

BASE: any of several nitrogen-containing chemicals in DNA and RNA that are the basis for the genetic code

CHROMOSOME: a double-stranded (duplex) DNA molecule that contains several segments, or genes, that are each transcribed into an mRNA molecule that is the blueprint for the synthesis of a protein

CODON: a three-base sequence in an mRNA molecule that pairs with the anticodon of a tRNA and specifies that a particular amino acid is incorporated into a protein during translation

RIBOSOME: the machinery, composed of many proteins and RNA molecules, which synthesizes proteins during translation

TRANSCRIPTION: the process in which genes are used to produce mRNA blueprints for protein synthesis

TRANSFER RIBONUCLEIC ACID (TRNA): a small RNA molecule that carries specific amino acids to the ribosome for use in protein synthesis

TRANSLATION: the process in which mRNA, amino acids, tRNA, and ribosomes interact to synthesize proteins

WOBBLE RULES: rules that explain the base-pairing of tRNA anticodons to mRNA codons

Summary of the Phenomenon

The genetic code is the system by which all organisms convert the hereditary information carried in genes—sections of giant polymeric deoxyribonucleic acid (DNA) molecules called chromosomes—into the many proteins that make up the basis for the sum total of biological processes called life. Some functions of proteins that emphasize their importance include biological catalysis to speed up chemical reactions; contractions that make cell movement possible; transport of food into cells; removal of cellular wastes; actions of substances such as blood-clotting factors, antibodies, and hormones.

The genetic information present in a gene is encoded in a language that has a four-letter alphabet (A, G, C, and T). These letters represent four nitrogen-containing chemicals (the bases) named adenine, guanine, cytosine, and thymine, respectively. A and G are purine bases; C and T are pyrimidine bases. The bases are found in linear array in DNA chains (strands), arranged like strings of four kinds of beads. Each DNA strand contains many thousands of these "beads." The arrangement of the series of bases in a given section of DNA strand (a particular gene) stipulates the exact nature of the protein that the translation process will ultimately produce.

DNA molecules (chromosomes) are each giant, two-stranded duplexes. The two strands of each duplex are joined together (base-paired) by hydrogen bonds between A and T or between G and C. For example, a partial sequence -AGCTAAT- in one strand of a DNA molecule will form a base pair with the sequence -TCGATTA- in the other strand. Each DNA strand is composed of a sequence of many thousands of As, Gs, Ts, and Cs. These units of a DNA molecule are joined together by intervening molecules of phosphate and the sugar deoxyribose.

The two strands in a duplex run in opposite directions because of the nature of the DNA polymer chains produced. Therefore, they are said to be antiparallel. Readout of a gene, however, occurs in only one direction along any DNA strand. Consequently, where a DNA sequence such as -AGCTAAT- in one strand is read directly, the antiparallel DNA sequence -TCGATTA- in the other strand is read as -ATTAGCT-.

The protein produced by translation is also a polymer; however, all proteins (polypeptides) are composed of amino acid subunits joined directly to one another by chemical bonds called peptide bonds. Twenty different amino acids are found in proteins. Each of these amino acids is coded for by a sequence of bases generated from the information in the gene that stipulates its production.

Genes do not act directly in protein synthesis. A major reason why they do not is the fact that there is only one gene for any protein in a cell, and at any given instant the cell may require thousands of copies of the protein for which this gene carries the hereditary information. Because of this, cells make large numbers of copies of genes called messenger ribonucleic acid molecules (mRNAs). These RNA molecules, manufactured by a process called DNA transcription, are exact copies of the region of single-stranded DNA that makes up the gene. The mRNAs differ from the genes from which they are transcribed in that they contain the sugar ribose in place of deoxyribose and that the pyrimidine base uracil replaces the thymine. Also, they are antiparallel copies of the gene that is transcribed. Therefore, when the sequence -AGCTAAT- is transcribed, the mRNA sequence made -UCGAUUA- is read as -AUUAGCU- by the machinery of protein synthesis.

Protein synthesis (translation) uses the information in mRNAs as three-letter code words (codons). If two-letter codons were used instead, the A, G, C, and U alphabet would only provide sixteen combinations (AA, AC, AU, AG, CA, CC, CG, CU, UA, UC, UU, UG, GA, GC, GU, and GG). That would not allow translation of all twenty amino acids into proteins. Three-letter codons, however, allow sixty-four combinations of A, G, C, and U, a number in excess of the twenty needed. Because of this excess, many amino acids have two or more codons that stipulate their translation. Only sixty-one codons stipulate translation of amino acids. The other three (UAA, UAG, and UGA) are stop (termination) signals that signal the end of translation of a given protein to the protein-synthesizing machinery.

CODONS AND THE TWENTY AMINO ACIDS WHOSE TRANSLATION THEY STIPULATE

Alanine(GCU,GCC,GCA,GCG)	Leucine(UUA,UUG,CUU,CUC,CUA,CUG)
Arginine(GGU,CHC,CGA,CGG,AGA,AGG)	Lysine(AAA,AAG)
Asparagine(AAU,AAC)	Methionine(AUG)
Aspartic Acid(GAU,GAC)	Phenylalanine(UUU,UUC)
Cysteine(UGU,UGC)	Proline(CCU,CCC,CCA,CCG)
Glutamic Acid(GAA,GAG)	Serine(UCU,UCC,UCA,UCG,AGU,AGC)
Glutamine(CAA,CAG)	Threonine(ACU,ACC,ACA,ACG)
Glycine(GGU,GGC,GGA,GGG)	Tryptophan(UGG)
Histidine(CAU,CAC)	Tyrosine(UAU,UAC)
Isoleucine(AUU,AUC,AUA)	Valine(GUU,GUC,GUA,GUG)

The translation process that uses the codons requires that the mRNA to be translated binds to the protein-synthesizing machinery, a ribosome. Ribosomes are protein-assembly sites composed of several structural RNAs (rRNAs) and fifty-five proteins that carry out the mechanics of translating the information in the mRNA blueprint. The rRNAs can be viewed as the framework to which ribosomal proteins, the assembly machinery, are attached.

Amino acids to be assembled into a protein, in the order stipulated by the mRNA to be translated, are carried to the ribosome by transfer RNA (tRNA) molecules. Amino acids and tRNAs are chemically joined together. In translation, a tRNA molecule attaches to the complex between the ribosome and the mRNA because it contains an anticodon (with a three-base sequence) that can form a base pair with one codon in the mRNA. This base-pairing occurs as in DNA duplex formation, so that the mRNA and tRNA strands involved are antiparallel. For example, the codon AUC base-pairs with the anticodon GUA, usually called UAG. Codons UAA, UAG, and UGA signal termination of protein synthesis because they have no anticodons.

There are fifty-three anticodons in the genetic code. Each is found in a tRNA molecule that will carry only one amino acid. The anticodons base-pair with codons according to the "wobble hypothesis," as named by Francis Crick. The wobble hypothesis explains why a tRNA can recognize two codons. The third base on the tRNA anticodon has a variance, or "wobble," that allows it to pair with the third base of different mRNA codons. Interaction between anticodons and codons positions amino acids so that they can be assembled into the protein chains stipulated by the mRNA being copied. When termination codons are reached, finished protein molecules leave the ribosome.

The genetic code is also involved in starting synthesis of proteins. The start (initiation) signal is UAG, the codon for methionine, paired with a special tRNA that is the only one that can start synthesis of a peptide chain. Once the chain has been started, methionines that appear in other positions of a protein use the same codon, but a different methionine-binding tRNA.

The flexibility of codon-anticodon interaction minimizes mutation-generated mistakes that can be made in the translation of proteins. The fact that several codons exist for most amino acids, called the "degeneracy" of the code, helps here too. That results from the fact that when one of several codons that translate an amino acid is changed by a mutation, proteins that contain that amino acid—translated by its other codons—can still be made. This device minimizes the life-threatening effects of many mutations. Furthermore, codons in the genetic code are designed so that most mutations that change a single base produce codons that stipulate translation of a structurally similar amino acid. All these aspects of the code are beneficial to living organisms, minimizing the effects of mutations on them.

It is remarkable that the genetic code is the same for all organisms that have been examined, from bacteria to whales. The only exception to this "universality" of the code occurs in mitochondria, energy-producing organelles in cells of higher organisms (eukaryotic cells). Mitochondria have their own DNA, transcription, and translation systems. Differences in the code in mitochondria include several different codons (for example, UGA and UGG code for tryptophan) and some differences in wobble rules. These differences are viewed as helping to keep mitochondrial proteins and other cell proteins distinguishable. They are also cited as evidence for the theory that mitochondria were originally organisms that invaded the ancestors of eukaryotic cells and stayed on as symbionts.

Methods of Study

Understanding of the genetic code began with the work of Marshall Nirenberg and Heinrich Matthaei in 1961. They carried out the following experiment with RNA-like polyuridylic acid (poly U), which can be viewed as being a synthetic mRNA composed of hundreds of Us (UUUUUU . . . U). Poly U was added to twenty test tubes that each contained one radioactive amino acid, ribosomes, and all the other ingredients that are required for protein synthesis. After incubation, the contents of each test tube were examined. It was shown that a radioactive polypeptide (proteinlike molecule) was made only in the tube that contained radioactive phenylalanine. That is how the first codon, UUU, was discovered. Similar studies were carried out with poly C and with poly A by Nirenberg's group and by the group headed by Severo Ochoa. These experiments showed that AAA and CCC were the codons for lysine and proline.

Next, more-complex synthetic RNAs of defined composition (for example, poly UG, poly AC, poly GU) were made with the enzyme (or protein biological catalyst) called polynucleotide phosphorylase. The base compositions of most of the other codons were identified on the basis of the codons that could be present in such polymers and the amino acids incorporated into proteins when they were used as synthetic mRNAs. The base sequences, or spellings of the codons, however, could not be shown in this way. For example, a codon that contains a U and two Cs can be UUC, CUU, or UCU.

The spellings of the codons were determined when Nirenberg and Phillip Leder found that it was possible for ribosomes mixed with codon pieces of RNA, such as AAA, CGU, or CGA, to bind to specific tRNAs. Use of this method, termed the binding assay, allowed exact identification of all the codons that are shown in the table. This entire effort, regarded as the greatest scientific discovery of the 1960's, was completed only four years after Nirenberg's group first showed that poly U produced polyphenylalanine. Since then, the code words have been shown to be correct by many other methods.

A modification of the "binding" assay that used six-base pieces of RNA allowed the assignment of the direction of readout of the code. For example, -AAAUUU- and -UUUAAA- made lysyl-phenyl alanine and phenylalanyl-lysine, respectively. This experiment also pointed out that the genetic code is commaless. That is, there are no punctuation marks present, and the beginning of each codon directly follows the preceding one. In 1968, Nirenberg and his coworkers received a Nobel Prize for their efforts in deciphering the genetic code.

Context

The genetic code is the crux of gene function because it is the language, carried in RNA molecules made from genes, that specifies the exact nature of each protein made by every type of living organism. Many normal individual differences between human beings result from differences in the proteins for which their chromosomes can code. For example, hair, eye, and skin color differences that demarcate and distinguish racial and ethnic groups are the result of the presence or absence of messages that code for different proteins. The best-known example occurs in blonds, whose hair cells do not possess the mRNAs that produce the proteins that make the melanin pigment found in darker-haired people.

Furthermore, identification of the code has helped researchers to understand that many serious diseases result from very small changes of the genetic message for an otherwise-normal protein. Examples of such diseases include sickle-cell anemia, Tay-Sachs disease, phenylketonuria, and diabetes. In every case, the diseases are caused by mutation-generated changes of one or a few codons, and it becomes clear, from the genetic code, how the changes happened.

For example, sickle-cell anemia—an often fatal disease found in people of African descent—results from a mutation that changes only one of 287 amino acid molecules in hemoglobin, the oxygen-carrying protein of blood. This change is the replacement of glutamic acid with valine. The RNA codon modifications that cause the disease can be identified from the accompanying table. They are the conversion of either glutamic acid codon (GAA or GAG) to the valine codons GUA or GUG. As mutations occur in the DNA of genes, the actual change involved is conversion of TTC to TAC or CTC to CAC. These mutations are then transcribed, producing inappropriate mRNA codons, and translation produces sickle-cell hemoglobin.

The tiny change in sickle-cell hemoglobin is disastrous. People with the disease exhibit low red blood counts, heart murmurs, frequent dizzy spells, heart palpitations, kidney damage, and crippling strokes. These problems are all from the fragility of their red blood cells and those cells' abnormal shapes. Many afflicted people die by their midtwenties, after heart or kidney failure. The basic problem is that sickle-cell hemoglobin makes the deoxygenated red blood cells (in veins) take on abnormal shapes that cause them to break apart easily, get trapped in small blood vessels, cause clots, and damage the kidneys.

Understanding of the codon changes that can cause sickle-cell anemia only came after years of intense study identified the changed amino acid in the protein. Many other genetic diseases, however, are presently being solved by codon analysis, which provides much quicker understanding of the amino acid modifications that cause them. Where there is a change in one or a few amino acids in a protein, life scientists are using the knowledge to help them to develop chemical methods to treat the resulting diseases.

In other cases, understanding the genetic code is expected to aid genetic engineers in devising means to make important human proteins to be utilized for treating debilitating diseases. These efforts are also expected to facilitate development of plant and animal species that will be improvements over nature. The genetic code is viewed as being so important that the U.S. Public Health Service is planning and implementing a project to identify the codon sequence of the entire human genome, an enormous project which is expected to cost billions of dollars.

Bibliography

Hall, B. D. "Mitochondria Spring Surprises." *Nature* 282 (1979): 129-130. This article shows that mitochondria provide exceptions to the universality of the genetic code. It led to examination of mitochondria that delineated difference in wobble rules, as well as in codons.

Ingram, V. M. "Gene Mutation in Hb: The Chemical Difference Between Normal and Sickle Cell Hemoglobin." *Nature* 180 (1957): 326-328. This article describes the discovery of the amino acid replacement in hemoglobin S. It is a definitive presentation, predating the genetic code. Readers wishing to understand it clearly are directed to background chapters on amino acids and proteins in Lehninger's biochemistry texts, as needed.

Lake, J. A. "The Ribosome." *Scientific American* 245 (August, 1981): 84-97. This article gives a detailed description of the structure of the ribosome and of the process of translation. It also emphasizes the roles of the shape of the ribosome, its subunits, and the ways in which ribosomal proteins participate.

Lehninger, A. L. *Biochemistry.* New York: Worth, 1975. This edition of the classic college biochemistry text provides exceptionally lucid coverage of protein synthesis and the genetic code in chapters 33 and 34. Lehninger deciphers the chemistry, biochemistry, history, and evolution of both areas in a masterful and scholarly fashion. Chapter 34 is particularly useful for coverage of the role of the ribosome, base sequences in the codons, genetic evidence for codon assignments, explanation of initiation and termination codons, wobble rules, and proof of code universality.

_____. *Principles of Biochemistry*. New York: Worth, 1982. This text, written at a somewhat lower level than the author's *Biochemistry*, covers most of the same topics and has the advantage of some newer information lacking in the 1975 book. The two texts are complementary.

Marshall, R. E., C. T. Caskey, and M. W. Nirenberg. "Fine Structure of RNA Codewords Recognized by Bacterial, Amphibian, and Mammalian Transfer RNA." *Science* 155 (1967): 820-825. This article provides conclusive evidence for the universality of the genetic code, based on study of fifty codons. It also discusses the phylogenetic and evolutionary significance of the codons.

Nirenberg, M. W. "The Genetic Code: 1." *Scientific American* 208 (March, 1963): 80-94. This article describes several important aspects of the genetic code. First described are the classical experiments with synthetic RNA that proved that the base sequence in an RNA polymer specifies the order of insertion of amino acids into a protein during translation. It also describes the nature of the genetic code and explains how triplet codons were identified in the laboratory.

Nirenberg, M. W., and Phillip Leder. "RNA Codewords and Protein Synthesis." *Science* 145 (1964): 1399-1407. This important article describes the development of the powerful and ingenious "binding assay" used to spell codons. It also shows how the codons that comprise the code were determined.

Nirenberg, M. W., and J. H. Matthaei. "The Dependence of Cell-Free Protein Synthesis in *E. coli* upon Naturally Occurring or Synthetic Polyribonucleotides." *Proceedings of the National Academy of Science (U.S.)* 47 (1961): 1588-1602. The classic paper in which Nirenberg's group demonstrated the dependence of protein synthesis in ribosomes on RNA messengers and described the production of polyphenylalanine by poly U. The article also describes how to carry out experiments that show that amino acids are incorporated into proteins.

Sanford S. Singer

Cross-References

DNA Replication, 692; DNA Sequencing, 698; DNA's Molecular Structure, 706; Genes and Nucleic Acids, 1134; Deciphering the Genetic Code, 1155; Genetics: A Historical Perspective, 1177; Nucleic Acid Structure, 1987; Proteins, 2272; Transcription of DNA to Form RNA, 2632.

DECIPHERING THE GENETIC CODE

Type of life science: Molecular biology
Other fields of study: Biochemistry and genetics

The scientists who deciphered the genetic code provided the answer to the oldest question in biology: How does an organic form transmit, through reproduction, inherited patterns to its progeny? Knowledge of this mechanism of inheritance led to advances in many fields of study and to potential changes in human society.

Principal terms

CHROMATIN: material in the nucleus of a cell that can be stained by dyes; later found to consist of deoxyribonucleic acid (DNA)

DEOXYRIBONUCLEIC ACID (DNA): a large helical molecule made up of a single strand of nucleotide; contains the genetic code for all living organisms

DOUBLE HELIX: the genetic material in the cell, which is shaped in the form of two clockwise spirals and separated by 180 degrees

MUTATION: a change or error in the genetic code of a section of the DNA molecule

NUCLEIN: a name given by Friedrich Miescher for the DNA material in the nucleus of pus cells

PROGENY: offspring, or children, from reproduction

TRANSFER RIBONUCLEIC ACID (TRNA): similar to DNA except for one of the bases; transfers the genetic code for making proteins

Summary of the Methodology

It is often noted that a progeny can resemble one parent and not the other in some traits. Farmers have learned to select seeds from the plants that produce the largest crops and to select from farm animals certain desired characteristics. Yet it is equally apparent that each organic individual is unique and not simply a collection of parental parts or a blending of those parts. The problem of inheritance has two aspects: the continuation of some trait or characteristic for many generations, even while variations are being produced within individuals of a species.

The deciphering of the genetic code was the result of multiple lines of biological research carried out over an entire century; it involved determining the mechanical functions of the cell and answering questions raised by a theory of evolution. The final step in the search for the genetic code, however, depended on isolating the chemical compounds within the cell.

By the early part of the nineteenth century, the cell was established as the fundamental unit of living organisms, and scientists proceeded to break down the components of the cell. In 1879, Walther Flemming studied the stages of cell division and dyed cells to accentuate their parts. He found that parts of the nucleus of the cell absorbed colored dyes, while others did not. To this colored material, Flemming gave the name "chromatin." While observing cell division, Flemming found that during one stage of this process, the chromatin material would change into threadlike objects, which later came to be called chromosomes.

The next stage in the exploration of the cell was to identify specific chemical compounds within the nucleus, and this work was taken up by Friedrich Miescher in 1868. He used pus, which was readily available from the hospitals. By washing the pus with dilute hydrochloric acid, the cytoplasmic material of the cell was destroyed, leaving only the nucleus. Within the nucleus, Miescher found a compound with an abundant amount of phosphorus, which he called nuclein. In retrospect, Miescher had discovered deoxyribonucleic acid (DNA), but since he was working on cell chemistry, he did not realize the significance of his find.

The initial analysis of the chemical composition of the nuclear material consumed nearly forty years. By 1910, it was generally agreed by biochemists that DNA was composed of four bases: two purines (guanine and adenine) and two pyrimidines (cytosine and thymine), in addition to a phosphate and a sugar compound. Guanine, adenine, cytosine, and thymine are commonly abbreviated simply as G, A, C, and T, respectively. The combination of these compounds came to be called nucleic acid; it was considered by scientists to be a small molecular compound with little relevance to the problems of inheritance. The key to the genetic mystery seemed to lie in the larger and more complex protein molecules that possessed twenty different amino acids to form unlimited combinations.

Other than noting the curious presence of DNA in all cell nuclei, researchers concentrated their efforts on other, more promising, compounds until the 1930's. At this time, new methods for the exploration of large molecules were developed, including advanced centrifuge machines, more efficient filters, and light-absorption methods. When the DNA molecule was displayed under these methods of scrutiny, it was discovered to be twice as large as earlier estimates had indicated. It was now seen as a likely candidate for the transmission of genetic information, but it was necessary to show if this compound could carry genetic information and how that was accomplished. The first part of this task was undertaken by Oswald Avery, who utilized a method developed in the creation of vaccines. One method for making a vaccine is to kill the cells of bacteria and inject the dead cells into a trial animal. The vaccinated animal then acquires information from the dead cells and, in some cases, is protected from the disease. In 1944, Avery and his associates demonstrated that it was the DNA that carried the protection in vaccination.

Avery's discovery initiated the beginnings of extensive research in nucleic acid. The goal was to find its structure, but a number of intermediary steps were necessary to arrive at the structure of DNA. In 1950, Erwin Chargaff showed that bases come in pairs. In DNA, there are always the same amounts of adenine (A) to thymine (T) as there are guanine (G) to cytosine (C). Yet the ratio of A and T to G and C is different for different organisms. As further chemical analysis of DNA became available, a race for determining the structure of DNA began.

Linus Pauling, who led a research program in California, was one scientist involved. He had unraveled the helical structure of protein and in doing so contributed to an understanding of protein chemical bonds. Maurice Wilkins led another group in London; their work concentrated on X-ray photography of the crystal forms of DNA. X-ray work performed by Rosalind Franklin suggested that DNA was also a helical structure, but the question remained as to the number of coils and how the bases were attached to the chemical coil to form the structure. The final answer came from an unlikely pair of scientists, James Watson and Francis Crick.

Both Watson and Crick lacked the technical expertise and depth of experience of others who led the search for the structure of DNA. Watson had only recently completed his Ph.D. and had been working on the effects of radiation on viruses. Crick was completing his work in physics at the University of Cambridge and had become interested in biochemistry. Despite their apparent lack of qualifications, in 1952 Watson and Crick talked to a number of people involved in DNA research and began to construct their own model. Using the Chargaff ratio of bases, they constructed several models of different helix patterns. Finally, they arrived at the model of the double helix with the bases on the inside of the backbone. This model was also consistent with the X-ray information developed by Wilkins and Franklin. Shortly after completing this work, it became apparent that the DNA molecule served as the blueprint that directed the biochemical processes of the cell. For their work in unlocking the mystery of inheritance and cell replication, Watson, Crick, and Wilkins received the Nobel Prize for Physiology or Medicine in 1962.

Applications of the Method

With the discovery of the double helix structure of DNA, the floodgates of genetic research opened wide. Three overall approaches to genetic research have been pursued. The first is the precise and painstaking work of determining the genetic code in a variety of organisms from viruses to the human population; work in this area is not yet complete. A second line of research activity has centered on genetic engineering, in which sections of genes have been replaced with new information, hence the creation of new and altered organic forms. This work has direct application in agriculture and medicine, in which recombined genetic forms serve as organic pesticides, frost-resistant plants, and new forms of medical treatments. A third area of research has centered on the genetic source of disease through an investigation of how shifts and changes in the genetic code can develop phenomena that range from those that produce minor physical deformities to others that totally debilitate the human body and lead to death.

After Watson and Crick produced the model of DNA in 1952, research immediately turned to the questions of the exact configuration of the four bases that allowed the genetic code to work. The presence of adenine, guanine, cytosine, and thymine had been known for some time. It took ten years of additional work to determine how these "letters" form into the "words" that are then read in terms of specific biochemical information. DNA is the blueprint that directs about twenty different amino acids to link into a specific sequence to form proteins. The proteins, in turn, act as enzymes, or catalysts, which direct the many hundreds of chemical reactions that take place within the cell. Each protein is a molecular chain that contains many amino acids. Because the blueprint for the protein is carried on a gene, the gene has to contain the same number of "words" to describe the protein. A gene is a part of the DNA chain, with even the smallest organisms, such as viruses, possessing several hundred genes. More complicated organisms, such as bacteria, contain perhaps one thousand genes, and human DNA may have as many as a million genes. The answer to the DNA language lies in the way in which the bases (A, G, C, and T) combine to form the words.

George Gamow provided a logical solution to the genetic code. Using only one letter at a time, there can only be four words. Two-letter combinations can produce sixteen words, and three-letter combinations can form sixty-four words. With twenty amino acids, three-letter combinations were the logical answer. The experimental evidence for the three-letter code was provided by Marshall Nirenburg and Philip Leder, with some surprising results. The code that indicates certain proteins uses at least two (and in many cases three or four) triplet codes. For example, the protein glutamic acid can be synthesized by either the code GAA (guanine, adenine, adenine) or GAG. The first two letters of the code are the most important part of the "word." There are also words that code for "stop" and "go." Other discoveries indicated that another nucleic acid, transfer ribonucleic acid (tRNA), matches the code words from the blueprint DNA and, acting as a signal from a master switchboard, proceeds to assemble the protein chain. One major difference between RNA and DNA is the presence of uracil (U) instead of thymine in RNA.

A major breakthrough in the language of the genetic code was evidence of how mutation occurs in individuals of a species, a crucial key to the theory of evolution. If changes were unable to occur in the genetic code, then each progeny would be a variation of its parents. In the process of transferring the message from the DNA through the tRNA, errors can develop. These misprints can cause both minor and large-scale changes in an organism. The errors may occur through outside agents, such as radiation or chemicals, or simply as the result of weak points in the genetic chain. For example, the codes for glutamic acid are GAA and GAG. Change the code to GUA (the U is uracil) or GUG and the amino acid valine is produced. Such a change is commonly found in the hemoglobin of persons suffering from sickle-cell anemia.

Research on the genetic code has produced a range of new biological techniques that raise serious ethical questions. The heart of the issue lies in the ability of microbiologists to break apart the DNA chain and create new organic forms. This technique of "recombinant DNA" provides a number of benefits that range from cheaper pharmaceutical products to more abundant food production to possibly finding the cause of cancer. There are also a number of grave risks, which include producing altered microbes for which human antibodies do not exist, creating ecological imbalances, and even changing the human population. Thus, this technique becomes the ultimate form of artificial selection. In the past, changes in a breed of cattle or chicken required hundreds if not thousands of generations. Genetic engineering can produce the required results in a much shorter time. Such biomedical issues generated a number of heated debates during the 1970's, focusing on whether human society should intervene in the very process of evolution. The result was a series of guidelines that have attempted to balance the benefits and risks of future genetic engineering.

The potential for the application of the genetic code is unknown. The U.S. government is funding research for the complete mapping of all the genes (the genome) of the human body. When this work is finished in the twenty-first century, knowledge in biological, medical, and even physiological fields will have been greatly increased.

Context

The discovery of the double helix structure of DNA and the research into the function of the bases that followed is one of the most significant moments in biological science, if not in all human history. With the isolation first of bacteria and then of viruses, human diseases were thought to be caused only by outside agents. It has become clear since, however, that a large range of human diseases have a genetic origin, and several hundred genetic diseases are known. To extend this one step further, human behavior and characteristics could have some basis in genetics. A cultural theory that originated in the seventeenth century and prevailed throughout the twentieth century suggests that human characteristics are shaped by the environment. This "nature versus nurture" argument has never been resolved. A current consensus links roughly half of human psychological and behavioral traits to the environment and half to inheritance.

Outside human genetics, there exists a vast area of exploration. Increased yields in meat, poultry, and egg production have come as a direct result of breeding programs based on genetic research. Similar results have been accomplished in creating crops that are resistant to certain diseases, as well as providing greater increases in yields. The results that breeders have sought over hundreds of years of human history have been accomplished in a decade.

The DNA molecule is a blueprint; it is never used directly in organic life. No part of this molecule can actually become incorporated into the amino acids, proteins, or biochemicals that are so essential to living organisms. From the DNA blueprint to the production of proteins, the process occurs in only one direction: Proteins do not have any influence on the message of the DNA. Thus, acquired characteristics cannot be inherited. For example, cutting the tails off rats over many generations will not produce short-tailed rats.

The genetic code is extremely consistent and allows for very few errors. The incidence of mutation in any population is less than 1 in 100,000. In addition, most cases of mutation are fatal to the individual prior to the age of reproduction. The genetic code is universal and identical for living organisms; by implication, life on earth is uniform and singular, and there are no known alternative life-forms that use another code. Yet at the same time that life is singular and derived from a single code, every sexually reproduced individual is unique, taking a combination of genetic information from each parent. Consequently, there exists a large supply of variation in any species, which provides the material for natural selection to create new varieties of species. Evolution occurs because successful species tend to remain consistent, yet variation and occasional mutation allow change to take place.

Bibliography

Crick, F. H. C. "The Genetic Code: III." *Scientific American* 215 (October, 1966): 16, 55-62. The article describes how the four DNA bases form a triple-letter code to control the linkage of twenty different amino acids to form proteins. Crick also describes the function of messenger RNA and how mutations occur. The article presents few problems to the general reader and provides a useful summary of work on the language of the genetic code.

Grobstein, Clifford. "The Recombinant-DNA Debate." *Scientific American* 237 (July, 1977): 22-33. The author covers the extensive controversy over the hazards of genetic engineering and gene-splicing methods by presenting both the benefits and risks of such biological experimentation. He describes in some detail the techniques of gene-splicing and guidelines for future genetic experimentation in this area. There is a useful bibliography of other positions in this debate on genetic engineering. The article requires the background of a high school biology class.

Mayr, Ernst. *The Growth of Biological Thought: Diversity, Evolution, and Inheritance*. Cambridge, Mass.: Harvard University Press, 1982. Mayr is the recognized authority on the history of biological development. Chapter 19 covers the history of the biochemical basis of inheritance, and for anyone interested in the development of DNA research, this chapter is the place to start. The material is sometimes difficult, but the treatment is definitive. The bibliography is extensive but not useful for the general reader.

Nirenberg, Marshall W. "The Genetic Code: II." *Scientific American* 208 (March, 1963): 33, 80-86. This article picks up the ideas presented by an earlier publication by Crick on the question of how DNA code is responsible for the manufacture of proteins. A useful article to read in conjunction with "Genetic Code: III." Both these articles offer a number of diagrams on the genetic code and how proteins are manufactured.

Olby, Robert. *The Path to the Double Helix*. Seattle: University of Washington Press, 1974. A comprehensive and detailed description of the scientists engaged in the search for structure of DNA. Large sections of this book, however, are only suited for students with some college background in biology and chemistry.

Watson, James D. *The Double Helix*. New York: Atheneum, 1980. This book is indispensable for the general reader interested in the history of how the genetic code was deciphered. There are three major sections: Watson's personal account of the discovery of the structure of DNA; other perspectives from Francis Crick, Linus Pauling, and Aaron Klug; and a collection of reviews of the discovery and original papers by those involved in the event.

Victor W. Chen

Cross-References

Cloning to Produce Recombinant DNA, 505; DNA's Molecular Structure, 706; Gene Therapy, 1128; Genes and Nucleic Acids, 1134; The Genetic Code, 1148; Genetics: A Historical Perspective, 1177; Nucleic Acid Structure, 1987; Sequence Comparison for Proteins and Nucleic Acids, 2466; Sex Linkage, Sex Limitation, and Sex Determination, 2487.

GENETIC EQUILIBRIUM: LINKAGE

Type of life science: Evolutionary biology
Other fields of study: Ecology and genetics

Genes located on the same chromosome are said to be linked because during cellular reproduction whole chromosomes migrate to the new nuclei. During meiosis, crossing over (the exchange of portions of one chromatid with like portions of a sister chromatid) can occur, so that alleles which once occurred on one chromosome now occur on the other.

Principal terms

CHIASMA (*pl.,* CHIASMATA): physical evidence of crossing over; a cross-shaped configuration indicating that two nonsister chromatids of homologous chromosomes have exchanged chromosomal material

COUPLING: the arrangement of linked genes on homologous chromosomes in which wild-type alleles are located on one chromosome and mutant alleles on the other; also called cis configuration

CROSSING OVER: the process of chromosomal interchange by which recombinants (newly linked genes) arise

LINKAGE: the tendency of genes on the same chromosome to be inherited together

LINKAGE MAP: a chart showing the relative positions of each of the known genes on a particular chromosome

PARENTAL TYPE: the phenotype or genotype of the parents in a cross

RECOMBINANT TYPE: a phenotype or genotype which varies from the parental type because of recombination

REPULSION: linked genes arranged so that one homologous chromosome has a mutant allele for one gene and a wild-type allele for the other, and the opposite arrangement on the homologue; also called trans configuration

Summary of the Phenomenon

The genetic complement of any organism is contained on one or more types of chromosomes. Whether there is only one chromosome, or many, in a diploid organism, each type occurs as a set of two, called homologues. Each gene at a particular locus (or site) along the chromosome normally occurs twice in the same cell. The particular information at each site may be different because genes come in several forms. An alternative form of a particular gene is called an allele. Each homologous chromosome, therefore, contains an allele at a locus which may or may not be the same as the allele on its homologue.

During reproduction, this chromosomal material is copied, thereby duplicating the individual genes which lie along the chromosome. During mitosis, a copy of each homologous chromosome is brought to the two new nuclei. But in meiosis, during gamete production, the chromosome copies are separated so that only a single chromosome is brought to each new nucleus. Before this happens, however, the homologues and their duplicates, called chromatids, are aligned. The arms of sister chromatids may at this time cross over, break, and become attached to a new chromatid.

The result of this crossing over is that alleles that were once on one chromatid are now joined to the other. In mitosis, genes on a single chromosome exhibit linkage and tend to remain together and be inherited by the daughter cell together; in meiosis, these linked genes can become recombined in new associations so that linkage is partial. The new combination of alleles are called recombinants.

Mendelian genetics (named for Gregor Mendel) predicts a 3:1 phenotypic ratio in a monohybrid cross (a cross involving only one gene having two alleles) and a 9:3:3:1 phenotypic ratio in a dihybrid cross (a cross involving two genes on different chromosomes, each having two alleles). Early in the twentieth century, geneticists began to notice that not all crosses produced offspring in the proportions predicted by Mendel's law of independent assortment. Cytologists discovered that not all the chromosomes of one type looked exactly alike. Geneticists used these morphological differences in chromosomes as cytological markers and associated them with genetic markers or alleles with specific effects.

In 1911, T. H. Morgan concluded that during segregation of alleles at meiosis certain genes tend to remain together because they lie near each other on the same chromosome. The closer genes are to each other on the chromosome, the greater their tendency to remain linked.

In 1909, chiasmata had been described. These are the physical evidence of exchanges between maternal and paternal homologues. Morgan hypothesized that partial linkage occurs when two genes on the same chromosome are separated physically from each other by a chiasma during meiosis. This crossing over provided new combinations of genes, genes which did not exhibit the linkage found in the parents, but which were recombined. In these crosses, the parental phenotypic classes were most frequent, while the recombinant classes occurred much less frequently.

Genetic recombination results from physical exchange between homologous chromosomes that have become tightly aligned during meiotic prophase. A chiasma is the site of crossing over. Crossing over itself is the exchange of parts of nonsister chromatids of homologous chromosomes by symmetrical breakage and crosswise rejoining. Two papers providing convincing evidence of this were published within weeks of each other in 1930.

Harriet Creighton and Barbara McClintock worked with corn. They studied two chromosomes that differed cytologically on both sides of the chromosomal segment in which the crossing over occurs. They determined that the dominant alleles that controlled seed color and the form of starch produced are on cytologically different homologous chromosomes. Whenever the alleles were recombined, the aberrant part of the chromosome is also recombined. No such exchange was evident in plants with parental characteristics.

Curt Stern also used genetic markers and cytological markers in his study of the carnation allele for eye color and bar-eye allele for eye shape in fruit flies. His cross involved the X chromosome, but the X that carried the carnation color allele and bar-eye allele was distinctly shorter than the X that carried wild-type alleles for both traits. (The Y chromosome inherited by male fruit flies from their fathers contained no relevant genetic markers.) Where there was no recombination of phenotypes, Stern found no exchange of chromosome parts. Where recombination of traits had occurred, there were physical exchanges between the chromosomes as well.

Both experiments, and many others performed later, indicate that when crossing over takes place during meiosis there is also an exchange of cytological markers. This evidence can be used to construct a genetic map. The more closely linked genes are, the less frequently crossing over will take place between them. The recombinants will occur much less frequently than they do in the offspring of crosses between individuals with more widely separated linked genes.

With widely separated genes, the chances of double crossovers increases, so that the recombination frequency may actually underestimate the crossover frequency and, hence, the map distance. The map distance is a relative distance based on the percent of recombination and is not an actual distance.

The presence of a chiasma in one region is thought to prevent the occurrence of a second chiasma between the two chromatids. This phenomenon is called interference. It becomes stronger the more closely genes are linked. Linkage is determined using experimental crosses involving known genotypes. In a single generation of random mating, autosomal loci separately attain equilibrium of genotype frequencies. This is not true when there are alternative alleles segregating at each of two independently assorting loci. If loci are unlinked, equilibrium occurs very rapidly. But if the loci are on the same chromosome, the speed of approach to equilibrium is proportional to the closeness of the linkage. At equilibrium, repulsion and coupling gamete frequencies do not depend on the degree of linkage. Another way of saying this is that the characters produced by alleles at linked loci show no particular association in an equilibrium population. When characters happen to be associated in a population, the association may form because alleles at separate loci that are in genetic disequilibrium result from recent population immigrations. They may also be the result of selection for certain allelic combinations. Like dominance, linkage can be detected only in prescribed breeding experiments.

Mutations are the ultimate source of variation. In populations, mutant alleles may accumulate over time because they are recessive to the normal allele. It is only when the mutant becomes widely distributed in the population or when mutants are recombined that they are revealed. The fundamental paradox of genetics is that it produces constancy and continuity in the face of unimaginable variability. With ten loci and four alleles at each locus, 10 billion different possible genotypes will occur with equal frequency if all the alleles occur with equal frequency and segregate independently. This describes a state of linkage equilibrium. In a natural population, however, these conditions are rarely met. The probability is that common genotypes will be produced.

Diploid organisms have several thousand, or more, gene loci. Since they have only a small number of chromosomes, usually less than forty, many loci lie on the same chromosome. The genotypes are highly biased toward already existing combinations. This does not alter the theoretical possibilities of genotypes, only the probability of their occurrence. It does ensure that variation is present in the population so that adaptability of the species to changed conditions is available while maintaining large numbers of individuals that are adapted to existing conditions.

Linked genes may control very different functions. For example, enzymes vary depending on the climate. Northern species may possess an enzyme which functions at a lower temperature than the variant of the southern species. Linked to the gene which controls this highly adaptive allele may be an allele of another gene whose adaptive value is less or neutral. This less adapted allele hitchhikes on the chromosome in the same direction as the adaptive allele.

Linkage disequilibrium is decreased by recombination. The possibility of maintaining favorable allelic combinations in linkage disequilibrium is enhanced by the reduction of frequency of recombination between the loci involved. This is achieved by inversions and translocations.

If two loci are on different chromosomes, a translocation may bring one of the loci to a position on the same chromosome as the other locus. If two loci are separated by a number of genes on the same chromosome, then an inversion, a twisting of a portion of a chromosome so that the order of the genes is reversed when the piece is reattached, will make recombination difficult because the two loci are brought closer to each other. Whenever linkage disequilibrium is favored by natural selection, chromosomal rearrangements increasing linkage between loci will also be favored by natural selection.

Supergenes are closely linked genes that contribute to the same function. Their close linkage allows the species to maintain a smoothly functioning phenotype. Such supergenes contribute to the development of two distinct phenotypes of primrose: "pin" and "thrum" flowers. The phenotypic variations promote cross-fertilization because in the "pin" flower, the stigma collecting the pollen is near the tip of the flower's mouth while the pollen-releasing anthers are located within the flower's bell. The positions of the stigma and anthers are reversed in the "thrum" flower. Multiple genes were suspected because other features, such as the size and shape of pollen grains, also varied. In rare recombinations, these traits can be mixed, but the rarity of these recombinations suggests close linkage of these genes in a supergene.

Methods of Study

Closely defined breeding experiments are necessary to determine linkage. The parents involved must exhibit alternate alleles for at least two traits. The parents must also breed true; this ensures that they are homozygous. One of the first crosses that displayed an exception to the law of independent assortment arose when two true-breeding strains of sweet pea were crossed. One strain had purple flowers and long pollen. The other had red flowers and round pollen. These were the parental, or "P" generation.

When the true-breeding parents' offspring were raised, they all had purple flowers and long pollen as expected. These offspring, called the "F_1," (for first filial) generation, all showed the dominant traits, and were actually heterozygotes. They had one dominant and one recessive allele for flower color and another dominant and recessive allele for pollen shape.

When these plants were crossed, the next generation, called F_2, was expected to have a 3:1 ratio of purple to red flowers and a 3:1 ratio of long to round pollen. There were 381 offspring, of which 305 were purple and 76 were red. The same numbers occurred in the distribution of pollen shape. If the two character pairs assorted independently in the cross, there should be a 9:3:3:1 ratio of purple flowers with long pollen to purple flowers with round pollen to red flowers with long pollen to red flowers with round pollen. Instead, approximately 75 percent were purple and long, only 5 percent were purple and round, another 5 percent were red and long, and 15 percent were red and round.

A second cross of the same type several years later produced 6,952 offspring of the F_2 generation. In this experiment, 70 percent had purple flowers and long pollen, 5 percent had purple flowers and round pollen, 5 percent had red flowers and long pollen, while 20 percent had red flowers and round pollen. The parental characteristics were found in 90 percent of the offspring of this cross. But 10 percent showed the parental characteristics recombined so that the phenotypes were different from the characteristics of one parent in respect to the flower color or pollen shape. The expected percentages, if there were independent assortment, would be 56 percent purple and long, 19 percent purple and round, 19 percent red and long, and 6 percent red and round. The observed values differ from the predicted values.

Even today, geneticists use the same types of experiments to determine linkage. Today, however, they do not use only cytological markers. The markers or linked traits may be biochemical ones, such as production of a particular enzyme or molecule. Biochemical tests ascertain the presence, character, and quantity of a gene product precisely and may even suggest modifications of diet or life-style to alleviate the aberrant condition.

In many linkage experiments, a testcross is made. This is a cross in which one parent is homozygous recessive for the traits being studied. The other parent's alleles will be expressed in the offspring, and crossovers can be detected. Double testcrosses, with two loci involved, are informative. Testcrosses involving three loci are even more instructive because the distances between the three genes can be calculated and their order on the chromosome determined.

Map distances are calculated two genes at a time. The frequency of genetic recombination (crossing over) is an indication of the distance between the two genes and, hence, of how closely linked they are. The percentage of offspring exhibiting crossover between two genes multiplied by a hundred is the map distance between the two.

Map distance is an indication of the probability of recombination of alleles located near it. The presence of a chiasma nearby will also reduce the probability of recombination. So the map distance is only an approximation of the actual cytological distance between two genes. Generally, the farther apart they are, the more likely they are to recombine. The closer they are, the more likely it is that they will not recombine but remain linked.

Context

Gregor Mendel defined the laws of inheritance; his work became known late in the nineteenth century. Scientists are always more fascinated by possibilities—the puzzle piece that does not fit—than by the known. Such a challenge (to explain what should not have been) occurred when aberrant ratios were found in the offspring of particular crosses.

Geneticists discovered that individual genes do not behave as independent entities. Genes that occur on the same chromosome are linked—and often inherited together. The exceptions provided insights into the transmission of traits and the behavior of chromosomes. Although these results are interesting, their real impact is in predicting genetic disease in offspring of affected individuals.

Genetic markers can sometimes be associated with disease conditions, such as Huntington's chorea or Tay-Sachs disease. Huntington's chorea manifests itself only when the bearer of the gene is over thirty years of age. Therefore, a person knows that he or she has the disease only after there is a possibility that the gene has been passed to their offspring.

The presence of a marker gene, a gene closely linked to the disease-causing gene but the presence of which can be detected more easily, enables geneticists to predict the probability of a person known to be at risk of developing the disease. Knowing does not cure the disease, but it does provide options in life planning for those carrying the allele. They can decide whether they wish to have children, knowing that they risk passing on the gene to their offspring. They can plan to enter a career that will not be disrupted by the onset of the disease. They can provide financially for their future or simply not postpone until the future what should be done in the present.

The ability to predict also brings up ethical issues. A person carrying the disease-causing gene has probably seen a relative suffer from its effects, and perhaps the person wishes to ignore the possibility until symptoms occur. Not everyone carrying the gene may develop the disease, yet insurance companies may discriminate against such individuals and not provide health coverage or life insurance.

Without the knowledge of gene linkage, these dilemmas would not present themselves. With it, treatments may be devised that begin before the disease manifests itself, limiting damage to the body so that the person is healthier and stronger longer.

Linkage will also be important in deciphering the meaning of the deoxyribonucleic acid (DNA) sequences discovered when the human genome is mapped. Eukaryotes have many chromosomal regions that contain no useful information. Some geneticists fear that the project will generate much data and little information. In other words, merely knowing the sequence of nucleotides will not tell which nucleotides are incorrect or where the gene controlling a particular trait is located. This more useful information will be obtained from studies of genes linked with disease-causing genes. If these linkage patterns are discovered, sequencing of nearby regions of the chromosome may reveal the presence of an aberration in affected individuals which may lead to treatment or, with genetic engineering, a cure.

Bibliography

Blixt, S. "Why Didn't Mendel Find Linkage?" *Nature* 256 (1975): 206. A short article describing the linkage patterns of genes not subjected to experiment by Gregor Mendel, even though they are noted in his records.

Croce, Carlo M., and George Klein. "Chromosome Translocations and Human Cancer." *Scientific American* 252 (March, 1985): 54-60. A well-written article detailing how changes in linkage can affect the functioning of certain genes.

Fedoroff, N. V. "Transposable Genetic Elements in Maize." *Scientific American* 250 (June, 1984): 84-98. The transposable genetic elements were first described by Barbara McClintock. In this lucid article, the elements are analyzed to show that by changing their position on a chromosome or by moving to another chromosome, they change the activity of nearby genes.

Ford, E. B. *Ecological Genetics.* 3d ed. London: Chapman and Hall, 1971. This scholarly work describes gene linkage and the contributions of supergenes to evolution.

Lerner, I. M., and W. J. Libby. *Heredity, Evolution, and Society.* 2d ed. San Francisco: W. H. Freeman, 1976. This is a clearly written work on genetics and the mechanisms which produce evolution. It relates these two topics to society and its functional and ethical problems.

McKusick, V. A. "The Mapping of Human Chromosomes." *Scientific American* 224 (April, 1971): 104-113. This article discusses the importance of knowing the physical locations of genes along a chromosome. He describes the usefulness of the "secretor" gene linked to the gene for myotonic dystrophy, a hereditary disease whose presence can be predicted in 90 percent of fetuses.

Scheller, Richard H., and Richard Axel. "How Genes Control Innate Behavior." *Scientific American* 250 (March, 1984): 54-62. A comprehensive article showing how the activation of genes and supergenes affects the responses of some cells to stimuli or alters their hormonal constitution.

Judith O. Rebach

Cross-References

Adaptations and Their Mechanisms, 22; Gene Mutation and Repair, 1103; Eukaryotic Gene Regulation, 1111; Prokaryotic Gene Regulation, 1119; Mitosis and Meiosis, 1753; The Mitotic Spindle Apparatus, 1760; Sex Linkage, Sex Limitation, and Sex Determination, 2487.

GENETIC SCREENING AND COUNSELING

Types of life science: Bioethics and genetics
Other field of study: Molecular biology

Genetic screening furnishes the basic information that permits effective genetic counseling. Genetic counseling requires knowledge of genetics and medicine as well as the skills necessary to interpret and convey knowledge of genetic disorders within an appropriate ethical context.

Principal terms

ALLELES: two or more alternative forms of a gene occurring at the same general sites (loci) on homologous chromosomes

AUTOSOMAL CHROMOSOMES: chromosomes not primarily involved in sex determination/differentiation of an organism

DOMINANT GENE: an allele that expresses itself to the exclusion of another allele (recessive allele) when the two exist together

GENE: the functional unit of inheritance; a segment of the deoxyribonucleic acid (DNA) molecule that codes for the synthesis of a single polypeptide or a functional ribonucleic acid molecule

GENOTYPE: the genetic makeup of an individual as coded for by the DNA as opposed to the appearance (phenotype) of an individual

HETEROZYGOUS: the genotypic condition in which one individual carries both members of a pair of alleles at a given locus

HOMOZYGOUS: the genotypic condition in which one individual carries a pair of identical alleles at a given locus

PHENOTYPE: the appearance or discernible characteristics of an organism produced by interaction of its genes with the environment

RECESSIVE GENE: a form of a gene (allele) that does not express itself in the heterozygous condition, that is, in the presence of another allele that masks it (dominant allele)

SEX CHROMOSOME: the chromosome(s) at least partly concerned with sex differentiation of an organism

Summary of the Methodology

Even though the basic knowledge of genetics may be well known to a physician or medical geneticist, it is recognized that making genetic predictions and advising persons who ask questions about genetic problems involves much more than genetic knowledge alone. Predicting and advising roles are the responsibility of the genetic counselor and his support staff of clinical personnel, who assist in the biochemical and chromosomal analyses (screening) as well as in the analysis of family pedigrees. Genetic counselors interpret genetic and medical information and counsel patients (prospective parents, parents, and family members) in a sensitive and factual manner so that the risks of genetic problems involved and possible ways of avoiding having children with genetic defects can be well understood by all persons involved. Frequently, genetic counseling is more an exchanging of information than the counselor giving directives to the client.

Genetic screening provides information necessary for detection of carriers of defective genes and provides a basis for subsequent counseling. Screening uses a variety of techniques ranging from genetic screening of large population groups to individuals. Prospective genetic screening (also called parental screening) is decidedly the most effective type of screening, since effects have not yet occurred. It employs procedures that furnish the genetic counselor and parents-to-be with information necessary to determine the likelihood that a genetic disorder may occur in the prospective child. Family pedigrees, family histories of mental or physical disorders, previous records of spontaneous miscarriages or stillbirths, phenotypes of previous children, and other factors involved in genetic expression provide important clues for prospective genetic screening. Retrospective genetic screening, on the other hand, uses a number of medical procedures, including amniocentesis, electrophoresis, fetoscopy, ultrasonography, chorionic villus biopsy, restriction enzyme analysis, and the like.

Most genetic screening is voluntary, and the information derived may be useful in detecting genetic disorders so that they may be anticipated in advance, treated prenatally or in early infancy, or used to reach decisions regarding possible therapeutic procedures for protection of either the mother, the prospective child, or both. Ideally, genetic screening programs should be accompanied by effective educational programs so that both medical personnel and the public become fully aware of the potential benefits, risks, and possible long-term consequences for society.

It is important to choose a genetic counselor carefully. Genetic counseling is done by a variety of professionals, some of whom may not have had rigorous, professional training in one or more aspects of the areas with which genetic counselors work. Ideally, a genetic counselor should have formal medical training, a firm knowledge of genetics, and counseling skills that guarantee realistic but sensitive analysis and clear presentation of information to the patient. While these skills may be possessed by different members of a genetic counseling "team" and in varying degrees for each individual genetic counselor, it should be recognized that not all genetic counselors possess these skills to the same degree, and not all medical clinics are able to provide the professional level of genetic counseling necessary in a particular case. The best advice is to seek the help of a well-trained physician who knows genetic counselors and medical clinics where the appropriate screening and testing can be reliably secured. Many persons who could benefit from genetic screening and counseling do not receive either of them for a variety of reasons, including ignorance of availability of genetic screening or counseling services and lack of economic resources necessary to obtain these services.

Applications of the Method
The risks of having a genetically defective infant are sufficiently small that few

patients are advised by physicians to seek genetic screening or counseling unless the physician is relatively certain that prospective parents are carriers of a deleterious gene or chromosomal defect, when the mother-to-be is more than thirty-five years old, when there have been one or more previously affected children or repeated fetal losses, or when there are apparent genetic defects in families of the prospective parents. Additionally, when parents are closely related or when mental illness or retardation appears in family histories, the physician may refer the prospective parents to counselors for risk assessment and analysis of available options.

Many diverse methods are used in genetic screening and genetic counseling. Pedigree analysis is one frequently used method in genetic screening. It incorporates several aspects of basic genetics and is helpful in most cases in which the family history is known and there is a desire for genetic analysis to be used in genetic counseling. In standard pedigree methodology, individuals are placed in generational lines, males are distinguished from females, and individuals showing symptoms of a genetic trait are indicated.

Pedigree analysis uses basic genetic information from the pedigree to view the occurrence of genetic traits or disorders in a family. It is also used to determine the probability of an individual being an asymptomatic carrier (heterozygous) of a defective gene such as the sickle-cell gene or the phenylketonuria (PKU) gene— both of which are recessive and must be present in two doses, one from each parent, for the phenotypic trait or disorder to be expressed—and to determine the probability of two such heterozygous people having an affected child. The genetic counselor must know basic probability theory as well as the genetics and medical significance of genetic disorders if the information inherent in the pedigree is to be fully understood.

Genetic screening includes a variety of techniques, such as amniocentesis, a method frequently employed to examine cells and fluids from a developing fetus for biochemical or chromosomal defects. It consists of withdrawing amniotic fluid with a device similar to a large hypodermic syringe. Amniotic fluid fills the amniotic sac, which surrounds the fetus in the womb of the mother and contains cells sloughed off from the fetus. Fetal cells may be grown in culture and their chromosomes stained and examined by karyotyping, a systematic comparison of chromosome numbers, morphology, and banding patterns from photographs taken of slides of the dividing cells. This method is used to detect chromosomal abnormalities such as trisomy 21 (Down's syndrome), X monosomy (Turner's syndrome), and many other genetic abnormalities associated with defective chromosome structure.

Ultrasonography employs harmless ultrasound waves to image the fetus within the womb of its mother. It not only permits the gross anatomical features of the fetus to be seen, so that physical deformities, twins, gender, and other conditions may be detected, but ultrasonography also permits more accurate insertion of the amniocentesis needle, thereby decreasing the risk of inadvertent physical injury. In addition, fetoscopy, which uses fiber optics within a needlelike tube inserted into the amniotic sac, permits more precise viewing of details of fetal anatomy and is particularly useful in determining the extent of fetal deformities. A physician may also insert a syringe within the fetoscopy tube to draw a sample of fetal blood from an appropriate fetal vessel.

Chorionic villus biopsy (or sampling) is accomplished by insertion of a thin tube into the uterus through the vagina, where the chorionic villi, the hairlike projections of tissue from the chorion (the outer epithelial wall of the membrane within which the embryo develops), are sampled. Another technique now widely used employs restriction enzymes to cut the DNA molecules obtained from cells in amniotic fluid into variably sized pieces. These pieces can then be sized, identified, and compared with similarly treated DNA from persons with and without symptoms of a given genetic disorder. Because this technique carries far lower risks than fetal blood sampling, restriction enzyme analysis will probably become one of the preferred methods for detection of genetic defects in a fetus.

Electrophoresis, another increasingly valuable method, utilizes electrical charge differences between biological molecules to separate components of substances found in blood or body fluids when placed in an electrical field on an appropriate substrate. It also compares these specific components from affected individuals with those from normal, unaffected individuals. It has been extremely effective in detecting heterozygous, asymptomatic carriers of recessive alleles such as the sickle-cell allele, Tay-Sachs allele, and others.

These and other techniques currently being developed promise to improve the detection and analysis of genetic abnormalities and to increase the effectiveness of both physicians and genetic counselors even as these techniques increase the complexity of accompanying technologies.

Context

Genetic counselors provide parents and families with both biological and statistical information, but it is frequently equally necessary to dispel misconceptions about hereditary diseases, explain precisely how the disorder arises, describe exactly what it is, and convey the risks involved in a sensitive and understandable manner. Genetic screening may provide information from biochemical tests indicating whether parents are heterozygous for a deleterious allele, but for many genetic diseases tests for heterozygosity do not exist or are equivocal. To make matters more complex, some diseases may have several genetic bases (genetic heterogeneity), the symptoms in known defective genotypes may vary in severity (genetic expressivity) from case to case (as in Down's syndrome and related disorders), and in some instances symptoms may range from none at all (lack of gene penetrance) to extremely affected (complete gene penetrance).

Genetic counselors walk the narrow path of being as effective and sensitive as possible, while at the same time minimizing the possible legal entanglements that may ensue from withholding information, from the physician's not telling patients that genetic counseling services were available, from cases in which genetic defects were not detected or diagnosed by prenatal screening, or even cases in which children might sue parents for not having prevented the birth when the parents had prior knowledge of a likely defect. Other troublesome problems also arise for genetic counselors, and answers are not always clear. The psychological effects of finding that one carries a "bad gene" are not well known, and one cannot fully predict the types of social pressures placed on affected individuals. It is known that some minority groups have been treated with discrimination. For example, stigmatization of blacks is well documented in cases in which they were found to be carriers of the sickle-cell allele, and their life insurance coverage was canceled, or their premium rates increased. Sickle-cell disease is a disorder occurring more frequently in blacks of northwestern African ancestry than in most other populations.

Another ethical problem is whether the births of all children known to have genetic defects should be prevented. Can one effectively compare "quality of life" with a given genetic defect with no life at all? Are selective contraception, abortion, sterilization, and other manipulative measures morally or ethically acceptable? Is it acceptable to keep a "human pet" alive when that individual may never lead a "normal life" or be self-supportive? Questions become even more complex as the screening technologies and therapeutic techniques become more advanced and sophisticated. The number of ethical dilemmas will only increase as medical and genetic advances continue.

Even when it is possible to make probability and risk understandable to those being counseled, recurrent risks are less easily determined. The precise inheritance pattern may not be clearly indicated or known, or its basis may be very complex. Each individual case is unique, and probabilities vary with parental age, other affected family members, previous patient histories of miscarriages, reproductive diseases, general health, and other factors. For example, even if both parents are known carriers for the Tay-Sachs allele, the probability of an affected child is only 25 percent. In the case of Huntington's chorea, or disease, however, the chance of an affected child is 50 percent when only one parent is affected because Huntington's disease is caused by an autosomal dominant gene. The affected parent may bear children well in advance of the onset of the disease. If the child inherits the defective gene but reaches the age of forty-eight without expressing Huntington's disease symptoms, the probability of that individual ever exhibiting the disease declines.

Patients' perceptions of identical probabilities may vary. Some think only of an either-or situation; some think that a one-in-four chance means that if they have one defective child the next three will be normal. Others may not understand that the probability of successive events is independent of previous events. The patient may see a one-in-four risk as too great for an extremely serious disorder but acceptable for a less-deleterious one, while another may view a one-in-ten risk for a disease as incompatible with their personal values or desires.

People vary not only in understanding and perception but also in disposition and the emotional maturity and stability necessary to accommodate severe physical or mental disorders. For example, medically induced abortion of a defective fetus may not be identical to elective abortion, but for some persons opposition to all kinds of abortion limits the applicability of both prenatal diagnosis and subsequent induced or elective abortion on the grounds that all abortions are morally unacceptable.

It is obvious that prenatal diagnosis need not result in a decision for abortion, and when informed of a defective fetus the parents may sometimes choose to prepare for and care for a child with a genetic defect rather than to choose elective abortion. The decisions based on prenatal diagnosis might either raise or lower the anxiety level of the parents, the patient, or the physician or counselor involved. Such decisions are influenced by the severity of the disability, the age of the parents, the economic status of the family, the religious or ethical and moral values of all concerned, and other elements.

The problem of who shall "play God" is often more than a cliché. Not all persons look with equal reverence to their physician or counselor, and not all physicians or counselors are comfortable in assuming a task of "divine guidance" in reaching decisions involving genetic disorders.

Bibliography

Epstein, C. J., and M. S. Golbus. "Prenatal Diagnosis of Genetic Diseases." *American Scientist* 65 (1977): 703-711. A well-written short article intended for the nonspecialist with scientific knowledge at the college level. Advanced high school students will also benefit from this article.

Fuhrman, W., and F. Vogel. *Genetic Counseling*. 3d ed. Translated by S. Kurth-Scherer. New York: Springer-Verlag, 1982. Well written at a rather advanced level but understandable to those with good basic science background at the advanced high school and college level.

Harper, Peter S. *Practical Genetic Counseling*. Baltimore: University Park Press, 1981. A good book for both the interested general reader and health professionals. It clearly explains processes and procedures in a thorough, though nontechnical manner.

Kieffer, G. H. *Bioethics: A Textbook of Issues*. Reading, Mass.: Addison-Wesley, 1979. A textbook written for health-sciences students in upper-level college classes or beginning-level professional training. Several chapters are devoted to topics such as prenatal diagnosis, amniocentesis, and genetic screening as these relate to bioethical perspectives, ethical problems, and consequences. Good reading for the advanced high school student and general public; written in a nontechnical style, with well-documented bibliographies at the end of each chapter and good line drawings and data tables from other sources.

Kowles, Richard V. *Genetics, Society, and Decisions*. Columbus, Ohio: Charles E. Merrill, 1985. A textbook for the college-level student, equally applicable for science and humanities students alike. This book has excellent discussions with reference to the role of genetics in decision making for topics including genetic counseling, genetic screening, amniocentesis, consanguinity, and judicial uses of genetics. Good illustrations, references, glossary, and index.

Milunsky, Aubrey, ed. *Genetic Disorders and the Fetus: Diagnosis, Prevention, and Treatment.* New York: Plenum Press, 1979. A thorough, well-written book considered the bible of genetic disorders by professionals and nonprofessionals alike. Technical issues are discussed in clear, nontechnical writing so that advanced high school, college, and interested general readers will find it interesting and understandable. Good index and glossary, modest but useful line drawings.

Reed, Sheldon Clark. *Counseling in Medical Genetics.* 3d ed. New York: Alan R. Liss, 1980. A technical but well-written book of interest to health professionals or students at the advanced college level. Good index to topics covered.

Donald M. Huffman

Cross-References

Eukaryotic Gene Organization, 871; Gene Therapy, 1128; The Genetic Code, 1148; Human Genetics, 1190; Karyotyping, 1506; The Polymerase Chain Reaction in Genetic Screening, 2141; Prenatal Diagnostic Techniques, 2194.

GENETICS: A HISTORICAL PERSPECTIVE

Type of life science: Genetics
Other fields of study: Biochemistry and molecular biology

Genetics is the study of the inheritance of biological traits. Modern genetics began with the discovery of the basic laws of inheritance in 1866 and has since become one of the most fundamental biological sciences, with tremendous potential for practical applications in medicine, industry, and agriculture.

Principal terms
CHROMOSOME: a cellular structure composed of DNA
DEOXYRIBONUCLEIC ACID (DNA): a complex organic molecule shaped like a double helix that makes up genes and that carries hereditary information as a genetic code
GENE: a sequence of DNA that codes for a cellular function
GENETIC MAP: the identification and order of specific genes on a chromosome
GENETIC RECOMBINATION: the production of offspring carrying new combinations of genes that are not present in parents
INDEPENDENT ASSORTMENT: random assortment of chromosomes resulting from the selection of one chromosome from each parental pair of chromosomes for transmission to an offspring
LINKAGE: physical coupling of genes linked together in a linear sequence on a chromosome, forcing them to be inherited as a unit
SEGREGATION: the random separation of the two homologous parental chromosomes during sexual reproduction so that only one is passed on to each offspring

Summary of the Phenomenon

In 1866, an Augustinian monk named Gregor Mendel published a paper, "Experiments on Plant Hybrids," describing the heredity of mutant characteristics of garden peas. Mendel founded the modern science of genetics with these experiments, because they led him to propose the existence of hereditary factors, now called genes, and rules describing their inheritance, now referred to as Mendel's laws. The importance of Mendel's work was not recognized until the year 1900, sixteen years after his death, but since then Mendel's laws have been shown to hold throughout nature, the biochemical nature of genes has been discovered, the genetic code has been broken, and genetics has assumed a central role in modern biology, medicine, and agriculture.

One of the reasons for Mendel's success was that he simplified the problem of heredity down to the analysis of a few simple hereditary differences in a species that was easy to breed. He began by selecting strains of garden peas that differed by a single trait from normal strains, such as wrinkled seeds in one strain versus smooth in another, green peas versus yellow, and tall plants versus short. Once each strain bred true for a mutant variation, he crossed it with a different strain to see which trait was passed on to the offspring. Mendel observed that all the hybrid offspring of a particular cross resembled one of the parent types and not the other, rather than a mixture of the two types or an intermediate form. Crosses between tall and short parent strains, for example, produced hybrids that were tall only. Mendel defined this phenomenon as "dominance" of one trait over another trait, which he called the recessive trait.

Mendel then discovered that crossing two hybrids resulted in the reappearance of the recessive trait, but only in one-fourth of the offspring. A cross between two "tall" hybrids, for example, produced about three-fourths tall plants and one-fourth short plants. Mendel thought of a novel explanation for these results. He proposed that hereditary factors (now called genes) existed for each of the traits with which he was working. He also proposed that they exist in pairs, such that each individual inherits one from each parent, and each parent passes on only one of their two factors to each offspring. Mendel assumed that one of the two factors would be chosen at random for inclusion in each gamete (egg or sperm cell in animals; pollen or ovule in plants).

Mendel tested this theory with further crosses. He predicted, for example, that the original tall parent had two tall genes for height (symbolized as *TT*), and the original short parent had two "short" genes for height (*tt*). The hybrid would inherit one of each (*Tt*), but since the tall one is dominant, the hybrid's appearance would be tall. Mendel predicted that crossing a *Tt* hybrid with one of the short (*tt*) plants should produce half tall (*Tt*) offspring and half short ones (*tt*). That is exactly what Mendel observed. He was also able to predict the outcomes of other crosses involving different traits. Mendel concluded that his theory worked: Paired hereditary factors must exist, and only one of the two, chosen at random, must be passed on to each offspring by each parent. Mendel labeled this phenomenon "segregation," meaning that the parent's two hereditary factors are physically segregated into different cells during the production of gametes. This principle of segregation is now called Mendel's first law of inheritance.

Mendel's second law of inheritance describes the principle of "independent assortment," which states that different hereditary factors segregate independently of one another. Mendel observed, for example, that if he crossed a tall and purple parent (*TT-PP*) with a short and white one (*tt-pp*), the hybrid offspring were both tall and purple, since these are dominant. Then, when he crossed the tall and purple hybrid (*Tt-Pp*) with another identical hybrid, the progeny showed an "assortment" of the two traits (tall and purple, tall and white, short and purple, short and white) in a 9:3:3:1 ratio, respectively. This is the ratio expected if each trait's genes segregate independently of the other, meaning that whether a parent passes on a tall or short factor does not influence whether they also pass on the purple or white factor.

These two laws of heredity summarize Mendel's discovery of genes and their patterns of inheritance.

Mendel proposed that genes exist, explained how they are passed on, and supported those proposals with experimental evidence. Mendel's discovery, however, was virtually ignored, and he died in 1884 without receiving recognition for his work. Mendel's laws were independently rediscovered in the year 1900, and then their fundamental importance and general applicability was widely recognized.

Microscopic bodies in the nuclei of cells, called chromosomes, had been discovered by this time, and in 1901 it was proposed that chromosomes are the physical structures that contain Mendel's hereditary factors, or genes. Chromosomes were a likely structure for the location of genes because they occur in pairs, duplicate when the cell divides, and segregate into sperm and egg cells such that only one of the two chromosomes is passed on to any single offspring by each parent. The chromosomal theory of heredity made it easier for biologists to think of genes as physical objects of analysis, and studies of Mendelian patterns of inheritance and their chromosomal basis began to progress rapidly. A geneticist named Thomas Hunt Morgan at Columbia University made several key discoveries using fruit flies between 1910 and 1920. He and his colleagues discovered mutations in flies that showed a different pattern of inheritance in males and females, which led to association of these genes with the sex-determining X and Y chromosomes. Traits affected by genes on these chromosomes show a sex-linked pattern of inheritance in which recessive traits appear more often in males than in females. Human sex-linked traits, for example, include hemophilia, color blindness, and pattern baldness.

Fruit flies have three pairs of chromosomes besides the sex chromosomes, and Morgan's laboratory team showed that traits could be grouped together in "linkage groups" corresponding to their four pairs of chromosomes. They realized that Mendel's second law describing the principle of independent assortment corresponded to the assortment of chromosomes being passed from parent to offspring. Any genes on different chromosomes would be passed on independently, while genes linked together on the same chromosome would be passed on together as a unit. The discovery of linkage groups supported the idea that chromosomes were made up of collections of a large number of genes linked together. Morgan's laboratory group, however, also observed occasional exceptions to this pattern of linkage, when offspring sometimes showed unexpected new combinations of linked genes that did not exist in either parent. Alfred H. Sturtevant, a student in Morgan's laboratory, proposed that the paired chromosomes carrying different forms of the same genes (one carrying recessive forms, for example, a-b-c, versus the other, carrying dominant forms A-B-C) could undergo a reciprocal exhange of part of the chromosome. One chromosome pair could exchange, for example, C for a c, resulting in new a-b-C and A-B-c combinations of the linked genes.

Sturtevant also discovered that such recombination events occur with different frequencies between different genes. Only 1 percent of the A and B genes might be switched in each cross, for example, but 20 percent of the A and C genes might recombine in the same cross. Sturtevant proposed that the genes are linked together in a linear sequence and that the frequency of recombination between them was a function of the physical distance separating them on the chromosome. Two genes that are far apart should recombine more frequently then two genes close together, since there would be a greater opportunity for the breakage and the exchange of different chromosomal material to occur between them. Sturtevant proposed that differences in the frequency of recombination among linked genes on the same chromosome could be used to "map" the genes in a linear sequence that would reveal their order and relative positions on the chromosome. This principle turned out to be universal, and it allows genes to be mapped to specific locations on each chromosome in all organisms that can be systematically bred in the laboratory in large numbers—or in humans, because parent and offspring traits can be observed from one generation to the next in large families. Mendel's genes had, by the 1920's, been associated with chromosomes, and individual genes on each chromosome could be ordered and mapped using recombination analysis.

The next two decades were marked by two important parallel developments in genetics. The first was a mathematical and experimental synthesis of Mendel's genetic theory with Charles Darwin's theory of evolution: It was shown that the genetic mechanism described by Mendel was compatible with the hereditary mechanism required for Darwin's evolutionary theory. The compatibility of Mendel's genetic theory with Darwin's evolutionary theory provided an important synthesis of the two theories that strengthened them both. The second development was progress in identifying the biochemical nature of genes, primarily by the extension of genetic analysis to bacteria and viruses. These studies led to the identification of deoxyribonucleic acid (DNA) as the hereditary molecule and to the identification of its biochemical structure by James Watson and Francis Crick in 1953. Once the biochemical structure of genes was identified, an understanding of how DNA replicates and carries a genetic code that directs the synthesis of proteins followed rapidly.

One more revolutionary breakthrough that set the stage for the current era of genetics was the rapid development of recombinant DNA technology in the 1970's and its refinement and broad application in the 1980's. Recombinant DNA technology is a collection of methods that allows DNA sequences of one organism to be recombined with those of another. The application of these techniques is commonly referred to as "genetic engineering." The fact that the chemical structure of DNA and the genetic code for protein synthesis are virtually the same for all organisms makes recombinant DNA a powerful technology, since there is no reason, in principle, that the DNA of any two organisms cannot be recombined. One of the first practical applications of recombinant DNA technology, for example, was the insertion of the human insulin gene into bacteria. The bacteria use it to produce insulin, which is then harvested from the bacteria for human use.

The theoretical understanding of heredity begun by Mendel, together with the discovery of the biochemical basis of heredity and practical techniques for working with DNA, is one of the major accomplishments of modern science.

Methods of Study

Mendel's original methods of crossing mutant strains to test for dominance and predictable patterns of inheritance are still widely used to discover new genetic traits. The technique of making genetic maps of recombination analysis developed by Sturtevant is also still widely used to locate genes on a genetic map. The ability of X rays to induce mutations was discovered in 1927; since then, a variety of treatments, such as ultraviolet light and mutagenic chemicals, have been used to induce mutations for genetic analysis in many diverse organisms. Another classical genetic method is artificial selection, which is accomplished by breeding individuals with desired traits together to concentrate their genes in a single lineage over many generations. Typically, artificial selection is a slow but reliable process producing gradual change over many generations. Most complex traits depend on many different genes, and genetic differences are common in most populations, so artificial selection almost always makes a significant difference within a few generations. Problems, however, may arise from inbreeding in small populations, from the occurrence of undesired side effects of selected genes on other unselected traits, or from unselected genes that are closely linked to those selected for and inherited along with them. Average yields of corn, wheat, milk, eggs, and beef have been improved dramatically through combinations of selective breeding and environmental enhancements.

These classical genetic methods have been augmented by molecular genetic techniques for more complete genetic analysis than either the classical or molecular methods alone allow. Genes that are identified and mapped by classical methods can now be physically isolated, and their DNA sequences can be analyzed and decoded. The gene can then be altered, reinserted, or spliced into the DNA of another species, using recombinant DNA techniques. Specific genes causing traits that have long been known to "run in families" can now be identified and isolated, such as genes involved in causing various forms of cancer, cystic fibrosis, sickle-cell anemia, Huntington's chorea, and many other diseases. Ultimately these techniques will allow many genetic disorders to be diagnosed and treated more effectively.

One of the most effective combinations of the classical techniques with new molecular techniques is the mapping of a new trait by searching for genetic linkage to a specific mutant DNA sequence identified by direct biochemical anlaysis of the DNA. Once a gene's position on the genetic map is identified relative to a known DNA sequence, its DNA sequence can usually be determined as well. A known DNA sequence that is found to be closely linked to a particular trait—for example, a disease such as sickle-cell anemia or cystic fibrosis—can serve as a diagnostic marker for it and can allow accurate genetic counseling and, potentially, genetic therapy to correct harmful mutations. The usefulness of the classical genetic techniques of Mendelian analysis and linkage mapping has been amplified dramatically by molecular genetic methods that allow a gene's DNA to be isolated once it has been identified and mapped.

Context

Genetics has become one of the central disciplines of the life sciences. Mendelian genetics provides a mechanistic explanation of the heredity of biological charactersitics, which has led to a universal theory of heredity, including the hereditary mechanisms underlying evolutionary change. Classical Mendelian genetics explains how biological information is transmitted from one generation to the next in organisms that reproduce sexually. Genetic mutations explain the origins of variation essential for evolutionary adaptation. Molecular genetics has identified DNA as the biochemical form of genes. It exists in long linear strands of DNA called chromosomes, which cells read and translate into proteins that make up the cell structure and regulate its metabolism. Control of the timing of protein synthesis controls the growth and development of complex organisms; differences in the number and specific chemical makeup of genes determine the essential biological differences among the variety of organisms and contribute to individual differences among organisms of the same species.

Recombinant DNA techniques, together with an understanding of the genetic code and the ability to identify and map specific genes, have opened up a new era of biological investigation. Genes can be altered in order to repair mutations or redesign their protein products and can be transferred from one organism to another. The application of these techniques will have a dramatic impact on the progress of basic biological research, as the genetic basis of more and more traits is understood; on medical science, as the genetic basis of more and more diseases is understood, allowing new treatments and cures to be developed; and on agriculture and animal husbandry, as the genetic characteristics of more plants and animals are understood in greater detail.

Genetics was, throughout most of its history, largely a textbook example of the creativity of science at its best in revealing the elegance and beauty of nature's solutions to some of the most fundamental mysteries of life. Now, however, genetics includes application of that knowledge, through genetic engineering techniques, to alter living organisms by introducing new traits that are not only new combinations of naturally occurring genetic characteristics but also the results of creative human engineering or biological heredity. The same knowledge that allows scientists to alter the genetic qualities of organisms also gives human society new responsibilities to use genetic technology wisely.

Bibliography

Cherfas, Jeremy. *Man-Made Life: An Overview of the Science, Technology, and Commerce of Genetic Engineering*. New York: Pantheon Books, 1982. A history of the origins and growth of recombinant DNA technology and its applications. The style is journalistic and nontechnical. Cherfas includes interesting biographical sketches of the people involved in the work and a lively discussion of its controversial aspects.

Jacob, François. *The Logic of Life*. New York: Pantheon Books, 1973. A history of the study of heredity, from the ideas of the Greeks through the discovery of the genetic code, by a Nobel Prize-winning molecular geneticist. Presented as a serious intellectual history.

King, Robert C., and William D. Stansfield. *A Dictionary of Genetics*. 3d ed. New York: Oxford University Press, 1985. A comprehensive dictionary defining common and technical terms in all areas of genetics, with a concise chronological history of genetics appended.

Olby, Robert. *Origins of Mendelism*. 2d ed. Chicago: University of Chicago Press, 1985. A scholarly account of the intellectual history of genetics, concluding with the "rediscovery" of Mendel's laws in 1900. Particular attention is paid to Mendel's contemporaries and to how Mendel's work began as an attempt to study the possible origin of new species from hybridization between existing ones.

Orel, Vitezslav. *Mendel*. New York: Oxford University Press, 1984. A detailed account of the life and work of Gregor Mendel. Orel is the head of the Moravian Museum exhibit on the history of Mendelian genetics at the site of Mendel's monastery and original garden laboratory in what is now the city of Brno, Czechoslovakia. A fascinating biography that makes Mendel come to life in nineteenth century Moravia.

Rothwell, Norman V. *Understanding Genetics*. 4th ed. New York: Oxford University Press, 1988. A popular college-level introductory genetics textbook that explains all the major areas of genetics in depth. Clearly written and well illustrated. Each chapter includes problems and questions for analysis, references to the scientific literature, and a summary of key points.

Sturtevant, Alfred H. *A History of Genetics*. New York: Harper & Row, 1965. A comprehensive history of genetics written by the discoverer of the technique of linkage mapping by recombination analysis. The book is clearly written and nontechnical, and is especially interesting for its firsthand account of the discoveries made in Thomas Hunt Morgan's "fly lab" in the early 1900's.

Voeller, Bruce R. *The Chromosome Theory of Inheritance*. New York: Appleton-Century-Crofts, 1968. An annotated collection of classic early papers in genetics, including a translation of Mendel's original paper. Other papers address the role of the cell nucleus in fertilization and heredity, the identification of chromosomes as the site of genetic material, and early experimental work verifying the existence of genes on chromosomes.

Bernard Possidente, Jr.

Cross-References

Cloning to Produce Recombinant DNA, 505; DNA Replication, 692; DNA's Molecular Structure, 706; Gene Therapy, 1128; Genes and Nucleic Acids, 1134; The Genetic Code, 1148; Deciphering the Genetic Code, 1155; Genetic Screening and Counseling, 1170; Mitosis and Meiosis, 1753; Transcription of DNA to Form RNA, 2632; Translation of Messenger RNA to Form Protein, 2647.

BACTERIAL GENETICS

Types of life science: Genetics and microbiology
Other fields of study: Biochemistry and molecular biology

Genetic material can be transferred among bacteria cells in three ways: conjugation, transduction, and transformation. Knowledge of this transfer of DNA has led to practical applications in medicine, agriculture, and industry.

Principal terms
> CONJUGATION: the transfer of genetic information from one bacterial cell to another in which there is direct physical contact of the cells
> PLASMID: an extrachromosomal piece of DNA found in some bacterial cells; its presence is often associated with the appearance of special characteristics such as drug resistance
> RECOMBINATION: the process whereby pieces of genetic information enter a bacterial cell and become incorporated into that cell's chromosome
> TRANSDUCTION: the transfer of genetic information from one bacterial cell to another by a bacterial virus
> TRANSFORMATION: the transfer of genetic information as cell-free, or naked, DNA from one bacterial cell to another

Summary of the Phenomenon

An important characteristic of an organism's genetic information is its ability to replicate itself accurately. Thus, its genetic information tends to remain constant from generation to generation. There are times, however, when small modifications of that information would be advantageous. Such changes might enable the organism to adapt better to changing physical or biological environments. In bacteria, there are two ways by which the genetic information can be modified. One is a process known as spontaneous mutation. This involves a physical alteration of the structure of a specific gene. It could be caused by radiation, chemicals, or excessive heat. Such changes occur approximately only once in every 100 million bacteria.

The other way that genetic information can be modified is by the transferal of genetic instructions from one organism to another. This will ultimately lead to genetic recombination. In bacteria, genetic transfer can be accomplished in three ways. The first involves a process known as conjugation. In this process a donor cell makes physical contact with a recipient cell. This contact is made with a structure called a pili. The genetic information can then travel through the pili from the donor to the recipient cell. The second method is called transduction. In transduction, genetic information of the donor cell is actually brought to the recipient cell by a bacterial virus. The final way in which genetic information can be transferred is by the process of transformation. In this case, cell-free deoxyribonucleic acid (DNA), also called naked DNA, is absorbed directly from the environment by the recipient cell. The genetic recombination that results from these three transfer mechanisms is considered a desirable process because it introduces new genetic information into a population of bacteria. It may allow the population to survive in adverse or changing environmental conditions. Normally, however, recombination occurs only about 1 percent of the time in bacterial populations.

Plants were the original candidates for genetic studies, which began in the late 1800's. Studies with animals shortly followed; bacteria did not become candidates for such study until the middle 1940's. This resulted primarily from a lack of adequate technology for handling bacteria. Nevertheless, bacteria have become extremely useful organisms for genetic studies since the early 1950's. Two major features of bacteria make them desirable subjects. First, the rate at which they can reproduce allows a very large number of bacteria to be produced in a short time. This, in turn, provides the researcher with more opportunity to detect the "rare genetic events" of mutation or recombination. Even more important, unlike all other organisms, bacteria have a single chromosome with a single set of genes. Thus, genetic modifications are more likely to result in immediately observable changes. In other organisms, which have multiple chromosomes, a change in a single gene may go undetected because its effect is masked by genes on other chromosomes.

All bacteria have a single circular chromosome, composed of DNA. The DNA is subdivided into specific message areas known as genes, and the chromsome carries from four thousand to five thousand individual genes. For many bacteria, this constitutes the entirety of its genetic information. A number of bacteria, however, have additional genetic information in the form of plasmids. A plasmid is a small additional circular piece of DNA, independent of the chromosome, which can hold an additional twenty to one-hundred genes. Plasmid-containing cells often have several plasmids.

Many researchers have described the plasmid genes as nonessential to the normal activities of bacteria. Under certain circumstances, however, those genes might provide a survival advantage to the possessor. For example, genes for antibiotic resistance are often carried on a plasmid. Normally, antibiotics are not present in the bacteria's environment; such genes would therefore be unnecessary. If the bacteria later were to come into contact with antibiotics, however, then having antibiotic-resistant genes would be to their distinct advantage.

The plasmid is a prerequisite to one type of genetic variation, conjugation. Two major types of plasmids exist: F plasmids, or fertility plasmids, and R plasmids, or resistance plasmids. Both types of plasmids can carry resistance genes. Only the F plasmids, however, are able to control the formation of a special cytoplasmic tube known as the sex pili. Cells with the F plasmids are known as F+, or donor, cells. Cells without the F plasmids are called F−, or recipient, cells.

During conjugation, the donor cell copies its plasmids and transfers them to a recipient cell to which it has attached itself by means of a sex pili. The recipient cell can now take advantage of whatever additional genes it has received. If, in the process, it received an F plasmid, it has also become a potential donor cell. Whenever bacterial cells undergo cell division, any plasmids they possess can potentially be passed on to their progeny. Originally, it was thought that conjugation could occur only between members of the same species, but that is not true. For example, it is now known that some strains of the bacteria responsible for causing gonorrhea, *Neisseria gonorrhoeae*, have received antibiotic-resistant genes from unrelated bacteria.

There is one other type of donor cell, the Hfr+, or high-frequency recombinant, cell. Instead of the plasmid remaining independent of the cell's chromosome, it inserts itself into the chromosome. When that plasmid gets ready to copy itself, the chromosomal genes are the first to be copied. Unless the donor and recipient cells are able to maintain direct contact for a fairly long period of time, the recipient cell will not receive the plasmid. It will, however, receive numerous chromosomal genes from the donor. Those genes may later be incorporated into the chromosome of the recipient, causing gene replacement. Not all species of bacteria participate in conjugation. Some rely on transduction as a means of receiving "new" genetic information. This is how *Staphylococcus aureus* has developed resistance to many antibiotics.

There are two types of transduction: generalized and specialized. In both cases, a donor cell becomes infected with a virus. Upon the death of that cell, donor genetic information is transferred as the escaping virus infects another bacterium. In generalized transduction, a virus infects a bacterial cell. Shortly after infection, the bacterial chromosome becomes fragmented, and viral components are produced. Later, the viral components are assembled to form a complete virus particle. Occasionally, during this assembly process, a particle becomes contaminated with fragments of the bacterial chromosome or plasmids. After assembly is completed, the bacterial cell ruptures, allowing the escape of all virus particles. Eventually, these virus particles will invade other bacterial cells. Any cells that are invaded by contaminated virus particles are said to be transduced, since they have received genetic information from another bacterium. The information received in this manner is strictly random.

Specialized transduction involves what is known as a latent virus. After the initial invasion of a bacterium, the virus attaches itself to a specific spot on that cell's chromosome. At some future time, the virus detaches itself from the chromosome and accidentally takes a few bacterial genes located near its original attachment point. When the bacterial cell finally begins making new viral components, it behaves as if those particular genes are part of the virus and replicates them as such. Therefore, all the newly formed virus particles will contain those bacterial genes. Transduction then occurs when these viral particles invade other bacterial cells.

The final method of genetic transfer is transformation. An extensively utilized organism for such investigation has been *Streptococcus pneumoniae*. The most famous studies involved converting nondisease-causing strains of *Streptococcus pneumoniae* into disease-causing strains. Transformation also occurs in a wide variety of other bacteria. The process of transformation requires that a population of actively reproducing bacteria come into contact with DNA fragments from closely related dead bacteria. These DNA fragments are referred to as either naked or cell-free DNA. A small portion of that DNA can be absorbed and utilized by the growing bacteria. These recipients can then take advantage of any usable genes that the fragments might contain.

Methods of Study

Researchers in bacterial genetics are faced with two particular problems. First, they must provide the opportunity for the transfer of genetic material. Then, they must be able to demonstrate that the transfer has actually occurred. Studies involving differences in nutritional requirements and resistance to various antibiotics are often used in providing such evidence.

Demonstrating that genetic transfer has occurred can be done by isolating the recombinant cell on a medium that will not support the growth of either the donor or the recipient cell. For example, neither a donor cell that is resistant to penicillin and requires lysine in its growth medium nor a recipient cell that is susceptible to penicillin and does not require lysine could grow on a medium that contains penicillin and lacks lysine. A recombinant cell, however, could. The recombinant cell in this case would be a former recipient cell that had received a gene for penicillin resistance from a donor and had then incorporated that gene into its own formation pool (genome).

When the actual research is conducted, it is not practical to use a single donor cell or a single recipient cell; liquid cultures containing thousands of donor or recipient cells are used instead. Recombinant cells are usually recovered in the form of a colony, which is a mass of identical cells visible to the naked eye. In order for a colony to be formed, the cells must be grown on a solid medium.

In 1944, Joshua Lederberg and Edward Tatum demonstrated genetic recombination in bacteria by conjugation. They grew two different nutritionally mutant cultures of bacteria in liquid media. Then they combined the media, allowing the opportunity for direct contact of the two cultures. Later, they transferred some of the combined culture to plates containing a nonliquid minimal medium. A few recombinant colonies were recovered from the plates. Prior to Lederberg and Tatum's work, transformation studies had been conducted by Frederick Griffith in 1928 and by Oswald T. Avery and his associates in 1944. They combined cell extracts containing DNA from donor cells with liquid cultures of recipient cells. They, too, had been able to recover recombinant populations of bacteria.

By 1952, Norton Zinder and Lederberg were conducting additional conjugational studies. In the course of their experiments, they put a liquid medium in a U-shaped culture tube that was divided in two by a sintered glass filter impervious to bacteria. Donor bacteria were put in one arm of the tube, and recipient bacteria were put in the other. Samples were later plated on minimal media, and recombinants were recovered. Conjugation could not have been not possible, since direct contact between the two cultures had been prevented. When an enzyme that destroys cell-free DNA was introduced into the system, similar results were obtained. This ruled out the possibility of transformation. With further investigation, it was discovered that one of the cultures had been infected with a virus. The small virus had been able to pass through the glass filter and transfer some of the other culture's genes. Information gathered by researchers in these and similar studies, along with the later development of the ability to make recombinant DNA in the laboratory, has brought about a revolution known as genetic engineering.

Context

Conjugation, transduction, and transformation are all mechanisms of genetic change within a bacterial population. These mechanisms allow a specific characteristic to be spread throughout the population within a few hours. A wide number of bacterial genes have been found to be transferred by these methods, including genes that control a bacterium's ability to cause disease, to produce toxins, and to develop resistance to antibiotics and other drugs, as well as genes that control a number of other characteristics. The purpose of these mechanisms, as far as the bacteria are concerned, is to enable the bacteria to adapt to changing environmental conditions so that their survivial is ensured. Scientists, however, have found ways to adapt some of these mechanisms for human benefit.

Scientists have used the mechanisms of genetic transfer along with new technology from DNA research to perform genetic engineering on bacteria. They can make numerous genes and recombinant DNA in the laboratory. Such genetic information is then inserted into bacteria, such as *Escherichia coli*. The bacteria will follow the new genetic instructions they have received. In this manner, bacteria can be used to produce a wide variety of products for medicine, agriculture, and industry. Examples include various vaccines, human insulin, growth hormones, vitamin supplements, amino acid supplements, a substance to dissolve blood clots, insecticidal toxins, various antibiotics, and a bacterium that can help dissolve oil slicks. Genetic engineering and the products that result from it would not be possible without the knowledge of genetic transfer gained from studies of bacterial conjugation, transduction, and transformation.

Bibliography

Brock, Thomas D., and Michael T. Madigan. *Biology of Microorganisms*. 5th ed. Englewood Cliffs, N.J.: Prentice-Hall, 1988. Chapter 7, "Microbial Genetics," covers kinds of genetic recombination and gene transfer, plasmids, genetic mapping, and general genetics of eukaryotic microorganisms. There are many illustrations and diagrams. Explanations are in-depth and tend to be technical. Aimed toward an intermediate college-level audience. Supplementary references are listed.
Cano, Raul J., and Jamie S. Colome. *Essentials of Microbiology*. St. Paul, Minn.:

West, 1988. Chapter 6, "Microbial Genetics," covers nucleic acid structure, DNA replication, protein synthesis, mutation, and genetic transfer. Explanations are nontechnical and easy to understand; many illustrations. Accessible to a general audience. Includes a list of references.

Lim, D. V. *Microbiology.* St. Paul, Minn.: West, 1989. Chapter 11, "Information Processing: Mutation and Recombination," discusses such topics as mutation, recombination, and genetic engineering. Includes good illustrations and diagrams. Explanations can easily be followed by anyone with an interest in science. For the college-level and general reader. Supplementary references are listed.

Pelczar, Michael J., E. C. S. Chan, and N. R. Krieg. *Microbiology.* 5th ed. New York: McGraw-Hill, 1986. Chapter 12, "Bacterial Genetics," covers general microbial genetics, mutation, recombination, and gene regulation. It is well written but slightly technical. References are included.

Tortora, Gerard J., Berdell Funke, and Christine Case. *Microbiology.* 3d ed. Menlo Park, Calif.: Benjamin/Cummings, 1989. Includes discussions of DNA replication in general, general bacterial genetics, gene expression, genetic transfer and recombination, and genetic engineering. Chapter 8, "Microbial Genetics," is especially valuable. It is well written and not overly technical, and it has illustrations and diagrams. Written at the college level, but accessible to the general reader. References are listed.

Randy Firstman

Cross-References

Cloning to Produce Recombinant DNA, 505; Extranuclear Inheritance, 960; Gene Mutation and Repair, 1103; Prokaryotic Gene Regulation, 1119; Genes and Nucleic Acids, 1134; The Genetic Code, 1148; Human Genetics, 1190; Viral Genetics, 1198; Transposable Elements, 2654.

HUMAN GENETICS

Type of life science: Genetics
Other fields of study: Anthropology, biochemistry, evolutionary biology, molecular
biology, and reproduction

Analyzing a pedigree requires studying a family's genetic history for the pattern of
transmission of its inherited traits. Study of cotransmitted traits may reveal a physi-
cal association between genes. Such gene linkage is measured by lod scores.

Principal terms

ALLELE: a genetic determinant; a recessive allele is expressed only if two
copies of it are present, whereas a dominant allele is expressed if
one copy of it is present, such as the A allele in an Aa heterozygote

CIS and TRANS: mutually exclusive terms for the relative location of
alleles of two linked genes; two dominant alleles on opposite
members of a chromosome pair are in a "trans" relationship; if on
the same member, there is a "cis" relationship

CROSSING OVER: the physical exchange of parts between two members
of a chromosome pair when they are aligned together during the
formation of sex cells

GENOTYPE: the gene(s) underlying an inherited trait

HETEROZYGOTE: having two different alleles for a particular gene,
exemplified by the genotype Aa

HOMOZYGOTE: having two identical alleles for a particular gene; the
genotypes AA and aa are both homozygous conditions

LINKAGE: the physical association of genes in a linear array on a
chromosome

LOD SCORE: the logarithm of the frequency of recombination estimated
for offspring of informative matings in which one parent is
heterozygous for two or more genes, which may or may not be
linked

MAP DISTANCE: linear distance between linked genes given in genetically
defined units called centimorgans; 1 percent recombination (0.01 R)
equals 1 centimorgan

PEDIGREE: a family genealogical tree with known, or suspected, genetic
traits indicated for each person in it

PHENOTYPE: the observable trait or traits that may be inherited, in whole
or in part, or that may be entirely acquired, having an environmental
basis

RECOMBINATION: the formation of new associations of alleles of different
genes during production of the sex cells; linked genes become
recombined when crossing over occurs between these gene sites

Summary of the Phenomenon

Humans have tens of thousands of genes, the determinants of inherited traits. Genes are composed of the chemical material called deoxyribonucleic acid (DNA) and are located in human cells on the linear bodies called chromosomes. Each chromosome contains hundreds of genes. Each human cell has forty-six chromosomes, consisting of a set of twenty-three from the mother and a matched, or homologous, set of twenty-three from the father. In general, each gene in an individual consists of two copies, one from each parent, borne on homologous chromosomes.

Geneticists are working to locate the position of each human gene on its particular chromosome, studying inherited anomalies both at the organismal and at the DNA levels, in order to construct a detailed genetic map of the biological makeup of the human species. A genetic map, even in its incomplete stages, provides a basic framework for understanding and predicting gene and chromosome behavior. Such understanding, in turn, is useful in the diagnosis and prediction of human genetic disorders.

By studying large families, geneticists can often determine the inheritance pattern of two or more genes, thereby revealing whether the genes are linked together on the same chromosome. Two genes chosen at random for study in a particular family are likely to be unlinked, to be located on different chromosomes. Genetic evidence for nonlinkage or linkage traditionally comes from observing the frequencies of the types of offspring produced in informative families.

To symbolize the genetic situation in one kind of informative family, let A and a be alternative versions, or alleles, of the gene A. Let B and b be alleles of the gene B. An individual having both A and a is said to be heterozygous for gene A. An individual having the combination AaBb is a double heterozygote. An individual carrying the same alleles for a gene is a homozygote: For example, aabb is referred to as a double homozygote.

For many genes, one allele is dominant over the other. The dominant allele, symbolized by a capital letter, is expressed in either single or double dose: Both AA and Aa genotypes express the allele A; they have the A trait, or A phenotype. The allele a is recessive: It is expressed only in a double dose; the aa genotype expresses the a phenotype.

During the formation of the sex cells (the gametes), segregation of alleles occurs as homologous chromosomes separate to different daughter cells. Sperm and egg cells have twenty-three, not forty-six, chromosomes, and they have only one of the two possible alleles of a gene. An Aa heterozygote produces two kinds of gametes, A and a, as a result of allele segregation.

More than a century ago, Gregor Mendel worked out the expected frequencies of different genotypes (and phenotypes) of offspring in various kinds of familial matings. Nonlinkage, also called independent allele segregation in Mendelian terminology, is evident in the case of the mating of A/a B/b × a/a b/b. Here, the offspring are expected to appear in four equally common classes: ¼ A/a B/b, ¼ a/a b/b, ¼ A/a b/b, and ¼ a/a B/b. Because genes A and B are unlinked, their alleles are passed on to offspring from the doubly heterozygous parent independent of each other. The gametes of this A/a B/b parent occur in all possible combinations of four equal classes: AB, ab, Ab, and aB. The gametes of the a/a b/b parent are all ab.

By analogy, the mating A/a B/b × a/a b/b produces results such as those found when flipping two coins simultaneously a large number of times. In that case, one obtains 25 percent HH (both heads), corresponding to ¼ A/a B/b; 50 percent HT (one head + one tail), corresponding to ¼ A/a b/b + ¼ a/a B/b; and 25 percent TT, corresponding to ¼ a/a b/b.

Human families are too small to produce idealized offspring frequencies of independently segregating (unlinked) or dependently segregating (linked) genes. An AaBb parent may have only two or three offspring, which may all be AaBb, or all aabb, or all Aabb, or some combination of the various possibilities. Geneticists must hence study a number of families of like mating, such as AaBb × aabb, to determine if the genes involved are linked or unlinked.

Such pedigree studies, especially of multigenerational families, can sometimes reveal close linkage. Consider the following family: The grandparental cross is AaBb × aabb, producing two sons who are AaBb. The elder son marries an aabb woman and they produce two daughters, both of whom are AaBb, and two sons, both of whom are aabb. The fact that all the offspring in this family have genotypes like one or the other of their parents suggests that genes A and B are linked. The possible nonparental genotypes, Aabb and aaBb, are not observed. Alleles A and B are thus linked on the same member of a chromosome pair, with the alleles a and b on the opposite homolog. The double heterozygote Aa Bb can be more precisely symbolized in this family as AB/ab. (In contrast, if A and B are unlinked, the genotype is symbolized as A/a B/b.)

In this three-generational family, the linkage between A and B must be very tight because nonparental, or recombinant, offspring are not observed. If, however, a fifth child who is Ab/ab is produced in the last generation, this new finding of a completely different combination of alleles from the AB/ab parent suggests looser linkage. The Ab/ab child is produced by the crossover, the exchange, or the recombination, of chromosome segments between the AB and ab homologues while these members of the chromosome pair are aligned during the process of gamete formation.

The five-child family consisting of four nonrecombinant offspring (genotypes AB/ab and ab/ab) and one recombinant (Ab/ab) can provide an estimate of the relative distance between genes A and B. The frequency of recombination (R) resulting from crossover is arbitrarily defined as the distance between A and B on a genetic map in which one map unit is equal to 0.01 R. As a general rule, the closer together two linked genes are, the fewer crossovers occur between them. In the five-child family, simple counting gives an estimate of R. R = 1 child out of 5 = 0.20, or a distance of 20 map units between genes and A and B. If the fifth child had not been produced, R would have been estimated as zero recombinants among four children: R = %4 = 0 map units between genes A and B, signifying that they are side by side.

An R value of 0.20 in the five-child family means that if other crosses of the type AB/ab × ab/ab were studied for linkage between genes A and B, the expected frequencies of the offspring of such crosses taken as a group would be approximately 0.30 AB/ab and 0.30 ab/ab (the two nonrecombinant classes) plus 0.20 Ab/ab and 0.20 aB/ab (the two recombinant classes). In contrast, if A and B were unlinked, the expected offspring frequencies would be 0.25 for each of the four classes, with R being at its maximum value of 0.50.

A methodological problem in linkage studies is that it is often impossible to tell the phase of linked genes in pedigrees, especially when only two generations are available for study. In a double heterozygote, the A and B alleles may be linked together in cis (AB/ab) or in trans (Ab/aB). In the five-child family mentioned earlier, if the A and B alleles had been on opposite homologues (the trans condition) the cross (indicated as Ab/aB × ab/ab) would not have been expected to produce so many AB/ab and ab/ab offspring.

Lack of knowledge of the phase of linkage, whether cis or trans, precludes determination of the map distance, R, between two genes by means of the direct counting of offspring types. The impasse arises because recombinants cannot be distinguished from nonrecombinants. To circumvent this problem, a statistical method of linkage analysis has been developed that does not depend on knowing whether the A and B alleles in a double heterozygote are linked in cis or trans. This method produces a numerical value for the likelihood of linkage at different postulated values of R, from very tight linkage (R at or near zero) to loose linkage (an R with a value of 0.30 or 0.40). The best estimate of R, its maximum value for the data available, is derived from maximum likelihood mathematics, a complex topic. Algorithms and computer programs have been devised that permit the analysis of large amounts of pedigree data about possible linkage between genes when the phase (cis or trans condition) is unknown. Further consideration of unknown-phase linkage studies is presented in the following section.

One of the problems geneticists encounter in pedigree studies is that not all families are informative about linkage. The family under study must have two or more segregating genes, the more the better. Crosses of the type AABB × AABB, aaBB × AABB, or aabb × AABb are not informative about linkage because crossovers occurring in the parents are not detectable via recombinant offspring. Even in informative matings, double crossovers between two genes do not give rise to recombinants for these genes because the second crossover reestablishes the original configuration.

In addition to revealing gene linkage, pedigree studies can provide information on the extent of inbreeding that occurs in families in which the parents are related; on the persistence or extinction of rare traits in family lineages; and on the genetic influence the first few individuals can exert on a colonizing, or insular, population. Every decade sees new uses for pedigree analysis in human genetics.

Methods of Study

In most pedigrees, linkage can be analyzed only by statistical methods because the phase of the doubly heterozygous parent is unknown, that is, whether the parent is genotypically AB/ab or Ab/aB. These methods give the odds, or chances, of linkage versus nonlinkage. The methods require use of recombination (R) frequencies. R refers to the fraction or percent of offspring that are recombinant, meaning genotypically unlike either parent. By definition, R also measures the distance between two genes on a linkage map.

If two genes A and B are unlinked (R = ½), the cross of A/a B/b × a/a b/b generates 0.25 A/a B/b, 0.25 a/a b/b, 0.25 A/a b/b, and 0.25 a/a B/b expected offspring. If the two genes are very tightly linked (R ≅ 0), the cross of AB/ab × ab/ab generates 0.50 AB/ab and 0.50 ab/ab expected offspring. With the same tight linkage, the cross of Ab/aB × ab/ab generates 0.50 Ab/ab and 0.50 aB/ab expected offspring.

Keeping all this in mind, consider a family in which the mother is a double heterozygote for genes A and B, the father is a double recessive homozygote, and it is not known whether A and B are linked. These parents have two daughters, both aabb. If the genes are unlinked (R = ½), the probability (P_2) for these daughters' genotype is ¼. If the genes are very tightly linked (R ≅ 0), moreover, the probability is that these daughters' genotype is ½ if the mother's genotype is AB/ab. With R ≅ 0, there is no chance at all that the mother's genotype is Ab/aB because crossover is virtually ruled out by the very tight linkage. Because the phase of the mother's genotype, whether cis or trans, is unknown, the overall probability (P_1) for R ≅ 0 must then be ½ + 0, or P_1 = ½.

Even without knowing if the mother's genotype reflects linkage in the cis or trans phase, therefore, the likelihood of R being zero can be given as P_1 divided by P_2. This is called a likelihood ratio, and for this family, this ratio is P_1/P_2—½ divided by ¼ = 2: The odds are 2 to 1 in favor of very tight linkage. Odds of this magnitude are not good enough to convince geneticists that the two genes are linked. More families must be studied to reach a greater level of certainty about linkage.

When surveying many families for the possibility of linkage between A and B, it is numerically easier to add the logarithms of the likelihood ratio (P_1/P_2) for each family rather than the ratios themselves. These logarithm values (Z scores) are known as "lod" scores, standing for log of the odds. For the two-daughter family previously discussed, Z = log 2 = 0.301.

If a large family were discovered in which the parents were an AaBb mother × an aabb father, and there were ten offspring, all either aabb or AaBb (apparent nonrecombinants), this finding strengthens the case for the two genes A and B being very tightly linked, with the mother being AB/ab. The Z score for this large family is 2.709. Adding it to the Z score of 0.301 obtained in the two-child family studied previously, the total Z score is 3.01. Now the odds of R being near zero are about 1,000 to 1 (the logarithm to the base 10 of 1,000 = 3), providing strong evidence for linkage. The odds of R being 0.1 or 0.3 or 0.5 become smaller and smaller. Z is therefore maximal at R = 0.

If one member of a nine-member family is recombinant (Aabb), the most likely value for R (above zero probability) is about 0.11—eleven map units. The one Aabb offspring points to a recombination (crossover) occurring between A and B, meaning that the two genes are less tightly linked than previously envisioned. If another recombinant offspring were produced in this family (Aabb or aaBb), the most likely value for the genetic map distance between genes A and B (R) moves beyond 0.11. The higher the percentage of recombinant offspring discovered, the greater the chance that A and B are farther apart. If recombinant offspring are as common as nonrecombinant (parental-type) offspring, R is therefore 0.5 and the genes are operationally unlinked—their alleles segregate independent of each other.

The strength of the lod-score approach can be seen in the following example. By studying many individuals from four generations in one extended family, the insulin gene and the ras-1 cancer gene were estimated to be 6.7 map units apart on human chromosome number 11 by maximum-likelihood methods. The lod score (Z) for this computer-aided analysis was 9.9, providing overwhelming evidence for linkage of this magnitude between the two genes.

Context

Linkage is an important aspect of the way genes are organized in human cells. Understanding the phenomenon of linkage aids in the understanding of the traits that are inherited together from a particular parent, traits that are inherited separately by different children in a family. An inherited disorder can be mapped by linkage studies even when detailed knowledge of the biochemical defect causing the disorder is not available.

By studying the genetic pedigree of a family, a medical geneticist can determine a number of factors important in the understanding of a familial defect or genetic disease. If a family member is too young to have expressed the disease, a linkage study may help estimate the chance of the person expressing the disease at a later age. Adult-onset conditions such as Huntington's chorea (Huntington's disease)—a progressive, incurable, neuromuscular disease—have been forecast in this way. They can be important as a means of prenatal diagnosis and in genetic counseling.

A rare, complex phenotype is occasionally found to cluster in a family, and the genetic reasons for this are not clear. Such phenotypes are often congenital, involving defects in various internal organs. This may be intrinsically genetic in origin, or it may be caused by some factor in the family's environment. If the rare phenotype exhibits strong linkage to a known gene (a genetic "marker"), the finding is evidence that it may have a strong genetic basis.

Linkage studies will ultimately lead to the construction of a detailed map of human genetics. Once constructed, the map can be used for a variety of purposes in genetic counseling and for determining the genetic past in the evolution of the human species. Once the position of a gene is known on this map (even if it is only a map of one portion of one chromosome), it may be possible to design methods for inserting a normal gene into certain cells of a fetus or child showing a genetic disorder. This is the essence of gene therapy, but it is not yet a reality.

Studies on human evolution show that individuals differ in terms of their gene maps. Some people have an extra copy or two of a particular gene. Such duplicate or triplicate genes do not usually produce an abnormal phenotype. Human prehistory shows that Micronesians and Polynesians have a high frequency of triplicate genes for a prenatal form of the red protein found in blood cells, called hemoglobin zeta. This gene triplication can be traced back to East Asia, presumably the source of this genetic characteristic in the mid-Pacific.

Bibliography

Batschelet, Edward. *Introduction to Mathematics for Life Scientists*. 3d ed. New York: Springer-Verlag, 1985. A good general review of basic mathematics for anyone interested in human biology. For example, it explains logarithms (both normal and natural) and their uses in clear terms; it also discusses probability. Contains illustrations, mathematical tables, bibliography, and an index.

Congress of the United States Office of Technology Assessment. *Mapping Our Genes: Genome Projects—How Big, How Fast?* Baltimore: The Johns Hopkins University Press, 1988. An overview of the science and the science-policy questions involved in the current efforts to develop a human-gene map. Contains illustrations, glossary, index, bibliography, and appendices.

National Research Council. *Mapping and Sequencing the Human Genome*. Washington, D.C.: National Academy Press, 1988. This report by an expert committee for the National Academy of Sciences discusses the national and international efforts in progress to decipher human heredity in terms of a gene map. The implications of this effort—for medicine, for science, and for society—are reviewed and evaluated. Contains a glossary, index, bibliography, and illustrations.

Reid, Russel M. *Human Population Genetics*. Minneapolis: Burgess, 1978. A quick introduction at the college level to human population genetics; discusses the importance of genetics in understanding human evolution, differences among human groups, and human biological adaptations to the environment. Illustrations, index.

Roberts, J. A. Fraser, and Marcus Pembrey. *An Introduction to Medical Genetics*. New York: Oxford University Press, 1985. This college-level text covers basic human genetics. Chapter 8, on genetic linkage, discusses how linkage is distinguished from nonlinkage, including the use of lod scores. Contains illustrations, bibliography, and an index.

Thompson, Elizabeth A. *Pedigree Analysis in Human Genetics*. Baltimore: The Johns Hopkins University Press, 1985. A college-level text containing much information about pedigree studies. Discussions of mathematics are kept to the minimum required for understanding basic principles. Examples of isolated populations are featured. Illustrations, bibliography, index.

White, Ray, and Jean-Marc Lalouel. "Chromosome Mapping with DNA Markers." *Scientific American* 258 (February, 1988): 40-48. This paper explains human genetic linkage in terms of genetic markers—variants of the chemical composition of genes (at the DNA level). This approach to linkage studies aims to produce a detailed gene map. It is also well illustrated.

A. S. Baer

Cross-References

Chromosomes, 462; Complementation and Allelism: The Cis-Trans Test, 555; Genes and Nucleic Acids, 1134; The Genetic Code, 1148; Genetic Equilibrium: Linkage, 1162; Genetic Screening and Counseling, 1170; *Homo sapiens* and the Diversification of Humans, 1329; Karyotyping, 1506; Mitosis and Meiosis, 1753; Prenatal Diagnostic Techniques, 2194.

VIRAL GENETICS

Types of life science: Genetics, microbiology
Other fields of study: Biochemistry and molecular biology

Viruses in general, and bacteriophages in particular, have been important systems for the study of gene regulation and for the better understanding of the processes of DNA replication and transcription.

Principal terms

COMPLEMENTATION: production of wild-type progeny when two different phage mutants are used in a mixed infection; the mutations must be in different functional genes

LYSATE: suspension of progeny phages released when a culture of phage-infected bacteria lyses (bursts)

LYSIS: the rupture and death of a bacterial cell that occurs as the last phase of a lytic phage infection; infective progeny phages are thus released from the cell

LYSOGENIC BACTERIUM: a host cell that contains a temperate bacteriophage that is integrated as a prophage; it is subject to lysis if the prophage uncouples itself from the host DNA and enters the lytic pathway

MULTIPLICITY OF INFECTION: the average number of phages that infect a single host cell in a particular experiment

PLAQUE: a clear, circular area on a lawn of bacterial host cells growing on solid media that results from progressive infections of a single phage particle and its descendants

PROPHAGE: the DNA of a temperate bacteriophage when it is physically integrated into the DNA of the host cell

RECOMBINATION: the physical exchange of segments of DNA between two genetically different phage parents, or the detection of progeny phages that have gene sequences derived from each parent

TEMPERATE BACTERIOPHAGE: a phage capable of entering the lysogenic cycle in the host; the phage DNA is integrated into the host DNA to become a prophage

Summary of the Phenomenon

Viruses are an extraordinarily diverse group of ultramicroscopic particles that are distinct from all other organisms because of their noncellular organization. Composed of an inert outer protein shell, or capsid, and an inner core of nucleic acid—either deoxyribonucleic acid (DNA) or ribonucleic acid (RNA) but never both—viruses are obligate intracellular parasites, depending to a great extent on host cell functions for the production of new viral particles. There is considerable variation in size and complexity among the viruses. Some have fewer than ten genes and depend almost entirely on host functions, while others are known to contain from thirty to one hundred genes and rely more on proteins encoded by their own DNA. Even the largest viruses are too small to be seen under the light microscope, so studies on viral structure rely heavily on observation with the transmission electron microscope.

From a historical perspective, definitive studies on viral genetics have primarily involved those viruses, called bacteriophages (or phages, for short), that specifically infect bacterial cells. Since scientists know more about the molecular and cell biology of the common bacterium *Escherichia coli* than about any other cell or organism, it is perhaps not surprising that the best-known phages are those that require *E. coli* as a host (coliphage). It is not possible to observe phage growth directly (as bacterial growth can be detected by the appearance of colonies on an agar plate), but phage growth can be indirectly observed by the formation of plaques, small interruptions in an otherwise confluent lawn of host bacteria growing on a solid growth medium in a petri dish.

There are two alternative life cycles found among the various bacteriophages, termed lytic and lysogenic. Some phages are capable only of lytic growth, while others retain the options of either lytic growth or entry into the lysogenic cycle. In the lytic cycle, phages first attach themselves to specific receptor sites on the host cell wall. The phage nucleic acid (DNA or RNA) is injected inside the host, while the protein capsid of the infecting particle remains outside of the host cell at all times. Once inside, transcription of phage genes begins, and phage-encoded proteins begin to be made. Some of these proteins serve to inactivate and destroy the host cell DNA, ensuring that the cell's energy resources will be directed exclusively toward the production of phage proteins and the replication of phage nucleic acid. Phage DNA or RNA replication ensues quickly and is followed by the packaging of this genetic material into the newly synthesized capsids of the progeny phage particles. The final step is host cell lysis—the bursting of the host cell to release the completed and infective phage progeny. The number of phages released in each burst varies with growth conditions and species, but ideal conditions often result in a burst size of from one hundred to two hundred per host cell.

For temperate bacteriophage, those capable of entering the lysogenic cycle, infection of the host cell only rarely causes lysis. Injection of the phage DNA into the host is followed by a brief period of messenger RNA (mRNA) synthesis, necessary to direct the production of a phage repressor protein, which inhibits the production of phage proteins involved with lytic functions. A DNA-insertion enzyme is also made, allowing the phage DNA to be physically inserted into the DNA of the host. The cell then can continue to grow and multiply, and new copies of the phage genes are replicated every cell generation as part of the bacterial chromosome. The host cell is said to be lysogenic, for it retains the potential to be lysed if the prophage pops out of the host DNA and enters the lytic cycle. The integrated prophage does confer a useful property on the host cell, however, for the cell will now be immune to further infection from the same phage species.

Most of the well-characterized mutant phenotypes in phages fall into one of two broad classes: plaque morphology mutants or host range mutants. Plaque morphology mutants are those that form plaques that are distinctly different in a predictable way from the wild type. These may be described as clear, turbid, large, small, pinpoint, fuzzy, and more. Host range mutants are those that have undergone either an extension or a change in the number of bacterial strains or species that they can successfully infect. Bacteriophages are in general quite specific with regard to their host cells. Most can infect only a single host species, and often successful infection is limited to one or a few strains of that species. For example, the wild-type coliphage φX174 grows well on *E. coli* strain C, but it fails to grow on other laboratory strains of this species. Host range mutants of φX174 have been identified that can grow on *E. coli* strain B, *E. coli* strain K, and others.

A third general class of phage mutants, called temperature-sensitive (t^s) mutants, are more difficult to study and characterize. For each, there is a permissive temperature, generally 20 to 30 degrees Celsius, at which they grow with efficiencies comparable to the wild type. At the restrictive temperature (usually 38 to 42 degrees Celsius), the t^s mutants fail to grow at all. These mutations occur in any of several essential genes whose protein products are necessary for phage growth. At the restrictive temperature, the altered protein becomes unstable and is unable to perform its biological function. In some cases, it is possible to infect host cells with t^s mutants at the restrictive temperature, lyse the hosts artificially after an hour or so of incubation, and determine from the contents of the lysate at which point in the lytic pathway phage growth was arrested. Genes involved with phage DNA replication or packaging and specific structural genes of the capsid have been identified in this way.

Once phage mutants have been identified, it is possible to perform standard types of genetic analyses, including mapping studies, determination of recombination frequencies, complementation tests, and the like. The basic tool for these studies is the phage cross, in which host cells are simultaneously infected with two genetically different phage strains. When these cells are allowed to lyse and the progeny phages are recovered, the phage can be plated on appropriate hosts for plaque formation to distinguish the two parental phenotypes as well as recombinant phenotypes. As in other genetic systems, closely linked genes will show little recombination, while genes widely separated from one another on the phage DNA molecule will approach the 50 percent frequency characteristic of unlinked markers.

Two special problems are often encountered in phage crosses. One is that a given mutant phenotype may result from a mutation at any of several or many different locations on the DNA, and these often include two or more functional genes. Sometimes exhaustive genetic analyses are required to characterize and distinguish between different independently isolated mutants that have identical phenotypes. A second problem is often termed phenotypic mixing, in which progeny phages may be produced whose DNA does not encode for all the capsid proteins surrounding it. This results from mixed infections, because new phage particles are self-assembled from cellular pools of constituents. It is thus possible that a phage DNA molecule of one parental type will be packaged into a capsid whose proteins were specified by the DNA from the other parental type. As long as the progeny phages are taken through more than one cycle of infection, as in a standard plaque assay, this will make no difference.

One of the best-known and most-useful lytic phages for genetic studies is the coliphage T4. Its protein capsid consists of three major sections—the head, the tail, and the tail fibers. The double-stranded circular DNA molecule of T4 is packaged into the icosahedral-shaped head, and during the infection process it is forced through the hollow core of the cylindrical tail and then directly into the host cell. Contact with the cell is established and maintained throughout the infection process by the tail fibers. Self-assembly of progeny phages occurs in at least three distinct cellular locations, since complete heads, tails, and tail fibers are first assembled separately and then pieced together in one of the last phases of the infection cycle. Packaging of the replicated T4 DNA is an integral part of the head assembly process. Each of the three subassemblies involves a reasonably complex and highly regulated sequence of assembly steps. For example, head assembly is known to require the activity of eighteen genes, even though only eleven different proteins are found as structural components of mature heads. Identification of the number and sequence of genes involved with each subassembly process has been facilitated by the analysis of artificial lysates from t^s mutants, as mentioned earlier.

For those temperate phage capable of entering the lysogenic cycle, many additional strategies for genetic control and regulation have evolved. The most thoroughly studied of the temperate coliphages is phage lambda (λ). Genes controlling phage DNA integration, excision, and recombination, and those involved with repressor functions, have been identified in phage λ, as well as structural genes involved with lytic functions that are similar to those studied in T4.

Methods of Study

In a standard phage cross involving two genetically distinct phage parental strains, designed for the study of complementation or recombination, host cells are mixed with lysates of each phage parent at a multiplicity of infection of approximately five phages per cell. There are multiple opportunities for pairing and recombination among different phage DNA molecules. The mixed infection is allowed to proceed through cell lysis, and the progeny phages can be isolated and separated from the cellular debris by differential centrifugation. These can then be used to infect additional host cells at a much lower multiplicity of infection, and the mixture can be plated to allow plaque formation. Sometimes a mixture of two or more different host cell types must be used to detect all the progeny phage phenotypes with respect to plaque morphology and host range. Calculation of the number of recombinant progeny divided by the total progeny gives the recombination frequency, which can then be easily converted into a map distance. This process yields a relative estimate of the physical distance separating the two genes or mutant sites on the phage DNA.

One of the first methods developed to study the mechanics of phage genetics is known as the single burst experiment. This experiment can provide important information about cell-to-cell variation by allowing one to analyze all the progeny of a single lytic event (burst). In particular, the molecular nature of recombination in phage T4 has been studied successfully in this way. Host cells are simultaneously infected with genetically different parents, as above, but then are immediately diluted in growth medium to an exceedingly low concentration and then dispensed in one milliliter aliquots into one hundred or more test tubes. The idea is to dilute the cells sufficiently, such that most of these tubes (perhaps 90 to 95 percent) have no cells in them at all. This degree of dilution ensures that the vast majority of tubes that are not "empty" of cells contain exactly one infected cell. The infection cycle is allowed to run to completion, and the contents of each tube are plated on appropriate host cells to detect the parental and recombinant phenotypes. Most plates will thus contain no plaques at all, but those that do will reflect the phage progeny of a single lysed cell. Numbers of parental and recombinant phenotypes can be compared for each single burst, and these figures can be compared with the overall average for all bursts. Using this technique, recombination in T4 was found to be nonreciprocal at the molecular level—that is, some bursts were identified that produced only one of the two possible recombinant types.

Phage T4 has also proven to be an excellent system for the study of genetic fine structure—the identification and mapping of many individual mutant sites, all within the same functional gene. Crosses of two different phage mutants that have identical phenotypes sometimes results in progeny phages that all have the wild-type phenotype. In this case, it is said that the two mutants complement each other, since each provides for the other the gene function that the other lacks. This relationship is possible only if the two mutations occur in different genes. In other cases, two mutants fail to complement each other, so they must result from different mutant sites in the same functional gene. Mutants can thus be classified into various complementation groups, each representing a cluster of mutations in a distinct functional gene. It is then possible to perform classical recombination and mapping studies between mutants in each complementation group, thus identifying a sequence of mutational sites within each gene.

While the methods of classical transmission genetics have been useful for the elucidation of the processes of phage growth, DNA replication, and plaque formation, so too have the methods of modern molecular biology had their impact. Recombinant DNA technology, DNA sequencing, and studies on purified phage RNA have all been used to begin to further understand the more complicated phenomena of gene regulation and the control of RNA transcription.

Context

One of the most important conclusions to be drawn from studies on viral genetics is that many of the results have universal implications. For example, the physical properties of DNA and RNA are remarkably identical in all organisms, and these are perhaps most easy to study in bacteriophage systems. The experiment that provided the final proof that DNA was the genetic material was performed using a coliphage very similar to T4. Studies on the origin of spontaneous mutations, first performed in phage, have extended to all higher forms of life as well. Some of the most basic questions concerning protein-DNA interactions are best addressed in viral systems, and the principles that emerge seem to hold for all other experimental systems. There is every reason to believe that many basic questions in cell and molecular biology will continue to be best studied in viruses, and that some of these investigations will spawn applications that can directly benefit humankind.

In the 1980's, the principles of viral genetics were put to a critical test with the unprecedented cascade of research on the acquired immune deficiency syndrome (AIDS) virus. This virus is one member of a special class of animal viruses called retroviruses. The nucleic acid in retroviruses is single-stranded RNA, which serves as a template for the production of a double-stranded DNA copy in the cytoplasm of the host cell. This DNA migrates to the nucleus, where it will undergo integration into a host chromosome as a provirus (similar to a prophage). Integration is a necessary part of the retroviral life cycle, and it must occur before the DNA can be transcribed into RNA copies for the progeny virus particles. The process of integration creates short, repeated DNA sequences in the host DNA and increases the likelihood that other host DNA sequences will recombine with the retroviral sequence. These recombined host sequences can then move to new locations with the retroviral DNA, often changing the properties of the host cell in the process. For example, several human cancers are known to be caused by retroviruses, and it is likely that tumor induction can be initiated in this way.

It is certain that the advances in molecular biology that have revolutionized the understanding of cell biology and the molecular architecture of cells will also continue to expand the frontiers of knowledge in the study of viral genetics. Applications in human medicine, veterinary medicine, and plant breeding are sure to follow, as scientists continue to unravel the complexities of these simplest of organisms.

Bibliography

Benzer, Seymour. "The Fine Structure of the Gene." *Scientific American* 206 (January, 1962): 70-84. Somewhat dated, yet still the best popular description of the author's pioneering studies on genetic fine structure in phage T4. Excellent illustrations help to distinguish the processes of complementation and recombination, and advanced genetic mapping techniques, such as deletion mapping, are introduced with clarity.

Birge, Edward A. *Bacterial and Bacteriophage Genetics: An Introduction.* New York: Springer-Verlag, 1981. An excellent supplementary text for a college student studying viral genetics for the first time. Chapter 4 gives a thorough coverage of T4, while chapters 5 and 6 cover other lytic phages and several different temperate phages. Some useful illustrations. References at end of each chapter are designated either "general" or "specialized."

Freifelder, David. *Microbial Genetics*. Boston: Jones and Bartlett, 1987. An intermediate-level college textbook focusing on the genetics of bacteria and their bacteriophage. Chapter 5 provides an excellent summary of the properties and life cycles of phages, and it should be accessible to readers with a limited background in biology. Chapters 15-18 give a more thorough coverage of phage genetics, with a special emphasis on the phages T4 and lambda. The text is well illustrated throughout, with many references for each chapter.

Russell, Peter. *Genetics*. 2d ed. Boston: Scott, Foresman, 1990. An introductory college text that is particularly well suited to the problem-solving approach to genetics. Parts of chapters 7, 8, 10, and 14 are of interest, but the most useful chapter is probably chapter 20, which presents a fine overview of gene regulation in phages. Well illustrated with a carefully conceived glossary and reference list.

Stahl, Franklin W. *Genetic Recombination: Thinking About It in Phage and Fungi*. San Francisco: W. H. Freeman, 1979. Probably the most technical of the references listed, this book might nevertheless be useful to interested readers with a limited background. In particular, chapter 4 provides a nice treatment of phage replication and the single burst experiment. Some illustrations, glossary, references.

Suzuki, D., A. Griffiths, J. Miller, and R. Lewontin. *An Introduction to Genetic Analysis*. 4th ed. New York: W. H. Freeman, 1989. Chapters 10-12 of this intermediate-level college text provide a historical perspective on the development of phage genetics and its applications to DNA structure and mutation. The summary of genetic fine structure and complementation is particularly well described and illustrated. Glossary and references included.

Jeffrey A. Knight

Cross-References

Complementation and Allelism: The Cis-Trans Test, 555; Gene Mutation and Repair, 1103; Genes and Nucleic Acids, 1134; Genetics: A Historical Perspective, 1177; Bacterial Genetics, 1184; Human Genetics, 1190; Monera and Viruses, 1768; Transcription of DNA to Form RNA, 2632; Viral Organization, 2681.

GERMINATION AND SEEDLING DEVELOPMENT

Type of life science: Plant physiology
Other field of study: Botany

Germination is the extrusion of one part of the seed embryo, usually the radicle (embryo root), through the seed coat. The radicle emerges as existing cells expand with the uptake of water before cells in the radicle begin to divide. Seedling development is the growth, cell division, and transformation of the germling into a young plant.

Principal terms

AFTER-RIPENING: a metabolic process that results in the removal of a germination block in seed

DORMANCY: a biological state characterized by environmental insensitivity, low or absent metabolism, and an inability to undergo cell division; it blocks an embryo's response to germination triggers

EMBRYO: a partially developed organism inside a seed with organs including the radicle, cotyledon (one or two), hypocotyl, epicotyl, and plumule

ETIOLATION: germinating a plant in the absence of light; this causes an elongation of the hypocotyl following germination, a mechanism for bringing the embryo from below ground up into the light

IMBIBITION: the intake of water by the seed; water uptake may be the first step to germination in nondormant seeds

PHYTOCHROME: a blueish pigment in seeds, which, when activated by white light, starts the germination

SEED: a propagule of a higher plant consisting of the embryo and storage reserve, surrounded by a hard, waxy membrane

STRATIFICATION: a condition that is necessary to allow the dormant propagule to after-ripen; dormancy and after-ripening are promoted simultaneously, but at a rate dictated by temperature

SUMMER ANNUAL: a plant whose seeds typically germinate in spring; winter temperatures are typically necessary to stratify the seeds

WINTER ANNUAL: a plant with seeds that germinate in autumn or early winter; seeds after-ripen in warm temperatures of summer

Summary of the Phenomenon

To germinate, seeds must be nondormant and be in a suitable environment. Seeds germinate within a restricted range of temperatures, moisture, oxygen, light, and freedom from chemical inhibitors. Wild seeds display many adaptations that predispose germination to specific habitats and seasons. By contrast, seeds of crops and other cultured plants usually lack controls that prevent germination. The control system was lost because some seeds in the population lacked controls and were chosen when they germinated in the care of a culturist. For that reason, most cultivated plants that start from seeds show no, or little, germination control. Most of the information on germination control, therefore, addresses wild species of plants.

Seeds are the exclusive means of regeneration for the flowering plants that are classified as annuals. In annuals, the following generation depends exclusively on regeneration by seeds. In other plants, seeds are an alternative strategy to regeneration by buds, bulbs, rhizomes, stolons, or tubers. In those plants, the primary roles of the seed are to disperse the population and to reinvigorate the genetic diversity of the germ line.

Dormancy is a stage in the life cycles of most plants. The dormant state may begin with maturation of the seed embryo, or it may develop in climate extremes after the seed falls from its parent. It prevents immediate germination when the mature seed is in an otherwise germination environment, and it is a programmed phase in the life cycle. Dormancy is scheduled to end, and a "germination window" to open, at a time when the emerging seedling has the optimum chance for making successful contribution to the population.

After-ripening removes the dormancy and allows the seed to respond to germination stimuli. Seeds of summer annuals after-ripen when exposed to winter and early spring temperatures, a treatment called stratification. Exposure to cold temperatures also promotes dormancy. Any given temperature, in fact, simultaneously promotes dormancy and after-ripening, although to differing degrees.

Not all nongerminating seeds are innately dormant. There are also nondormant and conditionally dormant seeds. Neither type may germinate when the seeds mature, simply because the parent prevents contact with the soil and absorption of water or because the temperature range is below that necessary for germination. Wild seeds may experience a deepening of dormancy as a result of exposure to the temperatures of the dormant season. Nondormant seeds may simultaneously experience biochemical reactions that deepen dormancy and cause them to after-ripen.

Many would-be culturists fail in their attempts to germinate wild seeds because there is a general misunderstanding of the communication, or coupling, of the seed with its environment. Seeds need to experience many conditions of the field, including temperature oscillations and natural daylengths. The reverse is also true: Removal of a seed in late summer may lead to the mistaken belief that the seed lacks a dormancy, which may only develop after it experiences the temperature and light conditions of autumn.

Dormancy is caused by one or more conditions of the seed. Physiological dormancy of the embryo is the most common. It may be caused by the presence of an inhibitor molecule, inadequate level of growth hormone, or some other inadequacy for active growth. Examples of the last include blockages in membrane function or in the synthesis of an enzyme or its nucleic acid messenger.

Other causes of dormancy are a hard or impervious seed coat, an underdeveloped embryo, or some combination of those factors. Physically dormant seeds usually have a region on the seed coat associated with the chalaza, or micropyle, where fluctuating temperatures cause cell layers to pull apart or cause a plug to rupture and permit exchange of ions, oxygen, and water.

Waiting to germinate in spring are the seeds from last year's crop of summer annuals. Seeds of many species will germinate when soil temperatures reach a threshold constant. Others require daily fluctuations of temperature. Such seeds are prevented from germinating until the daily fluctuation becomes sufficiently large. Seeds of other species, and by far the largest number, require a light stimulus to germinate. The light is absorbed by the pigment, phytochrome, which is positioned in the cotyledons of the embryo. Phytochrome acts as a shade detector. White light, and especially red light, convert the phytochrome molecule to an active form. The rearrangement of the molecule causes it to attach a different part of itself to a new location on a cell membrane within the cotyledons of the seed. Transformed phytochrome allows seeds to germinate. By contrast, far-red light, which is absorbed by the transformed phytochrome molecule, transforms the molecule back to its original shape—that is, it deactivates it.

When sunlight is transmitted through green leaves to the forest floor, much of the visible light with wavelengths shorter than 700 nanometers is absorbed or scattered. This "shade light" is rich in far red, and it tends to deactivate phytochrome. Other mechanisms may also control germination. Some seeds are sensitive to daily temperature fluctuations and insensitive to light. Such seeds delay germination until their temperature is free to undergo a large daily fluctuation, sometimes of 5 degrees Celsius or more.

Not all seeds germinate at the beginning of the following growing season. Light-demanding seeds that have become buried or have fallen into the shade will be stressed by the absence of an activating light signal while the embryos experience an environment that is otherwise growth-promoting. Stressed seeds may enter a secondary dormancy and will need to undergo a second interval of after-ripening before again becoming nondormant. Seeds emerging from secondary dormancy may require a smaller light stimulus. Following primary dormancy, one or more complete light cycles may be necessary. By contrast, seeds may be fully activated by only a brief pulse of light when they emerge from secondary dormancy.

Most seeds used by humans—cereal grains, legumes, and vegetables—become dry on the parent plant as a part of maturation. Drying is believed to end the seed-building phase and start the pre-germination phase. Most domestic seeds require no after-ripening but will germinate if allowed to take up water. Water uptake is a first step in germination. Biochemical events that begin with water uptake in domestic seeds include metabolism along three separate pathways and an increased use of oxygen.

Excessive moisture, even at temperatures too low for germination, may lower seed viability. Seeds that are best preserved in cold, dry environments are called orthodox seeds. With proper storage, a reasonable percentage of seeds may live for many years. Record long-lived species include seeds of *Canna* (six hundred years), *Albizzia*, and *Cassia* (about two hundred years). Seeds of *Verbascum* have survived at 40 percent viability for a hundred years. The question is whether the seed is unable to germinate or whether the germination mechanism has failed.

Reputable records of longevity show seeds remaining viable for thousands of years, although the actual age of the seeds is questioned. Weed seeds in soil banks may need to wait for hundreds of years before the forest is cleared by catastrophe and the environment once again is favorable for such pioneer species. By contrast, recalcitrant seeds require their embryos to be kept moist, or viability is quickly lost. Examples include trees with large seeds, such as walnut, oaks, hazel, and chestnut. These seeds usually live less than one year.

Seedling development begins with the close of germination. Cells in the embryonic root (the radicle) begin to divide and grow. In some seeds, or in unusual environmental conditions, other parts of the embryo emerge before the radicle. Development of the seedling is marked by the growth and elongation of the embryo stem. Seeds are classified according to which part of the stem grows more rapidly. In the epigeal type, the hypocotyl, which is the basal part of the stem between the radicle and the embryonic leaves (the cotyledons), grows, thereby thrusting the cotyledons above the soil.

Exposed to light, phytochrome in the cotyledons calls for an end to subterranean elongation, called etiolation, and the beginning of plantlike growth. Among its functions, phytochrome triggers the synthesis of chlorophyll; photosynthesis soon turns the cotyledons into sugar factories. At the same time the epicotyl region of the embryo above the cotyledons is extending the "plumule" to form the first true, or foliage, leaves. In other seeds (hypogeal type seeds), the cotyledons remain beneath the soil. The epicotyl grows and the tip of the epicotyl, known as the plumule, extends. The first leaves emerge from the plumule.

Mobilization of food reserves comes with germination. Food reserves that are stored in the endosperm, cotyledons, and embryo will nourish the early growth of the plant until it can synthesize the necessary machinery for making its own food. Foods are stored in seeds as starch and other complex carbohydrates, fats, and proteins. Cereal grains contain large amounts (65-80 percent) of carbohydrates, which are stored in the endosperm. Seeds of legumes are famous for their high protein contents, which reach 37 percent in soybeans. The peanut, a legume, stands out by having both high protein (30 percent) and high fat content (50 percent). Legumes store food reserves in the embryonic leaves (cotyledons).

Foods are transferred to the growing sites, primarily as sucrose and amino acids. Starches and other carbohydrates and fats are first converted to simple sugars and then to sucrose for transport. The rate of mobilization and transport from storage organs to the growing embryo is orchestrated by the embryo. Synthesis of active phytochrome, second messengers, and the plant hormone gibberellin are involved. Their function is to promote synthesis of enzymes such as those that break down food reserves into simple sugars.

The embryo selects one part of the root-stem axis for rapid growth, changing the relationship of the other parts to the external environment. The cotyledons are also versatile: They may act as first leaves or may remain attached to another part of the embryo, such as the endosperm. There they act as absorptive organs to transport mobilized food reserves to the growing parts of the seedling. In the onion, a single cotyledon performs both functions. The exposed part carries out photosynthesis, while the buried part absorbs foods from the endosperm.

Seed technology is concerned with proper seed care and storage and the testing of viability. It also involves genetic improvement of seed crops, the production and distribution of improved varieties, and the education of growers to provide proper environments for each new seed variety. The technology of seeds also includes the search for, discovery, and development of new domestic species from wild species. Such searches consider food value, digestive quality, resistance to diseases, and suitability for growth in mechanized agriculture.

Unusual seed properties are sought, such as the ability of popcorn to explode when heated. Popcorn technology involves knowledge of both seed structure and genetics. In popcorn, a starch rich, or floury endosperm, is tucked within a shell of protein-rich and horny endosperm. Starch grains in the horny endosperm are encased in an elastic colloid that traps seed water with the starch. When the popcorn seed is heated, the water turns to steam. The resulting pressure explodes the seed. Good popping ability requires a minimum amount of horny endosperm.

Methods of Study

After-ripening and seed germination are usually studied experimentally. Seeds are collected from specific locations on each plant and stratified in a range of temperatures, light qualities, irradiance levels and durations, and moisture levels. They are germinated in one of a range of each environmental variable until a multidimensioned envelope is constructed that depicts the range of environment that permits germination. Mechanisms are studied in the laboratory, and their purposes are verified with experimentation in the field.

The study of the biochemistry of food-storage mobilization employs modern techniques. Investigating metabolic pathways, the synthesis and release of hormones, and other regulative biochemistry requires the latest advances in enzyme recognition, pathway analysis, and gene transcription control.

Context

Wild seeds are equipped with germination control mechanisms. Each mechanism operates to control both when and where a seed may germinate. Germination is the act that "decides" the time and space boundaries of active growth for each species. Actual boundaries may evolve through natural selection. Selection starts with the operation of a "germination window," which is determined by when after-ripening frees the seed from dormancy. Normal evolutionary processes may select the best time for germination. Summer annual plants germinate in spring, and winter annuals germinate in autumn. Precise control is achieved by two mechanisms: dormancy and its control, and the "germination trigger."

When the seed becomes freed of dormancy, it may only germinate when exposed to an activating stimulus, which may be light or some facet of the temperature environment, such as suitable range or a minimum amplitude of daily fluctuations in temperature. Seeds that require light, and most do, may find that major obstacles in the environment prevent germination and hold them in an ungerminated state for decades, possibly centuries, until the seed bank of which they are a part is free of the obstacle.

When meadows of annual plants, such as weeds, are invaded by shrubs and trees, the shade created by the canopy of such vegetation prevents further regeneration of the meadow species. Yet their seeds may accumulate in the soil. When the canopy falls as the trees die or are destroyed, seeds in the soil bank may germinate if exposed to light. Plowing of soils is a sure way of starting the annual plants in motion by giving their seeds access to the light. The phytochrome molecule can function as a shade detector in shallow water. An unknown detector operates in deep, clear water, sensing in the blue rather than in the red/far-red part of the spectrum (the way plants of terrestrial and shallow water environments behave).

Other germination mechanisms control where a seed may germinate. In wild plants of wetlands, the seeds are sensitive to daily temperature fluctuations and insensitive to light. Such seeds delay germination until the winter's accumulation of water has drained off. Once the water is drained and air reenters the soil, the temperature is free to undergo a large daily fluctuation, warming when the sun strikes the soil at a direct angle and cooling at night as the heat reradiates into space.

Temperature requirements for germination may act to restrict the range of a species. Seeds dispersed too far south may find themselves unable to germinate following after-ripening because the environment has become too warm. The converse may happen beyond the northern limit. When temperatures become warm enough for germination, the long nondormant seed may have already exhausted its temporal window of germination and reentered secondary dormancy.

The replacement of shade-sensitive seed plants, such as weed seeds, pine trees, and birches, with nonlight-requiring seeds of oaks, maples, and beeches was a phenomenon described by Henry David Thoreau in 1859, although the mechanism behind it was not known until 1937, when researchers discovered photoreversibility of a then-unidentified molecule. The molecule, phytochrome, was isolated and purified in the early 1950's at the Plant Industry Station of the U.S. Department of Agriculture in Beltsville, Maryland. The mechanism centering on temperature control is unexplored. New discoveries, however, are expanding science's understanding of how germination regulators may control the seasonal, geographic, and habitat preferences of plants.

Bibliography

Baskin, J. M., and C. C. Baskin. "The Annual Dormancy Cycle in Buried Weed

Seeds." *Bioscience* 35 (1985): 492-498. This article describes the function and seasonal position of seed dormancy in the annual cycle of plants. The reader is able to envisage the timing mechanisms for germination and the ecological significance of dormancy control in a cyclic environment. Paper marked a strong departure from traditional linear-time thinking in ecology.

Bewley, J. D., and Michael Black, eds. *Seeds: Physiology of Development and Germination.* New York: Plenum Press, 1985. An extensive examination of seed structure and biochemistry in relationship to its maturation and germination. Condensed from two earlier volumes. The topics force an emphasis on domestic seeds.

Bradbeer, J. W. *Seed Dormancy and Germination.* New York: Routledge, Chapman & Hall, 1988. Gives a brief but thorough introduction to seed formation, germination, viability and vigor, longevity, and seed technology. Author adopts the philosophical stance that a plant is only a seed's way of making more seeds. The advanced student will want to contrast that with the biological reality that seed and plant are phases of a recurring cycle, as described in the Baskin and Baskin article.

Campbell, Neil A. *Biology.* 2d ed. Menlo Park, Calif.: Benjamin/Cummings, 1990. Two chapters in this fine introductory biology text deal with various aspects of the plant life cycle, including germination; chapter 34, "Plant Reproduction," and chapter 35, "Control Systems in Plants." The text has excellent illustrations as well as a glossary and index.

Fenner, Michael. *Seed Ecology.* New York: Routledge, Chapman & Hall, 1985. Presents the function of the seed in the regeneration of plants and the strategies that seeds have evolved to meet the conditions of various land environments. Successive chapters introduce the reader to seed production as one option of reproduction, to seed dispersal (the hazards and the vehicles), to formation of seed banks in soil, and to dormancy, germination, and seedling establishment.

Raven, Peter H., Ray F. Evert, and Susan Eichorn. *Biology of Plants.* 4th ed. New York: Worth, 1986. This text covers material also found in the Campbell text, but in much greater detail. Refers to original experimental work. Written at an introductory college level, but accessible to high school readers as well.

Ray Stross

Cross-References

Angiosperms, 95; Flowering Regulation, 1010; Gymnosperms, 1247; Leaf-Fall Regulation, 1542; Plant Hormones, 2103; Plant Tissue Types, 2119; Pterophyta, 2294; Seeds, 2452; Succession, 2566; Tropisms and Their Control in Plants, 2669.

GILL, TRACHEA, AND LUNG ANATOMY

Type of life science: Animal anatomy
Other field of study: Histology

Gills, tracheae, and lungs are respiratory organs that are the primary sites of gas exchange in certain groups of animals. Gills are present in water-breathing animals, and tracheae and lungs are found in animals that breathe air. The structure and design of these organs are related to the particular manner of their function.

Principal terms

BRONCHUS (*pl.* BRONCHI): an individual tube that is part of a lung and leads to one of the smaller lung parts

DIFFUSION: the passive movement of molecules from an area of high concentration (or pressure) to an area of lower concentration, often across a distance or a barrier

EPITHELIUM: a thin membrane that lines or coats a surface; in respiratory organs, the layer of cells that covers or lines the surface is called the respiratory epithelium

GILL: an extension or outpocketing of the body wall of an animal that creates a limblike structure, much as the fingers of a glove extend from the palm; gills are found almost exclusively in animals that breathe water

LAMELLA (*pl.* LAMELLAE): lamella means "platelike," and an individual lamella can be any one of several structures in the context of gas-exchange organs, these are usually found in gills

LUNG: a concave inpocketing of the body wall of an animal (in contrast to a gill); lungs occur in air-breathing animals

TRACHEA (*pl.* TRACHEAE): a tubular inpocketing of the body found mostly in insects and the spiders (arachnids), both of which are air breathers

Summary of the Phenomenon

The anatomy of a respiratory organ—gills, tracheae, or lungs—determines the way in which the organ functions. The design of the organ is specifically related to the way in which the animal functions in the world. Design refers to whether the structure is internal or external, large or small, and concerns some aspects of how it works. In order to understand the function of most organs and organ systems, it is necessary to know the structure.

The structure, or anatomy, can be considered from several different levels of organization. "Gross" structure is the size, shape, and position of the whole organ within the animal. "Fine" structure, on the other hand, refers to the microscopic level of organization. The microscopic structure includes the type and thickness of cells, the number of cells, and a description of the cell surface.

There are a few common features among gills, tracheae, and lungs in terms of both the gross structure and the fine structure. All three are organs of gas exchange and are therefore designed to permit oxygen and carbon dioxide gas to diffuse passively across this specific part of the body wall. Because one of the factors that directly affects diffusion is the total surface area, respiratory surfaces are greatly increased in order to maximize the movement of gas. Thus, the largest part of the total surface of an animal is the respiratory surface, no matter whether it is a lung, gill, or trachea. All three types of respiratory organs have openings to permit air or water to flow in (and out), tubes for conducting air or water to the exchange surface, the exchange surface itself, and the necessary support to hold the surface in place. The exceptions are those animals that have external gills with no enclosing cover.

The commonality of gas exchange function also imparts similar features to the microscopic level of structure. The epithelia of all three types of organs are thin and made of cells that are individually thin, providing less of a barrier to gas movement (although there is an exception to this in gill structure).

Gills are the most diverse and varied of all respiratory organs. Gills are found in aquatic animals, both vertebrate (animals with internal skeletons) and invertebrate (animals with external skeletons or no hard skeleton). With few exceptions, all animals with gills live in and breathe water, even if the volume of water is small and only one life stage of the animal breathes water. Most people are familiar with several types of animals that breathe water and use gills: fish, crabs, lobster, shrimp, crayfish, clams, aquatic insects, many worms (but not all), and numerous other animals. The form and function of gills have been variously modified in different animals through the process of natural selection.

The gills of many marine worms and of the marine sea hare and sea slug (both are related to snails) are thin, blind-ending tubules representing extensions of the body wall that form an elaborate treelike structure. For the most part, these are not complicated either in the pattern of blood flowing through them on the inside or in the way water is passed over them on the outside. Worms and sea slugs usually extend the gills into the water above and let the water's own movement bring the oxygen-filled water to the gills. Sea hares, however, cover the gills with a flap of skin, an extension of the body wall, and pump water over the gills by the beating action of numerous tiny cilia.

The gills of crabs are formed from a central structure called an arch and platelike extensions of the gill arch, called lamellae. Each lamella has a thin layer of epithelium, but because it is formed as an extension of the outside layer of the body, the epithelium is covered with a very thin layer of shell, called chitin. This is true of crabs, lobster, shrimp, and all the crustaceans. Nevertheless, the layer still permits the exchange of gases between the blood on the inside and water on the outside.

Each lamella is exposed to the water on both sides and has numerous supporting cells on the inside that keep the two sides apart so that blood may flow between. These support cells are called pillar cells, and if an observer could look down between the sides, the inside would look something like a forest. Blood comes into each lamella from a single channel, an artery, located at the top, and flows out through a vein located at the bottom of the lamella.

Not all lamella are alike even in the same crab, much less in crabs from habitats as different as the deep ocean and a tropical forest. One of the major differences is that some epithelia are specialized to transport salts actively across the gill in much the same way as the kidney does in a mammal. These gill lamella are thicker, with cells that are modified to transport sodium and chloride. Blue crabs, land crabs, and crayfish (which have podia instead of lamellae) are examples of animals with this type of specialization.

Not all crustaceans have gills that are lamellar in form; the crayfish and lobster have fingerlike projections of the gill arch. These projections are called podia and are more like the blind-ending tubules found in some worms than they are like the lamellae of crabs. The inside of the podia is divided, however, so that blood flows to the tip of the tube on one side and back to the animal on the other side of the podia.

Fish gills are not unlike those of a crab in many ways, but those of fish are more complex. Both are composed of flattened extensions of a trunklike support structure that contains the blood vessels. Gills of most teleost fish (bony fish, such as perch and bass) have further, or secondary, extensions from these, which are oriented perpendicular to the main lamella. The result is that the primary lamellae form a flat surface in a horizontal plane, and the secondary lamellae form the largest surface area, extending in a vertical plane. Some primitive fish, or those with adaptations to special conditions have reduced secondary lamellae.

Some of the major differences between vertebrate and invertebrate gills are that fish gills are thinner, so that the layer separating the blood from the water is not as thick in fish. Fish-gill epithelia are usually about 20 percent as thick as those of the invertebrates described. Many fish have two different types of lamellae on the gill arch: primary and secondary lamellae. Many fish gills also contain specialized cells to transport salts across the border between the animal and the water, as happens in blue crabs.

Tracheae, found in insects, spiders, and related invertebrates, are long, thin tubes that extend from the outside of an animal to the inside, similar to the way a trachea leads to the lung in humans. The tracheal system, however, is made up entirely of branching tubules, each somewhat smaller than the one leading to it. The major tubes are called tracheae and the smaller ones are tracheoles; the smallest ones are as thin as hairs and reach within a very short distance of the cells inside the body. The outside opening to each trachea is controlled by a special structure, a spiracle, that can open and close the trachea.

Lungs are actually the simplest type of respiratory system to describe in terms of animal type, distribution, and variations on the common form. Lungs are found only in air-breathing vertebrates, are always internalized, and have a single opening through which air flows both in and out. A single tube, the trachea, is the conducting passage for inspired and expired air. This tube branches into two smaller tubes, the bronchi, that lead to each of the individual sides, or lobes, of the lung. Tracheae and bronchi are usually, if not always, reinforced with cartilage rings for structural support to prevent collapse. Thus, animals with lungs actually have two, one on each side.

Tracheae and bronchi are not designed for gas exchange but are conducting tubes that also serve to "condition" the air before it reaches the lungs. Both tubes are lined with special cells that have hairlike projections called cilia on the surface. The cilia continually sweep small particles (such as dust) toward the outside to protect the lungs. Other cells in tracheae and bronchi secrete mucus to keep the surface moist and maintain high humidity so that air will be 100 percent humid when it reaches the alveoli.

At the end of the tubes of the lungs are the sac structures that form the gas-exchange surface. These very thin structures are the alveoli and are the site of gas movement into and out of the body. On the inside of each alveolus is an entire network of tiny blood vessels, capillaries, that supply the blood which is the source of the carbon dioxide that is exhaled and is the sink for the oxygen taken up at the alveoli.

Methods of Study

The anatomy of gas-exchange organs is studied in whole living animals, in preserved specimens, and in sections prepared for microscopic examination. Both light microscopy and electron microscopy are used to study these organs. Light microscopy is simply the use of a microscope that requires standard lighting with the type of lens systems that have been used for decades; there are also some much more sophisticated systems that use specialized optics and lighting techniques. Electron microscopy uses beams of electrons to enable magnification of more than 100,000 times and the visualization of cells and their component parts. In some cases, miniaturized laser optics are used to examine the relatively large organs, such as lungs, while they are functioning. This application is often used in health-related studies and diagnosis of disease.

Studying the gross morphology of gills, tracheae, and lungs involves the dissection of a whole animal, either preserved or freshly deceased. Each option offers advantages, and both methods will be employed in a complete examination. Part of the dissection will be to determine qualitative features such as attachment points, spatial relations, and general appearance. A thorough study of the anatomy of an organ also includes measurements of features such as surface areas, number of parts, distances, and volumes. These are the quantitative measures, and they are applicable to all the organs. These numerical values are absolutely necessary in order to quantify the functions.

In the case of small animals, including shrews, insects, and fish the size of minnows, a dissection of the whole animal may have to be carried out with additional magnification, using a microscope designed for such work. These microscopes are called dissection microscopes and have enough distance between the lens and the object to allow dissection with small instruments by hand. In a few cases, the material is so small that microdissecting techniques developed by neurobiologists must be used. Traditional histological examination of respiratory organs has also revealed much about the design and nature of these structures. Histological examination (examining tissue structure, usually under a microscope) reveals the thickness of the epithelium, the number of layers, and some information about the nature of the material in the layers.

Context

One of the purposes for studying the anatomy of all respiratory structures, and lungs in particular, is to improve medical applications. Knowledge of the general structure of lungs is useful, even crucial, in treating diseased lungs and in operating on patients with lung disorders. For the same reasons, specific anatomy of the human lung is essential in treating human respiratory problems, regardless of the type of treatment (surgery or chemical or mechanical therapy). The same is true in veterinary medicine—intricate knowledge of the organ is needed to treat respiratory problems effectively.

The use of animals in research has always been a controversial topic, but if such research is to be conducted properly, then accurate knowledge of the anatomy of the experimental animals is necessary. In this way, the animals can be kept healthy and monitored properly so that the intended purpose of the research may be realized. The common features of respiratory anatomy, particularly within a group such as the vertebrates, are useful for instructional purposes. Lungs of other mammals can be used to demonstrate human lung anatomy, and even nonmammalian vertebrates are used in some cases.

Evolutionary and taxonomic relationships are revealed in comparisons of respiratory structures in some groups of animals. Other relationships are evident in making comparisons between very different groups. There are only subtle differences in lung structure among the air-breathing vertebrates with lungs: amphibians, reptiles, and mammals. These differences occur more in the gross structure than at the cellular level, indicating how evolutionary pressures create successful adaptations.

The differences in the gill structures of crabs, worms, and fish from various habitats give valuable insight into evolutionary changes. Land crabs and air-breathing fish have fewer gills, fewer lamellae with thicker surfaces, and special structures to hold them in position. These latter are needed in air because without the support offered by water the gill lamellae would otherwise adhere to one another and not function. Similarly, some fish that live in water that contains too little oxygen must depend on air breathing and show these same adaptations.

One of the most widely studied aspects of comparing respiratory structures in different animals is the evolutionary transition from breathing water to breathing air. The transition from water to land has always interested scientists, and this level of anatomy is part of that interest. Biologists have examined the differences between air and water breathers in many groups of animals generally, and in groups that have both, such as the crabs and the amphibians, in particular. The features of interest include the surface area, thickness, position in the body, and pattern of circulation.

Few groups of animals display such a clear example of the evolution of structure and function in the tracheal system as do insects. Insects have a respiratory system, the tracheae, that reaches nearly to the cells themselves, bringing them oxygen-laden air and removing the carbon dioxide produced by the cells. It would seem, then, that there would be little need for a circulatory system to serve that function, and indeed there is but a rudimentary one in insects.

Anatomy of respiratory structures is also studied in relation to other functions and organ systems. The circulatory system provides the blood that exchanges gases with the water or air on the outside of the animal. Thus, the anatomy of the blood vessels is an important part of the anatomy. Similarly, the control of the flow of blood to the lungs or gills is critical for respiratory system function.

The fine structure of several types of respiratory systems, but primarily gills, is part of the study of other, nonrespiratory functions. The gills of some aquatic animals play an important role in regulating the animal's salt balance. In these animals, the fine structure of the gills shows where this process takes place and what special modifications are needed.

Bibliography

Barnes, Robert D. *Invertebrate Zoology.* 5th ed. Philadelphia: Saunders College Publishing, 1987. This invertebrate zoology text complements the Romer and Parsons vertebrate zoology text listed. Barnes's book for advanced high school or (more likely) college level is considered by many to be the best, and it contains excellent illustrations and a rather complete bibliography. The reader must get the information for each group from the appropriate chapter, but the index is sufficiently detailed so that this is not a problem. Most of the phyla have gills or trachea, so the reader must look carefully.

Comroe, J. H. "The Lung." *Scientific American* 214 (February, 1966): 56-68. This magazine only features a subject once, so the story on the lung is dated, but it still gives an accurate description of basic lung anatomy and includes information on function.

Hill, Richard W., and Gordon A. Wyse. *Animal Physiology.* 2d ed. New York: Harper & Row, 1989. This text is intended for college students who have had general biology and understand the basics. It gives good explanations of the structures of gills, tracheae, and lungs as well as of other types of respiratory systems. It is well written and illustrated and lists additional readings. Especially useful for relating structure and function. (Any good recent text on animal physiology will cover similar material.)

Klystra, J. A. "Experiments in Water Breathing." *Scientific American* 219 (August, 1968): 66-74. This article is somewhat dated, but the illustrations effectively compare lungs and gills; there are accompanying explanations of the function of each.

Raven, Peter H., and George B. Johnson. *Biology*. 2d ed. St. Louis: Times Mirror/ Mosby, 1989. A text for college freshmen; includes much more than only the anatomy of the three respiratory systems. It does a better than average job of explaining gills, tracheae, and lung structure, and it includes some material on function, evolution, and related matters. The illustrations are clear and there is a glossary.

Romer, Alfred S., and Thomas S. Parsons. *The Vertebrate Body*. 6th ed. Philadelphia: Saunders, 1986. This is one of several texts on the market that deal with comparative anatomy of vertebrates, and it is considered to be one of the best. Written for college students, this is certainly the most comparative and gives an excellent evolutionary perspective. The figures are good; the glossary is extensive but succinct.

Storer, Tracy I., Robert L. Usinger, Robert C. Stebbins, and James W. Nybakken. *General Zoology*. New York: McGraw-Hill, 1979. The authors are four of the finest zoologists of the past several decades, each with his own specialization to bring to the book. Every part is written by a specialist in the field, a feature of which few general textbooks can boast. Unlike most texts, the material is covered by function and by animal group. The respiratory structures are described in the section on that topic and for each group as presented. College level with illustrations.

Peter L. deFur

Cross-References

Adaptations and Their Mechanisms, 22; Animal Cell Types, 105; Cellular Membrane Specializations, 388; Cilia, Flagella, Basal Bodies, and Centrioles, 470; Circulatory Systems of Vertebrates, 483; Gas Exchange in Animals, 1069; Histology, 1307; Osmosis, Free Diffusion, and Facilitated Diffusion, 2022; Respiration: Adaptation to Low Oxygen, 2369; Respiration in Birds, 2383.

GLYCOLYSIS AND FERMENTATION

Type of life science: Respiration
Other fields of study: Animal physiology, biochemistry, microbiology, and plant physiology

Glycolysis refers to the chemical process of splitting a molecule of glucose in order to obtain energy for other cellular processes. Fermentation includes glycolysis and deals with the fate of its products when oxygen is not available. The end products of fermentation are different according to the type of organism carrying out the process.

Principal terms

ADENOSINE TRIPHOSPHATE (ATP): an important biological molecule that represents the energy currency of the cell; the energy in a special "high-energy" bond in ATP is used to drive almost all cellular processes that require energy

AEROBIC: in the presence of oxygen

ANAEROBIC: in the absence of oxygen

CELLULAR RESPIRATION: a complex series of chemical reactions by which chemical energy in food molecules is released and used to form ATP

CHEMICAL ENERGY: the energy locked up in the chemical bonds that hold the atoms of a molecule together; food molecules, such as glucose, contain much energy in their bonds

ELECTRON: a small particle that makes up part of an atom; an electron has a negative charge and negligible weight; electrons are removed from or added to molecules in many biological reactions

ENZYME: a biological catalyst that speeds up a chemical reaction without itself being used up; enzymes are made of protein, and a single enzyme can usually only catalyze a single chemical reaction

NICOTINAMIDE ADENINE DINUCLEOTIDE (NAD): a molecule used to hold pairs of electrons when they have been removed from a molecule by some biological process; the empty molecule is denoted by NAD^+, while it is denoted as NADH when it is carrying electrons

PHOTOSYNTHESIS: the process by which plants and many microbes trap the energy of sunlight to build organic molecules

PROTON: a small particle present in the nucleus of an atom; it carries a positive charge and detectable weight; a hydrogen atom has a single proton as its nucleus

Summary of the Phenomenon

The simple sugar glucose is generally considered the starting point for looking at the basic processes of glycolysis and fermentation. Glucose is a simple carbohydrate, consisting of only carbon, hydrogen, and oxygen atoms. Most glucose molecules are produced by plants; organisms that cannot photosynthesize must obtain glucose (or more complex carbohydrates) from their surroundings. Animals obtain food molecules by eating. Simpler forms of life, such as bacteria and yeast, simply absorb their food from their environment. Glycolysis begins the process of extracting usable energy from food. Fermentation disposes of the products of glycolysis when there is no oxygen available.

The energy in glucose is locked up in the chemical bonds that hold the molecule together. The process of fermentation breaks these chemical bonds in a series of carefully controlled chemical reactions. Each chemical reaction can be greatly speeded up by the appropriate enzyme, but the control process is automatic. Generally, cells have sufficient quantities of the necessary enzymes present at all times. Each chemical step is regulated by either the amount of raw materials present or the amount of finished product. If the raw materials are in short supply, the rate of reaction will be slow. If the finished products build up to a high concentration, the reaction will also slow down. The energy of the chemical bonds in glucose must be released gradually. During most of the chemical steps, small amounts of energy are released. The amount of energy released is often not enough to perform significant biological work, in which case it is simply wasted as heat. The energy released during some steps, however, is captured in the special high-energy bond of ATP. ATP is such an important and ubiquitous molecule that it requires further examination.

Adenosine triphosphate (ATP) belongs to a class of organic molecules known as nucleotides. While the monophosphate has many other important functions, the triphosphate has an important role in the energy reactions in the cell. The term "triphosphate" indicates that there are three phosphate groups attached to the base molecule. The last two of these phosphates are held by a special kind of chemical bond known as a high-energy bond. It takes a greater amount of energy to form one of these bonds than to form the normal kinds of bonds that hold the atoms of other molecules together. When one of these bonds is broken, this large amount of energy is released and is available to the cell to do work. Examples of such work are production of heat, synthesis of complex molecules, movement of molecules across a membrane, and the physical movement of a muscle. When energy is required in a cell, the third phosphate of ATP is released. While the third phosphate group is routinely split off to release energy the second one is rarely split off in cellular reactions. The cell must maintain a supply of ATP by means of the reverse reaction. The energy required for this reaction may come from fermentation when oxygen is unavailable. When oxygen is available, other components of cellular respiration are used, which include the Krebs cycle and electron transport.

Fermentation may be treated in two stages. In the first stage, glycolysis, the glucose molecule is split into two smaller molecules. The initial glucose molecule contains six carbon atoms. Splitting this initial molecule produces two molecules of pyruvic acid, and each pyruvic acid molecule contains three carbon atoms. During glycolysis, energy is released from the bonds of the glucose molecule and captured in the form of high-energy bonds of ATP. This production of ATP is the whole reason for carrying out the process. As a by-product, however, electrons are also stripped from the glucose molecule. These electrons are immediately trapped and held by another very important and ubiquitous molecule, usually known by its abbreviation: nicotinamide adenine dinucleotide, or NAD. By convention, the empty electron carrier is denoted as NAD^+. When the molecule is carrying a pair of electrons, it is denoted as NADH, an appropriate designation since as well as receiving the two electrons, the molecule also picks up a hydrogen nucleus, or proton. The electrons held by NADH represent additional energy; however, oxygen is required to convert this energy into ATP. Since fermentation is carried out in the absence of oxygen, this energy cannot be used. Instead, the NADH must be relieved of its electrons in order to accept more electrons produced by the splitting of additional glucose molecules. The mechanism by which NADH loses its electrons to regenerate NAD^+ varies according to the type of organism.

A glucose molecule is relatively stable and not inclined to split readily. To make the glucose split, it is energized, which is accomplished by adding two phosphate groups to the molecule from two ATP molecules. The third phosphate from each ATP is transferred, along with its high-energy bond to the glucose molecule. Therefore, the initial steps of glycolysis actually use ATPs, depleting some of the cell's energy stores. Once the glucose is energized, it readily splits under the influence of the appropriate enzyme. Each half of the glucose molecule then attaches another phosphate group from the cell's pool of inorganic phosphate. In a series of reactions, the two phosphate groups on each half of the glucose molecule are transferred to ATP molecules, causing ATP to replace the two ATPs used initially and generate two more. Therefore, glycolysis results in a net gain of two molecules of ATP. After the phosphate groups have been transferred, the three-carbon molecule, pyruvic acid, remains.

Under aerobic conditions, further energy from the chemical bonds of pyruvic acid is harvested by the Krebs cycle and electron transport system. When oxygen is not available (anaerobic conditions), however, the electrons must be removed from the NADH to regenerate NAD^+. While there are many ways of accomplishing that, the most common methods are alcoholic fermentation as observed in yeast, where the end products are ethyl alcohol and carbon dioxide, and lactic acid fermentation as observed in the muscles of a mammal during strenuous physical exercise. In any event, no further energy is gained for the cell.

In yeast cells cultured in the absence of oxygen, a carbon atom and two oxygen atoms are first split from the pyruvic acid, releasing a molecule of carbon dioxide. This carbon dioxide gas is responsible for the bubbles that make bread rise and those that produce the carbonation in champagne. The remainder of the pyruvic acid molecule then receives a pair of electrons from NADH, producing a molecule of ethyl alcohol. The alcohol evaporates from bread when it is baked but is retained for its mildly euphoric effect in alcoholic beverages. As far as the yeast is concerned, the alcohol is only produced as a way of regenerating NAD^+. It is not a desirable product and will eventually kill the yeast cells. Most yeast cells cannot tolerate an alcohol concentration greater than about 12 percent.

In the muscles of an exercising human or other mammal the demand for energy may exceed the supply of oxygen from the blood. In this case, NAD^+ is regenerated when the NADH donates its electrons to a pyruvic acid molecule to produce lactic acid. Accumulation of lactic acid in the muscles may cause fatigue; however, it is removed by the bloodstream to the liver. In the liver, lactic acid is converted back to pyruvic acid, using oxygen. Strenuous exercise results in an oxygen debt in mammals. After the exercise is over, this debt must be repaid. Anyone who ever ran to catch a bus has observed how this debt is repaid by a period of panting or at least heavy breathing.

Methods of Study

In the late 1800's and early 1900's, scientists began the serious study of the steps involved. The process can be more easily controlled and investigated in a cell-free system. Cells are broken apart in carefully prepared salt solutions. By various chemical and physical processes, the different components of cells can be separated and mixed with glucose or intermediate molecules to determine their effect. Since most of the steps of fermentation are the same in different organisms, almost any type of cell will work. One of the pioneering experiments was performed in 1927 by Otto Meyerhof. He extracted an enzyme from muscle that could add the phosphate from ATP to glucose molecules. This activity decreased as the muscle extract aged. The activity could be restored, however, by adding yeast extract. Thus, it was shown that at least the initial steps of fermentation are the same no matter what organism is performing it.

The process of splitting a glucose molecule is indeed fundamental to cells. Enzymes extracted from plants during the study of photosynthesis have been shown to catalyze many steps of glycolysis. The enzymes catalyze reactions in opposite directions in photosynthesis and glycolysis. Most enzymes simply speed up a chemical reaction; the direction of the reaction is usually determined by the concentrations of the reactants.

Context

Cellular respiration is the process by which organisms harvest usable energy in the form of ATP molecules from food molecules. Fermentation is the form of respiration used when oxygen is not available. Fermentation is much less efficient than aerobic cellular respiration, which needs oxygen. Fermentation harvests only two molecules of ATP for every glucose molecule used. Aerobic respiration reaps a yield of more than thirty molecules of ATP. Additionally, the typical products of fermentation, alcohol or lactic acid, are toxic to the organism producing them. Most forms of life will resort to fermentation only when oxygen is absent or in short supply. These are described as facultative anaerobes. While higher forms of life such as animals can obtain energy by fermentation for short periods, they enter an oxygen debt, which must eventually be repaid. The yield of two molecules of ATP for each glucose molecule used is simply not enough to sustain their high demand for energy. A few simple forms of life, mostly bacteria, rely solely on fermentation for their source of ATP. To some of these, oxygen is actually poisonous. These are described as obligate anaerobes, and they are only found under the completely anaerobic conditions of the deeper layers of the mud in salt and fresh water marshes.

Alcoholic fermentation has been known since biblical times. It took Louis Pasteur working for the French wine industry, however, to prove conclusively that living cells were responsible. Fortunately for the ancient wine-makers, the yeast responsible for the process occurs naturally on grape skins. Modern wine-makers prefer not to leave fermentation to chance. Instead, they treat the grapes with sulfites to kill the wild yeast. When ready to ferment, they add their own (often jealously guarded) strains of cultivated yeast. Yeast has been used to leaven bread for as long as history has been recorded. In the making of bread, yeast, with a small amount of sugar, is trapped in the anaerobic conditions inside raw dough. The thick dough prevents oxygen from reaching the yeast, resulting in the production of carbon dioxide bubbles, which raise the bread. Baking drives off the small amount of alcohol produced. In the making of still wines, the carbon dioxide is allowed to escape. Sparkling beverages were traditionally produced by bottling and sealing the wine or beer before the carbon dioxide production had stopped. Since it is often difficult to judge exactly when to bottle the brew, modern processes allow all the carbon dioxide to escape and the correct amount is added under pressure at bottling time. To make the more alcoholic spirits, fermentation is allowed to run to completion and the product is distilled. Since alcohol boils at a lower temperature than water, the fermented product is heated and the resulting vapors condensed and collected. The impurities of the various juices and other fermentable substrates impart the particular flavors to the spirits.

Lactic acid fermentation is an important source of ATP for humans during strenuous physical exercise. Even though it is an inefficient use of glucose, it can provide enough ATP for a short burst of activity. After the activity is over, the lactic acid produced must be converted back to pyruvic acid with the use of oxygen. Most exercise regimes stress aerobic activity. Aerobic exercises do not stress muscles to the point where the blood cannot supply enough oxygen. These exercises are designed to improve the efficiency of the oxygen delivery system so that there is less need for anaerobic metabolism.

Bibliography

Asimov, Isaac. *Life and Energy*. Garden City, N.Y.: Doubleday, 1962. Chapter 2, "Life Without Air," provides an overview of glycolysis with a chronology. It is written in the typical light, flowing style of one known best for his science fiction.

Camp, Pamela S., and Karen Arms. *Exploring Biology*. 2d ed. Philadelphia: Saunders College Publishing, 1984. A lighter introductory biology text. Chapter 12,

"Cellular Respiration," provides an overview of the whole process and a clear, stepwise description of glycolysis. The pronunciation guide in the margin is a unique feature.

Campbell, Neil A. *Biology*. 2d ed. Menlo Park, Calif.: Benjamin/Cummings, 1990. A very thorough and complete introductory biology text. Chapter 9, "Respiration: How Cells Harvest Chemical Energy," covers both aerobic and anaerobic respiration. The author points out the interconnectedness of many processes. Although aimed at college students, the text is easily read, and many of the diagrams stand by themselves.

Demain, Arnold L., and Nadine A. Solomon. "Industrial Microbiology." *Scientific American* 245 (September, 1981): 66-75. This piece is an introduction to an issue of the magazine devoted to this topic. It provides a brief history of industrial fermentation and lists examples of the wide variety of economically important products dependent upon the vast array of fermentation processes.

DuPraw, Ernest J. *Cell and Molecular Biology*. New York: Academic Press, 1968. Although older and more detailed, this text is useful for its historic summary of the acquisition of knowledge of the subject. Chapter 6, "Energy-Releasing Processes," deals with the production of ATP and includes the process of releasing light energy in bioluminescence.

Lehninger, Albert L. *Bioenergetics*. New York: W. A. Benjamin, 1971. Chapter 4, "Generation of ATP in Anaerobic Cells," provides a detailed but very readable account of the anaerobic portion of respiration. The chapter also provides a succinct account of enzyme action in general.

_____. "How Cells Transform Energy." *Scientific American* 205 (September, 1961): 62-73. This older, but classic, review article covers glycolysis and other aspects of respiration as well as photosynthesis.

Margaria, Rodolfo. "The Sources of Muscular Energy." *Scientific American* 226 (March, 1972): 84-91. This article points out the relative amounts of energy from aerobic and anaerobic sources used by active muscle. The discussion leads to tips on developing the most effective training regimen.

Rose, Anthony R. "The Microbial Production of Food and Drink." *Scientific American* 245 (September, 1981): 126-136. An article from the single-topic issue on industrial microbiology, this piece describes the organisms and types of fermentation that produce a wide variety of foods and drinks. The author outlines the fermentation processes that produce everything from beer and wine to cheeses and single-cell protein supplements.

James Waddell

Cross-References

ATP and Other Energetic Molecules, 134; Electron Transport and Oxidative Phosphorylation, 751; Exergonic and Endergonic Reactions, 939; Heterotrophs and Anaerobes as the Earliest Organisms, 1284; The Krebs Cycle, 1520; Metabolic Pathways, 1691.

THE GREENHOUSE EFFECT

Type of life science: Ecology
Other fields of study: Bioethics, botany, evolutionary biology, photosynthesis, plant physiology, and respiration

The greenhouse effect is the elevation of global average temperatures as a result of the absorption of infrared radiation by trace gases in the atmosphere. Industrial activity elevates the amount of carbon dioxide in the atmosphere—a process that has the potential to change drastically the climate of the earth.

Principal terms

CARBON CYCLE: the set of mechanisms via which carbon is transported through the ecosystem

ELECTROMAGNETIC WAVE: a phenomenon involving oscillating electric and magnetic fields capable of transferring energy

GREENHOUSE GAS: a gas that absorbs infrared radiation and will produce elevated temperatures if its atmospheric concentration is increased

INFRARED RADIATION: a form of electromagnetic radiation that the human body detects as heat

TROPOSPHERE: the region of the atmosphere in which the weather occurs, approximately the lowest fifteen kilometers of the atmosphere

WAVELENGTH: the distance between the adjacent peaks (or troughs) of a wave

Summary of the Phenomenon

Water vapor, carbon dioxide, ozone, and methane are often referred to as the greenhouse gases. These gases are called the greenhouse gases because they are transparent to visible light yet they absorb infrared radiation, just as the glass in a greenhouse is transparent to visible light and traps infrared radiation. This is the origin of the term "greenhouse effect," and just as the temperature inside a greenhouse is higher than the temperature of its surroundings, an increase in the percentage of greenhouse gases in the atmosphere can lead to the elevation of the temperature of the earth.

The definition of the term "greenhouse effect" is sometimes restricted to the absorption of infrared radiation by carbon dioxide, but it properly applies to any gas whose presence in the atmosphere leads to an increase in the absorption of infrared radiation. The concentration of study, however, is on the role of carbon dioxide, because the burning of fossil fuels, such as coal, and the clearing of forests for agriculture have led to an elevation of the amount of carbon dioxide in the atmosphere. Some scientists predict that increasing levels of carbon dioxide and other greenhouse gases will cause significant increases in temperatures on the earth; some researchers, moreover, believe that warming caused by an increasing greenhouse effect has already begun.

In order to understand the greenhouse effect, it is first necessary to know some of the basic properties of electromagnetic radiation. The average temperature of the earth is determined by the balance between the electromagnetic radiation received from the sun and the amount emitted by the earth. Electromagnetic radiation is a way of transferring energy as a wave without transferring matter. The energy is transported by an electromagnetic wave; this electromagnetic wave can be visualized in terms of the waves on the surface of water, as an undulating pattern of peaks and troughs. The difference between water waves and electromagnetic waves is that instead of the level of the water fluctuating, there are fluctuations in electric and magnetic fields. In water waves, and in electromagnetic waves, the distance between the adjacent peaks of a wave is called the wavelength.

Electromagnetic waves of different wavelengths are given different names; the longest wavelength electromagnetic waves are called radio waves, then (in order of decreasing wavelength) there are microwaves, infrared radiation, visible light, ultraviolet light, X rays, and gamma rays. There is a considerable variation in the wavelength of electromagnetic waves: The wavelength of radio waves is measured in hundreds of meters while the wavelength of electromagnetic radiation from the infrared to visible light varies between ten-thousandths of a meter and hundreds of nanometers.

All objects emit electromagnetic waves—the amount of energy transferred—and the wavelength at which most of the energy is emitted depends on the temperature of the object emitting the radiation. This is a familiar phenomenon—if a piece of metal is heated, it will first begin to radiate heat (that is infrared radiation) and then it will begin to emit light, and the material will begin to glow. If the range of temperatures were extended, a wider range of emitted electromagnetic radiations would be observed: The hotter an object became, the shorter the wavelength of the peak emission.

Most of the energy received by the earth from the sun is received in the form of visible light—it passes through the atmosphere and is absorbed by the earth's oceans and continents. The oceans and continents then radiate energy, but since the earth is at a lower temperature than the sun, the energy is radiated as infrared radiation. The infrared radiation emitted by the earth then warms the atmosphere as energy is absorbed by the greenhouse gases. There is also some warming by heat conduction between the earth and the layers of the atmosphere close to the surface of the earth. Then, as the temperature of the earth increases, the wavelength at which most of the energy is emitted decreases until some of it can pass through the greenhouse gases and a stable temperature is achieved.

If the atmosphere of the earth did not contain any greenhouse gases, the balance between emitted and absorbed radiation would result in an average global temperature of −19 degrees Celsius. The actual global average temperature is approximately 14 degrees Celsius, leading to the conclusion that the greenhouse effect is already operating. Calculations show that the presence of the greenhouse gases in the atmosphere has caused the average global temperature to be 33 degrees Celsius higher than it would be if the greenhouse gases were not present. It is difficult to determine the exact contributions of each of the greenhouse gases to the temperature increase, but it is generally accepted that the contribution of the water vapor is the greatest and that the contribution of the ozone is the smallest. Roger Barry and Richard Chorley ascribe 21 degrees Celsius of the temperature increase to the water vapor, 7 degrees to the carbon dioxide, and 2 degrees to the ozone.

The layer of the earth's atmosphere closest to its surface is called the troposphere; it is in this layer that the earth's weather occurs. The carbon dioxide released by humankind's industrial activities is also released into the troposphere, which means that any additional atmospheric warming will occur in the troposphere and so will have the potential to cause major changes in the earth's climate.

The amount of carbon dioxide in the atmosphere and the average global temperature have both increased since the end of the nineteenth century. Prior to large-scale industrialization, the atmospheric concentration of carbon dioxide was 290 parts per million; by 1986, the concentration had increased by about 19 percent to 345 parts per million. The average temperature of the earth's continents increased by more than 0.7 degrees Celsius between the 1880's and the 1980's. Thus, it would appear that there is a direct correlation between the increased concentration of atmospheric carbon dioxide and average global temperatures. Unfortunately, however, the situation is more complicated. Between the 1880's and 1940, average land temperatures had increased by about 0.6 degrees Celsius but between 1940 and 1965 average temperatures dropped slightly — as the atmospheric carbon dioxide content continued to increase. After 1965, temperatures again began to increase, and up to 1989 the five warmest years globally occurred in the 1980's, with 1987 being the hottest. The temperature decrease observed between 1940 and 1965 is thought to have been caused by an increase in the amount of small particles in the atmosphere, but its occurrence underlines the difficulty in determining the cause of observed effects in the atmosphere. If the rate of global temperature increase measured since 1965 continues until the year 2010, the earth will be warmer than it has been for more than 100,000 years, and it would be difficult to ascribe that result to the earth's normal climatic variations.

In order to account for the observed increase in the level of carbon dioxide between 1870 and the 1980's, it is necessary to consider the carbon cycle. The carbon cycle is the set of mechanisms and reactions through which carbon is transferred among different parts of the environment. The carbon cycle is not completely understood, but it plays a major role in food production, energy production, and waste disposal.

Carbon dioxide is water soluble, and large amounts of it can be dissolved in the oceans — a process that happens continuously. Yet, the carbon dioxide does not remain in solution; it is removed by photosynthesis, the formation of calcium carbonate shells, and by the formation of other carbonate compounds that are eventually deposited as sedimentary rocks, such as limestone. On land, carbon dioxide is used in photosynthesis: Approximately half the carbon dioxide absorbed by plants is returned to the atmosphere through respiration; the remainder is converted to wood or appears as carbon in the soil. That photosynthesis is responsible for removing carbon dioxide from the atmosphere is confirmed by the seasonal variations of atmospheric carbon dioxide content—it is apparent that plants absorb large amounts of carbon dioxide in the spring and summer.

The main sources of increased carbon dioxide in the atmosphere are the burning of fossil fuels and the production of cement. The amount of fossil fuels burned between 1870 and 1986 is enough to have increased the concentration of atmospheric carbon dioxide by 30 percent, rather than the observed 19 percent. The oceans provide the major mechanism for removing carbon dioxide from the atmosphere. Photosynthesis can have little effect on the overall average level of carbon dioxide in the atmosphere, because increased levels of atmospheric carbon dioxide do not stimulate photosynthesis. The average amount of carbon dioxide stored in the earth's plants and trees depends on the aggregate amount of the earth's vegetation: Much carbon dioxide is stored in the trees of tropical rain forests, and their destruction in the twentieth century is thought to have contributed to the increase in atmospheric carbon dioxide levels.

Although it is expected that a buildup of carbon dioxide will increase average global temperatures, there are relevant questions that are very difficult to answer. It is not known, for example, how much of the carbon dioxide introduced into the atmosphere will remain there or to what degree the additional carbon dioxide will actually contribute to an elevation of global temperatures.

Methods of Study

The greenhouse effect is difficult to study, as are all phenomena that involve the atmosphere and climate. The source of the difficulty is that small events may produce large consequences, which is usually described as nonlinear behavior. The major tool used to study the greenhouse effect is mathematical models of the atmosphere. The models used are similar to the models that are used in weather prediction; the difficulties in the greenhouse models are also similar to the problems in the weather prediction models: The atmosphere is too complex an environment to allow reliable long-term predictions. Global climate models must consider more than the variability of atmospheric carbon dioxide—the effects of clouds and the variability of other greenhouse gases must also be considered. The result of this situation is that the many competing models predict a wide variety of consequences and that the future effects of increasing atmospheric carbon dioxide are not completely understood.

The models of the greenhouse effect are based on data that have been collected on atmospheric carbon dioxide content and global temperatures since 1870; however, there are some problems associated with these data. The temperature measurements are made at a variety of sites around the world but they are overwhelmingly measurements of land temperatures. The greenhouse model predict that the continents should warm faster than the oceans because the oceans have a larger heat capacity. (Heat capacity is a measure of temperature increase as a function of heat absorption; the larger the heat capacity, the smaller the temperature increase for a given heat transfer.) The available temperature measurements show that temperatures have increased faster in the Southern Hemisphere, which is mostly ocean, than they have in the Northern Hemisphere. All greenhouse models predict the reverse. The carbon dioxide content of the atmosphere has not been widely monitored; the base figure of 290 parts per million prior to large-scale industrialization is an estimate. Many models of the greenhouse effect have assumed that the global increase of atmospheric carbon dioxide is similar to the increase observed at the monitoring station at the Mauna Loa volcano in Hawaii, though it is not clear whether that is a valid assumption.

There is another uncertainty in the models of the greenhouse effect. The ocean ultimately removes carbon dioxide from the atmosphere, but the rate at which it does that is not well determined. In order to determine the rate at which the ocean removes carbon dioxide from the atmosphere, it is necessary to know how much carbon dioxide is entering the atmosphere and how much of it remains in the atmosphere; there is a degree of uncertainty in both of these quantities. The uncertainty is caused by the limited number of carbon dioxide monitoring stations and doubt about the amount of carbon dioxide produced by natural and artificial means. Models of the greenhouse effect will improve as more data on temperature variations and carbon dioxide increases are collected. As yet, however, the information available (particularly as it covers only a limited span of years) does not allow the formulation of solid long-range predictions.

Context

There is no question whether a greenhouse effect exists: The greeenhouse effect that currently exists keeps the earth about 33 degrees Celsius warmer than it would otherwise be and helps make the earth habitable. Carbon dioxide levels, however, are increasing. The question is what the effect of an increased level of atmospheric carbon dioxide will actually be. Mathematical models of the atmosphere predict that a doubling of atmospheric carbon dioxide will cause an increase of at least 2 degrees Celsius in the global average temperature (some models predict as much as 4 degrees). Projections of population growth and energy usage formulated in the late 1980's predict a doubling of atmospheric carbon dioxide by the year 2050. The temperature increases predicted by a doubling in atmospheric carbon dioxide would drastically alter the earth's climate. The polar ice caps would recede, thus reducing the amount of available land, and the most fertile crop-growing regions could be expected to occur closer to the poles than they currently are.

An enhanced greenhouse effect would undoubtedly have potentially drastic consequences. Increased carbon dioxide levels will cause elevated temperatures; carbon dioxide is the major atmospheric constituent of the planet Venus, and the greenhouse effect has given that planet the hottest surface of any planet in the solar system. It is uncertain, however, how much of the temperature increase that occurred on the earth between 1870 and 1989 should be attributed to the increase in the levels of atmospheric carbon dioxide. Throughout the history of the earth there have been fluctuations in its average temperature—these have usually been of the order of 0.5 degrees Celsius per century—it may well be that the earth is in the middle of a warming trend and that the contributions of carbon dioxide have been overestimated. The increasing amounts of data that have been collected since the 1970's will improve scientific models, and if the global average temperatures continue to rise at the same rate as they did between 1965 and 1989, the models in use in the late 1980's will have been substantially correct.

If global average temperatures continue to increase, and if it is determined that the increase is a result of the increase in atmospheric carbon dioxide, the world will be presented with a simple choice: Either the consequences of an altered climate must be suffered, or the amount of carbon dioxide in the atmosphere must be controlled. Climatic changes associated with elevated global temperatures could be catastrophic—elevated temperatures would affect global rainfall patterns and would be likely to increase the extent of the world's deserts. If the carbon dioxide-induced greenhouse effect is proved to be real, the only realistic choice will be to reduce the amount of carbon dioxide introduced into the atmosphere by humans. The simplest method to reduce atmospheric carbon dioxide is to eliminate the production of electricity in coal-fired generators. Human beings will indeed have a difficult choice, because the earth has more coal than any other fossil fuel.

Bibliography

Barry, Robert G., and Richard J. Chorley. *Atmosphere, Weather, and Climate*. 5th ed. New York: Methuen, 1987. This book is an excellent introductory textbook in meteorology and climatology. The book is intended for college-level geography and meteorology courses, but the level is such that it is accessible to anyone wanting to learn more about the environment. An extensive bibliography is included.

Bolin, Bert, E. T. Degens, S. Kempe, and P. Ketner, eds. *The Global Carbon Cycle*. New York: John Wiley & Sons, 1979. A thorough study of global sources of carbon dioxide and of the mechanisms through which carbon dioxide is removed from the atmosphere. Many references to the effects of carbon dioxide on biological systems are included.

Fowler, John M. *Energy and the Environment*. 2d ed. New York: McGraw-Hill, 1984. A textbook for liberal-arts students which focuses on energy. One of the best starting places for those who are interested in the effects of different modes of energy production on the environment. A balanced and complete treatment.

Gribbin, John R. *Future Weather and the Greenhouse Effect*. New York: Delacorte Press, 1982. One of many books with the words 'greenhouse effect' in the title. This book has been included for its representative title; many books with similar titles will be found. Contains information on climatic changes and an extensive bibliography.

MacCracken, Michael C., and Frederick M. Luther. *Projecting the Climatic Effects of Increasing Carbon Dioxide*. Washington, D.C.: United States Department of Energy, 1985. This report is a review of the climatological effects of increasing carbon dioxide and a review of the degree of the scientific understanding of the phenomenon. A good general introduction of the degree of reliability of scientific studies of the eco-system.

National Research Council, Carbon Dioxide Assessment Committee. *Changing Climate*. Washington, D.C.: National Academy Press, 1983. A report on the climate of the United States from 1800 to 1980. The effects on the industrialization of the United States and the increase in production of carbon dioxide are detailed. An ideal companion to the work cited below.

National Research Council, Climate Research Committee. *Carbon Dioxide and the Climate: A Second Assessment*. Washington, D.C.: National Academy Press, 1982. An assessment of the climatological effects of atmospheric carbon dioxide written for the intelligent layman. This work is unusual in that the assumptions inherent in different greenhouse models are explicitly stated and analyzed. At 72 pages, the book is an ideal introduction.

Trabalka, John R. *Atmospheric Carbon Dioxide and the Global Carbon Cycle*. Washington, D.C.: United States Department of Energy, 1985. A collection of reports on the atmospheric carbon dioxide prepared for the Department of Energy. An unrivaled study of natural and man-made sources of atmospheric carbon dioxide and its environmental effects. The reports are accessible to the general reader.

Stephen R. Addison

Cross-References

Bioethics: Ecological Decisions, 171; Biomass Related to Energy, 203; The Biosphere, Biomes, and Habitats, 210; Carbon 13/Carbon 12 Ratios in Photosynthesis, 330; Ecological Principles, 736; The Gaia Hypothesis, 1054; Life's Effect on Earth, 1589; Photosynthetic Light Absorption, 2073; Photosynthetic Light Reactions, 2080; The Water Cycle, 2695.

GROWTH AND GROWTH CONTROL IN PLANTS

Type of life science: Plant physiology
Other fields of study: Biochemistry, botany, and cell biology (cytology)

The size of a plant body can increase by the lengthening of its principal axis (primary growth) or by branching or an increase in girth (secondary growth). Both patterns of growth are influenced by genetic and environmental factors that affect the hormonal balances within the organism.

Principal terms

AXIS: the central structure of a plant, usually the primary stem and the primary root, about which the other structures (such as branch roots, branch stems, and leaves) are organized

GROWTH: a natural process of change involving an increase in the size or the number of cells

HORMONE: a chemical produced at low concentrations in one part of an organism that controls the physiology (such as growth and development) in another part of the organism

MERISTEM: a tissue that functions in increasing the number of cells in the plant body, usually located at the growing tips (apical meristems) or within the body of the plant (the cambia)

PHLOEM: the vascular tissue in some plants that moves nutrients throughout the plant; it consists of sieve elements shaped like elongated tubes

SEED: a propagative part of many plants, consisting of a seed coat, a food layer, and an embryo; the embryonic root and stem define the principal axis of seed plants

TISSUE: a group of cells that together carry out a single function; the cells may be similar or dissimilar

VASCULAR CAMBIUM: a type of lateral meristem that forms a ring of cells that produce secondary xylem and phloem

VASCULAR TISSUE: circulatory tissues; in the plant these are the xylem and the phloem

XYLEM: the vascular tissue in some plants that moves water and minerals up from the root to structures such as the leaves

Summary of the Phenomenon

Plant growth is considered to be of two distinct types: primary growth and secondary growth. Primary growth results in increased length of stems or roots; secondary growth increases the width of the plant and allows differentiation of cells into various distinct types of tissues. Both types of growth occur at plant tissues called meristems. A meristem consists of tissue where extensive cell division takes place, creating the new cells that allow a plant to grow. There are two general types of meristems, and they correspond to the two types of plant growth. Primary growth occurs at the apical meristems, and secondary growth occurs at the lateral meristems (which are known as the vascular cambium and the cork cambium).

Apical meristems are located at the growing tips of the plant; there are apical meristems in the roots and in the buds on shoots of the aboveground part of the plant. New cells produced at the meristems are undifferentiated, nonspecialized cells. Cells produced at the apical meristems enlarge in the adjacent "zone of elongation," where they become larger mostly by increasing their water content. Primary growth produces the plant's primary tissues, which comprise three tissue systems: dermal tissue, vascular tissue, and ground tissue.

Secondary growth also usually occurs in both stems and roots, but it increases the girth (diameter) of the plant rather than its length or height. One type of meristem responsible for secondary growth produces a structure called the vascular cambium. The lateral growth of the vascular cambium produces new vascular tissue for the plant (known as secondary xylem and phloem). In plants that live for many years, this continual lateral growth produces wood. The other type of lateral meristem that produces secondary growth is the cork cambium. It produces cells at the outer edge of the plant, which are dead by the time they perform their function of protecting the plant and providing some structural support. The walls of cork cells contain a protective waxy substance called suberin.

The use of the adjectives "primary" and "secondary" to describe plant growth is fraught with potential confusion, because these adjectives are also applied to organs, to tissues, and to cell walls. Primary indicates a simpler structure than secondary structures, a structure that occurs early in development, or a structure with less specialization and less elaboration than secondary structures. The primary root and stem are the primary organs; that is, they are elongations of the original embryonic axis. Yet, these primary organs may be composed exclusively of primary tissues (derived directly from the apical meristems) or they may have increased in girth through the formation of secondary tissues derived from the cambia.

Secondary organs are the branch roots and branch stems. Secondary organs form from meristems other than the apical meristem of the primary organs, but they are always initially formed of primary tissues. The tissues of the secondary organs are originally derived directly from primary growth at the apical meristems, but if these secondary roots and stems increase in girth, secondary tissues derived from cambia will also be found in the structure.

The need to understand primary and secondary growth arises from a desire to understand plants' patterns of growth, especially the growth patterns of plants that develop elaborate structures and plants that grow for long periods. Growth is among the most basic functions of the bodies of plants. The specific form of the plant body results from the pattern of growth and the subsequent differentiation of the tissues produced by this growth.

Although growth and differentiation are important to all multicellular organisms, plants approach growth in ways that are very different from those used by most animals. Principal among these differences is the fact that many plant bodies have the potential to grow forever. Secondary growth that results in increases in the girth of the stem and root provides support for plants whose principal axis is greatly elongated. Secondary growth resulting in branching provides broad expanses of roots and stems to support the gathering of energy, the development of reproductive structure, and competition with surrounding plants for light and nutrients.

Terrestrial plant species (including the mosses and vascular plants) and those aquatic species derived from these terrestrial forms, have life cycles that include the formation of two potentially independent bodies called the gametophyte and the sporophyte. The gametophyte, which is responsible for the production of egg and sperm, is the smaller and less conspicuous of the two bodies in most plant species, whereas in the mosses it is the larger of the two bodies.

Both the gametophyte and the sporophyte develop from single cells—the spore and the zygote, respectively. The first cell division of the spore or zygote often defines the root cell line (or its equivalent) and the stem cell line (or its equivalent). The body produced by this early development is initially linear in many cases; this linear form lays out the primary axis of the plant body. For example, in seed plants, the zygote forms in the developing seed. The embryo grows from the zygote and is a miniature version of the adult sporophyte. The organs that make up this embryo are called the primary root and the primary stem. They grow from a root apical meristem and a shoot apical meristem, respectively.

In the meristems, individual cells divide to produce pairs of cells which have the ability to divide further or to enlarge and differentiate. Primary tissues develop from cells derived from the apical meristems. These cells grow and differentiate to produce roots (or rootlike structures), stems (or stemlike structures), and leaves (or leaflike structures).

In many species, the new cells in the plant body are produced primarily by the division of apical meristems. These plant bodies therefore consist almost exclusively of primary tissues. In most terrestrial species, this is true for the gametophyte body. In some species, the sporophyte body also consists almost exclusively of primary tissues. There are, however, some species in which the sporophytes grow in girth. Some of these species, such as the *calamites* (giant horsetails), the *Lepidodendron* (tree lycopods) and the seed ferns, are known only from the fossil record. Others are the trees and shrubs that characterize the modern forests. Most species which grow in girth are characterized as woody.

The wood of woody plants is composed almost entirely of secondary xylem—xylem which is not derived from the apical meristems but instead grows from the vascular cambium, a cylindrical meristem located under the bark. The bark of woody plant is also a secondary tissue; it is made of phloem and corky layers. The vascular cambium produce the cells which will differentiate to form both secondary xylem and the secondary phloem of woody species. The corky layers develop from a second cylindrical meristem, the cork cambium. The cork cambium produces the corky cells in the outside of the bark.

In addition to the secondary tissues, many plants as they grow produce secondary organs: branch stems and branch roots. These secondary organs are not derived from the original axis of the plant; in the early stages of their growth they are composed of primary tissues that are essentially identical to the primary tissues of primary organs. Cambial growth will produce secondary tissues in these branch stems and roots. The patterns of secondary tissue formation determine the form of the wood and bark of woody species. The patterns of secondary organ formation determine the architecture of the plant: the shape of the crown and the root system. This architecture plays an important role in the ability of the plant to compete for sunlight, water, and soil nutrients.

The patterns of secondary organ formation are controlled both by genetic factors and by environmental conditions. Horticulturalists use plants which have a genetic predisposition to form branches early as a source of dwarfing stock. In many cases, the dwarfing results from a failure of the stem to elongate in the internodes (the regions between leaves). Since branches form at the nodes, failure of the internodes to elongate results in a dwarf variety.

Dwarfing appears to be particularly influenced by the hormone family known as the gibberellins. These hormones stimulate internodal elongation in the type of plants known as dicots; this action is dependent on an appropriate balance of the other hormones within the plant. The synthesis of gibberellins in young leaves provides the plant with a chemical signal describing the proportion of the crown to the trunk, allowing the production of new branches to respond to the current form of the plant in relation to its total photosynthetic potential.

Columnar plants also represent a genetically controlled growth pattern influenced by the relationship of the secondary organs to the axis of the plant. Lombardy poplar has greatly reduced branching compared to the European poplar; the branches also exhibit an upright growth pattern. This results in the apparent elongation of the principal axis and therefore in a form similar to that found in forest trees growing in the shade of the surrounding forest. The shaded environment of the forest stimulates the growth of the main axis of many tree species while inhibiting growth of the secondary stems. As a result, the stem reaches above the surrounding trees and is better able to compete for light.

The inhibition of the formation of secondary stems seems to be influenced primarily by chemicals in the hormone family called auxins. High auxin concentrations inhibit the development of secondary stems, while low auxin levels stimulate the formation of branches. In some species, high cytokinin levels also stimulate secondary stem growth. Since cytokinins are produced in large quantities in the root tips, and auxins are produced in large quantities in the stem tip, the relationship between these two chemicals reflects the balance between the root system and the stem system.

Less is known about the mechanisms of control of branching in the root system. Some species, especially those that are monocots, have many secondary roots of approximately equal size. Others have dominant primary roots with little development of the secondary roots; carrots carry this pattern to an extreme. Largely because the root systems are underground, less study has been focused on their architecture and the control of the development of that architecture.

The patterns of secondary tissue formation are also controlled both by genetic factors and by environmental conditions. Many plants complete their life cycles in a single year. This quick passage from seed to seed is under genetic control. Annuals rarely develop significant amounts of wood and bark; other plants survive many seasons and show increases in stem girth throughout their lives. The annual rings seen in the cross-section of a tree are a result of seasonal variations in the production of various types of cells in the secondary xylem. The formation of these rings is influenced both by genetic controls and by the environmental signals which indicate the passage of the seasons. Wood and bark that form in stems and grow horizontally, whether this orientation is a result of the branching pattern of the trees or is caused by windfalls or landslides, develop patterns of secondary tissue formation that reflect the strains on the various parts of the stem. Different sizes and numbers of cells buttress the various parts of the stem against the stress of gravity.

Secondary tissues are extraordinarily complex. The patterns of cell division, apparently under genetic control, are influenced by a whole concert of hormones. Secondary wood in stems begins forming each season in emerging buds. The differentiation of the secondary tissues passes down from these buds in a wave toward the base of the stem. Larger xylem channels open earlier in the season, followed later by smaller channels. Hormonal gradients and seasonal gradients of sugars and amino acids may play a role in these patterns of secondary tissue formation. The activity of mature phloem tissues and the concentrations of auxins, gibberellins, cytokinins, and perhaps of the gaseous hormone ethylene may all be important in regulating the activity of the cambia.

Methods of Study

Growth is as difficult to measure as it is to define. An organism may increase in size as a result of an increase in its water content, for example, without any concurrent increase in cell numbers or in the quantity of biologically produced chemicals in the cell body. Conversely, the number of cells in an organism may increase, but if those cells do not increase in size, there may be no subsequent change in the size of the organism. Yet, differentiating between primary and secondary growth is an easier process: The origin of the cells produced is the critical question.

The fate of individual cells in the differentiation of tissues is not so easily studied. Fortunately, the patterns of plant tissue formation, which separate the elongation and growth in girth temporally, make it easy to assign tissues to origins in the apical meristems or the cambia. Only after elongation has been completed are there significant increases in cells of cambial origin. Thus, the temporal separation of primary tissue formation and secondary tissue formation provides a mechanism for the study of the physiology of the processes.

Plant tissues are most often studied by observing thin slices (sections) of plant organs through the microscope. The arrangements of vascular tissues in scattered bundles, in broken rings, or in complete rings may all occur in the differentiation of primary tissues of various species, but the development of concentric rings of xylem and phloem is limited to secondary tissues derived from the cambia.

To be observed microscopically, the tissues must be killed with chemicals that immobilize (fix) the structures within the cells. The tissues are then embedded in plastic or wax and sliced (sectioned) using metal or glass knives. The sections are mounted on glass slides and observed. Special dyes or stains can reveal much about the structure and chemistry of the tissues. The presence of a chemical called lignin, for example, signals the presence of secondary cell walls.

A variety of tissues can grow in tissue cultures. By understanding the chemical and physical environment in which a tissue will grow in a culture, biologists can draw inferences about the conditions that will lead to growth of the tissue in nature. Large explants (tissue samples that are removed from a living plant) which include apical meristems or cambial tissues can be grown in culture as well. The culture of these explants provides insights into the particular chemical environments that support primary and secondary growth.

No single technique informs botanists about a plant's growth. Instead, understanding has grown by combining observations made by many researchers using many different tools. In this way, the study of plant growth illustrates the way in which knowledge of nature in general has grown.

Context

Wherever it is available, wood is used by humans for fuel, for construction, for the manufacture of paper, and for creating cultural artifacts. Wood products are made from the secondary xylem tissues harvested from hundreds of tree species. The grain and the physical characteristics (such as heat content, density, hardness, and absorbancy) of the wood are all influenced by the patterns of secondary tissue development. An understanding of the patterns of development is especially important when the wood is sawed or milled. Lumber cut from the wood of stems which were not growing vertically can take some unusual forms because of the patterns of secondary tissues laid down to cope with the stresses. Bark is also sometimes used in the production of cloth, paper, and cultural artifacts. One unique product derived from the bark of a few species is cork. Many of the uses of cork relate to its resilient character and its insulating properties. Most commercial production of cork depends on the bark from the cork oak.

Patterns of seasonal growth, branching, and wood formation may all be related to fruit production and yields. Tomatoes have been bred to produce an abundant crop in a single season. These varieties of tomato have some limited secondary tissue formation but rarely would they be described as woody. In the wild, tomatoes are woody shrubs with limited fruit production at any one time.

Patterns of secondary tissue and organ formation may significantly influence the nature of commercial agricultural practices. Mechanical harvesting may be made more practical as shrubby forms (with short, branched, woody stems) are derived from viney species. Crop yields per acre may also be influenced when dwarf varieties are derived from standard forms, although in some cases the yields will improve and in others they will be hurt.

Human interference in the development of plant tissues can change the appearance of the tissues and therefore affect their utility to humans. As the development of wood is better understood, it may be possible to affect the density and grain of a wood significantly. This use of knowledge may seem rather whimsical, but it could result in a reduced dependence on harsh and potentially dangerous chemicals in the manufacturing of products such as paper. An understanding of secondary tissues and organs may help humans to utilize land planted in woody species more effectively. The use of dwarfing stock in orchards has revolutionized fruit production practices. As the understanding of the basic biology of plant growth and development improves, new abilities to manipulate plants in the laboratory and the field will enable more efficient feeding, housing, and warming of the people of the world.

Bibliography

Beazley, Mary, ed. *The International Book of the Forest.* New York: Simon & Schuster, 1981. A beautifully illustrated, oversized book dealing with forests and forest products. The International Paper Company cooperated in the publication of this interesting volume. The illustrations are among the best and most artistic available.

Böhm, W. *Methods of Studying Root Systems.* New York: Springer-Verlag, 1987. A surprisingly easy-to-read college botany text that focuses on the anatomy, physiology, and ecology of roots. This book illustrates well the difficulties of studying root tissue and organ development. Illustrated in black and white with both line drawings and photographs. There is an extensive bibliography.

Forest Products Laboratory. *Wood Handbook: Wood as an Engineering Material.* Washington, D.C.: Government Printing Office, 1987. Everything you want to know about wood and wood products in a weighty volume that is easy to use but is hardly casual reading material. Illustrated in black and white. Chapter 2, "Structure of Wood," and chapters 3-5 on the properties of wood and lumber relate directly to the topics of this piece.

Hartmann, Hudson, A. M. Kofranek, V. E. Rubatzky, and William J. Flocker. *Plant Science: Growth, Development, and Utilization of Cultivated Plants.* 2d ed. Englewood Cliffs, N.J.: Prentice-Hall, 1988. An easily read introductory college botany text that places the plants in a context of their biology and economical uses. Chapter 2, "Structure of Higher Plants," describes the relationship between plant tissues and cell types and between plant tissues and organs. Chapter 6, "Vegetative and Reproductive Growth and Development," covers the mechanisms controlling plant growth. Heavily illustrated in black and white with both line drawings and photographs.

Kaufman, Peter B., T. F. Carlson, P. Dayanandan, M. L. Evans, J. B. Fisher, C. Parks, and J. R. Wells. *Plants: Their Biology and Importance*. New York: Harper & Row, 1989. Illustrated with both black-and-white and color drawings and photographs, this college-level botany text is very easily understood. Chapter 3, "Structure and Function of Roots, Stems, and Leaves," chapter 26, and chapter 27 provide a useful survey of material related to secondary growth and growth control.

Klein, Richard M. *The Green World: An Introduction to Plants and People*. 2d ed. New York: Harper & Row, 1987. An extraordinarily readable text that focuses on the importance of plants to humans. Illustrated primarily with line drawings in black and white. Relates the importance of parts of plants to human use of those parts. Chapter 1, "What Plants Are and What Plants Do," has sections that focus on stem and root growth.

Raven, Peter H., and George B. Johnson. *Biology*. St. Louis: Times Mirror/Mosby, 1986. Beautifully illustrated with many color drawings and photographs, this college-level biology text places plant growth in context with the biology of plants and places plants in context with the living and nonliving world. Chapter 31, "Vascular Plant Structure," provides a simple review of plant cell types, tissues, and organs. Chapter 32, "Plant Development," deals clearly with many questions concerning growth and growth controls.

Roberts, Lorin W. *Cytodifferentiation in Plants*. New York: Cambridge University Press, 1976. An advanced college-level text, which deals with patterns and controls of tissue differentiation. Chapter 5, "Regulation of Secondary Xylem Differentiation," provides a review of the techniques used to study patterns of secondary wood formation.

Craig R. Landgren

Cross-References

Angiosperms, 95; Germination and Seedling Development, 1205; Growth in Animal Development, 1240; Gymnosperms, 1247; Plant Cell Types, 2095; Plant Hormones, 2103; Plant Life Spans, 2110; Plant Tissue Types, 2119; Roots, 2437; Seeds, 2452; Stems, 2535.

GROWTH IN ANIMAL DEVELOPMENT

Type of life science: Developmental biology (embryology)
Other fields of study: Cell biology (cytology) and zoology

Animal development begins with a single cell, the fertilized egg. Continued growth and formation through numerous cellular replications result in the formation of the complex animal body.

Principal terms
DIFFERENTIATION: the process during development by which cells obtain their unique structure and function
FERTILIZATION: the union of two gametes (egg and sperm) to form a zygote
GAMETE: a functional reproductive cell (egg or sperm) produced by the adult male or female
GROWTH: the increased body mass of an organism that results primarily from an increase in the number of body cells and secondarily from the increase in the size of individual cells
MITOSIS: the process of cellular division in which the nuclear material, including the genes, is distributed equally to two identical daughter cells
ZYGOTE: a fertilized egg

Summary of the Phenomenon

Animal development has been a source of wonder for centuries. Development involves the slow, progressive changes that occur when a single cell—the zygote, or fertilized egg—undergoes mitosis. Mitosis is the process by which a cell divides into identical daughter cells. During development, mitosis occurs repeatedly, forming multiple generations of daughter cells. These cells increase in number and ultimately form all the cells in the body of a multicellular animal, such as a frog, mouse, or human being. The simple experiment of opening fertile chicken eggs to observe the embryos on successive days of their three-week incubation period illustrates the process of embryonic development. A narrow band of cells can be seen increasing in number and complexity until the body of an entire, but immature, chick is seen.

An organism's growth occurs because of the increasing number of cells that form as well as because of the increasing size of individual cells. For example, a mouse increases from a single cell, the zygote, to about 3 billion cells during the period from fertilization to birth. Embryology is the study of the growth and development of an organism occurring before birth. Growth and development, however, continue after birth and throughout adulthood. Growth ceases only at death, when the life of the individual organism is ended. The bone marrow of human adults initiates the formation and development of millions of red blood cells every minute of life. About 1 gram of old skin cells is lost and replaced by new cells each day.

Development produces two major results: the formation of cellular diversity and the continuity of life. Cellular diversity, or differentiation, is the process that produces and organizes the numerous kinds of body cells. The first cell that determines an individual's unique identity, the zygote, ultimately gives rise to varying types of cells having diverse appearances and functions. Muscle cells, red blood cells, skin cells, neurons, osteocytes (bone cells), and liver cells are all examples of cells that have differentiated from a single zygote.

Morphogenesis is the process by which differentiated cells are organized into tissues and organs. The continued formation of new individual organisms is called reproduction. The major stages of animal development include fertilization, embryology, birth, youth, adulthood—when fertilization of the next generation occurs—and death. A new individual animal is begun by the process of fertilization, when the genetic material from the sperm, produced by the father, and the egg, produced by the mother, are merged into a single cell, the zygote. Fertilization may be external, occurring in fresh water or the sea, or internal, occurring within the female's reproductive tract. While fertilization marks the beginning of a new individual, it is not literally the beginning of life, since both the sperm and egg are already alive. Rather, fertilization ensures the continuation of life through the formation of new individuals. This guarantees that the species of the organism will continue to survive in the future.

Following fertilization, the newly formed zygote undergoes embryological development consisting of cleavage, gastrulation, and organogenesis. Cleavage is a period of rapid mitotic divisions with little individual cell growth. A ball of small cells, called the morula, forms. As mitosis continues, this ball of cells hollows in the middle, forming an internal cavity called the blastocoel. Gastrulation immediately follows cleavage. During gastrulation, individual cell growth as well as initial cell differentiation occur. During this time, three distinct types of cells are formed: an internal layer called the endoderm, a middle layer, the mesoderm, and an external layer, the ectoderm. These cell types, or germ-cell layers, are the parental cells of all future cells of the body.

Cells from the ectoderm form the cells of the nervous system and skin. The mesoderm forms the cells of muscle, bone, connective tissue, and blood. The endoderm forms cells that line the inside of the digestive tract as well as the liver, pancreas, lungs, and thyroid gland. The transformation of these single germ layers into functional organs is called organogenesis. Organogenesis is an extremely complex period of embryological development. During this time, specific cells interact and respond to one another to induce growth, movement, or further differentiation; this cell-to-cell interaction is called induction. Each induction event requires an inducing cell and a responding cell.

In the formation of the brain and spinal cord, selected cells from the ectoderm form a long, thickened plate at the midline of the developing embryo. Through changes in cell shape, the outer edges of this plate fold up and fuse with each other in the middle, forming a tubular structure (a neural tube). This tubelike structure then separates from the remaining ectoderm. At the head region of the embryo, the neural tube enlarges into pockets that ultimately form brain regions.

For differentiation and development to occur, cells must be responsive to regulatory signals. Some of these signals originate within the responding cell; these signals are based in the genetic code found in the cell's own nucleus. Other signals originate outside the cell; they may include physical contact with overlying or underlying cells, specific signal molecules, such as hormones, from distant cells, or specialized structural molecules secreted by neighboring cells that map out the pathway along which a responding cell will migrate.

Embryological development climaxes in the formation of functional organs and body systems. This period is concluded by birth (or hatching, in the case of some animals). Following birth, development normally continues. In some animals, such as frogs, newly hatched individuals undergo metamorphosis during which their body structures are dramatically altered. Newly hatched frogs (tadpoles), for example, are transformed from aquatic, legless, fishlike creatures into mature adults with legs that allow them to move freely on land.

In mammals, development and growth occur primarily after birth, as the individual progresses through the stages of infancy, childhood, adolescence, and adulthood. Mature adulthood is attained when the individual can produce his or her own gametes and participate in mating behavior.

Embryonic growth is especially impressive because the rate of cellular mitosis is so enormous. In the case of the mouse embryo, thirty-one cell generations occur during embryonic development. Thus, the zygote divides into two cells, then four, then eight, sixteen, thirty-two, and so on. This results in a newborn mouse consisting of billions of cells—produced in a period of only twenty-one days. When the newborn passes through its life stages to adulthood, its body cells may number more than 60 billion. One marine mammal, the blue whale, begins as a single zygote that is less than 1 millimeter in diameter and weighs only a small fraction of a gram. The resulting newborn whale (the calf) is about 7 meters long and weighs 2,000 kilograms: The embryonic growth represents a 200-million-fold increase in weight. Yet, for some animals, impressive growth periods also occur in the juvenile and adolescent stages of life. In humans, the end cells of long bones undergo a high rate of mitosis in response to growth hormone; this causes the typical adolescent growth spurt.

In many cases, once an individual animal reaches its typical adult size, the rate of mitosis slows so that the number of new cells simply replaces the number of older, dying cells. At this maintenance stage, the individual no longer grows in overall size even though it continuously produces new cells. Since most of the cells in the mature adult have reached a final differentiated state, the function of mitosis is simply to replace the degenerating, aging cells. The slowing of the rate of cellular mitosis during this time may be attributable to the presence of specialized cell products called chalones. Chalones are thought to be local products of mature cells that inhibit further growth or mitosis.

Methods of Study

Historically, much study of animal development and growth was performed by simple observation. Aristotle, perhaps the first known embryologist, opened chick eggs during varying developmental periods. He observed and sketched what appeared to be the formation of the chick's body from a nondescript substance. With the invention of lenses and microscopes, growth and development could be studied on a cellular level. The concept of cellular differentiation arose, since investigators could see that embryonic muscle cells, for example, looked different from embryonic nerve cells. Again, much of the investigative information was descriptive in nature. Embryologists detailed the existence of the three germ-cell layers in gastrulation as well as the various tissues and primitive cells involved in organogenesis.

Experimentation as a method of investigating animal growth and development began during the nineteenth century. Lower animal species, such as the sea urchin and frog, were frequently investigated; their developmental patterns are simpler than those of mammals, their development occurs outside the maternal body, and they can be found in abundant numbers. Many of these experiments used separation or surgical techniques to isolate or regraft specific tissues or cells of interest. An attempt was made to determine how one tissue type would interact with and influence the development of another tissue type. Thus, the ideas of induction, in which some tissues affect other tissues, came into being. During this time, the descriptive and comparative observations resulting from these experimental manipulations were the major contributions of investigators.

The early embryologists of the twentieth century paid little attention to genetics. They believed that the major influences on development and growth were embryological mechanisms, although genes were thought to provide some nonessential peripheral functions. Chemical analyses of embryos attempted to establish the chemical basis for the cell-to-cell interactions that were seen during development and differentiation. During the middle portion of the twentieth century, geneticists began to investigate the role of the gene in cell function. The function of genes in the cellular manufacturing of specific proteins led to the hypothesis that each kind of cellular protein was the product of one gene. During this time, bacteria and fruit flies (*Drosophila*) were primary organisms of study because of their relatively simple genetic makeups.

In the latter part of the twentieth century, molecular biology techniques were applied to the study of development. Using techniques for transferring and replicating specific genes, researchers have greatly clarified the central importance of genes in development. Scientists came to believe that all the major developmental and differentiation influences that control cell growth are regulated through specific genes that are turned off or on.

The combination of molecular biology techniques with embryological investigations has led to a new field of study—developmental biology. New methods have been developed and used. Radioactive tracer technology has allowed the investigator to label particular genes or gene products and trace their movements and influences on cell growth through several generations. Recombinant DNA technology has allowed the isolation and replication of significant genes that are important in development. Immunochemistry uses specific proteins (antibodies) to bind to differentiating cell products and quantify them. Cell-cell hybridization allows the introduction of specific genes into the nuclei of cells in alternate differentiation pathways.

Context

Developmental biology, with its multidisciplinary approach, is solving many of the fundamental questions of development. As scientists become better able to understand the role of genetics and cell-to-cell interactions, they gain insight into the mechanisms that control cell growth and development. Consequently, the potential to control undesirable growth or to enhance underdeveloped growth is within reach.

In vitro fertilization for mammals essentially involves combining gametes in a petri dish, thus bypassing internal fertilization. This technique has provided some formerly infertile couples with children. Other related techniques involve embryo splitting and embryo transfer: With these procedures, the animal agriculturalist can separate the cells of an early morula from a quality cow into several identical subgroups. Each subgroup can be reimplanted into the womb (uterus) of a surrogate cow. Since each subgroup of cells is undifferentiated at this stage of development, each implant will develop into a normal embryo and form an individual calf. Thus, instead of one zygote producing one morula and ultimately one individual, each high-quality morula may produce several identical calves. This creates an economic advantage for the dairy farmer who wants to raise quality cows that are genetically predisposed to produce large quantities of milk.

Genetic engineering holds the promise of repairing or preventing developmental defects. Some diseases result from an improperly functioning gene or from the lack of a particular gene product; an example is the person with diabetes, who is unable to produce insulin. Since this disease has a hereditary component, future preventive measures may involve replacing the defective gene with a properly functioning gene during an early developmental period. Thus, the inherited bad gene that will not produce insulin would be replaced with a good gene that functions normally. Future research in the molecular aspects of development may allow humans to manipulate the developmental period of their lives. In the case of agricultural animals, growth-promoting substances that enhance the rate and the extent of growth are already being used commercially and continue to be investigated experimentally. The result has been the production of larger offspring in shorter periods of time.

The problem of cell aging is also under investigation. Questions about why mature cells stop dividing and growing and what the causes of aging are constitute important areas of developmental research. While various theories have been presented, the fundamental key to cellular aging remains to be discovered. One of the most challenging areas of continuing research is the determination of how developmental patterns guide evolutionary changes. Developmental principles may provide the answer to why evolution has given rise to animal diversity. In addition, developmental biology may give scientists the information needed to predict and determine future evolutionary trends. The individual animal is a growing organism that begins as a zygote and passes through the stages of embryonic development, birth, youth, adulthood, aging, and death. Preservation of the species depends on adult individuals' producing gametes that result in the formation of a future generation of zygotes and individuals. Remarkably, each zygote contains the necessary genetic instructions to regulate the orderly processes of growth and development. Thus, animal life continues from generation to generation.

Bibliography

Alberts, Bruce, Dennis Bray, Julian Lewis, Martin Raff, Keith Roberts, and James D. Watson. *Molecular Biology of the Cell*. 2d ed. New York: Garland, 1989. This encyclopedic college text is greatly enhanced by its superior diagrams and illustrations. While all aspects of cell biology are covered in great detail, of special interest are chapter 16, "Cellular Mechanisms of Development," and chapter 17, "Differentiated Cells and the Maintenance of Tissues." Highly recommended for the serious student who wishes to understand developmental processes on a cellular level.

Balinsky, B. I. *An Introduction to Embryology*. Philadelphia: Saunders College Publishing, 1981. While somewhat dated, this very well written text covers the essentials of classical animal embryology while integrating with them the cellular and molecular mechanisms that regulate them. Of specific interest is chapter 16, "Growth," which integrates this topic into the study of developmental biology.

Baserga, Renato. *The Biology of Cell Reproduction*. Cambridge, Mass.: Harvard University Press, 1985. This illustrated book can be read by the layperson who is interested in understanding more fully the role of cell division and reproduction in growth. The basics of the cell cycle are covered in detail, as are many of the influences that regulate it. In the latter portion of the book, the author describes the genetic mechanisms involved in growth and development.

Gilbert, Scott F. *Developmental Biology*. 2d ed. Sunderland, Mass.: Sinauer Associates, 1988. This is a college-level text written for the upper-level student who has a serious interest in development. The author's approach to development uses a historical experimental analysis of the progress of investigators in the research field. About half of the text deals with specific cell or genetic mechanisms that regulate growth and development. An excellent resource for advanced and accurate information regarding the field of development.

Hartwell, Leland H., and Ted A. Weinert. "Checkpoints: Controls That Ensure the Order of Cell Cycle Events." *Science* 246 (November 3, 1989): 629-634. An excellent review article describing the biochemical controls of cell division and cell proliferation. Information is a bit technical and is written at the level of the more advanced reader who has some background in biology.

Sachs, Leo. "Growth, Differentiation, and the Reversal of Malignancy." *Scientific American* 254 (January, 1986): 40-47. This article describes in detail an example of specific growth and regulation using normal and leukemic blood cells. Research approaches to development are discussed in this context. Differentiation patterns are well illustrated for the interested reader.

Wessels, Norman K., and Janet L. Hopson. *Biology.* New York: Random House, 1988. Chapter 16, "Animal Development," gives an overview of classic embryology including the role of growth. Chapter 17, "Developmental Mechanisms and Differentiation," takes the reader through the major cellular and genetic regulatory mechanisms involved in development. This extremely well written introductory college text is easily read; it is well illustrated with color photographs and self-explanatory diagrams.

Roman J. Miller

Cross-References

Animal Cell Types, 105; The Cell Cycle and Cell Division Control, 353; Cleavage, Gastrulation, and Neurulation, 490; Determination and Differentiation, 606; Development: An Evolutionary Perspective, 615; Fertilization, 969; Gametogenesis, 1061; Mitosis and Meiosis, 1753; Morphogenesis and Pattern Formation, 1783; Organogenesis, 2008.

GYMNOSPERMS

Type of life science: Systematics (taxonomy)
Other fields of study: Botany, plant anatomy, and plant physiology

The gymnosperms are one of the two major plant groups that dominate the modern land surface. Although they are not as abundant or diverse as the flowering plants, they have a long evolutionary history during which they have shown considerable ability to survive and adapt to changing environmental conditions.

Principal terms

ARCHEGONIUM (*pl.* ARCHEGONIA): female sex organ containing the egg
ARIL: the red, juicy outer covering of the yew seed that is eaten by birds
BISPORANGIATE: containing both sexes in the same reproductive structure and not simply on the same plant
EUSPORANGIUM (*pl.* EUSPORANGIA): a massive sporangium producing large numbers of spores (frequently in the thousands) that are passively dispersed
HETEROSPOROUS: producing two types of spores; the smaller develops into the male gametophyte, the larger into the female gametophyte
HOMOSPOROUS: producing only one type of spore; the spore develops into a gametophyte having both male and female reproductive structures
MICROPYLE: a pore which passes through the integument at one end of the ovule
OVULE: an unfertilized seed
POLYSTELIC: the vascular tissue of the stem is present as several separate units
SPORE: a reproductive body

Summary of the Phenomenon

Lower land plants such as the whiskferns (members of the division Psilophyta), the horsetails (of the division Sphenophyta), and the abundant common fern (of the Pterophyta division) require the presence of water for fertilization to occur. Two kinds of higher plants—the gymnosperms and angiosperms—have developed to become the dominant type of land plant. They do not require water for fertilization and are thus free to live in a wide variety of habitats. Gymnosperms and angiosperms differ primarily in the amount of protection they provide their ovules, with gymnosperms usually providing less than angiosperms.

The first group of gymnosperms to appear was the progymnosperms. These plants evolved from the trimerophytes about 365 million years ago. *Archaeopteris*, the best-known progymnosperm, was described in 1871 by Sir William Dawson. As its name implies, Dawson believed that *Archaeopteris* was an ancient fern. Dawson reached this conclusion because the large, leafy branch systems of *Archaeopteris* resembled a fern frond. In 1960, Charles Beck proved that these branch systems were borne on a stem having typical gymnospermous wood. This discovery led to the recognition of the progymnosperms as a distinct plant group and completely altered biologists' view of gymnosperm evolution.

Archaeopteris reached an estimated height of about 18 meters. The main axis of the plant gave rise to a series of lateral branch systems, bearing primary branches in a single plane. The flattened branch system resembled a fern frond. The primary branches were covered with spirally arranged leaves. Some leaves bore eusporangia. The earliest progymnosperms were homosporous. Later progymnosperms were heterosporous. Seeds have not been found attached to any progymnosperm.

Two major lines of gymnospermous evolution arose from the progymnosperms—the cycadophyte and the coniferophyte lines. Two plant groups make up the cycadophyte line—the pteridosperms, or seed ferns, and the cycads. These plants have large, compound, frondlike leaves. The cordaites and the conifers make up the coniferophyte line. These plants have simple leaves.

The pteridosperms and the cordaites appeared first. These plants were common in the wet tropical and subtropical coal swamps that covered much of the central United States between 345 and 225 million years ago. One of the best-known pteridosperms is *Medullosa*. *Medullosa* had an upright stem between 3 to 8 meters high. The lower portion of the stem was covered with adventitious roots. A number of large compound leaves arose from the stem tip. Ovules and pollen organs occurred singly on the leaves and not in cones. Pteridosperm pollen organs consisted of a number of elongate eusporangia that were commonly fused to form a ring. The seeds of *Medullosa* were quite large. Some reached lengths of up to 11 centimeters. Unlike other pteridosperms, *Medullosa* was polystelic. Other gymnosperms have only a single conductive strand in their stems. They are monostelic.

The cordaites were derived from archaeopteroid progymnosperms. The dispersed fossil remains are often reconstructed as a plant called cordaites. Some species of *Cordaites* were trees, others were shrubs, and some were similar to modern mangroves. Cordaites was common in swamp, floodplain, and upland environments. Long strap-shaped leaves up to a meter in length occurred at its branch tips. Cordaites resembled modern mangroves in having stilt roots.

Cones developed between the upper surface of some leaves and the stem of cordaites. Four rows of "bracts" were borne on the cone axis. Above each bract was a dwarf shoot that terminated in either male or female reproductive structures. Rudolf Florin believed that the woody seed-bearing scale of modern pine could be derived from the dwarf shoot of cordaites through a series of extinct coniferalean intermediates. His interpretation has been adopted in many textbooks. It has also been shown that the conifers did not evolve directly from the cordaites, although both groups undoubtedly shared a common ancestor.

When the coal swamps dried up, the pteridosperms and the cordaites were replaced by the cycads, cycadeoids, and conifers. The cycads and cycadeoids evolved from the medullosan seed ferns. The cycads and cycadeoids were among the dominant plants during the age of the dinosaurs. The conifers are related to the cordaites.

Some cycadeoids had slender, branching trunks. Others were short and had trunks that resembled the wicker beehives made by the American pioneers. Both types had compound leaves. Cycadeoid cones contained both male and female reproductive structures. Earlier researchers thought that the cones of the beehivelike cycadeoids resembled primitive angiosperm flowers, but detailed reinvestigation of the cones showed that this was not true. The cycadeoids became extinct about 65 million years ago.

The cycads were more abundant in the past than they are now. Eleven genera and 160 species exist worldwide. They are dispersed in the modern tropics—in Africa, Cuba, Mexico, Australia, India, China, Japan, and Madagascar. *Zamia floridana* (coontie) is the only cycad native to the United States. Some cycads are small, unbranched trees (18 meters tall) that resemble palm trees. Others have subterranean stems and only their leaves and cones show above the ground. All the cycads possess stiff, leathery, compound leaves. The male and female reproductive structures are borne apically in separate cones on different plants. Cycad cones are the largest cones that have ever been produced. Cycad ovules are also very large. Some reach lengths of 6 centimeters. Their ripe seeds are often brightly colored.

The dominant group of living gymnosperms is the conifers. About 550 species are divided among fifty-one genera. Conifers are common in temperate areas such as western North America, eastern Asia, Australia, and New Zealand. The conifers are divided into seven families—the Araucariaceae (examples are the kauri pine and Norfolk Island pine), Podocarpaceae (typified by the yellow woods), Pinaceae (pine, spruce, hemlock, and fir), Cupressaceae (juniper and arborvitae), Taxaceae (the yew), Cephalotaxaceae (cultivated in the United States as plum-yew or cow's-tail pine, it also has at least one Asian genus), and Taxodiaceae (bald cypress and the redwoods). Some researchers separate the Taxaceae from the conifers on the basis of their arillate ovule. Several extinct conifer families are also known.

The most distinctive features of the gymnosperms are their ovule and seed complex. In the center of the ovule is the female gametophyte. Surrounding the female gametophyte are layers of tissue called the nucellus and the integument. The nucellus is a nutritive tissue from which the developing female gametophyte draws its nourishment. The integument surrounds the nucellus and is the outermost layer of the ovule. After fertilization, the integument develops into the seed coat.

The gymnosperms have exploited land habitats more successfully than the lower plants and pterophytes because the gymnosperms do not require water for fertilization. The male gametophyte (pollen grain) is carried to the female gametophyte (ovule) through the air. The ovule exudes a sticky fluid (the pollination drop), which traps the pollen grains. As the sticky fluid dries, the pollen grains are drawn through the micropyle into the ovule. The archegonia are located directly below the micropyle. When the sperm are released, they fertilize the egg; a fertilized ovule is called a seed.

Pine is the standard example of a gymnosperm. The pine family is the largest family of living gymnosperms. It contains about two hundred species of ten genera. The pine tree is typically conical and represents the sporophyte generation. The leaves are needle-shaped, and confined to short, lateral shoots. Unlike a few conifers such as bald cypress and dawn redwood, which shed their leaves in the fall, pine and most conifers are evergreens.

Sexual reproduction takes three years to complete in pine. In the first year, the pollen (male) and seed (female) cones are formed. The cones are borne on different parts of the same plant. The small, upright male cones are borne in clusters on the lower branches of the tree. The mature seed cones are very large and hang down from the upper branches. The next spring, the male cones shed millions of pollen grains into the air. Only a few grains reach an ovule. Once there, the male gametophyte must wait from twelve to fourteen months before the female gametophyte matures and fertilization occurs. The seeds mature in the fall of the third year and are shed.

Included within the gymnosperms are four plants whose affinities are uncertain—ginkgo or the maidenhair tree (*Ginkgo biloba*) and the gnetaleans (*Gnetum, Ephedra,* and *Welwitschia*). Ginkgo is a large tree covered with fan-shaped leaves that turn golden yellow before being shed in the fall. Although a common ornamental in the United States, ginkgo is native to southeastern China. *Gnetum* is a broad-leafed vine found in the tropical rain forest of South America, western Africa, and southeastern Asia. *Ephedra* is found worldwide in cool, arid regions. Sixteen species of *Ephedra* occur in the western United States. Most species are highly branched shrubs with scalelike leaves. *Welwitschia mirabilis* is the most unusual plant of the four. The exposed portion of the stem gives rise to two strap-shaped leaves that are never shed and never stop growing during the life of the plant. *Welwitschia* is found only in coastal desert and inland savanna regions in southwestern Africa.

Methods of Study

Botanists approach the study of the gymnosperms with a variety of analytical techniques. Nevertheless, the successful solution of most classificational and evolutionary problems rests in a solid understanding of the characteristics shown by the gymnosperms in comparison to the characteristics shown by their immediate ancestors, the trimerophytes, and their offspring, the angiosperms. This approach, known as comparative morphology, can be illustrated by two questions being asked by botanists.

The first question is how seeds originated. The basic changes involved in the origin of seeds seem fairly obvious. The plants that gave rise to the progymnosperms, the trimerophytes, were homosporous. The earliest progymnosperms were also homosporous, but by the time the progymnosperms became extinct, some members, such as *Archaeopteris*, had become heterosporous. A reduction in the number of female spores to one, combined with the development of the integument, produced the first seeds. Fossil evidence is needed to document the actual changes that occurred leading up to the seed.

In 1960, Albert Long described a rich seed flora from Scotland representing pteridosperms that flourished approximately 345 million years ago. These seeds were very complex. Therefore, older, more primitive seeds related to the progymnosperms were eagerly sought. In 1968, a seed, *Archaeosperma*, that lived approximately 350 million years ago was discovered in Pennsylvania. Although the seeds were not found attached to its branch system, botanists speculated that these seeds might possibly have been borne on *Archaeopteris*, a progymnosperm. Surprisingly, *Archaeosperma* was even more complex than the younger seeds from Scotland. *Archaeosperma* is probably the reproductive structure of a pteridosperm and not of a progymnosperm. The fossil record still has not yielded any specimens that are intermediate between heterosporous and seed-bearing plants.

A second questions concerns which group of gymnosperms gave rise to the angiosperms. Angiosperms, or flowering plants, first made their appearance about 141 million years ago. Based on comprehensive studies of living angiosperms, botanists have concluded that the first angiosperms resembled the living members of the magnolia family (*Magnoliaceae*). The first angiosperms were woody shrubs with simple leaves and bisporangiate flowers.

Several groups of gymnosperm have been suggested as possible ancestors for the angiosperms. Included are the cycadeoids, cordaites, pteridosperms, and gnetaleans. Detailed morphological comparisons have shown that none of these groups gave rise to the angiosperms. The cycadeoids had compound rather than simple leaves. Their reproductive structure was not a flower as was once thought. Similarities in cone structure indicate that the cordaites are more closely related to the conifers than to the angiosperms. The most promising groups are the pteridosperms and their younger derivatives, the caytonias and glossopterids. The pteridosperms and their derivatives have compound rather than simple leaves as well as separate male and female reproductive structures. Recent computer-generated classifications indicate that the angiosperms, cycadeoids, and gnetaleans have a reasonable number of characteristics in common. These classifications are highly speculative because of the small number of characters and species involved. The origin of the angiosperms remains a mystery.

Context

The gymnosperms are important in manufacturing. In particular, pine (*Pinus*) has a large number of commercial uses. Pine is the most common wood used in the construction of homes. Because hardwoods are becoming scarce and costly, the use of pine in manufacturing furniture is increasing. Pine is a poor quality fuel. Oak, hickory, beech, maple, elm, and cottonwood are all better heat sources than pine.

Longleaf pine (*Pinus palustris*) and loblolly pine (*Pinus taeda*) are used to make what were once called naval stores—pitch, turpentine, and rosin. These resin products can make wood and rope resistant to seawater. Pine trees are tapped to extract their resin. Rosin precipitates from the resin and is distilled to produce turpentine.

Baseball pitchers use rosin bags to help them grip the ball better, and rosin is applied to the bows of violins and other stringed instruments to increase friction and enhance the quality of tone and timbre. Turpentine is used as a solvent in oil-based paints. In addition, deodorants, shaving lotions, and some medicines contain turpentine or its chemical derivatives. Amber, the only jewel of plant origin, is made of fossilized resin.

Conifers are preferred for making paper. The water-conducting cells (tracheids) of the conifers are from two to four times longer than the equivalent cells in woody angiosperms. The longer the paper fibers, the greater the paper's strength. Douglas fir (*Pseudotsuga menziesii*) and hemlock (*Tsuga canadensis*) are used for making paper.

Cedar (*Juniperus*) is used for making rail fences. Bald cypress (*Taxodium distichum*) is used for railroad ties. Redwood (*Sequoia sempervirens*) is used in a highly wasteful manner to make patio furniture. Violins and other stringed instruments are made from red spruce (*Picea rubens*). Larch (*Larix occidentalis*) provides a gum which is used in lithography. Hemlock is a source of tannin, which is used to convert rawhide into leather.

In China and Japan, the seeds of ginkgo are eaten. Native Americans foraged for juniper berries and piñon (*Pinus edulis*) nuts. An extract of Pakistani ephedra (*Ephedra gerardiana*), ephedrine, has been used to treat asthma, toxic shock, Alzheimer's disease, and circulatory problems. "Mormon tea" (*Ephedra nevadensis*) is used as a folk remedy for colds and several sexually transmitted diseases.

The second major use of the gymnosperms is as cultivated ornamentals. Ginkgo and dawn redwood (*Metasequoia glyptostroboides*) have been rescued from extinction by ornamental planting. Sago palm (*Cycas revoluta*) is grown both indoors and outdoors in California, Louisiana, and Florida. Sago palm, a cycad, resembles the true palms in growth form but can be distinguished from them by the presence of persistent leaf bases on its stem.

The yew (*Taxus baccata* or *Taxus cuspidata*) forms a beautiful hedge that is easy to prune. Juniper is often substituted for yew, but it does not prune well and tends to become bushy. An acceptable substitute for yew in hedges is hemlock Arborvitae (*Thuja occidentalis*) can be pruned into beautifully symmetrical columns. Pine and spruce can be planted to provide shade or as windbreaks.

Bibliography

Beck, C. B. *Origin and Evolution of Gymnosperms*. New York: Columbia University Press, 1988. This text deals solely with the gymnosperms, and is intended for specialists. A number of detailed, theoretical points are covered that could not be included in more general texts.

Elias, T. S. *The Complete Trees of North America*. New York: Van Nostrand Reinhold, 1980. This reference book discusses the characteristics and uses of all native North American gymnosperms.

Florin, Rudolf. "Evolution in Cordaites and Conifers." *Acta Horti Bergiani* 15

(1951): 285-388. Florin did important work on the evolution of conifers. In this article, he explores his theory that parts of modern pine could be derived from cordaites, an idea that has been fairly widely adopted.

—————————. "Upper Carboniferous and Lower Permian Conifers." *Botanical Review* 16 (1950): 258-282. In this article, Florin relates early conifers to aspects of earlier plants, particularly the cordaites.

Gensel, P. G., and H. N. Andrews. *Plant Life in the Devonian.* New York: Praeger, 1984. This book contains a very detailed analysis of the progymnosperms (chapter 8) as well as a thoughtful discussion of the origin of seeds (chapters 9 and 10). It also makes excellent use of line drawings to clarify individual points.

Gifford, E. M., and A. S. Foster. *Morphology and Evolution of Vascular Plants.* 3d ed. New York: W. H. Freeman, 1989. This book provides one of the most comprehensive treatment of the living gymnosperms available (chapters 14 to 18). Of particular merit are its numerous labeled drawings and photographs. The pine life cycle is covered in exacting detail (chapter 17).

Gould, R. E., and T. Delevoryas. "The Biology of *Glossopteris:* Evidence from Petrified Seed-Bearing and Pollen-Bearing Organs." *Alcheringa* 1 (1977): 387-399. While the vegetation of the Northern Hemisphere was undergoing a transition from a flora containing pteridosperms and cordaites to one containing cycads, cycadeoids, and conifers, the Southern Hemisphere was dominated by the glossopterids. This article summarizes the literature on these unique plants from the Southern Hemisphere.

Long, A. G. "Some Lower Carboniferous Fructifications from Berwickshire, Together with a Theoretical Account of the Evolution of Ovules, Cupules, and Carpels." *Transactions of the Royal Society of Edinburgh* 66 (1966): 345-375. Long presents an excellent summary of the various viewpoints on how seeds originated as well as a summary of his work on seed fern ovules.

Stewart, W. N. *Paleobotany and the Evolution of Plants.* New York: Cambridge University Press, 1983. More than one-third of this book is devoted to a discussion of fossil gymnosperms (chapters 19 to 26). The line drawings are excellent, and they complement the photographs of the actual specimens nicely. Stewart treats the basic evolutionary questions paleobotanists are asking about the gymnosperms in a very readable fashion. His treatment of the origin of seeds (chapter 20) could serve as a model for the cautious and careful blending of paleobotanical knowledge with the inferred paths of evolution.

Gary E. Dolph

Cross-References

Angiosperms, 95; Electron Microscopy, 744; Leaf Anatomy, 1535; Leaf-Fall Regulation, 1542; Plant Cell Types, 2095; Plant Tissue Types, 2119; Lower Plants, 2127; Pterophyta, 2294; Sexual Reproduction in Plants, 2326; Seeds, 2452.

HABITUATION AND SENSITIZATION

Type of life science: Ethology
Other field of study: Neurobiology

Habituation is learning to ignore irrelevant stimuli that previously produced a reaction. Results of habituation studies have been used to explain, predict, and control behavior of humans and other organisms.

Principal terms

ACETYLCHOLINE: a neurotransmitter produced by a nerve cell that enables a nerve impulse to cross a synapse and reach another nerve or muscle cell

APLYSIA: a large sluglike mollusk that lives in salt water and has been used in habituation experiments; its outer covering is called the mantle

IMPULSE: a "message" traveling within a nerve cell to another nerve cell or to a muscle cell

MOTOR NEURON: a nerve cell that causes a muscle cell to respond

NEUROTRANSMITTER: a chemical substance which enables nerve impulses to cross a synapse and reach another nerve cell or muscle cell

ORIENTING REFLEX: an unspecific reflex reaction caused by a change in the quantity or quality of a stimulus; it will disappear or decrease after repeated presentations of the stimulus

SENSITIZATION: an arousal or an alerting reaction which increases the likelihood that an organism will react; also, a synonym for loss of habituation with increased intensity of response

SYNAPSE: the minute space or gap between the axon of one nerve cell and the dendron of the next; also, the gap between a nerve cell and a muscle cell

Summary of the Phenomenon

Habituation is a simple form of nonassociative learning that has been demonstrated in organisms as diverse as protozoans, insects, *Nereis* (clam worms), birds, and humans. The habituated organism learns to ignore irrelevant, repetitive stimuli which, prior to habituation, would have produced a response. With each presentation of the habituating stimulus, the responsiveness of the organism decreases toward the zero, nonresponse level. If habituation training continues after the zero-response level, the habituation period is prolonged. Habituation to a particular stimulus naturally and gradually disappears unless the training continues. If training is resumed after habituation has disappeared, habituation occurs more rapidly in the second training series than in the first. Habituation is important for survival of the individual. Many stimuli are continuously impinging upon it: Some are important, others are not. Important stimuli require an immediate response, but those which result in neither punishment nor reward may be safely ignored.

When a new stimulus is presented (when a sudden change in the environment occurs), the organism—be it bird, beast, or human—exhibits the "startle" or "orientation" response. In essence, it stops, looks, and listens. If the stimulus is repeated and is followed by neither reward nor punishment, the organism will pay less and less attention to it. When this happens, habituation has occurred, and the organism can now respond to and deal with other stimuli. On the other hand, if, during habituation learning, a painful consequence follows a previously nonconsequential stimulus, the organism has been sensitized to that stimulus and will respond to it even more strongly than it did before the learning sessions, whether they are occurring in the laboratory or in the field.

Young birds must learn to tell the difference between and respond differently to a falling leaf and a descending predator. A young predatory bird must learn to ignore reactions of its prey which pose no danger, reactions that the predator initially feared. Humans learn to ignore the normal presence of saliva in the mouth, the pressure of their underclothes, and daily background noises.

A theory known as the dual-process habituation-sensitization theory was formulated in 1966 and revised in 1973. It establishes criteria for both habituation and sensitization. Criteria for habituation (similar to those proposed by E. N. Sokolov in 1960) are that habituation will develop rapidly; the frequency of stimulation determines the degree of habituation; if stimulation stops for a period of time, habituation will disappear; the stronger the stimulus, the slower the rate of habituation; the frequency of stimulation is more important than the strength of the stimulus; rest periods between habituation series increase the degree of habituation; and the organism will generalize and therefore exhibit habituation to an entire class of similar stimuli. Stimulus generalization can be measured: If a different stimulus is used in the second habituation series, habituation occurs more rapidly; it indicates generalization.

Sensitization, a very strong response to a very painful, injurious, or harmful stimulus, is not limited to stimulus-response circuits but involves the entire organism. After sensitization, the individual may respond more strongly to the habituating stimulus than it did prior to the start of habituation training.

These are eight assumptions about sensitization in the dual-process theory. Sensitization does not occur in stimulus-response circuits but involves the entire organism. Sensitization increases during the early stages of habituation training but later decreases. The stronger the sensitizing stimulus and the longer the exposure to it the greater the sensitization; weaker stimuli may fail to produce any sensitization. Even without any external intervention, sensitization will decrease and disappear. Increasing the frequency of sensitization stimulation causes a decrease in sensitization. Sensitization will extend to similar stimuli. Dishabituation, the loss of habituation, is an example of sensitization. Sensitization may be time-related, occurring only at certain times of the day or year.

According to the dual-process theory, the response of an organism to a stimulus will be determined by the relative strengths of habituation and sensitization. For example, the intensity of a sensitizing stimulus—a book being slammed on the table, for example—may be strong enough to overcome the somnolence of a bored student, habituated to a lecturer's voice. Charles Darwin, the father of evolution, observed and described habituation, although he did not use the term. He noted that the birds of the Galápagos Islands were not disturbed by the presence of the giant tortoises, *Amblyrhynchus*; they disregarded them just as the magpies in England, which Darwin called "shy" birds, disregarded cows and horses grazing nearby. Both the giant tortoises of the Galápagos Islands and the grazing horses and cows of England were stimuli which, though present, would not produce profit or loss for the birds; therefore, they could be ignored.

Within the bodies of vertebrates is a part of the nervous system called the reticular network or reticular activating system; it has been suggested that the reticular network is largely responsible for habituation. It extends from the medulla through the midbrain to the thalamus of the forebrain. (The thalamus functions as the relay and integration center for impulses to and from the cerebrum of the forebrain.) Because it is composed of a huge number of interconnecting neurons and links all parts of the body, the reticular network functions as an evaluating, coordinating, and alarm center. It monitors incoming message impulses. Important ones are permitted to continue to the cerebral cortex, the higher brain. Messages from the cerebral cortex are coordinated and dispatched to the appropriate areas.

During sleep, many neurons of the reticular network stop functioning. Those that remain operational may inhibit response to unimportant stimuli (habituation) or cause hyperresponsiveness (sensitization). The volunteer fireman who is accustomed to have his wife tend the infant at night will sleep through the child's wailing (habituation) but will bounce out of bed when the fire siren sounds (sensitization).

Researcher E. N. Sokolov concluded that the "orientation response" (which can be equated with sensitization) and habituation are the result of the functioning of the reticular network. According to Sokolov, habituation results in the formation of models within the reticular activating system. Incoming messages that match the model are disregarded by the organism, but those that differ trigger alerting reactions throughout the body, thus justifying "alerting system" as a synonym for the reticular network. Habituation to a very strong stimulus would take a long time. Repetition of this strong stimulus would cause an even stronger defensive reflex and would require an even longer habituation period.

Neurotransmitters are chemical messengers that enable nerve impulses to be carried across the synapse, the narrow gap betwen neurons. They transmit impulses from the presynaptic axon to the postsynaptic dendrite(s). E. R. Kandell, in experiments with *Aplysia* (the sea hare, a large mollusk), demonstrated that as a habituation training series continues, smaller amounts of the neurotransmitter acetylcholine are released from the axon of the presynaptic sensory neuron. On the other hand, after sensitization, this neuron released larger amounts of acetylcholine because of the presence of serotonin, a neurotransmitter secreted by a facilitory interneuron.

When a sensitizing stimulus is very strong, it usually generates an impulse within the control center—a ganglion, a neuron, or the brain. The control center then transmits an impulse to a facilitory interneuron, causing the facilitory interneuron to secrete serotonin.

Increased levels of acetylcholine secretion by the sensory neuron result from two different stimuli: direct stimulation of the sensory neurons of the siphon or serotonin from the facilitory interneuron. Facilitory interneurons synapse with sensory neurons in the siphon. Serotonin discharged from facilitory interneurons causes the sensory neurons to produce and secrete more acetylcholine.

On the molecular level, the difference between habituation and adaption—the failure of the sensory neuron to respond—is very evident. The habituated sensory neuron has a neurotransmitter in its axon but is unable to secrete it and thereby enable the impulse to be transmitted across the synapse. The adapted sensory neuron, by contrast, has exhausted its current supply of neurotransmitter. Until new molecules of neurotransmitter are synthesized within the sensory neuron, none is available for release.

In 1988, Emilie A. Marcus, Thomas G. Nolen, Catherine H. Rankin, and Thomas J. Carew published the multiprocess theory to explain dishabituation and sensitization in the sea hare, *Aplysia*. On the basis of their experiments using habituated sea hares that were subjected to different stimuli, they concluded that dishabituation and sensitization do not always occur together; further, they decided, there are three factors to be considered: dishabituation, sensitization, and inhibition.

Methods of Study

Habituation studies have utilized a wide variety of approaches, ranging from the observation of intact organisms carrying out their normal activities in their natural surroundings to the laboratory observation of individual nerve cells. With different types of studies, very different aspects of habituation and sensitization can be investigated. Surveying the animal kingdom in 1930, G. Humphrey concluded that habituation-like behavior exists at all levels of life, from the simple one-celled protozoans to the multicelled, complex mammals.

E. N. Sokolov, a compatriot of Ivan P. Pavlov, used human subjects in the laboratory. In 1960, he reported on the results of his studies, which involved sensory integration, the makeup of the orientation reflex (which he credited Pavlov with introducing in 1910), a neuronal model and its role in the orientation reflex, and the way that this neuronal model could be used to explain the conditioned reflex. Sokolov measured changes in the diameter of blood vessels in the head and finger, changes in electrical waves within the brain, and changes in electrical conductivity of the skin. By lowering the intensity of a tone to which human subjects had been habituated, Sokolov demonstrated that habituation was not the result of fatigue, because subjects responded to the lower-intensity tone with the startle or orientation reflex just as they would when a new stimulus was introduced. Sokolov concluded that the orientation response (which is related to sensitization) and habituation are the result of the functioning of the reticular network of the brain and central nervous system. Sokolov emphasized that the orientation response was produced after only the first few exposures to a particular stimulus, and it increased the discrimination ability of internal organizers. The orientation response was an alerting command. Heat, cold, electric shock, and sound were the major stimuli that he used in these studies.

E. R. Kandell used the sea hare, *Aplysia*, in his habituation-sensitization studies. *Aplysia* is a large sluglike mollusk, with a sheetlike, shell-producing body covering, the mantle. *Aplysia* has a relatively simple nervous system and an easily visible gill-withdrawal reflex. (The gill is withdrawn into the mantle shelf.) Early habituation-sensitization experiments dealt with withdrawal or absence of gill withdrawal. Later experiments measured electrical changes that occurred within the nerve cells that controlled gill movement. These were followed by studies which demonstrated that the gap (synapse) between the receptor nerve cell (sensory neuron) and the muscle-moving nerve cell (motor neuron) was the site where habituation and dishabituation occurred and that neurohormones such as acetylcholine and serotonin played essential roles in these processes. Kandell called the synapse the "seat of learning."

Charles Sherrington used spinal animals in which the connection between the brain and the spinal nerve cord had been severed. Sherrington demonstrated that habituation-sensitization could occur within the spinal nerve cord even without the participation of the brain. Pharmaceuticals have also been used in habituation-sensitization studies. Michael Davis and Sandra File used neurotransmitters such as serotonin and norepinephrine to study modification of the startle (orientation) response.

Habituation studies conducted in the laboratory enable researchers to control variables such as genetic makeup, previous experiences, diet, and the positioning of subject and stimulus; however, they lack many of the background stimuli present in the field. In her field studies of the chimpanzees of the Gombe, Jane Goodall used the principles of habituation to decrease the distance between herself and the wild champanzees until she was able to come close enough to touch and be accepted by them. The field-experimental approach capitalizes on the best of both laboratory and field techniques. In this approach, a representative group of organisms that are in their natural state and habitat are subjected to specific, known stimuli.

Context

Habituation is necessary for survival. Many stimuli are constantly impinging upon all living things; since it is biologically impossible to respond simultaneously to all of them, those which are important must be dealt with immediately. It may be a matter of life or death. Those which are unimportant or irrelevant must be ignored.

Cell physiologists and neurobiologists have studied the chemical and electrical changes that occur between one nerve cell and another and between nerve and muscle cells. The results of those studies have been useful in understanding and controlling these interactions as well as in providing insights for therapies. Psychologists utilize the fruits of habituation studies to understand and predict, modify, and control the behavior of intact organisms. For example, knowing that bulls serving as sperm donors habituate to one cow or model and stop discharging sperm into it, the animal psychologist can advise the semen collector to use a different cow or model or simply to move it to another place—even as close as a few yards away. Safety engineers use the principles of habituation to prevent people from becoming so habituated to dangerous or life-threatening objects or situations that accidents occur.

Speakers, be they teachers or public lecturers, who understand the principles of habituation will use them to keep their audiences from becoming so habituated that they ignore the speaker's words. Changes in voice, volume, rate of speaking, and position would be new stimuli that would produce the alerting or orientation reaction and would stop or at least interfere with habituation.

Conservationists and wildlife protectionists can apply the principles of habituation to wild animals, which must live in increasingly closer contact with one another and with humans, so that both animal and human populations can survive and thrive. For example, black-backed gulls, when establishing their nesting sites, are very territorial. Males which enter the territory of another male gull are rapidly and viciously attacked. After territorial boundaries are established, however, the males in contiguous territories soon exhibit "friendly-enemy" behavior: They are tolerant of the proximity of other males that remain within their territorial boundaries. This has been observed in other birds as well as in fighting fish.

Serotonin affects the nervous systems of vertebrates. When asleep, vertebrates produce more serotonin, which causes a heightened sensory condition. On the other hand, the brain of a person who has committed suicide contains much less serotonin than those of people who die from other causes. This is another example of the potential value of information obtained from habituation studies to understanding, and possibly treating, defects in the human nervous system. Physicians have used information about the physics and chemistry of neurotransmission, including how neurotransmitters are produced within and secreted by sensory neurons and how neurohormones such as acetylcholine and serotonin function, to treat neurohormonal disorders.

Humans are subject to stress from stimuli such as sounds, lights, and the proximity of other people over long periods of time. Sanity and survival will become increasingly dependent upon the individual's ability to habituate to those stimuli that cannot be avoided and must be endured.

Bibliography

Alcock, John. *Animal Behavior: An Evolutionary Approach.* 4th ed. Sunderland, Mass.: Sinauer Associates, 1989. A comprehensive study of the behavior of many different animals. Throughout, the authors emphasize how behaviors of different organisms have developed and changed and how these modifications have enabled different groups to survive.

Alkon, Daniel L. "Learning in a Marine Snail." *Scientific American* 249 (July, 1983): 70-84. A detailed description of experiments in which the saltwater snail, *Hermissenda crassicornis*, is conditioned to associate two different stimuli. Carefully and precisely written, though it abounds with technical terms, it is readily understandable because of the many line drawings, diagrams, and physiographic recordings.

Barash, David P. *Sociobiology and Behavior*. New York: Elsevier, 1982. An easily and understandable introduction into the evolution of social behavior in different organisms, with many examples. Sociobiological hypotheses are tested and test results are evaluated.

Eckert, Roger, and David Randall. *Animal Physiology*. 2d ed. San Francisco: W. H. Freeman, 1983. Includes an excellent, lavishly illustrated discussion of how nervous systems function. Highly recommended for background reading as well as for detailed explanations of more technical terms and concepts.

Gould, James L. *Ethology: The Mechanisms and Evolution of Behavior*. New York: W. W. Norton, 1980. An excellent ethology textbook that provides an in-depth analysis of the most complex organisms. Describes the functioning of their life processes and body parts. The evolutionary approach provides insights into the behavior of organisms from the simplest to the most complex. Persuasive, well written, and readily understandable.

Gould, James L., and Peter Marler. "Learning by Instinct." *Scientific American* 256 (January, 1987): 74-85. The authors maintain that a sharp distinction cannot be made between instinct and learning. Gould and Marler argue that learning occurs in many animals, both invertebrates and vertebrates, and that human learning evolved from a few types which appear in other organisms. Specific examples are given of learning in bees, birds, and humans. This well-illustrated article is easy to read and understand.

Kandell, E. R., and J. H. Schwartz. "Molecular Biology of Learning: Modulation of Transmitter Release." *Science* 218 (October 29, 1982): 433-442. Coauthored by one of the foremost experts in habituation of *Aplysia*, this article summarizes earlier studies and describes studies which regulate release of neurotransmitters. Though it appears in a highly regarded scientific journal, most of this article can be easily understood by the high school student.

Klopfer, P. H., and J. P. Hailman. *An Introduction to Animal Behavior: Ethology's First Century*. Englewood Cliffs, N.J.: Prentice-Hall, 1967. An easily understandable historical perspective on the scientists and the studies that established ethology as a science. The major ideas are discussed in terms of their originators.

Schneider, Allen M., and Barry Tarshis. *An Introduction to Physiological Psychology*. 2d ed. New York: Random House, 1980. A well-written, lavishly illustrated textbook that has easy-to-understand sections devoted to the nervous system, learning, and habituation. Suitable for upper high school-level and more advanced students.

Walter Lener

Cross-References

THE HARDY-WEINBERG LAW OF GENETIC EQUILIBRIUM

Type of life science: Evolutionary biology
Other fields of study: Ecology and genetics

The Hardy-Weinberg law of genetic equilibrium is one of the foundations of mathematical population genetics. A description of the genetic makeup of a population under ideal conditions, it acts as a benchmark against which the effects of natural selection or other evolutionary forces can be measured.

Principal terms

ALLELE: one of several alternate forms of a gene; the DNA of a gene may exist as two or more slightly different sequences, which may result in distinct characteristics

ALLELE FREQUENCY: the relative abundance of an allele in a population; to calculate, count the number of times an allele occurs in the population (twice in each homozygote and once in each heterozygote) and divide by the number of times it could have occurred (twice the number of individuals in the population)

DIPLOID: having two chromosomes of each type; the two chromosomes (a homologous pair) contain the same set of genes

GENE: a section of the DNA of a chromosome, which contains the instructions that control some characteristic of an organism

GENE POOL: the array of alleles for a gene available in a population; it is usually described in terms of allele or genotype frequencies

GENOTYPE: the set of alleles an individual has for a particular gene; a diploid individual may be a homozygote (two like alleles) or a heterozygote (two different alleles)

GENOTYPE FREQUENCY: the relative abundance of a genotype in a population; to calculate, count the number of individuals with a given genotype in the population and divide by the total number of individuals in the population

HAPLOID: having one chromosome of each type; gametes (eggs or sperm) are usually haploid

POPULATION: the individuals of a species that live in one place and are able to interbreed

RANDOM MATING: the assumption that any two individuals in a population are equally likely to mate, independent of the genotype of either individual; this is equivalent to saying that all the gametes of all the individuals in population are placed into a large pool, from which gametes are paired at random

Summary of the Phenomenon

Genetics began with the study of inheritance in families: Gregor Mendel's laws describe how the alleles of a pair of individuals are distributed among their offspring. Population genetics is the branch of genetics that studies the behavior of genes in populations. The population is the only biological unit that can persist for a span of time greater than the life of an individual, and the population is the only biological unit that can evolve. The two main subfields of population genetics are theoretical (or mathematical) population genetics, which uses formal analysis of the properties of ideal populations, and experimental population genetics, which examines the behavior of real genes in natural or laboratory populations.

Population genetics began as an attempt to extend Mendel's laws of inheritance to populations. In 1908, Godfrey H. Hardy, an English mathematician, and Wilhelm Weinberg, a German physician, each independently derived a description of the behavior of allele and genotype frequencies in an ideal population of sexually reproducing diploid organisms. Their results, now termed the Hardy-Weinberg principle, or Hardy-Weinberg equilibrium, showed that the pattern of allele and genotype frequencies in such a population followed simple rules. They also showed that, in the absence of external pressures for change, the genetic makeup of a population will remain the same, at an equilibrium. Since evolution is change in a population over time, such a population is not evolving. Modern evolutionary theory is an outgrowth of the "New Synthesis" of R. A. Fisher, J. B. S. Haldane, and Sewell Wright, which was done in the 1930's. They examined the significance of various factors that cause evolution by examining the degree to which they cause deviations from the predictions of the Hardy-Weinberg equilibrium.

The predictions of the Hardy-Weinberg equilibrium hold if the following assumptions are true: The population is infinitely large; there is no differential movement of alleles or genotypes into or out of the population; there is no mutation (no new alleles are added to the population); there is random mating (all genotypes have an equal chance of mating with all other genotypes); and all genotypes are equally fit (have an equal chance of surviving to reproduce). Under this very restricted set of assumptions, the following two predictions are true: Allele frequencies will not change from one generation to the next, and genotype frequencies can be determined by a simple equation and will not change from one generation to the next.

The predictions of the Hardy-Weinberg equilibrium represent the working through of a simple set of algebraic equations and can be easily extended to more than two alleles of a gene. In fact, the results were so self-evident to the mathematician Hardy that he at first did not think the work was worth publishing.

If there are two alleles (A, a) for a gene present in the gene pool, let p = the frequency of the A allele and q = the frequency of the a allele. As an example, if $p = 0.4$ (40 percent) and $q = 0.6$ (60 percent), then $p + q = 1$, since the two alleles are the only ones present and the sum of the frequencies (or proportions) of all the alleles in a gene pool must equal one (or 100 percent). The Hardy-Weinberg principle states that at equilibrium the frequency of AA individuals will be p^2 (equal to 0.16 in this example), the frequency of *Aa* individuals will be 2*pq*, or 0.48, and the frequency of *aa* individuals will be q^2, or 0.36.

The basis of this equilibrium is that the individuals of one generation give rise to the next generation. Each diploid individual produces haploid gametes. An individual of genotype *AA* can make only a single type of gamete, carrying the *A* allele. Similarly, an individual of genotype *aa* can make only *a* gametes. An *Aa* individual, however, can make two types of gametes, *A* and *a*, with equal probability. Each individual makes an equal contribution of gametes, since all individuals are equally fit and there is random mating. Each *AA* individual will contribute twice as many *A* gametes as each *Aa* individual. Thus, to calculate the frequency of *A* gametes, add twice the number of *AA* individuals and the number of *Aa* individuals, then divide by twice the total number of individuals in the population (note that this is the same as the method to calculate allele frequencies). That means that the frequency of *A* gametes is equal to the frequency of *A* alleles in the gene pool of the parents.

The next generation is formed by gametes pairing at random (independent of the allele they carry). The likelihood of an egg joining with a sperm is the frequency of one multiplied by the frequency of the other. *AA* individuals are formed when an *A* sperm joins an *A* egg; the likelihood of this occurrence is $p \times p = p^2$ (that is, 0.4 × 0.4 = 0.16 in the first example). In the same fashion, the likelihood of forming an *aa* individual is $q^2 = 0.36$. The likelihood of an *A* egg joining an *a* sperm is *pq*, as is the likelihood of an *a* egg joining an *A* sperm; therefore, the total likelihood of forming an *Aa* individual is 2*pq* = 0.48. If one now calculates the allele frequencies (and hence the frequencies of the gamete types) for this generation, they are the same as before: The frequency of the *A* allele is $p = (2p^2 + 2pq)/2$ (in the example, (0.32 + 0.48) ÷ 2 = 0.4), and the frequency of the *a* allele is $q = (1 - p) = 0.6$. The population remains at equilibrium, and neither allele nor genotype frequencies change from one generation to the next.

The Hardy-Weinberg equilibrium is a mathematical model of the behavior of ideal organisms in an ideal world. The real world, however, does not approximate these conditions very well. It is important to examine each of the five assumptions made in the model to understand their consequences and how closely they approximate the real world.

The first assumption is infinitely large population size, which can never be true in the real world, as all real populations are finite. In a small population, chance effects on mating success over many generations can alter allele frequencies. This effect is called genetic drift. If the number of breeding adults is small enough, some genotypes will not get a chance to mate with one another, even if mate choice does not depend on genotype. As a result, the genotype ratios of the offspring would be different from the parents'. In this case, however, the gene pool of the next generation is determined by those genotypes, and the change in allele frequencies is perpetuated. If it goes on long enough, it is likely that some alleles will be lost from the population, since a rare allele has a greater chance of not being included. Once an allele is lost, it cannot be regained. How long this process takes is a function of population size. In general, the number of generations it would take to lose an allele by drift is about equal to the number of individuals in the population. Many natural populations are quite large (thousands of individuals), so that the effects of drift are not significant. Some populations, however, especially of endangered species, are very small: The total population of California condors is less than twenty-five, all in captivity.

The second assumption is that there is no differential migration, or movement of genotypes into or out of the population. Individuals that leave a population do not contribute to the next generation. If one genotype leaves more frequently than another, the allele frequencies will not equal those of the previous generation. If incoming individuals come from a population with different allele frequencies, they also alter the allele frequencies of the gene pool.

The third assumption concerns mutations. A mutation is a change in the deoxyribonucleic acid (DNA) sequence of a gene—that is, the creation of a new allele. This process occurs in all natural populations, but new mutations for a particular gene occur in about one of ten thousand to 100,000 individuals per generation. Therefore, mutations do not, in themselves, play much part in determining allele or genotype frequencies. Yet, mutation is the ultimate source of all alleles and provides the variability on which evolution depends.

The fourth assumption is that there is random mating among all genotypes. This condition may be true for some genes and not for others in the same population, as, for example, with human beings: The alleles that determine skin color often play a major role in mate choice. At the same time, little attention is paid to ABO blood type in the choice of a prospective mate. Another common limitation on random mating is inbreeding, the tendency to mate with a relative. Many organisms, especially those with limited ability to move, mate with nearby individuals, which are often relatives. Such individuals tend to share alleles more often than the population at large.

The final assumption is that all genotypes are equally fit. Considerable debate has focused on the question of whether two alleles or genotypes are ever equally fit. Many alleles do confer differences in fitness; it is through these variations in fitness that natural selection operates. Yet, newer techniques of molecular biology have revealed many differences in DNA sequences that appear to have no discernible effects on fitness.

Methods of Study

The field of population genetics uses the Hardy-Weinberg equations as a starting place, to investigate the genetic basis of evolutionary change. These studies have taken two major pathways: theoretical studies, using ever more sophisticated mathematical expressions of the behavior of model genes in model populations, and experimental investigations, in which the pattern of allele and genotype frequencies in real or laboratory populations is compared to the predictions of the mathematical models.

Theoretical population genetics studies have systematically explored the significance of each of the assumptions of the Hardy-Weinberg equilibrium. Mathematical models allow one to work out with precision the behavior of a simple, well-characterized system. In this way, it has been possible to estimate the effects of population size or genetic drift, various patterns of migration, differing mutation rates, inbreeding or other patterns of nonrandom mating, and many different patterns of natural selection on allele or genotype frequencies. As the models become more complex, and more closely approximate reality, the mathematics becomes more and more difficult. This field has been greatly influenced by ideas and tools originally devised for the study of theoretical physics, notably statistical mechanics. Some of the most influential workers in this field were trained as mathematicians and view the field as a branch of applied mathematics, rather than biology. As a consequence, many of the results are not easily understood by the average biologist.

Experimental population genetics tests predictions from theory and uses the results to explain patterns observed in nature. The major advances in this field have been determined, in part, by some critical advances in methodology. In order to study the behavior of genes in populations, one must be able to determine the genotype of each individual. Some human traits, such as ABO blood type, are controlled by a simple genetic system and have been the basis of studies. The pattern of bands on the giant chromosomes found in the salivary glands of flies such as *Drosophila* form easily observed markers for groups of genes. Since these animals can be easily manipulated in the laboratory, as well as collected in the field, they have been the subjects of much experimental work. Using population cages, one can artificially control the population size, amount of migration, mating system, and even the selection of genotypes, and then observe how the population responds over many generations. More recently, the techniques of allozyme or isozyme electrophoresis and various methods of examining DNA sequences directly have made it possible to determine the genotype of nearly any organism for a wide variety of different genes. Armed with these tools, scientists can address directly many of the predictions from mathematical models. In any study of the genetics of a population, one of the first questions addressed is whether the population is at Hardy-Weinberg equilibrium. The nature and degree of deviation often offer a clue to the evolutionary forces that may be acting on it.

Context
As the cornerstone of population genetics, the Hardy-Weinberg principle pervades evolutionary thinking. The advent of techniques to examine genetic variation in natural populations has been responsible for a great resurgence of interest in evolutionary questions. One can now test directly many of the central aspects of evolutionary theory. In some cases, notably the discovery of the large amount of genetic variation in most natural populations, evolutionary biologists have been forced to reassess the significance of natural selection compared with other forces for evolutionary change.

In addition to the great theoretical significance of this mathematical model and its extensions, there are several areas in which it has been of practical use. An example is the role of population genetics in counseling for human genetic diseases. In order to understand the likelihood of passing on a genetic disease, one must understand how different genotypes are distributed in the population. A second area in which a knowledge of population genetics is important is agriculture, in which a relatively small number of individuals are used for breeding. In fact, much of the early interest in the study of population genetics came from the need to understand the effects of inbreeding on agricultural organisms. A related example, and one of increasing concern, is the genetic status of endangered species. Such species have small populations and often exhibit a significant loss of the genetic variation that they need to adapt to a changing environment. Efforts to rescue such species, especially by breeding programs in zoos, are often hampered by an incomplete consideration of the population genetics of small populations. A third example of a practical application of population genetics is in the management of natural resources such as fisheries. Decisions about fishing limits depend on a knowledge of the extent of local populations. Patterns of allele frequencies are often the best indicator of population structure. Population genetics, by combining Mendel's laws with the concepts of population biology, gives an appreciation of the various forces that shape the evolution of the earth's inhabitants.

Bibliography

Audesirk, Gerald, and Teresa Audesirk. *Biology: Life on Earth*. 2d ed. New York: Macmillan, 1989. An introductory college textbook designed for nonscience majors. Chapter 14, "The Processes and Results of Evolution," includes a complete explanation of basic population genetics, presented in a nontechnical way. The chapter is well illustrated and includes a glossary and suggestions for further reading.

Avers, Charlotte J. *Process and Pattern in Evolution*. New York: Oxford University Press, 1989. A text that introduces modern evolutionary theory to students who already have a background in genetics and organic chemistry. Chapter 7, "Gene Frequencies in Populations," covers basic population genetics. The book introduces most of the techniques used in the study of evolution and includes references to original research, as well as other suggested readings.

Ayala, Francisco J., and John A. Kiger, Jr. *Modern Genetics*. 2d ed. Menlo Park, Calif.: Benjamin/Cummings, 1984. This genetics text assumes an audience that has had college-level biology and some chemistry. It provides a good description of classical as well as molecular genetics. Chapters 22 and 23, "Genetic Structure of Populations" and "Processes of Evolutionary Change," cover most of the methods and major results of population genetics. Chapters include a bibliography as well as problem sets, and there is a glossary.

Ayala, Francisco J., and James W. Valentine. *Evolving: The Theory and Processes of Organic Evolution*. Menlo Park, Calif.: Benjamin/Cummings, 1979. This textbook is designed to introduce the major concepts of evolutionary theory to readers with only a high school biology background. Chapter 4, "Processes of Evolutionary Change," introduces the major concepts in population genetics, while the rest of the book consists of numerous examples of both evolutionary mechanisms and history. Each chapter includes suggestions for further reading, and there is an extensive glossary.

Dobzhansky, Theodosius. *Genetics of the Evolutionary Process*. New York: Columbia University Press, 1970. An older book, this text is an introduction to experimental population genetics, by one of the architects of the field. There are numerous references to the original literature and many examples. The book is suitable for anyone with at least some introduction to biology and provides one of the clearest explanations of the major concepts of modern evolutionary thought.

Futuyma, Douglas J. *Evolutionary Biology*. 2d ed. Sunderland, Mass.: Sinauer Associates, 1987. An advanced text in evolution for students with previous exposure to calculus and a strong biology background, including genetics and various courses in physiology and ecology. The great strength of this book is in the presentation of areas of current research and argument in evolution, rather than a cut-and-dried array of "facts." There are numerous references to original research and a glossary.

Hartl, Daniel L. *A Primer of Population Genetics*. 2d ed. Sunderland, Mass.: Sinauer Associates, 1987. This text is intended for students with a college-level knowledge of biology but does not require prior exposure to genetics, statistics, or higher mathematics. There are examples of the significance of population genetics ideas in many areas of biology and medicine, and each chapter has problem sets with answers. There are numerous references to original research.

Spiess, Eliot B. *Genes in Populations*. New York: John Wiley & Sons, 1977. This text does not require much biological or mathematical training, although some prior exposure to statistics would be helpful. It is well provided with examples and problems, and many of the mathematical and statistical methods are dealt with in separate appendices. An extensive bibliography includes original research.

Starr, Cecie, and Ralph Taggart. *Biology: The Unity and Diversity of Life*. 5th ed. Belmont, Calif.: Wadsworth, 1989. A textbook for an introductory college biology course. Chapter 36, "Population Genetics, Natural Selection, and Speciation," covers population genetics and mechanisms of evolution. The book is well provided with examples and many striking photographs.

Richard Beckwitt

Cross-References

DNA Sequencing, 698; Gene Flow, 1097; Genetic Screening and Counseling, 1170; Isozyme Analysis by Electrophoresis, 1500; Mitosis and Meiosis, 1753; Natural Selection, 1870; Neutral Mutations and Evolutionary Clocks, 1944; Nonrandom Mating, Genetic Drift, and Mutation, 1965; The Polymerase Chain Reaction in Genetic Screening, 2141.

HEART-OUTPUT AND BLOOD-FLOW REGULATION

Type of life science: Animal physiology
Other field of study: Neurobiology

Heart output and blood flow are produced by the contraction of muscle: heart muscle and blood vessel smooth muscle. Each of these can be regulated by signals originating within or near the muscle or by neural or hormonal signals from outside. By learning how the functions of both the heart and the blood vessels are controlled and how they interact, scientists have learned and continue to learn ways to treat heart and blood vessel disease.

Principal terms

BARRORECEPTORS: receptors located in some artery walls that detect changes in blood pressure and trigger a reflex response from the brain in order to alter cardiac output and blood flow

BLOOD FLOW: the volume of blood in motion per unit time, measured in milliliters per minute

CARDIAC OUTPUT: the volume of blood per minute that leaves the heart; the flow coming out of either the left or right ventricle

HORMONE: a chemical messenger released by a gland, which is carried by the blood to its target

NEUROTRANSMITTER: a chemical messenger released by a nerve cell

OPTIMAL LENGTH: the length of a muscle cell at which stimulation can elicit the maximum possible force development

PACEMAKER CELLS: electrically excitable cells in the heart that set the heart rate

PARASYMPATHETIC NERVOUS SYSTEM: a branch of the peripheral nervous system that controls automatic body functions, releases acetylcholine, slows heart rate, and relaxes blood vessels

SYMPATHETIC NERVOUS SYSTEM: a branch of the peripheral nervous system that controls automatic body functions, releases norepinephrine, increases the rate and force of cardiac contraction, and usually constricts blood vessels

VASCULAR RESISTANCE: the resistance to blood flow presented by the blood vessels; caused by the drag of blood on the wall of the blood vessel as it flows

Summary of the Phenomenon

The heart and the blood vessels work together to generate blood pressure and to determine the amount of blood that will reach muscles, organs, or any of the body's tissues. The heart's output determines the total amount of blood flow available to the body, whereas blood vessels, by varying their resistance to blood flow, divide the heart's output and thus determine the amount of flow that will reach each tissue. Muscle contraction is the basis of both heart and blood vessel function. Heart muscle (cardiac muscle) contracts and relaxes in a coordinated manner in order to drive a volume of blood out of the heart with each beat. In blood vessels, smooth muscle encircling the wall of each vessel (vascular smooth muscle) contracts or relaxes to narrow or widen blood vessels; thus, it profoundly alters the ease with which blood can pass through.

The contraction of cardiac and vascular smooth muscle must be controlled in order to regulate heart output and blood flow. The contractile activity of both muscle types is subject to two kinds of control: intrinsic, that is, from within the heart or blood vessel itself, and extrinsic, coming to the heart or blood vessel by means of chemical signals delivered by the neurotransmitter or hormones. The heart output, or cardiac output, is the total amount of blood flow leaving each side of the heart. Blood flow is usually expressed in milliliters per minute; average resting cardiac output is about 4,900 milliliters per minute. Cardiac output is determined by two things: the volume of blood that leaves each side of the heart with each beat, or stroke volume, and the number of beats that occur in each minute, or heart rate. Left and right sides are matched so that cardiac output is the same whether it is measured at the left or right side. For example, a stroke volume of 70 milliliters per minute, multiplied by a heart rate of 70 beats per minute, would produce a cardiac output of 4,900 milliliters per minute. The strength of cardiac muscle contraction will determine how much the size of the ventricle decreases upon contraction and, thus, the stroke volume. The frequency of cardiac muscle contraction will determine the heart rate.

Intrinsic regulation of the stroke volume depends upon cardiac muscle length. Cardiac muscle usually operates at a muscle length that is less than optimal. Therefore, when cardiac muscle is stretched, it will contract with greater force on the next beat. Thus, when the amount of blood returning to the heart increases and stretches the muscle in the walls of the heart, the heart will contract with greater force, ejecting a greater volume of blood. This phenomenon, called the Frank-Starling mechanism, was first demonstrated in isolated heart muscle by Otto Frank and in functional hearts by Ernest Henry Starling in the early part of the twentieth century.

Extrinsic control of stroke volume relies on chemical messengers which can enhance cardiac muscle contraction. The most important of these include the neurotransmitter norepinephrine, which is released from the sympathetic nervous system, and the hormone epinephrine, released from the adrenal gland. Both of these chemical messengers increase the entry of calcium ion into cardiac muscle cells. When more calcium ions are present, the force of cardiac muscle contraction is enhanced.

The intrinsic heart rate is determined by specialized heart cells which generate an electrical impulse on their own. They are spontaneously or intrinsically electrically active. The fastest ones are located in the wall of the right atrium in a region known as the sinoatrial (SA) node. Slower intrinsically active cells are located elsewhere in the heart. The fastest cells usually set the pace for the rest of the heart. Thus, the intrinsically active cells of the SA node are the normal pacemaker cells of the heart. When these spontaneously active heart cells fire an electrical impulse, they stimulate their neighbors to do the same, since all heart cells are interconnected. In this way an electrical signal can be conducted sequentially through the entire heart, stimulating a coordinated contraction which ejects blood.

· Pacemaker cells can be extrinsically modulated by both neural and hormonal mechanisms. The most significant chemical messengers are acetylcholine (released from the parasympathetic nervous system), norepinephrine, and epinephrine. Acetylcholine decreases the spontaneous excitability of the pacemaker cells and thus decreases heart rate. By contrast, the same epinephrine and norepinephrine that cause the heart muscle to increase contractile force cause the pacemaker cells to increase excitability and thus increase heart rate. All these extrinsic regulators are present in the normal heart, and the heart rate is determined by the total effects of these external influences superimposed on the intrinsic rate set by the pacemaker cells. At rest, the effects of acetylcholine predominate, so the resting heart rate (70 beats per minute) is somewhat slower than the intrinsic rate set by the pacemaker cells alone (100 beats per minute).

The magnitude and pattern of blood flow through any tissue is determined by the networks of arteries, arterioles, capillaries, and veins that make up the circulation and by the resistance that they present to the movement of blood: the vascular resistance. The single most important characteristic that determines vascular resistance is blood vessel radius. Narrow blood vessels have very high resistance; wide ones have very low resistance. A tiny change in the radius of a blood vessel can result in a very large change in resistance and thus in a large change in the amount of blood flow through the vessel.

A blood vessel decreases its internal radius by contracting vascular smooth muscle cells that are oriented in a circular pattern within the blood vessel wall. Of all the blood vessels in the circulatory system, the arterioles, tiny arteries 100 microns or smaller in diameter, are most important in controlling vascular resistance and thus blood flow to the tissues. Veins, which are generally large and thin-walled, can accommodate as much as two-thirds of the body's blood volume. They function as a kind of blood reservoir. When veins contract, the size of the reservoir is reduced, and more blood returns to the heart. Thus, contraction of the vascular smooth muscle controls both blood flow reaching the tissues and blood flow returning to the heart.

The intrinsic control of vascular smooth muscle includes local metabolic control and myogenic control. Local metabolic control refers to the ability of working tissue to produce its own signal to relax vascular smooth muscle and increase blood flow to meet metabolic needs. For example, when skeletal muscle contracts and its oxygen demands increase, its vascular smooth muscle relaxes, blood vessels dilate, and blood flow increases. Many substances have been proposed as possible signals for such a response, including oxygen, potassium, adenosine, and histamine. Myogenic control refers to the tendency of some vascular smooth muscle to contract when it is stretched or to relax when stretch is relieved. Although the mechanism for this stretch-dependent contraction and relaxation is not well understood, it may be responsible for some kinds of vascular relaxation.

Norepinephrine released from the sympathetic nervous system and circulating hormones such as vasopressin and angiotensin are among the critical extrinsic chemical modulators of vascular smooth muscle contraction. They rely on specialized cell membrane receptors to recognize the chemical messenger and trigger a response. In most arteries and veins, the majority of norepinephrine receptors cause contraction. In some blood vessels, such as those in the heart and skeletal muscle, however, other norepinephrine receptors, ones which cause vascular smooth muscle relaxation, predominate. The blood vessels in the brain have neither type of norepinephrine receptors and thus rely almost exclusively on local control. This variability of blood vessel response is very common and permits vascular smooth muscle control to vary with the special needs of each tissue. Vasopressin from the pituitary gland and angiotensin, which is activated by the release of a kidney hormone called renin, both constrict vascular smooth muscle and thus increase vascular resistance. Because they are carried in the blood rather than delivered from nerves, they have a general effect throughout the circulation.

The heart and blood vessels can influence each other. When arterioles constrict, increasing vascular resistance and blood pressure, the heart must overcome that increased pressure in order to eject blood. When veins constrict, they decrease the amount of blood stored in the venous circulation and thus increase the volume of blood that returns to the heart. This stretches heart muscle to a more optimal length and thus increases stroke volume and cardiac output.

The interplay between heart and blood vessels can also be mediated through the central nervous system. Specialized stretch receptor cells, called barroreceptors, are located in some arteries (in carotid arteries and in the arch of the aorta). These barroreceptors are excited through the distension of the blood vessel wall caused by the blood pressure. When blood pressure increases, further distension increases the frequency of electrical impulses from these receptors. Those impulses, interpreted in the cardiovascular control center in the brain, trigger an alteration of neuronal signals to the heart and blood vessels that decreases contraction in both cardiac output and vascular smooth muscle resistance. The consequent decrease in cardiac output and vascular resistance helps to lower blood pressure to approach normal levels. Thus, heart and blood vessels are controlled together by this neural mechanism in order to regulate blood pressure.

Methods of Study

The basic principles used to measure cardiac output were first outlined by Adolf Fick in 1870. His ideas about adding or removing substances from the blood in order to calculate blood flow are still in use today. Furthermore, magnetic fields, sound waves, X rays, radioactive particles, and computer imaging have been applied to create new, more flexible methods which can be used to examine the regulation of cardiac output and blood flow in a broad array of clinical or experimental conditions.

Fick's original ideas about measuring cardiac output were based on the fact that all the cardiac output passes through the lungs. Thus, knowing the amount of blood flow through the lungs is the same as knowing the cardiac output. In the lungs, a certain amount of oxygen is taken up (and carbon dioxide removed). If each milliliter of blood that passes through the lungs in a minute picks up the same amount of oxygen as it passes, then knowing the total amount of oxygen taken up in a minute will permit the calculation of the total number of milliliters of blood passing through the lungs in the same minute. The same is true for the amount of carbon dioxide lost. Thus, two values must be known in order to calculate cardiac output by Fick's principle: the amount added to or removed from each milliliter of blood as it passes through the lungs and the total amount absorbed or produced. Physicians and scientists routinely employ a thin tube called a catheter, which is directed through the veins or arteries in order to take blood samples at selected regions and measure the amount of gas added to or removed from a volume of blood. Catheters can also be used to inject a dye or a chilled salt solution for a more rapid measurement of cardiac output. The changes in the dye concentration or blood temperature can then be measured in the blood "downstream." This method is called indicator-dilution. These indirect methods can also be used to measure regional blood flow.

More direct measurements of blood flow can occur by placing a device called a flow probe directly on the blood vessel in which flow is to be measured. Two types of flow probes can be used. In an electromagnetic flow probe, a magnet creates a field around the blood vessel. The blood carries positively and negatively charged particles through the magnetic field, creating an electrical signal that is proportional to the amount of blood flow. In an ultrasonic flow probe, sound waves projected across the blood vessel are reflected by red blood cells; the reflection alters the frequency of the sound waves. The speed of the red blood cells (and thus the flow) is proportional to the frequency alteration. These probes, placed on the major artery leaving the heart, measure the cardiac output. On the artery leading to the kidney, they would measure kidney blood flow. Flow probes require surgery to be put in place, however, and so are of greater value experimentally than clinically.

Since cardiac output can be calculated as the product of stroke volume times heart rate, techniques that allow a calculation stroke volume can be used to ascertain cardiac output. Any technique that can create a picture of the interior of the heart's chambers during contraction and relaxation can be used to estimate the change in volume which takes place, the stroke volume. The closer the picture comes to a three-dimensional image, the better the estimate of stroke volume will be. Many noninvasive techniques can create such pictures. X rays can record such an image of the heart's interior when a contrast dye is infused through a catheter into the heart's chambers. This is a type of angiogram. Sound waves, used the way sonar is used by a submarine, can also create an image, in a process called echocardiography. Radioactive isotopes injected into the circulation can be detected in the heart's chambers by a device called a gammacamera or nuclear scanner. More recently, the dynamic spatial reconstructor, a descendant of the CAT scan (computerized axial tomography), has used fourteen X-ray tubes, a fluorescent screen, and elaborate computer processing to create truly three-dimensional images of the heart in motion. This promises to be a diagnostic tool that will provide highly accurate measurements of stroke volume as one of its many uses.

Context

The heart and the blood vessels are able to respond flexibly to the needs of the body because of their extrinsic and intrinsic regulatory mechanisms. In response to a changing environment, the action of cardiac and vascular smooth muscle can be fine-tuned to direct blood flow to deliver nutrients, oxygen, or hormones to working tissues, to dispose of wastes, and to maintain temperature and water balance. For example, when the skin is exposed to the cold, neural signals stimulate smooth muscle in skin blood vessels to contract. This reduces the blood flow that reaches the skin and therefore reduces the amount of heat that is lost from the warm blood in the skin to the cooler environment. During exercise, heart rate and skeletal muscle blood flow increase, both as the result of neural and hormonal signals directed to cardiac muscle and as the result of intrinsic local relaxing factors directed by the skeletal muscle to its blood vessels. Furthermore, when an individual merely anticipates exercising or perceives some other stress, heart output and skeletal muscle blood flow can be increased by using neural and hormonal control signals to heart and vascular smooth muscle.

The treatment and prevention of malfunctions in the heart or blood vessels are the major medical benefits gained from an understanding of the regulation of heart output and blood flow. Medical instruments and drugs have been designed to adjust both intrinsic and extrinsic signals to the heart and vascular smooth muscle. For example, when the normal coordinated, intrinsic contraction of heart muscle is replaced by uncoordinated contraction, heart muscle cells can be restored to orderly contraction by a device called a defibrillator. The device sends a single large pulse of electric current through the heart muscle, resetting all the muscle cells to a resting state so that they are prepared to contract when the next contraction signal is generated by the normal intrinsic pacemaker cells. If the normal, intrinsic pacemaker cells in the heart are damaged or die, other slower cells located in the heart can take over. These cells, however, may do more than only set a slower pace. Occasionally they can initiate an uncoordinated contraction of the heart muscle. To prevent this, a small electronic device is sometimes implanted to substitute for the normal pacemaker cells and to stimulate a coordinated contraction at a constant heart rate.

Sometimes the stimulus for an uncoordinated contraction or even a failure to contract can come from too much neural stimulation reaching the heart muscle. Drugs can be used in such cases to reduce the work of the heart by slowing the heart rate and reducing the force of cardiac contraction. One such drug, propranolol, operates on extrinsic control mechanisms by reducing the heart's response to neural transmission. If heart muscle is overworked or undersupplied with oxygen and nutrients, it can also be damaged. Drugs such as nitroglycerine can help heart muscle by acting directly on the vascular smooth muscle of the heart's blood vessels, causing them to relax and therefore increasing the amount of oxygen that can reach the heart muscle.

Bibliography

Berne, Robert M., and Matthew N. Levy. *Cardiovascular Physiology*. 5th ed. St. Louis: C. V. Mosby, 1986. An upper-level physiology text that contains all the basics of cardiovascular physiology in a very small volume. Challenging reading with some mathematics. An excellent resource.

Campbell, Neil A. *Biology*. 2d ed. Redwood City, Calif.: Benjamin/Cummings, 1990. A general textbook with an excellent treatment of cardiovascular function and disease in chapter 38. Outstanding illustrations, very accessible. College level, but suitable for the high school student as well. Glossary.

Davis, Goode P., Jr., and Edwards Park. *The Heart: The Living Pump*. Washington, D.C.: U.S. News Books, 1981. A beautifully illustrated and photographed volume for the general public. Historical, experimental, and clinical aspects of the heart's function are presented simply and accurately. Treatment and prevention of cardiovascular disease are given ample consideration, as are experimental and clinical techniques. Excellent for high school or college students. Glossary.

Eckert, Roger, David Randall, and George Augustine. *Animal Physiology*. 3d ed. New York: W. H. Freeman, 1988. General physiology text for upper-level college students, with excellent illustrations and a comparative approach to the cardiovascular system. Supplementary reading is listed at the ends of chapters. The figures would be particularly useful for high school or college students.

Fishman, Alfred P., and Dickinson W. Richards, eds. *Circulation of Blood: Men and Ideas*. Baltimore: Waverly Press, 1982. A historical account of cardiovascular physiology. Excellent reading, from high school to college and beyond.

Patton, Harry D., et al., eds. *Textbook of Physiology: Circulation, Respiration, Body Fluids, Metabolism, and Endocrinology*. 21st ed. Vol. 2. Philadelphia: W. B. Saunders, 1989. Upper-level physiology text with considerable experimental detail and some mathematics. A very comprehensive book with considerable information about techniques in cardiovascular sciences. A reference book.

Raven, Peter H., and George B. Johnson. *Biology*. 2d ed. St. Louis: Times Mirror/ Mosby, 1989. A general textbook with an excellent treatment of cardiovascular function, including some comparative vertebrate cardiac physiology in chapter 51. Outstanding illustrations, very accessible. College level, but suitable for the high school student as well. Glossary.

Sherwood, Lauralee. *Human Physiology: From Cells to Systems*. St. Paul: West, 1989. A basic physiology textbook oriented toward an understanding of human function and disease. Superbly well written, with excellent illustrations. Chapters 9 through 11 cover cardiovascular function and include a specific treatment of how it is affected by exercise.

Tortora, Gerald J., and Nicholas P. Anagnostakos. *Principles of Anatomy and Physiology*. 5th ed. New York: Harper & Row, 1987. General physiology text for upper-level college students, with superb illustrations and an anatomical approach to the cardiovascular system. Supplementary reading is listed at the ends of chapters. The figures would be particularly useful for high school or college students. Glossary.

Laura Gray Malloy

Cross-References

Blood Circuits, 248; Blood Pressure, 270; Circulatory Systems of Vertebrates, 483; Diffusion in Circulation, 621; Fluid Balance, 1017; Muscle Anatomy in Vertebrates, 1822; Muscular Contraction: The Molecular Basis, 1849; Neural Receptors, 1904; The Sympathetic and Parasympathetic Nervous Systems, 2580.

HEMOCYANINS, HEMOGLOBINS, AND MYOGLOBINS

Type of life science: Respiration
Other field of study: Animal physiology

Hemocyanins, hemoglobins, and myoglobins are special proteins that bind oxygen and then release it to the tissues for use in metabolic processes. Much of the oxygen used by higher animals is delivered through the blood by means of these proteins.

Principal terms

BOHR SHIFT: the change in a molecule's oxygen-binding ability caused by a change in the acidity of the surrounding solution

IN VITRO: occurring in the test tube under known and controlled conditions, often simulating conditions in a living animal or tissue

IN VIVO: having to do with the living conditions as they naturally occur in the animal

OXYGEN AFFINITY: the ability to bind oxygen under a given set of conditions, measured as the partial pressure of oxygen at which the respiratory protein is 50 percent saturated with oxygen

PARTIAL PRESSURE: the physical pressure attributable to only one gas as a part of the pressure exerted by a whole mixture of gases

RESPIRATORY PIGMENT: one of the several types of proteins that contain a metal ion, copper or iron, within an organic molecule; it is able to reversibly bind oxygen

SUBUNIT: one part of a respiratory protein, often considered the smallest functional unit that can bind oxygen or that can be identified as that specific protein

Summary of the Phenomenon

Hemocyanin and hemoglobin are proteins that are found in the blood of many animals and serve to supercharge the blood with oxygen. Myoglobin is a smaller protein found in cells that have a high rate of oxygen utilization, such as muscle cells; the myoglobin serves as an oxygen reservoir. Respiratory pigments such as hemoglobin and hemocyanin dramatically increase the amount of oxygen that can be carried in the blood; hemoglobin can increase the amount by as much as seventy times. All such proteins are called respiratory proteins or respiratory pigments. The references to pigments is attributable to the color that results from the presence of the protein when it is in the oxygenated state and to the fact that it changes color when deoxygenated. Hemoglobin, in fact, does have a pigment portion of the molecule, the heme. Hemoglobin and myoglobin are red, and hemocyanin is blue when oxygenated. Hemoglobin appears bluish, and hemocyanin clear when deoxygenated. All respiratory proteins function by binding oxygen under one set of conditions and releasing the oxygen under a different set of conditions. This ability to bind oxygen reversibly is the single most important property of all the respiratory pigments.

For the respiratory pigments that circulate in the blood (all but myoglobin), the conditions for the binding of oxygen are determined by the anatomy and function of the parts of the body through which the respiratory pigments pass in the blood. Specifically, blood is exposed to conditions of high oxygen at the lung or other gas-exchange organ and to low-oxygen conditions as it passes through the tissues where oxygen is used by the cells. Respiratory pigments bind oxygen under high-oxygen conditions (oxygenated) and release oxygen under low-oxygen conditions (deoxygenated). In this way, respiratory pigments may be considered an extra reservoir of oxygen in the blood or other fluid. Many pigments, notably human hemoglobin, also combine with carbon dioxide, but this function is not universal to all pigments; it may be very small and is secondary to the oxygen transport.

The most important factor determining the binding of oxygen to the pigment is the partial pressure of oxygen in the liquid (blood) surrounding the respiratory pigment. The partial pressure is simply that part of the total pressure attributable to a single gas—in this case, oxygen. The partial pressure is a measure of the energy in the gas, whether it is in air or dissolved in a liquid. In an animal, the partial pressure of oxygen is highest in those parts of the body that are closest to the external source of oxygen. These places are in the lungs or gills, in the mouth, at the skin, and any other body surface exposed to the air or water in which the animal lives. The lungs and gills are the primary sites, and they are modified for oxygen uptake and carbon dioxide loss. At these sites, the partial pressure of oxygen is quite high in the blood (near 1.9 pounds per square inch), and oxygen binds to the respiratory pigment readily. As blood travels through the body, some of it is used by the cells, and the partial pressure of oxygen falls. When blood flows through the capillaries (the smallest blood vessels within the tissues), much of the oxygen is used, and oxygen partial pressure declines to one-third or less than at the gills or lungs. At low partial pressures, far less oxygen is bound to the respiratory pigment, oxygen being released as the partial pressure declines. This release of oxygen, in fact, constitutes the function of the respiratory pigment in the animal.

The relationship between oxygen partial pressure and the amount of oxygen bound to the pigment is an important measure of how the respiratory pigment operates. The relationship is expressed in terms of the maximum amount of oxygen that can bind to the pigment when it is fully saturated with oxygen. Thus, the amount bound under any given conditions is expressed as a percentage of the maximum amount; this is also called the percent saturation. At the lung or gill, the pigment should be 100 percent oxygen saturated; at the tissues, it is usually about 25-50 percent oxygen saturated. This relationship between oxygen saturation and the partial pressure of oxygen is not linear, and when plotted on graph paper it does not form a straight line; it is curved in the form of an "S." As oxygen partial pressure increases from zero to the maximum, saturation increases very slowly at first, then increases rapidly, and finally levels off at high partial pressures. The shape and position of this curve are measures of how the respiratory pigment binds oxygen.

When hemoglobin or hemocyanin is able to bind oxygen even at very low oxygen partial pressures, it is said to have a high affinity for oxygen. Another way to look at this property of the pigment is to consider how much oxygen pressure is required to bring the pigment to a given level of saturation. If the partial pressure of oxygen must be high, then pigment has a low affinity for oxygen. If a low oxygen partial pressure results in a high level of saturation, then the pigment has a high affinity and can operate at low oxygen partial pressures. The oxygen affinity of a respiratory pigment is usually closely related to the conditions under which the pigment functions. Animals that live in low-oxygen conditions or face conditions in which oxygen supply is limited often have respiratory pigments with high affinities.

The oxygen-binding properties of respiratory pigments are influenced by a variety of conditions in which they exist. These include the acidity of the liquid; the temperature; and the concentration of calcium, magnesium, chloride, and some of the end products of cellular metabolic processes. Thus, in some animals, the oxygen-binding properties of the hemoglobin or hemocyanin are modified by one of the chemical waste products produced by the cells. Hemoglobin is affected by some chemicals, hemocyanin by others, and the effect may vary from one species of animal to another. Most are affected by temperature, and in the same way: The oxygen affinity increases at lower temperatures.

One of the best-known examples of chemical effects is the influence of acidity on oxygen affinity. This influence is known as the Bohr effect and refers to the decrease in oxygen affinity caused by exposing the respiratory pigment to more acidic solutions. Acidic conditions change the shape of the site where oxygen binds to the pigment, making it more difficult for oxygen to bind, thus lowering the affinity. As the solution becomes less acidic and more basic, the reverse change takes place and the pigment has a higher affinity. The Bohr effect is used as an example of how conditions affect hemoglobin function, because the acidity of blood can change with the addition and loss of carbon dioxide from normal cell activities. In resting animals, the change in blood acidity is so small that the Bohr effect is not large and has little effect. In other cases, such as that of a low oxygen supply, blood acidity may decrease substantially. The oxygen affinity then increases, with the oxygen binding taking place at a lower oxygen pressure. This change is functional if the oxygen pressure is lower.

Hemoglobin, myoglobin, and hemocyanin all function in a similar way yet are three quite different molecules and represent a diverse group. The three are similar in that a metal ion (iron in myoglobin and hemoglobin, copper in hemocyanin) is bound to an organic molecule, a protein, creating a site where oxygen can bind. Hemoglobin and myoglobin are actually composed of two different parts: a heme, or pigment, and a protein, the globin. Myoglobin contains only one of these pigment-protein combinations, and hemoglobin contains four of them. The heme is where the iron is located. The binding site is created by the presence of the metal and is dependent on it. Thus, if the metal is changed chemically and remains in the pigment, the binding will be affected—usually reduced. The binding site may also be occupied by another chemical, preventing binding of oxygen, as happens when hemoglobin is exposed to carbon monoxide. Carbon monoxide is such a dangerous poison because the molecules bind to the site on hemoglobin (or hemocyanin) where the oxygen should bind. The real danger in carbon monoxide exposure is that oxygen cannot remove the carbon monoxide from the binding site; rather, the site remains occupied by the carbon monoxide, greatly reducing oxygen transport by the respiratory pigment.

The major differences among the three molecules are the metal, the specific location, the size, the properties determining the binding of oxygen, and the sensitivity of the binding to various conditions. Hemocyanin is always found dissolved in the blood of some invertebrates: the crab, lobster, crayfish, conch, squid, octopus, and even horseshoe crab (which is not a true crab at all). Hemoglobin is also found in the blood, but it may be inside the red blood cells or may be dissolved directly in the blood, as is hemocyanin. Red blood cells are found not only in humans and other vertebrates but also in some worms (polychaete annelids) and clams. Myoglobin is found in muscle and nerve cells of several different kinds of animals, but it is most obvious in the muscle cells of vertebrate animals, where it gives muscle a red appearance.

There is a major difference in size among myoglobin, hemoglobin from red blood cells, hemoglobin dissolved in blood, and hemocyanin. Myoglobin is approximately one-fourth the size of red cell hemoglobin, primarily because it is a single subunit from which hemoglobin is composed. Four subunits form a hemoglobin molecule of the kind found in red blood cells. The respiratory pigments that occur dissolved in the blood, such as hemocyanin and dissolved hemoglobin, are on the order of ten to one hundred times as large as those found in cells in the blood. These large respiratory pigments are made of many subunits, frequently twelve in the hemocyanins and sometimes as many as thirty-six.

Methods of Study

There are two basic approaches to studying respiratory pigments and their function. One approach is to measure the oxygen levels and conditions under which the pigment operates in the animals, known as in vivo research. The other is to remove the protein from the animals and measure the function under carefully controlled conditions in the laboratory (in vitro). Neither approach alone will fully explain the role of the respiratory pigment in oxygen uptake, transport, and supply. Some measurements can only be made outside the animal, and the functions are meaningless without knowledge of the conditions under which they occur in the animal.

In vivo research has included measurements of the function of the respiratory pigment in terms of oxygen levels and the conditions that determine oxygen binding. These data must be obtained under carefully described conditions and with precise knowledge of the biological source of the data. Experimental animals must be in known conditions, such as at rest, fed, and of known age, sex, and developmental stage. Data are obtained from blood samples, which must be withdrawn from specific sites and then analyzed appropriately. All the variables must be included in the analytical design. The variables measured most often are oxygen partial pressure and concentration (the amount of oxygen in a given volume of blood), the blood acidity (pH), the concentration of the respiratory pigment, and the concentrations of those chemicals (or other variables) known to influence or suspected of influencing oxygen binding. The blood oxygen levels and acidity must be measured immediately and at the same temperature as in the animals. Many of the chemicals (such as calcium and sodium) can be measured at a later time, using samples frozen or otherwise preserved. These data are then compared with values obtained from in vitro measurements. The object of the comparison is to determine if the values measured in vivo are the same as those predicted solely on the basis of the in vitro data. Much has been learned from observations in which the actual and predicted values have not matched. Such lack of agreement indicates either that other factors are involved in determining respiratory pigment function or that the interaction of known factors is not as expected. Frequently, the in vivo changes involve more than one variable, and if these do not simply add or subtract, then the result cannot be accurately predicted.

The specific techniques used in studying respiratory pigments in vitro are based on oxygen-binding ability and on the color change accompanying oxygen binding. The color change, or the optical property, has been used for many years to determine the percentage of oxygen saturation. The protein absorbs a particular kind of light when it is oxygenated, and this property is directly related to the percentage of oxygen saturation. Thus, the percentage of oxygen saturation can be determined by measuring the amount of light that is absorbed by a solution containing the pigment when a beam of light passes through it. This measurement is made over the full range of oxygen levels to assess the oxygen-binding properties. By carefully changing the conditions (such as temperature and acidity) under which the pigment is oxygenated in vitro, researchers examine the factors that affect the function of the respiratory pigment.

Other methods used are based on the fact that a solution containing hemoglobin or hemocyanin has additional oxygen. The concentration of oxygen, instead of optical property, is measured under differing conditions for a range of oxygen pressures. The same variations in temperature, chemical composition, and acidity may then be used in this type of measurement system. The result in either case is a numerical description of the change in oxygen binding for a given change in an operating condition, such as temperature.

Context

Research on hemoglobin, myoglobin, hemocyanin, and the other respiratory pigments has focused either on their role in oxygen delivery to the tissues or on evolutionary questions concerning these common and critically important molecules. Oxygen delivery to the tissues by hemoglobin or hemocyanin is important to basic respiratory physiology, including gas exchange, exercise physiology, and adaptation to low oxygen. Questions about evolutionary aspects often are based on the chemical properties of the molecule itself, the distribution in different animal species, the chemical structure of the molecule, and the sensitivity to modifying factors.

The oxygen transport function of the respiratory pigments has been studied in the live animals and in isolated solutions in the laboratory. In vivo research requires using live animals held under known and controlled conditions in order to determine the operating conditions in the animal and to discover how these conditions affect oxygen binding to the respiratory pigment and release to the tissues. Some measurements, however, can only be made on isolated samples outside the animal in order to determine how the pigments function under known conditions. It is not possible to manipulate the chemical conditions within an animal exactly, so these experiments are performed on isolated and purified pigment.

The other context in which in vitro research is conducted is an evolutionary one. Hemoglobin exists in a diverse number of forms and in totally unrelated animals. Red blood cells occur in clams, worms, fish, and mammals. Hemoglobin can be found in cells that circulate in the blood or as a much larger molecule that is not in cells but is dissolved directly in the blood. Protein biochemists as well as biologists studying respiratory pigments have sought the explanation for this apparent whimsical distribution among animal groups. Hemocyanin and myoglobin are distributed in almost as wide an array of animals as is hemoglobin.

Bibliography

Comroe, Julius H. *Physiology of Respiration*. Chicago: Year Book Medical Publishers, 1974. Chapter 14, "The Transport of Oxygen by Blood," is good basic material. The text does use scientific abbreviations and expressions, but not to excess. The explanations are understandable and clear, much more so than in most medical texts currently in use. The figures are illustrative of the principles and not merely displays of data.

Hill, Richard W., and Gordon A. Wyse. *Animal Physiology*. New York: Harper & Row, 1989, Chapter 13, "Exchanges of Oxygen and Carbon Dioxide 2: Transport in Body Fluids," gives an excellent and thorough explanation of the respiratory pigments. This textbook has a clear and complete description of the respiratory pigments and how they function in an animal. It is aimed at college students, but it does not require a science background to understand it. There are well-labeled diagrams and section headings.

Kendrew, John C. "The Three Dimensional Structure of a Protein Molecule." *Scientific American* 205 (December, 1961): 96-110. This paper is a landmark, representing a breakthrough in understanding the relationship between the structure and function of the molecule. Deals with the technical aspects of the methodology of early determinations of structure.

Perutz, Max F. "The Hemoglobin Molecule." *Scientific American* 211 (November, 1964): 64-76. Perutz describes both the structure and the function of the hemoglobin molecule in understandable terms and language. This paper is a classic and still provides many students with their first introduction to the topic. Includes a description of the technique used to determine the structure and drawings of the structure. His explanation of how the oxygen binds to the hemoglobin is the basis for the descriptions in many textbooks.

———————. "Hemoglobin Structure and Respiratory Transport." *Scientific American* 239 (December, 1978): 92-125. This second article by Perutz follows from the first and is written in the same style. He explains the specifics of oxygen binding at the molecular level for hemoglobin and myoglobin, with reference to the change in shape of the molecule at the binding site. Discusses the effects of carbon dioxide and acid on oxygen binding. Another classic paper, directed more toward function than structure.

Weber, R. E., and F. B. Jensen. "Functional Adaptations in Hemoglobins from Ectothermic Vertebrates." *Annual Review of Physiology* 50 (1988): 161-179. This review deals with the different kinds of hemoglobins and how they work in cold-blooded vertebrates. It is for those who wish more detail and want information on trends in research. Requires some knowledge of hemoglobins but also includes a section on basic structure and function of hemoglobins.

Peter L. deFur

Cross-References

Allosteric Regulation and Covalent Modification, 65; Blood Chemistry Analysis, 240; Blood Components, 262; Diffusion in Circulation, 621; Gas Exchange in Animals, 1069; Gill, Trachea, and Lung Anatomy, 1212; Isozyme Analysis by Electrophoresis, 1500; Proteins, 2272; Respiration: Adaptation to Low Oxygen, 2369.

HETEROTROPHS AND ANAEROBES AS THE EARLIEST ORGANISMS

Types of life science: Evolutionary biology and the origin of life (paleontology)
Other fields of study: Biochemistry and microbiology

The first organisms evolved in, and therefore reflected, the environmental conditions of the early earth. They were simple heterotrophs consuming readily available organic molecules produced by abiotic reactions in an anaerobic atmosphere. The heterotrophs used simple biochemical reactions, such as fermentation, to release energy from the molecules.

Principal terms

ANAEROBIC: used to describe an organism capable of living and functioning in the absence of free oxygen

ANOXIC: used to describe an environment where free oxygen is absent

FERMENTATION: an energy-producing series of biochemical reactions performed in the absence of oxygen

FOSSIL: the remains of trace of an organism preserved by natural causes in earth materials

OXIDATION: any of a broad range of reactions involving the reaction of oxygen with an element or molecule; in biochemical reactions, the use of free oxygen to release energy from organic molecules

PALEONTOLOGIST: an earth scientist who examines the fossil remains of organisms

PRECAMBRIAN: a time unit in earth history encompassing all rocks and events from the formation of the earth (about 4.8 billion years ago) to the start of the Cambrian period, 570 million years ago

Summary of the Phenomenon

Heterotrophs are organisms that cannot produce their own food. For their energy requirements, they must consume organic molecules produced by processes or organisms beyond their control. Anaerobes are organisms that do not require free oxygen gas in order to survive. In fact, free oxygen is a poison for many anaerobes.

Heterotrophs are common organisms (for example, animals) on the earth whose present existence is tied to primary producers, such as photosynthesizing plants, which create energy-storing organic molecules. Anaerobes also are common, though less apparent. Typically, they are microscopic organisms and restricted to living in a few surface environments where oxygen is absent. It may seem strange then that these organisms were perhaps the first organisms to evolve on the earth. Yet, the combination of the heterotrophic life-style and the anaerobic life requirement is consistent with what is known about the conditions of the early earth's surface environment.

Geologists seek to understand earth history by studying the record of events preserved in rocks. Paleontologists, geologists who study the remains of organisms preserved in rocks, are especially keen to understand the relationship between the environment, which is often evident in characteristics of the rock, and the life-form they are studying. A geologist can usually tell something about the environment of deposition, such as whether it was marine or fresh water, deep or shallow water, or cold or warm, by examining aspects of the rock. A paleontologist tries to reconcile aspects of the environmental conditions with the remains of organisms found in the rock.

The historical record, preserved in rocks, is good for the recent past but gets progressively worse as one looks further back into earth history. The earth is about 4.5 billion years old; the first 500 million years of that history are not preserved in any rocks. When the earliest rock record is examined, it reveals evidence for an earth surface environment that was much different from what it is today.

Rocks formed at, and exposed to, the earliest surface environment contain unusual minerals. The minerals, some of which contain iron and uranium, are stable in the absence of free oxygen but react quickly and irreversibly when exposed to free oxygen. They exist as particles in early Precambrian rocks that formed at the surface and in contact with the atmosphere. For these minerals to survive unaltered means that free oxygen was scarce or nonexistent in the early atmosphere.

What was the early atmosphere like if it did not contain free oxygen? Scientists think that the atmosphere was formed by gases released from the earth's interior by volcanic eruptions. It is possible to estimate the composition of the early atmosphere based on the composition of gases from modern volcanoes. Those gases are dominated by nitrogen, methane, carbon monoxide, carbon dioxide, hydrogen sulfide, water vapor, and traces of others. The evolution of life began at a time when the surface environment was in contact with a reducing atmosphere.

In the early 1950's, scientists began studying simulated Precambrian atmospheres in the laboratory by mixing likely gases in a flask. In one experiment, an electrical spark, to simulate lightning discharge, was introduced into the flask. In a matter of weeks, reactions in the simulated atmosphere had produced a complex mixture of organic molecules. Some of the molecules, sugars and amino acids, are, respectively, important energy sources and the building blocks for more complex molecules called proteins.

The experimenters found that by changing the composition of the starting gas mixture, within reasonable limits, they could produce a wide range of complex organic molecules. As the gas mixture was made more reducing, the range and supply of organic molecules increased. At the same time, small quantities of organic molecules, such as formaldehyde, were found in interstellar space. Amino acids, in addition to other organic molecules, have been found in certain types of meteorites.

It became apparent that, given a mixture of common starting gases and an energy source, organic molecules will be produced. These organic molecules are interesting not only because they include the precursors to life but also because they act as storehouses for some of the energy that went into making them.

Regardless of how the first organism evolved from these starting materials, it evolved in what has been called a "prebiotic soup" of energy-rich organic molecules. Heterotrophic organisms would exploit this environment by absorbing the molecules. A continuing supply of energy-rich molecules depends on the absence of free oxygen and the functioning of the abiotic synthesis.

The energy-rich molecules of the soup are converted to energy by a series of biochemical reactions. One of the simplest, and therefore perhaps one of the oldest, types of energy conversion reaction is anaerobic fermentation. During anaerobic fermentation, an energy-rich molecule, such as the simple sugar glucose, is dismantled to release energy and waste by-products. Several lines of evidence suggest that this form of energy conversion was utilized by the early heterotrophs.

One indicator that fermentation is a very ancient biochemical process is that the reaction used to release energy from the glucose molecule is very common among modern organisms. The ability to utilize the fermentation reaction is evident in the anaerobic reaction of yeast using sugar and releasing ethyl alcohol. Less obviously, an anaerobic environment is generated in the tissues of a human athlete during strenous exercise. Under these conditions, the body's biochemistry switches gears and utilizes anaerobic fermentation to produce energy. The waste by-product in this case is called lactic acid, which, when it builds up in muscle tissue, causes soreness.

Despite that fact it is not the primary energy releasing reaction for most organisms, fermentation's widespread availability suggests that it is very old and perhaps inherited from an early simpler ancestor.

The fermentation reaction is not very efficient. For example, it releases two units of energy for every glucose molecule, whereas oxidation of the same glucose molecule releases more than thirty energy units. Such an inefficient reaction for energy release could not be tolerated by an advanced organism with many energy demands (such as maintaining body heat and locomotion). Alternatively, single-celled heterotrophs surrounded by, and absorbing, energy-rich molecules such as glucose (which is unlikely to decompose in an anoxic environment) do not expend much energy in gathering their food.

Thus, two very different types of evidence, that which points to an anoxic early atmosphere and evidence for the ancient ancestry of the glucose fermentation reaction, suggest that the earliest organism was a single-celled heterotroph that absorbed energy-rich molecules from the surrounding anaerobic environment. Modern analogues for such an organism exist. Single-celled bacteria, called obligate anaerobes, exist in a few anoxic environments today. It is likely that the modern obligate anaerobes have not changed significantly (especially in their morphology, or shape, and size) from their Precambrian ancestors. Given this much information, paleontologists know that their search for early Precambrian fossils, or the petrified remains of organisms, will not be easy.

The process of fossilization, that is, the preservation of the shape of an organism in rock, is best at preserving the details of hard body parts. Hard skeletons and shells or their impressions are easier to preserve than soft body parts. In the case of early Precambrian fossils, not only are the most likely organisms (bacteria) small but they also do not contain any hard body parts.

Despite these barriers to preservation, and despite the very poorly preserved Precambrian rock record, some early Precambrian fossil remains have been found and described. The fossils are usually found preserved in rock called chert, which probably began as a gelatin-like material. Microscopic remains of organisms embedded in this gelatin were delicately preserved when the chert lost some of its water and solidified.

The oldest fossil remains identified have been found in cherts from southern Africa. The cherts, part of what is called the Fig Tree formation, are more than three billion years old. The fossils consist of the wispy, spherical remains of what may have been a type of alga and the rod-shaped remains of a possible heterotrophic bacterium.

Methods of Study

Micropaleontologists, those who identify and study the remains of microscopic organisms in rocks, will lead the search for the oldest earth organism. Even before the search begins, the paleontologist must have an understanding of the Precambrian rocks in a given location. The relative ages (that is, which are oldest, which are youngest) of the rocks should be known so the search can focus on the oldest rocks. The candidate rock should be capable of preserving the delicate remains — clearly, chert seems to be an ideal way to preserve these fossils. The general history of the rocks should be known. For example, if the rocks have been exposed to very high temperatures (but not melted) during their existence, the delicate fossils may have been obliterated.

Once a candidate rock is identified and described in general terms, the paleontologist will collect rock samples for study. The rocks are first cut into slices thin enough for light to pass through them. The paleontologist then examines the rock slice under a light microscope for evidence of fossils. If the sample warrants further study, the rock slice is prepared for examination by a scanning electron microscope. With this instrument, the smallest fossil remains are visible, and their ranges of shapes can be photographed. Ultimately, the paleontologist is looking for similarities in body shapes between fossils and more recent organisms. From morphological similarities, the paleontologist can speculate about the life function of the fossil organism. Geochemical and biochemical studies provide supporting evidence for association between fossil organisms and their biochemical functions.

Geochemists, examining Precambrian rocks for early signs of life, are looking for chemical fossils. Chemical fossils are the remains, usually somewhat altered over time, of distinctive complex molecules used by organisms in their life functions. Geochemists use chemical methods to digest the rock without altering or damaging the chemical fossils. The concentrate of molecules from the rock are examined using standard techniques for identifying organic molecules (for example, gas chromatography or mass spectrometry). The presence of chemical fossils derived from an anaerobic heterotroph provides evidence for the biochemical reaction in the absence of body remains. As in the case of body fossils, chemical fossils are influenced by the history, especially exposure to high temperatures, of the rock containing them.

Biochemists have identified a number of molecules that are common to most modern organisms. One example, ferredoxin, is a relatively small protein containing iron and sulfur atoms. It is a component of a number of biochemical reactions, including photosynthesis. Despite its almost universal presence, the molecule is slightly different in each organism. It appears to be simpler and smaller in bacteria, whereas it is more complex and larger in more complex organisms. Biochemists, using chemical techniques that have helped them to unravel other complex organic molecules (for example, deoxyribonucleic acid), have examined the size and composition of ferredoxin in a number of organisms of varying complexity. In a process that is much like tracing a family tree, it seems that the molecule's ancestry can be traced to an original use in a fermentation biochemistry.

The search for the earliest organism will rely most heavily on the work of paleontologists and geologists. Discerning the nature of the biochemical functions of that organism will call upon evidence gathered by geochemists and biochemists.

Context

Human activities are impacting the earth's surface environment to an extent rarely equaled in the past. Humankind's concerns with how it may be altering its own environment have given rise to a new science concerned with global change. It is interesting to note that the earth's earliest organisms began to alter their environment in much the same way. The earliest anaerobic heterotrophs laid the biochemical foundations for the evolution of photosynthesis, free oxygen in the atmosphere, and the rise of complex organisms. All those events had the adverse impact of limiting the range of environments available to the anaerobes.

Studying the development of the earth's surface environment through the evolution of Precambrian organisms may yield several benefits. Humankind will begin to understand the range of variability, and the limits on that range, of the environment. Studies of the biochemical evolution of fundamental organic molecules (such as ferredoxin) have yielded new insights into the workings and interrelationships of humans' varied metabolisms. Finally, the environmental restrictions imposed on anaerobes as a result of the changing atmosphere may serve as an object lesson to put limits on the damage that humanity is doing to its environment.

Bibliography

Barghoorn, E. S. "The Oldest Fossils." *Scientific American* 224 (May, 1971): 30-42. This article, by one of the first to discover Precambrian microbial fossils, is very readable. The article touches on a combination of the paleontological and biochemical evidence known at the time. There are several helpful diagrams as well as illustrations and photographs of the fossil evidence. Accessible at the high school level.

Cloud, Preston. *Oasis in Space: Earth History from the Beginning*. New York: W. W. Norton, 1988. The author provides a very readable account of geologic history, concentrating the first twelve chapters on the history of the Precambrian. There are numerous tables of data and illustrative diagrams that add to the text's explanation of the more technical concepts. There are very few references for the original technical literature, but there is a bibliography of supplemental readings for each chapter. The book is written for the college-level reader.

Dickerson, R. E. "Chemical Evolution and the Origin of Life." *Scientific American* 239 (September, 1978): 70-86. The author provides a comprehensive discussion of the evidence for nonbiological production of organic, biologically important molecules in the early history of the earth. Despite the age of the article, the arguments have not changed substantially. The article relies heavily on chemistry and biochemistry, and knowledge in those areas would help in getting the most out of the discussion. Although there is no formal bibliography, there are suggested readings for further information. Accessible at the college level.

Holland, Heinrich D. *The Chemical Evolution of the Atmosphere and Oceans*. Princeton, N.J.: Princeton University Press, 1984. A very technical book that concentrates on the chemical, and especially the geochemical, aspects of atmospheric and oceanic evolution. Chapters 4, "The Chemistry of the Earliest Atmosphere and Ocean," 7, "Oxygen in the Precambrian Atmosphere: Evidence from Terrestrial Environments," and 8, "Oxygen in the Precambrian Atmosphere: Evidence from Marine Environments," are the most applicable. Despite its formidable technical content, the text contains numerous references to recent technical literature cited in its extensive bibliography. This book is accessible by those with a minimum of a college chemistry background.

Miller, S., and H. C. Urey. "Organic Compound Synthesis on the Primitive Earth." *Science* 130 (July 31, 1959): 245-251. This early review article is most interesting for its historical perspective. The article contains some chemical equations, but it is still surprisingly accessible, which perhaps results from it being basically a discussion of unknowns and perceived directions for future research at the time. The references are extensive but, again, useful for their historical perspective, especially the reference to Miller's original experimental work published in 1953.

Schopf, J. William. "The Evolution of the Earliest Cells." *Scientific American* 239 (September, 1978): 110-134. This early summary article by Schopf provides a good introduction, without the level of detailed chemistry, to the following reference. There are discussions of the fossil remains (illustrated with numerous photographs), the evolution of metabolic pathways (fermentation to oxidation), and the other lines of evidence for an early, anoxic atmosphere. The reader with some background in chemistry, especially biochemistry, will get the most out of this article. Although there is no bibliography, there is a list of suggested readings. Accessible at the college level.

——————————, ed. *Earth's Earliest Biosphere: Its Origin and Evolution*. Princeton, N.J.: Princeton University Press, 1983. A collection of works by members of the Precambrian Paleobiology Research Group, an informal group of experts in the field. This one volume is the single best source for information on Precambrian chemical evolution, for both the biota and the environment. Chapters 4 ("Prebiotic Organic Synthesis and the Origin of Life"), 5 ("Precambrian Organic Geochemistry: Preservation of the Record"), 6 ("Biochemical Evolution of Anaerobic Energy Conversion: The Transition from Fermentation to Anoxygenic Photosynthesis"), and 9 ("Archean Microfossils: New Evidence of Ancient Microbes") are especially relevant. The text is very technical, with numerous allusions to the technical literature. There is a central section containing about twenty pages of photographs illustrating many of the classic microbial fossils. The bibliography is exhaustive and recent. It is college level, with chemistry and biochemistry background helpful.

Richard W. Arnseth

Cross-References

Anaerobic Photosynthesis, 87; Evolution: A Historical Perspective, 903; Glycolysis and Fermentation, 1219; The Definition of Life, 1564; The Origin of Life, 1572; Life's Effect on Earth, 1589; Metabolic Pathways, 1691; Prebiotic Evolution in the Laboratory, 2170.

THE HINDBRAIN AND MIDBRAIN

Type of life science: Neurobiology
Other fields of study: Animal anatomy, animal physiology, developmental biology (embryology), and evolutionary biology

The hindbrain and the midbrain are primitive parts of the vertebrate central nervous system which automatically regulate many vital body functions at a subconscious level

Principal terms

AXON: an extension of a neuron's cell membrane that conducts nerve impulses from the neuron to the point or points of axon termination

CENTRAL NERVOUS SYSTEM: that part of the nervous system consisting of the brain and spinal cord

CEREBRAL CORTEX: the outer layer of the forebrain in higher vertebrates

FOREBRAIN: the part of the brain located farthest in front and consisting of all brain structures above the midbrain

NERVE: a cordlike bundle of sensory and motor axons outside the central nervous system

NEURON: a complete nerve cell that responds to specific internal or external environmental stimuli, integrates incoming signals, and sometimes sends signals to other cells

NUCLEUS (*pl.* NUCLEI): a cluster of neuron cell bodies within the central nervous system

TRACT: a cordlike bundle of parallel axons within the central nervous system

Summary of the Phenomenon

The hindbrain and midbrain are very primitive parts of the vertebrate central nervous system (CNS). The hindbrain is essentially an extension of the spinal cord that is located between the cord and the midbrain. Together, the hindbrain and midbrain make up the brain stem, which connects the spinal cord with such higher portions of the CNS as the forebrain.

Despite their relatively small sizes and ancient evolutionary roots, the hindbrain and midbrain are more important to the basic functioning of an animal than any other comparably sized parts of the nervous system. Essentially, all functions occur automatically and do not need conscious attention. They contain various centers that regulate such physiological phenomena as breathing, sleeping-waking rhythms, levels of conscious arousal, heart activity modulation, and others. There are also many ascending and descending fiber tracts (bundles of nerve-cell extensions) that transfer neural signals through the brain stem to permit direct communication between the spinal cord and forebrain.

The midbrain (also called the mesencephalon) is smaller than the hindbrain (rhombencephalon), which is subdivided into the medulla oblongata, the pons, and the cerebellum. The medulla oblongata joins the hindbrain with the spinal cord, and the pons joins the hindbrain with the midbrain. The cerebellum, situated on the back side of the brain stem, is connected to the pons and the midbrain. Ten of the brain's twelve pairs of cranial nerves emerge from the brain stem.

Deep within the brain stem and extending throughout its core is a complex network of neurons (nerve cells) and axons (neuron fibers) called the brain-stem reticular formation. All sensory signals ascending into the forebrain also stimulate the reticular formation. The reticular formation sends axons into the spinal cord and widespread areas of the brain, with some reticular neurons having more than twenty-five thousand connections to other cells in the CNS. Reticular activation, especially in these parts of the midbrain and pons, can thus have profound effects on levels of awareness, sleep-wake cycles, emotions, sensory perceptions, and motivation. The entire system of reticular neurons and their axonal projections into the forebrain is called the reticular activating system (RAS).

Destruction of the RAS or interruption of its connections to the forebrain results in coma (deep, prolonged unconsciousness). This can occur because of infectious brain-stem diseases, brain tumors causing pressure on the upper brain stem, death of upper brain-stem neurons resulting from oxygen deprivation, interruption of the blood supply to these tissues, and other insults.

When injury severs the connections between reticular structures below the mid-pons to the higher brain-stem reticular regions, the result is a state of forebrain arousal that resembles being continuously awake. Scientists therefore conclude that the upper pontine and mesencephalic reticular formation causes brain activation, while reticular structures below the midpontine level can cause sleep by inhibiting the brain activating reticular regions.

In the anterior midbrain reticular formation there is a collection of neurons called the substantia nigra. Some neurons in this nucleus degenerate in patients suffering from Parkinson's disease. These neurons normally inhibit others in the forebrain. As the substantia nigra degenerates, there is a progressive loss of this inhibition. The result is stiff posture, slowed and spastic voluntary motions, tremors when not moving, and an expressionless face.

The medulla oblongata and pons contain vital nuclei within their reticular formation. These include centers for regulating heart rate, breathing rate, blood pressure, and the diameter of blood vessels. There are also nuclei that control the automatic activities involved in swallowing, vomiting, sneezing, coughing, and regulation of the release of saliva.

The vasomotor center is spread through the reticular formation of the hindbrain. Signals from this center cause blood vessels to constrict and the heart to increase its pumping activity. The result can increase blood pressure dramatically or help to maintain it at near normal levels during blood loss.

Also distributed through the hindbrain reticular formation are respiratory centers.

These cooperate to produce automatic, appropriate breathing adjustments by modulating the signals sent to the muscles (motor commands) used for inspiration and expiration. The rhythmic nature of breathing results from neural activity generated at these respiratory centers.

The hindbrain reticular formation also participates in relaying signals from the forebrain which regulate body temperature, digestive tract secretions, and other important bodily functions.

Immediately under the frontal surface of the medulla are clusters of neurons that are very sensitive to changes in either the blood's carbon dioxide concentration or its acidity. These chemosensitive areas (areas sensitive to chemicals) exert strong influences on the respiratory centers in the medulla and pons, and can bring about rapid, dramatic changes in breathing patterns to maintain the nearly constant blood concentrations of carbon dioxide and acid.

The cranial nerves IX (glossopharyngeal), X (vagus), XI (accessory), and XII (hypoglossal) exit from the sides of the medulla. The nuclei from which the outgoing (efferent) motor signals originate and in which the incoming (afferent) sensory signals terminate are also located within the medulla. Cranial nerve IX relays sensations from the tongue, including taste, and from the back of the oral cavity. Its nucleus helps to regulate salivation and swallowing.

Many hindbrain functions are possible because of the sensory and motor activities of the vagus nerve. The vagus has the widest distribution of any cranial nerve. It innervates parts of the head, neck, thorax, and abdomen. Important vagal fibers convey information among the hindbrain and the esophagus, respiratory tract, heart, most of the digestive tract, and many abdominal organs and glands. Some of the sensory signals concern blood levels of oxygen and carbon dioxide, and the blood pressure. The vagus can slow the heart rate drastically and, consequently, lower the blood pressure. The vagus also regulates salivation and helps to coordinate the muscle contractions for swallowing.

Cranial nerve XI controls several neck muscles important for voice production and head and shoulder movements. The sensations it transmits relate to the upper trachea and vocal cord regions. The hypoglossal nerve controls tongue movements. It is also used to control some of the muscles used for speaking and swallowing.

Cranial nerves VI (abducens), VII (facial), and VIII (vestibulocochlear) emerge at the junction of the medulla and pons. The abducens helps control eye movements. The facial nerve conducts taste sensations and also regulates salivation, tear production, and the movement of facial muscles. Its nuclei extend from the medulla into the pons.

The vestibulocochlear nerve relays to the hindbrain sensory information for hearing (the cochlear nerve) and balance and for the positioning and movement of the head (the vestibular nerve). The cochlear nerve terminates in the cochlear nuclei, while the vestibular nerve terminates in the vestibular nuclei. Both of these upper medullary nuclei send their axons further into the brain stem and higher CNS areas. Many axons from the vestibular nuclei, however, enter the spinal cord and control skeletal muscles of the torso, shoulders, and hips (especially those muscles supporting the body against gravity). The vestibular nucleus (together with the ocular nuclei) participates in reflexes which permit eye fixation on an object even though the head is moving.

The anterior half of the pons contains a number of pontine nuclei. They are the recipients of signals from the forebrain. Most axons of pontine nuclear cells immediately cross to the opposite side of the pons and then enter the cerebellum, located behind the hindbrain. This pathway is important in regulating muscular activity because it is the route by which the forebrain's cerebral cortex communicates with the cerebellum.

Finally, cranial nerve V (trigeminal) emerges from the pons. It relays to the CNS sensory signals from the face, teeth, oral cavity, tongue (excluding taste), nasal cavity (excluding smell), and surface of the eyeball. It also controls the muscles for chewing. Its nuclei extend from the midbrain down to the upper spinal cord.

Cranial nerves III (oculomotor) and IV (trochlear) emerge from the mesencephalon. The oculomotor nerve controls muscles for eye movements and for raising the upper eyelid. It is the nerve used to focus visual images by controlling the ciliary muscles which change the shape of the lens. Control of the pupil of the eye is another motor task of this nerve. The nucleus of the trochlear nerve is also in the midbrain and helps to control muscles for eye movement.

There are four lumps on the back surface of the midbrain. The upper two are the superior colliculi, which function in the reflex control and coordination of eye and head movements. The lower two lumps are the inferior colliculi, which are important centers along the auditory pathway to the forebrain. They contain cells sensitive to the position of a sound source relative to the ear.

Finally, the midbrain contains the red nucleus, which is the recipient of motor signals from the forebrain's cerebral cortex and from the cerebellum. Axons leaving the red nucleus enter the spinal cord. All skeletal muscles of the body, but especially those near the ends of the arms and legs, can be controlled to a certain degree by specific neurons in the red nucleus.

The cerebellum is the second largest brain structure. It is attached to the brain stem by three paired, large bundles of axons called the cerebellar peduncles. All information enters and leaves the cerebellum through the peduncles. The inferior cerebellar peduncles connect the cerebellum with the medulla oblongata and contain both afferent (incoming) and efferent (outgoing) axons. The middle cerebellar peduncles contain only afferent axons to the cerebellum. The superior cerebellar peduncles connect to the midbrain and contain mostly efferent axons from the cerebellum.

The general functions of the cerebellum relate to the coordination of subconscious movements by the skeletal muscles. There is a continuous flow of signals into the cerebellum from the eyes, the vestibular organs (balance and equilibrium), and from sensory receptors in the skeletal muscles, joints, and muscle tendons (information related to muscle stretch and tension, joint position, and the rates of change for all of these). The cerebellum is always being updated on the body's present posture and momentary movements; whenever any other CNS areas send motor signals to the skeletal muscles, the cerebellum also receives a "copy" of these commands. The cerebellum can thus serve as an "error detector" by comparing the intended movement with the actual state of the body. If an error is detected, the cerebellum sends signals to the other CNS motor centers to cause appropriate corrections in the activity of the skeletal muscles.

Finally, the cerebellum is very important in the prediction of the future positions of moving body parts. This function is used when running or walking or even reaching to grasp an object.

Methods of Study

Scientific knowledge of the functions associated with the hindbrain and the midbrain has been accumulated over the entire history of the study of the nervous system. Almost every branch of the sciences has contributed techniques that have been applied to brain research.

Some of the earliest approaches are still used today: comparing the behaviors and functions of normal animals or people with those of animals or people who have suffered some sort of damage to a part of the nervous system under study. Although the observation of behavioral or functional deficits in such "experimental" subjects does not provide unmistakable proof that the damaged area is responsible for the now missing normal behavior or function, this technique has often provided much useful knowledge.

Among the problems associated with this approach is that very seldom is the damage restricted to the boundaries of any given anatomical region. It is difficult to take possible damage to neighboring areas into account; moreover, some undamaged tissue still may be able to function within the supposedly damaged area. Another problem is that the damaged region may contain "fibers of passage" which have also been damaged. These are axons whose source and target areas may be far removed from the damaged region. Interruption of these connections may produce deficits totally unrelated to the true functions regulated by the area under study.

Another commonly used technique is electrical stimulation of brain regions. This usually involves the use of very fine wires which are insulated except at their tips (called microelectrodes) in order to restrict the area being exposed to the electrical stimulus. Insertion of the microelectrode until the tip is located in, or immediately next to, the area to be stimulated is facilitated by use of brain atlases, which are detailed anatomical guides for the brains of specific animals. Brain atlases allow the experimenter to determine reliably the three-dimensional spatial coordinates of any given brain structure. Using this knowledge and externally visible anatomic "landmarks," it is not difficult to position the tip of the electrode accurately into the desired area.

Applying weak electrical impulses through the stimulating electrode can stimulate the target neurons to generate their own neural signals. Careful observation for behavioral changes in response to the stimulation, or the recording of electrical activity within suspected areas of termination for the axons originating from the stimulated area, can reveal much about the functions and connections of the brain.

Depending on the phenomenon being studied, there are many other techniques used. These range from the simple recording of heart rates or breathing rates after stimulating suspected control areas to the use of very sensitive and complex chemical tests to measure the release of a hormone or other chemical substance as a result of brain stimulation. Although many brain scientists are highly trained specialists, many must work as generalists, employing a wide variety of seemingly unrelated techniques and instruments to discover how the brain functions. The study of the brain is thus one of the most interdisciplinary branches of the natural sciences, which is one reason for its popularity as well as its challenge.

Context

One of the body's primary control and integration centers is the nervous system. It can function as a receiver of the sensory information pouring into it from both the internal and external environments, it can process (or interpret) this sensory information by comparing it to expected or desired values and by combining multiple types of sensory information with each other and with previously experienced and stored information, and it can generate responses (motor commands to muscles or glands) based on the interpretation appropriate to the momentary situation.

At any moment, there is a virtual flood of sensory information being transmitted into the central nervous system: body temperature, blood pressure, light intensity, sounds, activity in the digestive organs, heart rate, the salt content of the bodily fluids, the acid content of the blood, pressure on various body surfaces, positions of the skeletal joints, the lengths of the skeletal muscles, and much more. Obviously, most of this information does not reach the level of conscious awareness. If it did, we would be so overwhelmed by it that we could not function as social beings. Much of this information, nevertheless, is necessary for existence. For example, if breathing stops, humans can live no longer than a few minutes.

How, then, does the body manage to deal with all of this vital information without distracting the consciousness? To a very great extent, this is the subconscious responsibility of the hindbrain and the midbrain parts of the vertebrate nervous system. Because of the efficient and automatic functioning of these parts of the central nervous system, our conscious existence is not burdened by such mundane body-maintenance tasks which must be continuously dealt with from the time we are born until our death.

With knowledge of the many physiological functions which are regulated by the hindbrain and midbrain structures, it is possible to understand why certain symptoms or deficits follow destruction of particular brain stem areas. The diagnosis of damage to a specific brain-stem region is made possible by combining such knowledge with the clinical symptoms observed in patients. Already, there are a number of treatments being tested for possible widespread use on those afflicted with Parkinson's disease. Without knowledge of the location and function of the damaged area (the midbrain's substantia nigra), not a single logical, responsible, and ethical treatment could even have been proposed for this debilitating disease. Future advances are inevitable in the understanding and treatment of other disorders which may have their origins in the disruption of normal brain-stem physiology. These advances will require the work of many researchers from a variety of scientific disciplines.

Bibliography

Diamond, Marian C., Arnold B. Scheibel, and Lawrence M. Elson. *The Human Brain Coloring Book*. New York: Barnes & Noble Books, 1985. Designed for anyone interested in the brain. Despite its title, this is much more than a coloring book restricted to the brain. It includes easy-to-follow treatments of the anatomy and physiology of the entire human nervous system. It is well illustrated and contains an extensive index.

Guyton, Arthur C. *Basic Neuroscience*. Philadelphia: W. B. Saunders, 1987. This college-level textbook is packed with information about the physiology and anatomy of the nervous system. The figures range in quality from very good to adequate and the references to each chapter are excellent, although a few are intended only for specialists. There is a good index but no glossary, but most terms are explained well in the text.

Hildebrand, Milton. *Analysis of Vertebrate Structure*. 3d ed. New York: John Wiley & Sons, 1988. This classic textbook is for college-level readers. Chapters 2, 5, 17, 18, and 19 present material relevant to the vertebrate nervous system. The index is complete, but the glossary is only adequate. The list of references for each chapter is good, but some are very advanced.

Nauta, Walle J. H., and Michael Feirtag. "The Organization of the Brain." *Scientific American* 241 (September, 1979): 78-105. This article is an excellent introduction to the anatomy and basic functions of the mammalian brain. The high-quality figures are very informative. One nice feature is the use of the same schematic brain diagram to illustrate the basic anatomy, the pathways for sensations from the skin, the pathways for sensations from the visual, auditory, and olfactory organs, the pathways for motor outflow, and the major looping circuits which center on the hypothalamus.

Netter, Frank H. *The CIBA Collection of Medical Illustrations.* Vol. 1, *Nervous System*. Summit, N. J.: CIBA, 1975. Sections 2 to 4 describe the anatomy and physiology of the human nervous system. Section 5 details the pathology of the brain and spinal cord. Classic, unforgettable illustrations make this an excellent companion text for college-level studies of the nervous system. There is an adequate index but no glossary of terms.

Patton, Harry D., John W. Sundsten, Wayne E. Crill, and Phillip D. Swanson. *Introduction to Basic Neurology*. Philadelphia: W. B. Saunders, 1976. Although this is an upper college-level text, the dedicated reader will be well rewarded for the effort required to read this very thorough treatment of the anatomy and physiology of the human nervous system. Adequate additional readings of both a general and an advanced, specialized nature are provided. There is a glossary and an extensive index.

Tortora, Gerard J., and Nicholas P. Anagnostakos. *Principles of Anatomy and Physiology*. 6th ed. New York: Harper & Row, 1990. This advanced high school or beginning college-level text has outstanding drawings and photographs to help present the subject matter. Chapters 12 through 17 cover the nervous system. The authors restrict their discussions to human anatomy and physiology, and they bring a large number of clinical cases into the text. The index and glossary are good; the selected readings excellent.

John V. Urbas

Cross-References

Blood Pressure, 270; Breathing Regulation, 300; Central and Peripheral Nervous System Functions, 404; Digestion Regulation, 650; The Forebrain, 1032; Heart-Output and Blood-Flow Regulation, 1269; Ingestion Regulation, 1422; Nervous Systems in Vertebrates, 1896; The Reticular Activating System, 2390; The Sympathetic and Parasympathetic Nervous Systems, 2580.

HISTOLOGICAL ANALYSIS

Types of life science: Animal anatomy and histology
Other field of study: Cell biology (cytology)

Histological analysis is a series of procedures designed to kill, preserve, and stain cellular architecture so that scientists can study thin slices of solid tissues with the light microscope. Pathologists use histological analysis to diagnose diseases; researchers rely on histological preparations to understand cells and multicellular relationships.

Principal terms

CLEARING: the use of a hydrocarbon compound such as xylene to enhance the penetration of paraffin (embedding medium) or Canada balsam (mounting medium) into tissues; tissues become "clear" because of the similar refractive index of the clearing agent

DEHYDRATION: the removal of water from tissues, usually through the use of a series of alcohols terminating in absolute alcohol (100 percent—no water present)

EMBEDDING: solidifying a tissue specimen in a mold filled with molten paraffin (or plastic compound to which a hardening agent has been added)

FIXATION: the process (usually chemical) whereby the cells making up tissues are killed and the structure of both cells and tissues is preserved as close to that of the living organism as possible

HISTOCHEMISTRY: localization and identification of specific chemicals within tissues

HYDRATION: the addition of water to tissues through a series of alcohols, usually before tissues are stained with aqueous stain reagents

INFILTRATION: causing either the embedding medium (paraffin or plastic compound) or mounting agent (Canada balsam or synthetic resin) to penetrate tissues; can be enhanced by the use of heat and/or reduced atmospheric pressure

MOUNTING: placing a drop of resinous medium on the tissue section and overlaying the preparation with a thin cover glass

PATHOLOGY: the study of the responses of different levels of an organism (plant or animal), such as the molecular, cellular, tissue, or organismal response, when exposed to injurious agents or deprivations

TISSUE: a collection of cells of similar type that are specialized to perform a common function or functions; the four basic tissues are epithelium, connective, muscle, and nerve

Summary of the Methodology

While some cells, such as blood cells, epithelial cells, and sperm cells, can be studied by smearing the cell suspension on a microscope slide, treating the smear with a stain solution, and subsequently observing the cells, many plant and animal cells are bound to one another in precise associations known as tissues. Since the late seventeenth century, when light microscopy began to be used to study living organisms, life scientists have worked toward developing a better understanding not only of cell structure, but also of the cellular architecture known as "tissues."

To enable life scientists to perform microscopic study of cells, cell types, and their arrangements as tissues, samples removed from plants or animals must be prepared according to fairly detailed procedures. Such techniques, generally known as "microtechniques," or specifically "histological techniques," result in a stained, thin (10-micrometer) slice of tissue sandwiched between a 25-by-75-millimeter glass microscope slide and a thin cover glass. The life scientist can then study the "tissue section" using light microscopy.

Specimens for histological analysis must be fresh, either surgically removed or from a recently dead organism. The first step is that of "fixation": The tissue (approximately 8 to 1,000 cubic millimeters) is placed in a liquid fixative solution that rapidly penetrates, kills, and preserves the cells making up the tissue. The chemicals in the fixative must immobilize the chemicals making up the cells of the tissue without causing significant distortion, such as shrinkage or swelling.

The process of chemical fixation can be enhanced, that is, accelerated, by the use of microwave oven treatment; however, only microwave ovens equipped with ventilation systems to exhaust toxic fumes should be used for this purpose. Many hospital pathology laboratories use a piece of equipment known as a "cryostat." A cryostat allows laboratory workers to freeze rapidly fresh tissue specimens and immediately cut tissue sections—without the use of chemical fixatives. Such a freezing process is especially useful for doing histological analysis on surgically removed human tissue specimens while the human is still in surgery: The pathologist can make a rapid microscopic examination and advise surgeons how to proceed. Generally, frozen sections are temporary and are not as useful as chemically fixed tissues for further histological analyses. Frozen sections may also be useful, however, for special stain and histochemical techniques when the life scientist wishes to demonstrate the presence or absence of certain tissue components (such as fats, enzymes, and radioisotopes).

After a period of time in the fixative (according to the size and type of tissue and choice of fixative), the tissue may be washed to remove certain fixative chemicals that could result in "artifacts" in the tissue. The tissue is then dehydrated, that is, passed through a series of increasing percentage concentrations of alcohol. Generally, ethyl alcohol concentrations of 15 percent, 30 percent, 50 percent, 70 percent, 85 percent, 95 percent, and 100 percent are used. Some life scientists, however, use isopropyl or tertiary butyl alcohol (especially good for plant tissues). The purpose of dehydration is to remove water from the tissue so that the tissue can be infiltrated with paraffin, which is not soluble in water. Because paraffin is not highly soluble in 100 percent ethyl alcohol, life scientists frequently use a "clearing agent" between the application of the 100 percent alcohol and the paraffin. Clearing agents include compounds such as xylene, toluene, chloroform, and methyl salicylate. Generally, life scientists use mixtures of a clearing agent and molten (approximately 58 degrees Celsius) paraffin before the tissue is placed in pure molten paraffin.

Once the tissue is infiltrated with paraffin (according to the size and type of tissue), the tissue is "embedded": It is placed in a container of molten paraffin, which is allowed to solidify.

The hardened paraffin block containing the tissue is attached to a pedestal that is inserted into an instrument called a microtome. The most commonly used microtome is known as a rotary microtome: A wheel is turned clockwise, causing the paraffin block to advance toward a very sharp knife, and sections are thus cut from the tissue block. The thickness of the sections can be adjusted from several micrometers to approximately 40 micrometers. Sections are attached to clean glass microslides with either an albumin or a gelatin adhesive solution. Paraffin tissue blocks or paraffin sections on microscope slides can be stored for long periods of time before further processing.

An alternative to the use of paraffin is that of specially formulated plastic compounds that are available as liquids and to which a hardening agent is added when the tissue is to be infiltrated. According to the formulation of the plastic compound, hardening is allowed to proceed until the tissue is embedded in a hardened plastic. Such plastic agents are used by life scientists who wish to routinely cut thin (2- to 5-micrometer) sections. While useful in a variety of histological analyses, sections of plastic-embedded tissues must be cut with special microtome knives and have not achieved the widespread applications of paraffin-embedded tissues.

The next step involves removing paraffin from the tissue sections, usually with a clearing agent such as xylene. The tissue sections are then hydrated (through a series of decreasing concentrations of alcohol) and stained.

There are many different staining procedures—some involving the use of four to six different dye stains. The most commonly used procedure is known as the hematoxylin-eosin procedure. In this procedure, hematoxylin is the primary stain (staining cell membranes, nuclei, and nucleoli) and eosin is a counterstain (staining cytoplasm and various tissue structures). Staining can be "progressive"—by checking the progress of the stain periodically under a microscope—or "regressive"—by overstaining and then destaining with a solution such as 3 percent acid alcohol.

In addition to routine staining procedures, life scientists use a variety of special stains and histochemical techniques. Special stains are those used for demonstrating various tissue components such as collagen, fibrin, striations of muscle cells, neurological elements, pigments, minerals, proteins, nucleic acids, lipids, carbohydrates, Golgi bodies, and mitochondria. Histochemical techniques are chemical methods used to demonstrate specific inorganic elements (such as calcium, copper, and lead) or organic compounds (such as amino acids, enzymes, and nucleic acids) at the sites where they occur in living tissue. The procedures for histochemical techniques are highly defined and frequently require the use of control as well as test tissue specimens.

After tissue sections are appropriately stained, they must be dehydrated (through a series of increasing concentrations of alcohol), cleared (for example, with xylene), and mounted. The most commonly used mounting agent has been Canada balsam, a resin that can be diluted with xylene. A drop of mounting agent is placed on the tissue section and then covered with a thin cover glass. Although the tissue sections can be studied immediately, they are usually placed on a "slide warmer," and the resin is allowed to harden before the slides are handled routinely. At no point, from the time the paraffin is dissolved from the sections until the mounting agent is placed on the sections, are the sections allowed to become air-dry; they are continuously immersed in the solutions.

Applications of the Method

Perhaps the major application of histological techniques is in the area of medicine—both human and veterinary. In their early training, physicians and veterinarians learn to recognize the characteristic microscopic structure of the various tissues making up the organs of multicellular organisms. They also develop an understanding of the arrangements and appearance of cells in normal tissues. These activities are known as histology. For example, the student of histology learns to recognize adipose (fat) tissue by the presence of fairly large cells that each contain a large, clear (in routine hematoxylin-eosin sections), fat-containing vacuole—so large that the nucleus of the cell is pushed to one side, giving the cell a "signet-ring" appearance. These cells appear similarly whether they occur in the outer capsule of the kidney, in bone marrow, or in the layer of the skin known as subcutaneous connective tissue. The presence of such fat cells (adipocytes) is characteristic of the normal histological structure of such organs.

In more advanced coursework, physicians and veterinarians learn to recognize changes in cells, tissues, and organs that are characteristic of disease processes. They learn to relate such changes to specific causes. This activity is a major component of the discipline known as pathology. For example, if, when a pathologist studies histological sections of a pancreas with associated mesentery (membranes), he finds fat cell vacuoles with solid bluish or pinkish material, occasional, minute clear slits (fatty acid crystals), and fat cell nuclei that are "pyknotic" (a shrunken, rounded, homogeneous black), he may report "pancreatic necrosis (death of cells or tissues) of fat." This observation indicates that pancreatic juice may be escaping from its normal channels and causing damage to such cells, which could be the result of a traumatic injury or the development of a tumor.

Pathologists frequently employ special stain techniques to demonstrate better the cellular structure as well as the specific components of tissues that may not be visible with routine hematoxylin-eosin stains. For example, nerve cells and nervous system tissue in general do not stain well with routine stain procedures; however, sections of nervous system tissue stained by various silver staining techniques (the Golgi and Cajal methods, for example) stain distinctly, with a highly defined blackened stain pattern. Another example, also with a staining procedure that includes a silver solution, would be that of special stains (such as the Gomori, Manuel, Snook, and Wilder methods) for reticular tissue—the tissue that makes up the framework of bone marrow, liver, lymph nodes, spleen, thymus, and other lymphoid tissues. In routine stained sections, reticulum fibers are difficult to observe; however, they are "argyrophilic," that is, "silver-loving," and when stained with one of the previously mentioned special stains, can be readily observed under the light microscope.

Special stain procedures serve another purpose in histopathology: They are used to demonstrate abnormal cellular or tissue inclusions, including disease-causing microorganisms that may be present but not visible in a hematoxylin-eosin stained tissue section. Bacteria, such as the spirochete of syphilis, may be virtually invisible in hematoxylin-eosin stained tissue sections. When such sections are stained by the Warthin-Starry technique (yet another special stain that includes silver solutions), however, the spirochetes are characteristic black-staining, spiral bacteria against a brownish-yellow overall tissue stain. There also are special stains for tubercle bacilli (Kinyon's Carbol Fuchsin), rickettsias (Pinkerton's method), fungi such as *Cryptococcus neoformans* and *Histoplasma capsulatum* (Grocott's methenamine silver method), and protozoans (Gridley's method for *Entamoeba histolytica*).

In the hospital histopathology laboratory, tissue specimens from biopsies, surgeries, and autopsies are routinely processed, and sections are stained using procedures such as those previously mentioned. Pathologists routinely examine such histological preparations and, in many cases, use the information they derive from tissue sections to make a diagnosis that will perhaps determine the nature or course of a patient's treatment (or, in the case of autopsy material, determine or confirm the cause of death).

Another major application of histological analysis is in the area of research in the life sciences. In developmental biology research projects, investigators frequently study "serial sections" of whole embryonic stages or of specific organs. Serial sections are histological preparations in which the technician uses a microtome to cut ribbons of sections from the paraffin tissue block. Such ribbons are kept in sequence, and thus the investigator can determine the presence or absence of certain structures, the orientation of structures relative to other structures, and any changes in the developmental histology of a structure. For example, it is through the study of serial sections that life scientists have developed a better understanding of an organ such as the pituitary gland. Although seemingly a single structure in the adult, the pituitary gland consists of two lobes, derived from very different sources. Through study of serial sections of early embryonic stages, life scientists observed that the roof of the mouth contributes to the formation of the anterior pituitary gland (adenohypophysis), while the floor of the developing brain (diencephalon) produces the posterior pituitary (neurohypophysis). Thus, the two lobes differ in their develop-

mental histology and, as life scientists have subsequently learned, in their physiological activities.

Another way researchers have found histological sections useful is in the processes of radioisotopic and immunocytochemical localization techniques. In the
former, radioisotopes can be administered to the organism and the tissue removed,
processed, and treated with a photographic emulsion. After a period of time, the
emulsion is developed by conventional photographic techniques and sites of radioisotope uptake can be demonstrated. Such a technique has been useful in developing understanding of where in cells substances such as genetic material and proteins
are synthesized and deposited.

Immunocytochemical techniques are used by researchers in many areas of the life
sciences (for example, cell biology, immunology, parasitology, invertebrate zoology). Generally, immunocytochemical techniques involve preparing or obtaining
"antibodies." Antibodies are specific protein molecules produced by vertebrate
lymphocytes in response to stimulation by specific chemicals known as antigens
(such as tubulin, a protein component of microtubules). The antibodies (for example, antitubulin antibodies) are treated ("labeled") with a fluorescent dye or a substance that can be made visible for light microscopy (such as the enzyme alkaline
phosphatase). When the labeled antibodies are reacted with the cells in the tissue
section, they will attach to the antigen if it is present. For example, the antitubulin
antibodies will attach to tubulin, a process that occurs in the microtubules of the mitotic spindle of a cell undergoing mitotic cell division. This reaction is highly specific and allows researchers to pinpoint the location of chemicals within cells and
tissues.

The applications of histological analysis have provided life scientists with a way
of obtaining information not only about cells and tissues but also about the organs
composed of those cells and tissues. This information is not only critical in the
practice of human and veterinary medicine but also provides many insights and answers in the life scientist's attempts to understand better the nature of life.

Context

The development of the compound light microscope is considered by many life
scientists to be one of the most important events in the history of the life sciences.
If that is true, the development of techniques for histological analysis is certainly a
significant factor in that claim. Without such techniques, life scientists would be
limited to looking at single-celled and simple multicellular organisms, such as
bacteria, protozoans, algae, and fungi, and cells that can be smeared on microscope
slides, such as blood cells.

The techniques of histological analysis have given life scientists the means for
looking at cells of multicellular organisms in their "natural habitats." Through the
use of histological techniques, life scientists have been able to understand the
effects of chemicals and microorganisms on the cells of different tissues and organs.
This ability has made the diagnosis of many human diseases fairly routine for pa-

thologists. Perhaps even more important, the use of histological analysis has given life scientists insights into the complex relationships of multicellularity.

Bibliography

Carleton, H. M., and R. A. B. Drury. *Histological Technique*. 3d ed. London: Oxford University Press, 1957. This text is a very useful reference in that it presents general techniques but then devotes approximately two thirds of the volume to descriptions of techniques for special organs, tissues, and cell components. The annotated text is more than a reprinting of published techniques.

Conn, H. J., M. A. Darrow, and V. M. Emmel. *Staining Procedures*. 2d ed. Baltimore: William & Wilkins, 1960. An excellent, well-documented handy reference, this work presents staining procedures—for sectioned animal and plant tissues—in a concise outline format.

Davenport, H. A. *Histological and Histochemical Techniques*. Philadelphia: W. B. Saunders, 1960. Although a general reference for histological techniques, this work provides explanations for routine histological techniques as well as more advanced techniques, including those of histochemistry.

Galigher, A. E., and E. N. Kozloff. *Essentials of Practical Microtechniques*. Philadelphia: Lea & Febiger, 1964. An excellent beginner's textbook, this work is an interesting and very readable presentation of histological techniques—from wholemounts and smears through freezing techniques and cytological methods.

Gray, Peter. *Handbook of Basic Microtechnique*. 3d ed. New York: McGraw-Hill, 1964. A very good general textbook, this work also presents the theory and practice of light microscopy, photomicrography, and eighteen detailed examples of microtechnique projects.

——————. *The Microtomist's Formulary and Guide*. New York: Blakiston, 1954. A historically indispensable reference. It is an extensive compilation of virtually all published techniques for microscopic preparations. The extensive number of citations and excellent index are unparalleled in microtechnique literature.

Guyer, M. F. *Animal Micrology*. 5th ed. Chicago: University of Chicago Press, 1953. Intended solely as a reference for animal specimens, this work frequently describes techniques for preparing unique specimens, for example, on page 108, "the radula or lingual ribbon of the snail or slug."

Humason, G. L. *Animal Tissue Techniques*. 4th ed. San Francisco: W. H. Freeman, 1979. Perhaps the most widely used textbook on microtechnique, this work has been significantly improved and updated with each edition. The author is firm about the distinction between histochemical and special stain procedures.

Lee, Bolles. *Microtomist's Vade-Mecum*. 9th ed. Edited by J. B. Gatenby and E. V. Cowdry. Philadelphia: P. Blakiston's Son, 1928. Although dated, this reference is an excellent synthesis of the techniques and formulations so successfully developed and used by nineteenth and early twentieth century microscopists. It is still a useful reference for many classical microtechnique procedures.

Thompson, S. W. *Selected Histochemical and Histopathological Methods*. Springfield, Ill.: Charles C Thomas, 1966. This extensive work is an outstanding reference in microtechnique, providing not only descriptions of techniques but also explanations of the theoretical basis (chemical and biophysical) for the results of important techniques (such as the Gram stain, pages 1004-1021).

David F. Oetinger

Cross-References
Animal Cell Types, 105; Blood Chemistry Analysis, 240; Gametogenesis, 1061; Histology, 1307; Mitosis and Meiosis, 1753; Muscle Anatomy in Vertebrates, 1822; Neurons and Glia, 1919; Plant Cell Types, 2095; Plant Tissue Types, 2119.

HISTOLOGY

Type of life science: Histology
Other fields of study: Animal anatomy, cell biology (cytology), evolutionary biology, and zoology

The primary concern of histology is the description of the microscopic anatomy, organization, and function of animal tissues and organs.

Principal terms

AXON: a single fiber that carries impulses away from the nerve cell body

DENDRITE: one of several fibers that carry impulses toward the nerve cell body

DEOXYRIBONUCLEIC ACID (DNA): the genetic material of cells; it has the molecular form of a double helix (twisted) and is linked together by purine and pyrimidine base pairs

GENE: the biological unit of heredity, which is composed of DNA and is located on a chromosome within the nucleus of a cell

GENOTYPE: the total set of chromosomal genes present in the cells of an organism

MYELIN: a white lipid surrounding the axon of a motor neuron and the dendrite and axon of a sensory neuron; it is the white matter of the brain and spinal cord

NEMATODE: a roundworm that exhibits a complete digestive tract and a false body cavity (a pseudocoel); nematodes have both free-living and parasitic representatives

ORGANELLE: a small organlike structure within a single cell that performs functions that are similar to those of organs in multicellular animals

PROTOPLASM: organized living substance; the cytoplasm and nucleoplasm of a cell

SPECIES: a taxonomic subdivision of a genus, containing populations of similar organisms that interbreed but usually do not breed with other species

Summary of the Phenomenon

Histology is defined as the study of the microscopic anatomy of tissues. A tissue is a group of similar cells that are specialized for performing a common function. A complete understanding of tissue and organ histology depends upon the knowledge of how they have developed—not only during the development of a particular animal but during the evolution of the whole species.

Protoplasm is the life substance of cells that all animals have in common. It is difficult to define protoplasm exactly, but it is known that the substance is a mixture of many chemicals that generally are similar in all animal species, to the degree that protoplasm may be discussed in general terms. Yet, this life substance does vary in subtle ways from species to species, and histologically it varies from one cell type to another within the same organism.

Each somatic cell of an individual animal will have the same chromosomes and the same genotypic makeup as every other cell. Therefore, a skeletal muscle cell will have exactly the same chromosomes and exactly the same genes as a motor neuron. Yet, both these cell types are otherwise greatly different from each other. The skeletal muscle cell has an elongated, cylindrical shape, contains several nuclei per cell, and has contractile myofibrils within its sarcoplasm (protoplasm of muscle cells). On the other hand, motor neurons have only one nucleus, many dendrites, and a single axon for the conduction of nerve impulses, and they are not directly concerned with contraction in any way. Other cells of the animal body also vary considerably from other cells within the same animal from the standpoint of both structure and function.

Lower forms of animal life, such as the animal-like protozoan (kingdom Protista) and the sponge, do not exhibit a tissue level of organization. The primitive coelenterates (Cnidaria), such as the hydra and the jellyfish, only have two tissue layers, an outer ectoderm and an inner endoderm. A true level of tissue organization appears in the flukes, tapeworms, and turbellarians constituting the phylum Platyhelminthes (flatworms), in which three germ layers are present: the ectoderm, the mesoderm, and the endoderm. This level of tissue organization persists in all the higher animal phyla.

Cells making up the three germ layers of the embryos of the higher forms of animal life play a role in the eventual development of specific adult tissues and organs. The ectoderm becomes the epidermis, or skin; the nervous system; hair; nails; scales; horns; feathers; and the enamel of the teeth. The endoderm becomes the lining of the alimentary canal, respiratory passages, and the lungs; secretory parts of the pancreas, liver, thyroid, parathyroid, thymus, and urinary bladder; and the lining of the urethra. Finally, the mesoderm forms the skeleton and muscles; excretory and reproductive systems; connective tissues; blood and blood vessels; lining of the coelomic cavity; and the mesenteries.

All cells of multicellular animals participate in the formation of tissues. Occasionally, the cells of a tissue may be of several types, and some tissues have a considerable amount of intercellular (between cells) materials. The different kinds of tissues have originated from the basic properties of cells. These basic properties along with the tissues that have originated from these properties are absorption and secretion (epithelial tissue), support and adhesion (connective tissue), irritability and conductivity (nervous tissue), contractility (muscle tissue), and fluidity and transportation (vascular tissue). Most of these five basic tissues are, in turn, divided into several subtypes that are specialized for several different functions.

Epithelial tissues cover the body surface (epidermis, hair, scales), line cavities, and form glands and tubes. The epithelial tissues are classified on the basis of cell structure and the number of cell layers. A simple epithelium is one cell-layer thick. The cells may be squamous (flat), as in the inner lining of blood vessels (endothelium of arteries and veins, whole structure of capillaries); cuboidal, as in glands (thyroid, liver, and in the formation of ducts such as bile ducts); or columnar (tall and thin), as in the inner lining (mucous membrane) of the stomach and intestines. These three forms of cells also may occur together in layers, as in stratified epithelia (epidermis of skin, inner lining of the cheeks, vagina, urethra, esophagus, and sweat glands). A special type of stratified epithelium, transitional epithelium, forms the inner lining of the urinary bladder. The outer cells are umbrella-shaped to allow for stretching. The pseudostratified ciliated columnar epithelia lining the trachea and bronchi seem to be in layers, but it is really that the cells are of varying heights and only appear to be layered. Other ciliated epithelial cells include the columnar epithelia of the oviducts, which function in moving the ovum toward the uterus.

Connective tissues bind and support all the other tissues. They are so widespread and abundant that the removal of the other tissues from an animal's body would still leave a clear image of the whole organism. Connective tissues generally have only a very few cells but a considerable amount of materials such as fibers and matrix (intercellular substance), in which the fibers are embedded. There are three kinds of fibers; the most common type is white collagenous fibers, which are nonelastic and very strong. They make up tendons, which attach muscles to bones (such as the Achilles tendon), and ligaments, and are found in the intervertebral discs; they are also involved in the repair reactions that form scar tissue. Yellow elastic fibers, along with the collagenous fibers, are found within the areolar connective tissue of the loose fibrous type. Yellow elastic fibers make up most of the ligamentum nuchae (large ligament in the back of the neck attaching to the thoracic vertebrae), which is particularly prominent in large animals such as horses, cattle, and giraffes. Reticular fibers form networks inside solid organs (such as the spleen and liver) and in bone marrow.

In many regions of the body, the connective tissue contains clusters of large cells that are fat storage cells. This adipose tissue is an energy reserve, and it also pads organs and angular areas (such as armpits) of the body. Fat usually accumulates as a single vacuole in each cell.

Cartilage cushions parts of the body and provides a framework for maintaining the shape of some body areas. It is made up of a dense network of white collagenous fibers (fibrous cartilage) and yellow elastic fibers (elastic cartilage) or has a matrix that contains no fibers at all (hyaline cartilage). Hyaline cartilage occurs on the ends of bones (joints), on the septum of the nose, between the ribs (intercostal cartilage), and on the larynx and the rings of the trachea and bronchi of the lungs, which serve to keep these important airways open. Embryos and fetus skeletons are composed almost entirely of cartilage, as is much of the skeleton of most infantile vertebrates. The skeletons of sharks, rays, and skates are composed entirely of cartilage throughout their lives. Elastic cartilage is found in only a few places, such as the Eustachian tube, which extends from the pharynx to the middle ear; parts of the larynx; and the external ear, or pinna. Fibrous cartilage makes up the intervertebral discs and the pubic symphysis.

Bones are attached to one another by joints. The bones support and protect softer tissues and organs, and serve as attachment points for most skeletal muscles. Bone is hardened by the deposition of calcium phosphate and calcium carbonate (67 percent of the weight). The ends of long bones (such as the femur and the humerus) and flat, compact bones (exemplified by the sternum, scapula, and skull) contain red bone marrow, which is the principal source of all blood cells and platelets. The shafts of long bones also contain yellow bone marrow, which is mostly lipidic, or fatty. Microscopically, bone is laid down in concentric layers (lamellae), forming elongated cylinders (Haversian systems). Bone cells (osteocytes) are contained within lacunae, or small cavities. Nutrients, oxygen, and other materials reach the bone cells and wastes are carried away from the cells through tiny canals within the hardened bone called canaliculi.

Nervous tissue is highly developed for the reception of stimuli and the conduction of impulses. The principal unit of structure and function is the neuron (nerve cell), which is composed of a nerve cell body containing the cell nucleus and processes (several dendrites and always only one axon). The nerve cell bodies are found only in gray matter within the central nervous system (brain and spinal cord) and in ganglia outside the central nervous system; however, the fibers may reach long distances throughout the animal body. Neurons are arranged in chains, with the point of contact being the synapse. Some fibers are myelinated, while others are not.

Sensory neurons are responsible for the conduction of impulses from receptors in the skin or sensory organs (such as eyes and ears) to the central nervous system. Motor neurons conduct impulses from centers in the central nervous system to muscles and glands bringing about contraction for movement and secretions, respectively. Association or connector neurons form interconnections between neurons within the central nervous system.

There are three types of muscle tissue, smooth or involuntary (visceral), voluntary or striated (skeletal), and cardiac (heart). The slow-contracting smooth muscle (composed of single-nucleus, spindle-shaped cells) is located in the walls of blood vessels and in the walls of internal organs such as the intestine, uterus, spleen, and urinary and gall bladders. Skeletal muscle is a more rapid-acting muscle, and the cylindrical cells are striated and multinucleated. Skeletal muscle is largely concerned with the movement of the skeleton; however, skeletal muscle may be found in the upper third of the esophagus and in the diaphragm. Cardiac muscle fibers resemble skeletal muscle, but they are involuntary and highly branched and fused in most directions and planes, so the heart can contract as a unit. Some cardiac muscle fibers (Purkinje fibers) do not contract but function in the conduction of nerve impulses. Special myoepithelial cells are located in sweat, salivary, and mammary glands. They wrap long contractile processes around the secretory cells of the glands to help squeeze out secretions.

The vascular tissues are made up of blood, lymph, and tissue fluid. Blood is a fluid tissue containing white blood cells (leukocytes, which are important in disease defense), red blood cells (erythrocytes, which carry oxygen), platelets (for blood clotting), and the liquid plasma. Blood transports materials such as oxygen, nutrients, and hormones through blood vessels to all the body cells, and from all the body cells it transports carbon dioxide, wastes, and hormones). Lymph and tissue fluids arise from the blood and body cells by processes of filtration, diffusion, and osmosis, and are necessary for the exchange of materials between the body cells and the blood.

Methods of Study

Histology usually involves the study of stained sections of dead tissues and organs with the compound microscope. Living tissues also are studied with such aids as the dark-field microscope, also known as the ultramicroscope, and the phase-contrast microscope. Certain dyes may be added (supravital staining) without harming the living cells, or dye solutions may be introduced into the living organism (vital staining). These procedures bring out structural details not easily seen in unstained living cells with ordinary light or bright field microscopes.

There are other methods used to investigate the detailed structure of cells and tissues, such as ultraviolet microscopy, fluorescence microscopy, and electron microscopy. Microspectroscopy, radioautography, and X-ray diffraction may also be employed. Special methods of tissue preparation and staining are required for these more specialized techniques.

The preparation of sections of tissues (histotechnology) for study with the compound microscope requires much skill and time. There are various methods that may be used; however, the usual technique first requires that the tissues are rapidly killed, or "fixed," by placing them in a protoplasm-coagulating solution such as mercuric chloride or picric acid. Second, water is removed from them with 70 percent alcohol, and they are infiltrated with melted paraffin that will solidify to form blocks containing the tissue. Third, thin (2- to 10-micrometer-thick) slices are shaved from the blocks with a precision-cutting microtome; then, these thin sections of tissues are affixed to glass microscope slides. The tissue sections (attached to the slides) are stained by placing them into hematoxylin-eosin dye and then made transparent by dissolving the paraffin with xylene. Finally, the sections are covered with a drop of transparent mounting medium (glue such as damar), and a thin cover glass is placed on the section of tissue. After the mounting medium has dried, the slide is ready for microscopic examination.

Fluid tissues, including blood and red bone marrow, can be spread in a thin film on a microscope slide, dried, and stained (as with Wright's or Giemsa stains), and then examined with a compound microscope. Imprints of soft tissues may also be prepared by merely pressing the cut end of a tissue against the surface of a slide. That will leave a one-cell-thick layer of cells adhering to the slide. These preparations may also be stained with Wright's or Giemsa stains.

Context

The science of histology is one of the most important diagnostic tools in human and veterinary medicine, enabling the pathologists to understand better the processes of infectious diseases as well as cancer. Zoological scientists generally must have a basic knowledge of histology in order to understand fully animal structure, behavior, and diversity.

Jan Purkyně proposed the name "protoplasm" for living matter, and Hugo von Mohl did extensive work describing its nature, but Max Schultze gave a clear concept of the relations of protoplasm to cells and its unity and importance in all organisms.

Histology was established as an important science by Rudolf Albert von Kölliker. This great investigator described many tissues with amazing insight, beginning with the first textbook in histology.

Since von Kölliker, many other eminent scientists have added significantly to the body of knowledge about animal cells and tissues. Because of these important contributions, it is now possible to recognize five grades of organization in animals. each grade is more complex than the previous one and represents increased complexities and more recent evolutionary advancements.

A protoplasmic grade of evolution is found in the kingdom Protista, which includes protozoans and algae, in which all life processes occur within the boundaries of a single cell. In some organisms, the protoplasm is specialized into organelles that carry out specific functions.

Cellular organization occurs when groups of cells live together that have different functions or divisions of labor. Some cells may be concerned with nutrition, while others are concerned with reproduction. The sponges belong to this level. A step beyond that is the cell-tissue grade of organization in which similar cells are grouped into patterns or layers. The jellyfishes, hydras, and other coelenterates are usually included in this group.

The tissue-organ grade of organization can be seen in the flatworms (Playthelminthes), in which there are many well-defined organs such as eyespots, reproductive organs, suckers, and digestive systems. Organs usually are composed of more than one type of tissue and are more specialized than tissues.

An organ-system grade of organization occurs when organs work together to perform important functions such as circulation, digestion, respiration, reproduction, and others. First observed in the primitive nematodes, this level is typical of all higher forms of animal life, including human beings.

Bibliography

Hickman, Cleveland P., Larry S. Roberts, and Frances M. Hickman. *Integrated Principles of Zoology.* 7th ed. St. Louis: Times Mirror/Mosby, 1984. Includes succinct, well-written discussions of levels of animal organization and animal tissues. The book also contains an up-to-date presentation of the regulation of gene function.

Knight, Bernard. *Discovering the Human Body.* New York: Lippincott and Crowell, 1980. An interesting historical background of the discovery of organ systems, along with good anatomical details.

Kuffler, Stephen W., John G. Nichols, and A. Robert Martin. *From Neuron to Brain.* 2d ed. New York: McGraw-Hill, 1983. A well-presented, detailed account of the nervous system. Good histological detail, along with excellent color plates.

Leeson, Thomas S., C. Roland Leeson, and Anthony Paparo. *Textbook of Histology.* Philadelphia: W. B. Saunders, 1985. A well-written, popular textbook, with a good coverage of human tissues.

Patt, Donald I., and Gail R. Patt. *Comparative Vertebrate Histology.* New York: Harper & Row, 1969. A well-integrated approach to animal histology showing evolutionary relationships. This text is a departure from the usual medically oriented books.

Ross, Russell, and Paul Bornstein. "Elastic Fibers in the Body." *Scientific American* 224 (June, 1971): 44-52. An in-depth discussion of elastic fibers in skin, around arteries, and in ligaments.

Vander, Arthur, and Dorothy Luciano. *Human Physiology: The Mechanism of Body Function.* 4th ed. New York: Harper & Row, 1985. A clear in-depth account of human organ systems and their functions.

Jon P. Shoemaker

Cross-References

HOMEOTIC GENES AND HOMEOBOXES

Types of life science: Developmental biology (embryology) and molecular biology
Other field of study: Genetic regulation in eukaryotes

Homeotic genes determine the identity of different body segments early in development. Research on these genes provides insight into how complex body patterns are established during development and how these patterns have evolved.

Principal terms

EMBRYO POLARITY GENES: genes whose expression in maternal cells results in products being stored in the egg that establish polarity, such as the anterior-posterior axis, after fertilization

GAP RULE GENES: expressed in the zygote, these genes divide the anterior-posterior axis of fruit flies into several regions

HOMEOBOXES: 180 nucleotide pairs that code for a protein called the homeodomain, found in such diverse organisms as insects, frogs, and humans; they are known to influence body plan formation in fruit flies

HOMEOSIS: a process that results in the formation of structures in the wrong place in an organism, such as a leg developing in place of a fly's antenna

HOMEOTIC SELECTOR GENES: genes that determine the identity and developmental fate of segments established in fruit flies by a hierarchy of genes

IMAGINAL DISK: a small group of cells that differentiate adult fruit fly structures after the last larval molt

IN SITU HYBRIDIZATION: a technique used to visualize the location of specific DNA or RNA sequences; typically, a radioactively tagged sequence of nucleic acids is paired (hybridized) to a complementary sequence of nucleic acids

PAIR-RULE GENES: segmentation genes of fruit flies that divide the anterior-posterior axis into two-segment units

SEGMENT POLARITY GENES: segmentation genes of fruit flies that divide the anterior-posterior axis into individual segments

SEGMENTATION GENES: these include the gap rule, pair-rule, and segment polarity genes; they establish anterior-posterior segmentation in fruit flies without specifying segment identity

Summary of the Phenomenon

The body plans of advanced animals and plants can be viewed as a series of segments with unique identities. This is especially obvious in the annelids (segmented worms), but even in vertebrates the muscular regions and the backbone are segmented. Occasionally, a segment takes on the identity of another segment of the organism. This is called homeosis, and it was first described in 1984. Numerous examples of homeosis have been cited, including the Antennapedia mutant of the fruit fly, which has a leg developing in the antennal socket of the head. Pea leaf mutants in which tendrils become leaflets or leaflets become tendrils are also homeotic. Many examples of homeosis in flower development exist, including flowers that have petals developing in place of stamens. Much has been learned about developmental patterns in organisms and about the evolution of these patterns, from the study of homeotic mutants.

The role of homeosis in elucidating genetic control of overall body plans is best illustrated in the development of the fruit fly. Early in its embryogenesis, the basic plan for the adult fly form is established, and this information is stored in imaginal disks (an adult fly is called an imago) through three larval stages and associated molts. Imaginal disks are small groups of cells that differentiate adult structures after the last larval molt. The early determination of these imaginal disks for specific developmental fates is controlled by a hierarchy of genes. This hierarchy of gene regulation has been carefully documented for the establishment of the anterior-posterior axis (a line running from the head to the abdomen) of larval and adult fruit flies. Three levels of genetic control—egg polarity genes, segmentation genes, and homeotic selecter genes—result in an adult fly with anterior head segments, three thoracic segments, and eight abdominal segments.

Egg polarity genes are responsible for establishing the anterior-posterior axis. Mutations of these genes result in bizarre flies that lack head and thoracic structures or lack abdominal structures. Maternal egg polarity genes are transcribed, and the resulting ribonucleic acid (RNA) is translocated into the egg and localized at one end. This RNA is not translated into protein until after fertilization. Following translation, the proteins are dispersed unequally in the embryo, forming an anterior-posterior gradient that regulates the expression of the segmentation genes.

Segmentation genes represent the second tier of the genes that establish the body plan of the fly. Within the segmentation genes, there are three levels of control—gap genes, pair-rule genes, and segment polarity genes—resulting in progressively finer subdivisions of the anterior-posterior axis. While there is hierarchical control within the segmentation genes, genes in a given level also interact with one another. Gap genes of the embryo respond to the positional information of the gradient established by the maternal egg polarity genes. Gap genes form boundaries that specify regional domains, and several gap genes with distinct regions of influence have been identified.

Pair-rule genes follow next in the sequence; they appear to function at the level of two-segment units. Mutant pair-rule genes are responsible for flies that have half the normal number of segments. Ultimately, the larval fly body is divided into visible segments, but while the patterns are forming, genes appear to exert their influence on parasegments. A parasegment is half a segment that is "out of phase" with the visible adult segments. Parasegments include the posterior of one segment and the anterior of the adjacent segment. Developmental programming of parasegments ultimately gives rise to visibly distinct segments. The final level of control of the segmentation genes focuses on individual segments and is controlled by the segment polarity genes. In response to the pair-rule genes, the segment polarity genes subdivide each segment into anterior and posterior compartments.

Thus, the segmentation genes create a series of finely tuned boundaries. It is the third tier of genes, however, the homeotic selector genes, that actually specify segment identity. Segmentation gene mutations result in missing body parts, whereas mutations of the homeotic selector genes result in a normal number of segments, but segments with abnormal identities. Homeotic selector genes are found in two gene clusters, the Antennapedia complex and the bithorax complex, both of which were identified based on mutant phenotyes. Genes associated with the Antennapedia complex appear to determine the fate of segments associated with the anterior body segments, whereas the bithorax complex is responsible for the more posterior segments, such as the abdominal segments. The pattern that arises is modulated both by interactions among the homeotic selector genes and by interactions with the segment polarity genes.

The genes found within the Antennapedia and bithorax complexes have been identified based on mutations that have arisen. These genes function within smaller regions of the anterior or posterior axis, much as pair-rule genes subdivide regions established by the gap genes. It is intriguing that the genes within the two complexes appear to be lined up in the same order that they function spatially. That is, the position of an Antennapedia complex gene on the chromosome relative to other Antennapedia complex genes correlates with the actual position of the segments controlled by the gene. Recent analyses of homeotic mutants in beetles indicate that the homeotic genes are also physically organized in a left-to-right sequence corresponding to the location of the segments they control on the anterior-posterior axis. Unlike the fruit fly, however, the beetle has a single homeotic gene complex controlling the entire anterior-posterior axis.

The interactions between homeotic selector genes and other genes in the hierarchy may, in part, be controlled by the homeodomain protein coded for by the "homeobox" associated with many of these genes. The homeobox is a 180-nucleotide-pair sequence that is included in many of the homeotic selector genes as well as in some segmentation genes (including the pair-rule gene). The homeodomain protein has a unique structure that may bind the deoxyribonucleic acid (DNA) and affect its transcription. It is possible that this allows genes to regulate expression of themselves and other related genes. For example, a pair-rule gene known as fushi tarazu (meaning "not enough segments" in Japanese) is found in the Antennapedia complex and has a homeobox, although fushi tarazu is not a homeotic selector gene. Its homeodomain can bind to the Antennapedia gene and thus can regulate when this gene is turned on and off. Antennapedia, a homeotic selector gene, was first identified when a mutation of it resulted in the replacement of an antenna with a leg. Thus, the ability of the homeodomain to bind to DNA provides a way for the hierarchical control of homeotic selector genes by segmentation genes to occur.

The homeotic selector genes are ultimately linked with gene expression that leads to the development of specific structures associated with different segments. It is not known exactly how homeotic selector genes regulate segment differentiation. Although the homeotic selector genes are active early in development, they appear to be involved in programming cells for fates that are not expressed until much later.

Methods of Study

Most of what is known about homeosis has been learned from studying mutations. Sometimes these mutations have arisen spontaneously; sometimes they have been induced by exposing organisms to mutagenic substances, such as chemicals or X ray or ultraviolet radiation. The large number of mutations identified in fruit flies accounts for the wealth of information on homeosis in this organism, in sharp contrast to the limited information on humans, for whom ethical considerations prohibit mutagenesis. Mutations affecting segmentation and determination of segment identity represent defective developmental switches and provide insight into the normal developmental sequence.

Classical genetic approaches have been used with homeotic mutants to map genes to chromosomes and to identify interactions between genes. For example, it can be determined whether two genes are on the same chromosome by making a series of specific matings between flies with mutations in these genes and wild-type ("normal") flies. If the genes are not on the same chromosome, offspring with one mutation will not necessarily have the other mutation. If the mutations are both on the same chromosome, they will be inherited together, except in rare situations where there is recombination between chromosomes. Geneticists use the frequency of recombination to assess how close together two genes are on a chromosome. This approach helped geneticists determine the order of genes within the Antennapedia and bithorax complexes. Matings between different mutants have also established the hierarchy of genetic control among egg polarity, segmentation, and homeotic selector genes. For example, a pair-rule mutant will have no effect on gap genes, but a gap gene mutant will affect pair-rule genes.

To visualize the results of these crosses of hierarchical mutants, researchers employed a second technique: in situ hybridization. To investigate the effect of gap genes on pair-rule genes, a wild-type fly embryo and one with a gap mutation affecting the middle section were exposed to radioactively labeled DNA that was a copy of the pair-rule gene fushi tarazu. The DNA hybridized (bound) to fushi tarazu RNA, and it thus labeled tissues where the fushi tarazu gene was turned on and was making RNA copies of itself. Excess radioactive DNA was washed away, and a photographic emulsion that was then placed over the tissue was exposed by the bound radioactive DNA. This permitted researchers to see that the fushi tarazu gene was being expressed in the middle of the wild-type embryo, but not in the gap mutant embryo. When this experiment was repeated using radioactive gap gene DNA in a pair-rule mutant, no effect on gap gene expression was observed.

In situ hybridization has also provided information on how egg polarity genes provide segmentation genes with positional information. The egg polarity gene bicoid was identified by mutations resulting in a fly with abdominal structures but no head or thoracic structures. When radioactive DNA copies of the bicoid gene were hybridized to eggs, it was found that all the RNA was located at the anterior tip after being transferred from the mother. When this RNA was translated into protein, the protein was tagged with an antibody specific for the bicoid protein. Tagging the protein with an antibody is similar to tagging RNA with a radioactive DNA segment; both techniques allow researchers to see how the RNA or protein is distributed in tissues. In this case, the bicoid protein formed an anterior to posterior gradient after the egg was fertilized, with more protein being found at the anterior end.

Homeotic genes have been isolated and used for in situ hybridization studies. In addition, the sequence of nucleotides in the DNA in these genes has been established. A variety of techniques is available for DNA sequencing. Generally the DNA is broken into smaller segments that can be more readily identified. Cutting the DNA yields overlapping segments, and the overall sequence can be established by piecing these overlapping fragments back together. The presence of the homeobox was established by comparing DNA sequences from different genes in flies and other organisms. It was evident, based on these types of data, that the homeobox sequence differs by only a small number of nucleotides even between very distantly related organisms.

The role of the homeobox was investigated by inserting DNA containing a homeobox from the fushi tarazu gene into a bacteria in such a way that the bacteria then produced large amounts of the homeodomain protein. This protein was then tested for its ability to bind the DNA and was found to bind to specific fragments of DNA that were involved in homeosis, such as the Antennapedia gene. Homeodomain protein from a mutant fushi tarazu gene was defective in its DNA binding ability. This provided evidence that the homeobox may regulate gene expression via the direct binding of the homeodomain to DNA. This is only one of numerous examples illustrating how researchers have utilized genetic mutants and molecular biology to investigate the role of homeotic genes in the development of segmented organisms.

Context

Research on homeosis and homeoboxes has made significant contributions to the fields of developmental biology and evolution. Since all higher animals and plants exhibit some form of segmented development, the common link of the homeobox has intrigued scientists interested in how body plans are established. Questions concerning the evolution of segmentation patterns in animals have also arisen as more is understood about the genes affecting segmentation and how they are regulated.

Significant similarities both among the homeoboxes identified in fruit flies and among the homeoboxes of distantly related species have been found. In fruit flies, homeoboxes have been identified in homeotic selector genes, segmentation genes, and egg polarity genes. Whether homeoboxes affect gene regulation and segmentation in other organisms is an exciting, and open, question. Segmented worms, leeches, earthworms, sea urchins, frogs, mice, and humans all have homeoboxes. Different mouse homeobox genes have been shown to be expressed in specific regions during embryogenesis. Relatively little is known about the process of segmentation in vertebrates, so it is more difficult to interpret the results of such experiments. Also, it appears that segmentation in vertebrates and in fruit flies (and other invertebrates) evolved separately. Thus, the presence of a homeobox may or may not indicate a common developmental process for segmentation among animals.

There is an intriguing possibility that addition and modification of homeotic selector genes were responsible for the evolution of insects from segmented worms. The presence of two homeotic gene complexes in fruit flies, contrasted with one in beetles, suggests that duplication of the gene complex, followed by subsequent specialization, may have allowed for greater fine-tuning of segmental identity. Evolutionary alterations of the initial homeotic gene complex may have been responsible for the addition of legs to a wormlike creature composed of similar segments, giving rise to a millipede-like creature. The reduction of all legs except for the walking legs in the thoracic region and, ultimately, the addition of wings to the thoracic region could also reflect changes in homeotic selector genes. Parts of this evolutionary journey can be reconstructed with homeotic fruit fly mutants that bear similarities to their ancestors. This is exemplified by the deletion of the Antennapedia gene, which results in a wingless fly; winged insects presumably arose from nonwinged insects. It is impossible, however, to create a millipede from a fly via mutations of the homeotic selector genes, so caution must be taken in speculating on the role of homeotic selector genes in insect evolution.

Bibliography

Alberts, Bruce, Dennis Bray, Julian Lewis, Martin Raff, Keith Roberts, and James D. Watson. *Molecular Biology of the Cell*. 2d ed. New York: Garland, 1989. Chapter 16 provides details on the molecular analysis of segment formation and specification. Illustrations of in situ hybridizations are especially helpful. Numerous examples using specific mutants would be informative for college students.

Bowman, John L., David R. Smyth, and Elliot M. Meyerowitz. "Genes Directing Flower Development in *Arabidopsis*." *The Plant Cell* 1 (1989): 37-52. Color photographs and scanning electron micrographs illustrate homeotic mutations in flowers. This paper provides insight into how homeotic mutations are being used to investigate pattern formation in a plant system. High school and college students would gain a broader understanding of homeosis from this article.

French, Vernon, Phil Ingham, Jonathan Cooke, and Jim Smith, eds. *Mechanisms of Segmentation*. Madison, Conn.: Research Books, 1988. Provides a good explanation of homeodomain binding studies and details on the spatial expression of mouse homeodomain genes. Clear illustrations and accompanying reference lists.

Gilbert, Scott F. *Developmental Biology.* Sunderland, Mass.: Sinauer Associates, 1988. Chapter 18 provides extensive coverage of segmentation in fruit flies with a somewhat general approach. The section on the evolution of homeotic genes would be good preparation for reading the text by Raff and Kaufman.

Raff, Rudolf A., and Thomas C. Kaufman. *Embryos, Genes, and Evolution.* New York: Macmillan, 1983. Chapter 8 is an exciting chapter focusing on the role of homeotic selector genes in the evolution of insects from segmented worms. Excellent illustrations provide the reader with a clear understanding of ancestral morphologies. Suitable for college students.

Sattler, Rolf. "Homeosis of Plants." *American Journal of Botany* 75 (1988): 1606-1617. Sattler reviews the history of homeosis and presents an overview of homeotic mutants in plants. (This paper is nicely complemented by the more in-depth analysis of a single plant in the article by Bowman and coauthors.)

Villee, Claude A., Eldra Pearl Solomon, Charles E. Martin, Diana W. Martin, Linda R. Berg, and P. William Davis. *Biology.* 2d ed. Philadelphia: W. B. Saunders, 1989. An introductory college text that is also suitable for high school students. Chapter 16 provides details on the development of the fruit fly from egg to adult and summarizes the hierarchy of gene control involved in segmentation. There is an excellent photograph of the Antennapedia mutant.

Watson, James D., Nancy H. Hopings, Jeffrey W. Roberts, Joan Argetsinger Steitz, and Alan M. Weiner. *Molecular Biology of the Gene.* Menlo Park, Calif.: Benjamin/Cummings, 1987. Chapter 22 provides a well-illustrated analysis of the genes associated with segmentation and the determination of segment identity. A clear explanation of maternal effects on embryo development is presented that provides additional insight into egg polarity genes. Suitable for an introductory-level college student.

Susan R. Singer

Cross-References

Autoradiography and Subcellular Fractionation of Radioactive Tracer Molecules, 148; Determination and Differentiation, 606; Development: An Evolutionary Perspective, 615; DNA Sequencing, 698; Genes and Nucleic Acids, 1134; In Situ Hybridization, 1408; Transcription of DNA to Form RNA, 2632; Translation of Messenger RNA to Form Protein, 2647.

HOMINIDS

Type of life science: Anthropology
Other fields of study: Animal anatomy, evolutionary biology, and systematics (taxonomy)

Though understanding of human ancestry is rudimentary at best, an astonishing series of discoveries since the nineteenth century has created a lively field of knowledge where there was none before.

Principal terms

APES: large, tailless, semierect anthropoid primates, including chimpanzees, gorillas, gibbons, and orangutans, and their direct ancestors — but excluding man and his ancestors

AUSTRALOPITHECINES: nonhuman hominids, commonly regarded as ancestral to present-day humans

DRYOPITHECINES: extinct Miocene-Pliocene apes (sometimes including *Proconsul*, from Africa) found in Europe and Asia; their evolutionary significance is unclear

HUMANS: hominids of the genus *Homo*, whether *Homo sapiens sapiens* (to which all varieties of modern man belong), earlier forms of *Homo sapiens*, or such presumably related types as *Homo erectus* and the still earlier (and more problematic) *Homo habilis*

PRIMATES: placental mammals, primarily arboreal, whether anthropoid (humans, apes, and monkeys) or prosimian (lemurs, lorises, and tarsiers)

Summary of the Phenomenon

The idea that humankind might be significantly older than the six thousand years previously allotted by biblical scholars, who tried to calculate the generations of man since Adam, was not widely maintained until 1859, when human stone tools and the bones of extinct animals were found lying close to each other in France. Charles Darwin's *On the Origin of Species* appeared on November 1 of the same year, but it suggested only that "light will be thrown on the origin of man and his history" by the theory of evolution he had just proposed.

A series of important and widely noticed books then followed, including J. Boucher de Perthes' *De l'homme antédiluvien et ses œuvres* (*Of Antediluvian Man and His Works*), published in Paris in 1860; Thomas Henry Huxley's *Evidence as to Man's Place in Nature* (1863); and Charles Lyell's *Antiquity of Man* (1863), with others later by John Lubbock, James Geikie, and W. Boyd Dawkins. In *The Descent of Man* (1871), Darwin sagely hypothesized that the human line evolved in Africa (not Asia, as had previously been assumed) from a long-tailed, probably arboreal, ancestor. Yet, in Darwin's time only two fossil apes were known at all, together with some controversial bones of a creature known as Neanderthal man. Extinct species such as the australopithecines and *Homo erectus* had not been discovered.

The scientific name for mankind is *Homo sapiens sapiens* (wise man); the taxonomic family is the Hominidae, which also includes chimpanzees and gorillas. This classification is reasonable because, bone for bone, their skeletons are almost identical to human skeletons. On other evidence as well, man and his cousins appear to be remarkably alike. The protein sequences in chimpanzee and human hemoglobin, for example, are identical; there are only two chemical differences between gorilla and human hemoglobin. Between humans and all other animals, there are more than two. Strands of deoxyribonucleic acid (DNA) from chimpanzees and humans, moreover, are 99 percent identical. Chimpanzees, finally, are second only to humans in intelligence; their brains closely resemble those of humans. These remarkable similarities attest a common ancestry for all the Hominidae, as the classification itself would imply, and a fairly recent differentiation among its members. Some biochemists have argued that man, the chimpanzee, and the gorilla shared a common ancestor no more than 6 or 8 million years ago.

Whatever the timing may have been, it is almost universally accepted that the link between humans and their protosimian ancestors was a now extinct genus of apemen, the australopithecines (Southern apes). The first of these, called, originally, the Taung child, was discovered in South Africa by Robert Dart in 1924. Its identity and significance remained controversial until 1936, when further discoveries by Robert Bloom convinced skeptical professionals and the public. Today, *Australopithecus* and *Homo* (man) are often grouped together as *Hominini*, as opposed to the *Pongidae* (apes), to which the chimpanzee and gorilla belong.

The australopithecines arose at least 4 million years ago, probably from dryopithecine ancestors. They lasted until 2 million years ago, evolving into a series of species. Of these, *Australopithecus afarensis* (found in the Afar region of Ethiopia) was the oldest and smallest. Males stood no taller than four feet, and the females were smaller. Most significantly, however, *afarensis* was fully bipedal; unlike the apes, it walked upright, with increasingly specialized hands, and with legs a bit longer than arms. Chimpanzee-like hips, together with curved toe and finger bones, suggest that it was essentially a tree-dweller living on fruits and seeds. A remarkably complete skeleton of *afarensis*, familiarly called Lucy, was found in 1974; it is about 3 million years old and is the oldest hominine skeleton yet found. *Afarensis* died out around 2.5 million years ago; it is thought to be ancestral to the later australopithecines and to modern humans.

Australopithecus africanus, deriving from Africa some 3 to 1 million years ago, probably evolved from *afarensis*. Most specimens come from Sterkfontein in South Africa, though others have been found in Ethiopia, Kenya, and Tanzania. This species was about the same size as *afarensis*, but it had a less apelike face. The arms were proportionately longer than a modern human's, yet shorter than those of *afarensis*; hands and teeth show similar "modernization." Dart's "Taung child" was the first (and is still the most famous) example of this species.

Australopithecus robustus (robust Southern ape), found only in South African caves thus far, was once thought identical to *Australopithecus boisei*; in older literature, it was also known as *Paranthropus* (past man). Larger and more strongly built than *africanus*, *robustus* was more than a foot taller and had a larger brain. His teeth indicate that *robustus* was a plant eater. There is also a remarkable specimen (discovered by C. K. Brain at Swartkrans) of a child's skullcap in which the imprint of a leopard's lower canines can be seen. Since an exact-fit leopard's jaw was found nearby, it is assumed that the leopard killed the child and was then itself killed by an adult *robustus* armed with some kind of weapon. (A diorama at the Transvaal Museum, Pretoria, reconstructs this hypothetical incident.) *Australopithecus boisei*—a famous discovery by Mary Leakey, named for the Leakeys' sponsor, Charles Boise—called *Zinjanthropus*, was even bigger than *robustus* and lived at the same time, though in East Africa. A *boisei* skull discovered in 1985 in Kenya proved not only to be particularly massive but also considerably older (2.5 to 2.6 million years) than any known *robustus* specimen. *Australopithecus boisei* must therefore have been a separate and earlier species probably *not* descended from *africanus*. If so, then there was more than one australopithecine lineage, and the previously held idea that the australopithecines became increasingly robust through time must be reversed. As a result of this one find, there no longer are widely accepted ideas as to who gave rise to whom.

Throughout their history, the australopithecines manifest a regular progression from apelike characteristics to human ones. All the australopithecines walked upright, a fact that evidently encouraged increasing height, hand specialization, and brain development. Gradual changes in australopithecine dentition, moreover, suggest not only changing diet but revised habits as well. With advanced hands and evolving arms and shoulders, *Australopithecus* probably carried loads and used weapons, regardless of whether he was capable of making them. Though australopithecines may have done some hunting, they probably depended primarily upon foraging and scavenging—filching from leopard kills, for example.

At what point *Australopithecus* evolved into *Homo* is unclear, in part because the distinction between them is rather arbitrary. Though still regarded by some researchers as an advanced form of *Australopithecus* (that is, as more than one species) *Homo habilis* (handy man), another Leakey family discovery, is otherwise usually accepted as the earliest member of a distinctly human line. He was still only about five feet high (perhaps an optimum height for the environmental conditions), but had a larger brain, a rounder head, a less projecting face, advanced dentition, reduced jaws, and essentially modern feet. Stone artifacts have been found in close association with his remains; *habilis*, who lived between 2 and 1.5 million years ago, almost certainly made tools, hunted, built shelters, gathered plants, and scavenged. He is assumed to be ancestral to *Homo erectus*, and may have exterminated *Australopithecus*.

In 1859, when the prehistory of mankind was first broadly acknowledged, the only remains then known belonged to Neanderthal man (now called *Homo sapiens neanderthalensis*). Until 1924, when *Australopithecus* was discovered, all the intervening finds (excluding "Piltdown man," a deliberately planted fake) have since been classified as varieties of *Homo erectus* ("erect man," a designation assuming that its predecessors stooped). Of these, the two best-known are Java man, discovered in 1891 by Eugène Dubois in Java, and Peking man, found in China by Davison Black in 1926. Only after a number of specimens had accumulated was it realized that Java man and Peking man were examples of the same species. An exceptionally complete *Homo erectus* skeleton was discovered in Kenya in 1984 and dated at 1.6 million years old. Overall, *Homo erectus* lived from some time before 1.6 million years ago to as recently as two hundred thousand years ago. He probably evolved in Africa but migrated from there (as no previous hominid had) to Europe and the Pacific shores of Asia. This species was as tall as modern humans, but more robust overall, with a noticeably thicker, somewhat "old-fashioned" skull that still included prominent brow ridges and a sloping forehead. He had large, projecting jaws, no chin, teeth that were larger than ours; he also had a bigger brain. *Homo erectus* was not only widespread in distribution, but also showed considerable regional variation. His success as a colonizer was attributable in large part to his intelligence, which was manifested in standardized but increasingly sophisticated toolkits, big-game hunting (almost certainly cooperative), the use of fire, and advanced housing. He lived during the Pleistocene, or glacial, epoch, and was probably stimulated to use his creative abilities by the deteriorating environments he sometimes encountered. Very late examples of *Homo erectus* are sometimes alternatively classified as *Homo sapiens*. Despite some continuing opposition, it is now usually accepted that *Homo erectus* gave rise to *Homo sapiens*.

Methods of Study

Considering the efforts that have been made to find them, hominid fossils are remarkably few. This is the case for three main reasons: First, the early hominids (unlike ourselves) did not exist in huge numbers; second, the majority of their bones were not preserved as fossils; and third, we have surely found only a small proportion of the hominid fossils that do exist.

The hominid line evolved in Africa, and its earlier members (including the australopithecines and *Homo habilis*) have been found only there. *Homo erectus* was both more widespread and more numerous, but none of these types practiced ritual burials (Neanderthals were the first to do that), so the most usual agent of presentation was some sort of nonhuman carnivore. Predators, such as the large cats, might actually have hunted the early hominids; in any case, they certainly scavenged hominid carcasses. Hyenas and other clean-up animals then grabbed what they could, taking the leftover pieces to their dens in limestone caves. (There must be some truth to this scenario, because leopards and hyenas have left their toothmarks on australopithecine bones.) The gnawed bones, now thoroughly disarticulated, were scattered about the cave — and eventually solidified by limy deposits into a bone breccia.

When twentieth century investigators find such embedded hominid bones, or suspect their presence, they collect chunks of the breccia and dissolve the limy matrix with acetic acid, a procedure that does no harm to fossil bones. It is unlikely that any of the latter will be whole. Once the fragmented bones have been freed from the matrix, they are cleaned, preserved, sorted by type, and tallied. Whether big or small, routine or not, each must be identified. By far the great majority of the bones will belong to antelopes of various kinds; less than one in a thousand, normally, proves to be hominid.

Such procedures are standard when dealing with cave deposits at the famous South African australopithecine sites of Sterkfontein, Kromdraai, and Swartkrans, all of which are adjacent to each other and to Pretoria. At Olduvai Gorge in Tanzania, where the Leakeys and others have found both australopithecine and *Homo habilis* remains, the geology is entirely different. Here, the erosive power of a now-defunct river has exposed primarily volcanic sediments that once bordered a shifting saline lake. The disadvantage of this site is that it lacked any obvious place for the location of bones; years of determined effort were required to locate productive sites. The advantages of the site were that the presence of early man was virtually assured because stone tools were scattered about plentifully (whole campsites were eventually found); the bones involved had not been dragged about and disarticulated by animals; and the involved stratigraphy made fairly precise dating at least theoretically possible. In general, a specimen from Olduvai Gorge brings with it more useful information than does one found in the South African caves. Still other sites have provided additional unique information.

The collection, preservation, and interpretation of hominid fossil bones is very much a multidisciplinary effort. In particular, detailed geological understanding of the site is essential. Only through stratigraphical analysis, usually, can the age and situation of the discovered fossil be understood. Stratigraphy aside, certain rocks can also be dated according to the radioactive elements they contain. More often, bones can be dated approximately because they occur in association with a particular assemblage of animal bones, the animal species themselves being of reliable short-term ages. In some cases, pollen samples have been of use. All this additional information, together with comparative anatomical analysis, helps to give hominid fossils a defensible identity.

Context

Thinking human beings have always been fascinated with the concept of origins, and of all origins, none has been of more interest than that of humans. Human groups have asserted deeply meaningful identities by attributing their present being to a particular origin. Most of these psychologically necessary genealogies relied upon some divine agency to explain the existence of man. From a surprisingly early time, however, civilized humans (such as the Greeks) recognized that there had been a time when mankind did not know the use of metals. Subsequently, many thinkers took the concept of cultural evolution for granted.

By the seventeenth century A.D., anatomy had become a popular field of study.

Comparisons soon established how like human anatomy that of the higher primates was. By the mid-eighteenth century, Carl Linnaeus, the originator of modern biological classification, even ventured to place man and the apes within the same family. Yet this classification did not imply any necessary common ancestry. Linneaus and others of his time created the notion that individual species arose through a special, divine plan. The idea of special creation lost credibility when the fact of extinction became established at the end of the eighteenth century and as the diversity of species and varieties came increasingly to be appreciated. Nature, moreover, was no longer seen to be a benign reflection of its creator. As opinions of a distinctly *human* nature likewise declined, the realization that humans are animals encountered lessening resistance.

Before human evolution was generally accepted during the twentieth century, the evolution of cultures, language, law, institutions, and at least some animals had already been established. Though the idea was there, reliable evidence for the biological evolution of humans remained elusive. Before 1891, the only known prehistoric human bones belonged to Neanderthals; they were quickly and effectively dismissed as pathological freaks. Since Raymond Dart's Taung child of 1924 was likewise dismissed with ridicule, only a few specimens of what would later be recognized as *Homo erectus* (Java man and Peking man) survived to satisfy the now fashionable quest for a "missing link." (There are still innumerable missing links, but the essential connection between ancestral apes and man was confirmed by the discovery of australopithecines.) It was Robert Broom who, during the 1930's, established the reality of the australopithecines and, by implication, of human evolution.

Though the evolution of the hominid line is certainly a worthwhile scientific topic, it has always been regarded as much more than that, because the claims to ancestry define humanity. Yet the formal constraints of science are limited. In a remarkable series of thirty-nine papers (published between 1949 and 1965), for example, Raymond Dart promulgated an interpretation of the australopithecines as aggressive, predatory, and cannibalistic hunters. Because of the recurrent wars in which civilization had engaged during this period and shortly before, this image of human (or almost human) nature appealed to the popular imagination—so much so that less technical restatements of the same views by Robert Ardrey were not only commercially successful but also politically influential. Interpretations of australopithecine and early hominid behavior have subsequently changed, however—many now see these species as abject scavengers disputing the possession of already picked-over animal corpses with hyenas. It is arguable whether such changing interpretations are attributable to scientific advances or are the result of changing philosophical views of humanity.

Bibliography

Brain, C. K. *The Hunters or the Hunted? An Introduction to African Cave Taphonomy.* Chicago: University of Chicago Press, 1981. In a sophisticated but readable style, Brain reports the evidence about the australopithecines—what they hunted and what hunted them. (Taphonomy is the study of entire bone assemblages.) His study is intended primarily for graduate students and professionals in the field.

Campbell, Bernard. *Humankind Emerging*. 5th ed. Glenview, Ill.: Scott, Foresman, 1988. A readable college-level text that is useful for its treatments of historical, biological, and anthropological topics. No other book presents so much information so well. Graphics and other illustrations are excellent. Campbell also includes topical bibliographies and a glossary. Chapters 7 through 10 are especially relevant.

Day, Michael H. *Guide to Fossil Man*. 4th ed. Chicago: University of Chicago Press, 1986. Despite some abstruse language (a glossary is included), this authoritative compilation can be of significant help. Organized geographically, it lists and often illustrates all known hominid fossils. Conflicting interpretations are reported but seldom reconciled. This is not, therefore, a book for those seeking the fast answer. Bibliographies accompany each section of the text. For college-level students and professionals, this is a standard work.

Jelínek, J. *The Pictorial Encyclopedia of the Evolution of Man*. Translated by Helga Hanks. New York: Hamlyn, 1975. See especially "The Development of Man and His Immediate Successors" (with *Homo sapiens* following). Some of the restorations and other opinions no longer represent current knowledge, but this is still an extremely useful introduction, copiously illustrated and pleasant to read.

Johanson, Donald C., and Maitland A. Edey. *Lucy: The Beginnings of Humankind*. New York: Simon & Schuster, 1981. Intended for a broad audience, this popular account recreates the excitement and explains the significance of the finding of an extraordinary specimen, known technically as *Australopithecus afarensis*. It is the oldest hominid whole skeleton extant.

Lambert, David, and the Diagram Group. *The Field Guide to Early Man*. New York: Facts on File, 1987. Featuring a brief but purposeful text and lucid, sometimes ingenious illustrations, this joint-effort popularization includes chapters on "'Man-Apes' and Early Man" (the australopithecines and *Homo habilis*) and "Upright Man" (*Homo erectus*). While making no original contribution itself, it is a responsible distillation of technical source material not easily available to students; precise documentation, however, is lacking.

Lewin, Roger. *Bones of Contention: Controversies in the Search for Human Origins*. New York: Simon & Schuster, 1987. This lucid but sophisticated treatment reviews scholarly debates regarding the Taung child (*Australopithecus africanus*), *Ramapithecus* (a fossil ape) and "Lucy" (*Australopithecus afarensis*). Too specialized for most high school students, it will appeal primarily to college graduates and professionals. Lewin has also written *Human Evolution: An Illustrated Introduction* (1984) and coauthored three popular books with Richard Leakey: *Origins* (1977), *People of the Lake* (1979), and *The Making of Mankind* (1981).

Pilbeam, David. *The Ascent of Man: An Introduction to Human Evolution*. New York: Macmillan, 1972. Chapters 5 through 8 discuss the hominids in chronological order—as then known. Much of the information remains valid, and Pilbeam is especially good at explaining physiology, but he himself no longer agrees with some of the interpretation that appears here (see Lewin).

Reader, John. *Missing Links: The Hunt for Earliest Man.* Boston: Little, Brown, 1981. Organized chronologically by date of discovery, chapters include Neanderthal man, Java man (*Homo erectus*), Piltdown man (a too-long-successful fake), the Taung child (*Australopithecus africanus*), Peking man (*Homo erectus*), later *Australopithecus* discoveries by Robert Broom, the Leakeys' *Australopithecus boisei* and *Homo habilis*, and Johnson's "Lucy" (*Australopithecus afarensis*), together with the Laetoli footprints (of uncertain origin). Outstanding original photographs by the author are featured. Though other treatments have been more detailed (and more technical), Reader's agreeable combination of history and science makes his book irresistible. For readers at all levels.

Shipman, Pat. "Baffling Limb on the Family Tree." *Discover* 7 (September, 1986): 87-93. The discovery of a new, older, and more primitive specimen of *Australopithecus robustus* has thrown all previous attempts at reconstructing the hominid lineage into confusion.

Szalay, Frederick S., and Eric Delson. *Evolutionary History of the Primates.* New York: Academic Press, 1979. Though not intended for beginners, and now somewhat dated in places, this remains a standard reference. (Lambert presents the same concepts in a more popular form.)

Theunissen, Berg. *Eugène Dubois and the Ape-Man from Java: The History of the First "Missing Link" and Its Discoverer.* Boston: Kluwer Academic, 1989. Java man, discovered by Dubois in 1891 (with one important discovery the previous year), was the first example of *Homo erectus* to be recovered. Theunissen's account of this historic addition to our knowledge of early man is detailed but nontechnical, suitable for readers at the high school level and beyond.

Dennis R. Dean

Cross-References

Apes to Hominids, 127; Evolution: A Historical Perspective, 903; Convergent and Divergent Evolution, 910; Cultural Evolution, 918; Extinction, 953; The Genetic Code, 1148; Human Genetics, 1190; *Homo sapiens* and the Diversification of Humans, 1329; Primates, 2202; Speciation and the Species Concept, 2521.

HOMO SAPIENS AND THE DIVERSIFICATION OF HUMANS

Types of life science: Anthropology and evolutionary biology
Other fields of study: Ecology and systematics (taxonomy)

By studying fossil, cultural, and genetic evidence, scholars have attempted to trace the evolutionary development of the human species. It is believed that the earliest form of Homo sapiens *appeared about 350,000 years ago and that the first modern humans (*Homo sapiens sapiens*) appeared somewhat before 100,000 years ago, with racial diversification following thereafter.*

Principal terms

GENE POOL: the total collection of genes available to a species
GENERALIZED: not specifically adapted to any given environment; used to describe one group of Neanderthal humans
HOMINID: any living or fossil member of the taxonomic family Hominidae ("of man") possessing a human form
HOMINOID: referring to members of the family Hominidae and Pongidae (apes) and to the taxonomic superfamily of Hominoidae
MORPHOLOGY: the scientific study of body shape, form, and composition
NATURAL SELECTION: any environmental force that promotes reproduction of particular members of the population that carry certain genes at the expense of other members
PLEISTOCENE: the sixth of the geologic epochs of the Cenozoic era; it began about three million years ago and ended about ten thousand years ago
WÜRM GLACIATION: the fourth and last European glacial period, extending from about 75,000 years ago to 25,000 years ago

Summary of the Phenomenon

All human beings on the earth today are highly adaptive animals of the genus and species *Homo sapiens sapiens* (Latin for "wise, wise human"). In terms of physical structure and physiological function, *Homo sapiens sapiens*—modern humans—are classified taxonomically as members of the order Primates, which is part of the class Mammalia. Since humans and other members of Primates (monkeys and apes) are biologically related, scientists presume both groups to be the products of an evolutionary process similar to that which affected other divergent categories of animals. The evolutionary process that produced *Homo sapiens sapiens* from previously existing species is also believed to account for diversifications within the modern human population such as racial differentiation.

Modern humans and modern apes (the two most closely related of modern primate species) are believed to possess a common biological ancestry, or line, that diverged perhaps 5 or 6 million years ago. The scanty fossil record of this early period, in conjunction with modern genetic studies, seems to indicate that the branch of hominoid evolution which eventually led to *Homo sapiens sapiens* first gave rise to the earliest hominid type, called *Ramapithecus*.

Next to appear, several million years ago, during the late Pliocene epoch, were the early forms of *Australopithecus*, which existed in Africa. They share certain characteristics with both humans and apes. Their brains are larger than those of apes but smaller than those of humans. There have been four species of *Australopithecus* identified.

Examples of the first undisputed members of the genus *Homo*—true human (though not *sapiens*)—appear in the fossil record about 1.5 million years ago. Samples of *Homo erectus* ("upright human") have been found in China, Africa, Java, and Europe. This creature habitually walked upright, made shelters, and used sophisticated tools. *Homo erectus* is also very important, since it is the first hominid to have used fire purposefully. It was suggested by John E. Pfeiffer, in a 1971 article entitled "When *Homo erectus* Tamed Fire, He Tamed Himself," that this first domestication of a natural force was a tremendous evolutionary step, changing the fundamental rhythms of life and human adaptability to environments. Most scholars accept the premise that *Homo erectus* was the hominid grade intermediate between the australopithecines and *Homo sapiens*.

Exactly when, where, and how advanced members of the species *Homo erectus* evolved into *Homo sapiens* are key questions in the study of human evolution, and they are questions that resist resolution. It might be thought that the closer one comes, in terms of time, to modern man, the easier it would be to find the answers. In actuality, such is not the case. The ancestral line or lines leading to modern man become hazy beginning approximately 500,000 years ago. Direct fossil evidence of the earliest members of the species *Homo sapiens* is scarce; moreover, finds of modern human fossils in the Middle East have intensified the debate about the immediate ancestry of *Homo sapiens sapiens*. All the evidence indicates, however, that the middle to upper Pleistocene epoch (beginning about 350,000 years ago), known as the Paleolithic or old stone age in archaeological terms, witnessed the emergence of early *Homo sapiens*.

In 1965, hominid fossil remains were found at a site named Vértesszöllös, near Budapest. They consisted of some teeth and an occipital bone (a bone at the back of the skull). The site also yielded stone tools and signs of the use of fire. Several features of the find recall *Homo erectus*, but the estimated cranial capacity of 1,400 cubic centimeters is well into the normal range for *Homo sapiens*. The age of the site was established at 350,000 years B.P. (before the present). These remains have been attributed to a *sapiens-erectus* intermediate type on the grounds that the remains, and the site, show a mixture of elements reflective of the transitional hominid evolutionary process. Such an assessment places Vértesszöllös man at the root of the *Homo sapiens* evolutionary line, some 100,000 years earlier than other specimens.

A better-known example of early *Homo sapiens* comes from a gravel deposit at Swanscombe, near London, England. In 1935, 1936, and 1955, three related skull pieces were unearthed that fit together perfectly to form the back of a cranial vault with an advanced (over *Homo erectus*) cranial capacity of about 1,300 cubic centimeters. This has been dated to around 275,000 to 250,000 years B.P. A more complete skull of approximately the same age (dated to the Mindel-Riss interglacial period about 250,000 years B.P.) was found at Steinheim, in southern Germany, in 1933. Swanscombe's and Steinheim's advanced morphological characteristics, in combination with relatively primitive ones, such as low brain-case heights, suggest that they are primitive members of the species *sapiens* and are representatives of a population intermediate between *Homo erectus* and *Homo sapiens*.

The finds at Swanscombe and Steinheim have been augmented by others from France and Italy, and especially from the Omo River region in southern Ethiopia. One Omo skull displays more mixed features (between *erectus* and *sapiens*) including flattened frontal and occipital areas, a thick but rounded vault, large mastoid processes (pointed bony processes, or projections, at the base of the skull behind the ears), and a high cranial capacity. Another skull is more fully *sapiens*, or modern in appearance. Some paleoanthropologists assert that the Omo group of fossils also helps bridge the gap between advanced *Homo erectus* and *Homo sapiens*.

The best-known examples of early *Homo sapiens* come from a group of fossils known collectively as Neanderthal man. Their name derives from the place where the first fossil type was discovered in 1865, the Neander Valley near Düsseldorf, Germany. Similar Neanderthal fossil types have been found at more than forty sites in France, Italy, Belgium, Greece, Czechoslovakia, the Soviet Union, North Africa, and the Middle East.

Neanderthal fossils tend to show an aggregate of distinctive characteristics that at one time led to their being regarded as a separate human species, *Homo neanderthalensis*. They are generally regarded as a subspecies of humans, with the designation *Homo sapiens neanderthalensis*. The characteristic features of their morphology include large heads with prominent supraorbital tori (thick brow ridges), receding jaws, stout and often curved bones, and large joints.

Most important, Neanderthal fossils disclose large brain capacities (1,500 cubic centimeters) and are found in sites revealing complex and sophisticated cultures. These two facts clearly separate Neanderthal humans from more primitive "presapiens" species that exhibit some of the same morphological features. Neanderthalers generally stood fully erect between 1.5 and 1.6 meters in height; they were not the stoop-shouldered brutes of early characterizations. They lived during the last glaciation (the Würm glacial stage) in Eurasia. The sites from which most examples of the Neanderthalers have been recovered have commonly yielded tools of the Mousterian complex, a stone-tool industry named for the kind found at Le Moustier, France, and dating from about 90,000 to about 40,000 years B.P.

In fact, two groups of Neanderthal humans seem to have existed. The first are referred to as classic Neanderthalers from such sites as Germany, France, Italy, Iraq (Shanidar man), and the Soviet Union. The second group, known as either generalized or progressive Neanderthalers, lived contemporaneously with, as well as later than, classic Neanderthal humans. They display a combination of modern *sapiens* features and typical Neanderthal characteristics (especially the prominent supraorbital torus, the forehead ridge). Included in this category for the sake of simplification are those specimens termed neanderthaloid. Examples include Rhodesian man (from Zambia, formerly Northern Rhodesia) and Solo man (from Java), both unearthed at upper Pleistocene deposits (100,000 to 10,000 B.P.). Neanderthalers were cave dwellers and were well adapted to cold conditions (especially the classic Neanderthal variety). They used fire, manufactured stone flake tools, and buried their dead with care. They also seem to have practiced fairly complex religious rituals.

Neanderthalers were a successful group for many thousands of years, flourishing from about 125,000 B.C. to 35,000 B.C., with a wide distribution geographically. Neanderthal traces suddenly and mysteriously disappear from the fossil record, however, and they seem to have been superseded around 35,000 B.C. by other *Homo sapiens* with a more advanced culture and different morphology. In Europe, these are known as the Cro-Magnon peoples, so named for the Cro-Magnon cave near Les Eyzies in southwestern France, where the first skeletons were found in 1868 and where more than one hundred skeletons have since been discovered. Indeed, Cro-Magnon skeletal anatomy is virtually the same as that of modern European and North African populations. The skull is relatively elongated, with a large cranial capacity of about 1,600 cubic centimeters; the brow ridges are only slightly projecting. The average height of Cro-Magnon man was between 1.75 and 1.8 meters.

Cro-Magnon humans produced a culture that, in variety and elegance, far exceeded anything created by their predecessors. They made weapons and tools of bone and stone, stitched hides for clothing, and lived in free-standing shelters as well as caves. Some Cro-Magnon people produced beautiful cave paintings (they have been found in southwestern France and northern Spain) and bone carvings, and they modeled in clay. Though Cro-Magnon samples are the best-known examples of early *Homo sapiens sapiens*, mounting fossil evidence from sites outside Europe as well as genetic research performed in the 1980's suggests a much older date of origin for the emergence of modern man.

At Qafzeh, a cave near Nazareth, Israel, anatomically modern fossils classified as *Homo sapiens sapiens* were discovered in 1988 and reliably dated to 92,000 years B.P. In addition, newer fossil finds of progressive Neanderthalers from Kebara Cave in Israel, taken together with earlier Neanderthal finds from the caves of et-Tabūn and es-Skhūl, also in Israel, make it certain that progressive Neanderthalers and modern humans coexisted for many thousands of years.

Anthropologists have puzzled over the disappearance of the Neanderthalers and, more important, over where they fit in the human family tree. It appears unlikely that classic Neanderthal humans were in the direct ancestral line of modern *Homo sapiens sapiens*. Reasons for their sudden disappearance are believed to include a combination of factors: extinction because of disease, lack of adaptation to the warmer climate following glaciation, and annihilation by the more advanced sapient groups.

Many scholars have considered the classic Neanderthalers to be a cold-adapted, specialized side branch from the modern human line that became extinct as the climate became warmer. The generalized or progressive Neanderthalers are considered by some to have avoided this specialization, perhaps continuing to exist through adaptation and ultimately being absorbed by flourishing modern human populations during the late Pleistocene epoch.

Although the exact time, place, and mode of the origin of the modern human species cannot yet be determined, genetic studies point to a date before 100,000 years B.C. Examination of mitochondrial DNA (mtDNA) from a sampling of present-day humans, representing five broad geographic regions, has allowed researchers to propose a genetic family tree and calculate roughly (assuming a fairly constant mutation rate) a temporal origin for the modern human population. Further studies seem to indicate that the modern human ancestral line emerged between 280,000 years and 140,000 years B.P. Genetic evidence, in concert with fossil finds, makes it plausible that a common ancestral population for *Homo sapiens sapiens* appeared in sub-Saharan Africa or the Levant (in the eastern Mediterranean region). Regional differentiation occurred, followed by radiation outward to other areas. The range of genetic and anatomical variability exhibited by fossil remains of modern humans is no greater than that known for the extant races of modern times.

During the late Pleistocene epoch (approximately 40,000 to 11,000 years B.P.), five different racial groups seem to have developed on the Eurasian and African landmasses. The last glaciation, approximately 30,000 to 10,000 years B.P., absorbed enough water to lower the oceans 90 meters below present levels. Emerging land bridges allowed people to move from Asia into North America, Australia, and elsewhere. In time the major racial roups became subdivided into smaller ones that resulted in the major races seen in modern times.

This view of racial diversification emphasizes the effectiveness both of geographic barriers in reducing free gene flow among varied groups of *Homo sapiens* and of environmental pressure in selecting different adaptive responses from the gene pool. These are also key factors in the entire evolutionary process by which modern humans developed over epochs into their present taxonomic position in the animal kingdom.

Methods of Study

The study of human evolution is primarily the concern of the physical anthropologist and the paleoanthropologist. Evolution may be defined as change in the genetic composition of a population through time. Because evolution is thought to operate according to several principles and factors, modern human evolutionary theory is studied in the light of ideas and practices taken from different disciplines, including archaeology, biochemistry, biology, cultural anthropology, ecology, genetics, paleontology, and physics.

Early investigations into human evolution sought to establish the sequence of the human ancestral line through chronological and morphological analyses of hominid fossil remains (bones and teeth), thus placing them in their proper phylogenetic context (their natural evolutionary ordering). This remains the principal method of study, but it has been augmented by sophisticated techniques in fossil dating and new avenues of exploration into the evolutionary process, such as genetic research.

Determination of the accurate age of a fossil is most important, since it sets the fossil in a correct stratigraphic context that allows comparison with remains from the same geologic layer or level a great distance away. Accurate dating also has helped determine the order of succession for fossils that could not be established on morphological grounds alone.

The most valuable absolute dating methods are the radioactive carbon technique, which can effectively date specimens between 60,000 years B.P. and the present; the potassium-argon technique, which most easily dates material older than 350,000 years B.P.; and the fission-track method, which helps bridge the gaps between other methods. These methods are based on the constant or absolute rates at which radioactive isotopes of carbon, potassium, and argon decay. When absolute dating is impossible, investigators have ascribed a relative age to fossil remains by noting the contents of the layer of rock or the deposit in which the remains were found. A layer containing remains of extinct animals is likely to be older than one containing remains of present forms.

In conjunction with dating, anatomical studies of fossil remains and comparisons with the morphological features of known hominid types, as well as comparisons to primate skeletal structures, have been primary approaches to the study of the evolutionary path of *Homo sapiens*. The species *Homo sapiens* (of which the modern human races compose a number of geographical varieties) may be defined in terms of the anatomical characteristics shared by its members. In general, these include a mean cranial capacity of about 1,400 cubic centimeters, an approximately vertical forehead, a rounded occipital (back) part of the skull, jaws and teeth of reduced size, and limb bones adapted to fully erect posture and bipedalism. Scientists assume that any skeletal remains which conform to this pattern and cannot be classified in other groups of higher primates must belong to *Homo sapiens*.

It is striking that the anatomical differences observed between *Homo erectus* and *Homo sapiens* have been confined to the skull and teeth. The limb bones thus far discovered for both are similar (though *erectus* appears more robust). Cranial capacity and morphology continue to be the dominant determining boundary separating sapient and presapient human species.

Human adaptability studies, using techniques from physiology, demographics, and population genetics, investigate all the biological characteristics of a population that are caused by such environmental stresses as altitude, temperature, and nutrition. It is believed that these normal stresses acted as genetic selectors in prehistoric times and continue to do so. Such racial variants as skin color and body hair are observable products of these stresses. The investigation of climatic changes during prehistoric epochs as revealed in the geologic record is important for understanding those pressures affecting the evolutionary history of man.

Genetic studies have become indispensable to the study of human evolution. Four forces have been identified as fundamental in the evolutionary process: mutation, natural selection, gene flow, and genetic drift. Since mtDNA is inherited through the female, it is possible to calculate how much time has elapsed since the mutations that gave rise to present variations originated in prehistoric populations.

Also important to the study of the evolution of *Homo sapiens* is the examination and classification of cultural remains preserved at hominid fossil sites. Not only can the relative date of a fossil be supported, but sometimes it is also possible to reconstruct the environmental situation that may have influenced the evolutionary process operating in a population. Cultural response is an integral part of hominid adaptation, and it in turn influences natural selection. Technology changes the physical and economic environment, and economic changes alter the demographic situation. Humans continue to promote or influence their own evolution by willingly or unwillingly altering the environment to which they must adapt.

The modern methods useful for investigating the evolutionary history of *Homo sapiens* are multidisciplinary. While each of them reveals an aspect of the emergence of modern man and complements the other methods of study, emphasis is placed on careful fieldwork, accurate dating, and comparative morphological analyses of hominid fossil remains. Increasing in importance, however, is the accumulating wealth of genetic data on human population relationships.

Context

Increasing attention is being given to the biological and behavioral changes that led to the emergence of *Homo sapiens sapiens*—the last major event in human evolution. Mounting evidence continues to push backward in time the point at which modern *Homo sapiens* made his appearance in the evolutionary scheme. The finds at Qafzeh, for example, indicated that modern man arose 50,000 years earlier than had previously been thought. A clearer understanding of the evolutionary history of modern *Homo sapiens* has not only helped to define the place of the modern human species more accurately in relation to the rest of the animal kingdom but also helped to illuminate the pressures, adaptations, and changes that have made humans what they are.

The accumulating data on the evolutionary appearance of *Homo sapiens* have allowed biologists and anthropologists to see the rise of modern man as part of the evolutionary development of the animal kingdom in general and of primates in particular. The primates that exist today make up a remarkable gradational series that links *Homo sapiens sapiens* with small mammals of very primitive types.

Through the pressures and process of evolution (including adaptation and natural selection), *Homo sapiens* has become one of the most successful and adaptive animals that ever lived, because he came to possess an elaborate culture (culture is based on learned behavior). The key is *Homo sapiens'* superior mental capacity. Only human beings can assign arbitrary descriptions to objects, concepts, and feelings and can then communicate them unambiguously to others. In the late Middle Pleistocene, the hominid branch that gave rise to early *Homo sapiens* witnessed an increase in brain size, complex social organizations, continual use of fire, and perhaps even language. As to what initiated these changes, many have suggested tool use and, in turn, a hunting economy.

In a classic article published in 1960, entitled "Tools and Human Evolution," Sherwood Washburn argued that the anatomical structure of modern man is the result of the change, in terms of natural selection, that came with the tool-using way of life. He stated that tools, hunting, fire, and an increasing brain evolved together. Washburn also argued that effective tool use led to effective bipedalism—another significant characteristic of *Homo sapiens*: Man is different from all other animals because he became a user of increasingly complex tools.

The other behavioral pattern that is seen to have been of utmost importance to sapient evolution is big-game hunting. Early *Homo sapiens* was undoubtedly a big-game hunter, as were all of his successors until approximately 8,000 years ago. It has been argued that human intellect, interests, emotions, and basic social life are the evolutionary products of the success of hunting adaptations. Success in hunting adaptation dominated the course of human evolution for hundreds of thousands of years. The agricultural revolution and the industrial and scientific revolutions are only now releasing human beings from conditions characteristic of 99 percent of their evolutionary history.

Scholars have suggested that research into human origins and development is much more relevant than is often realized. It has been argued that, although man no longer lives as a hunter, he is still physically a hunter-gatherer. Some investigators in the field of stress biology, the study of how the human body reacts to stressful situations, feel that man is biologically equipped for one mode of life (hunting) but lives another. Thus, there would be some link between an emotional reaction, such as explosive aggression, and human evolutionary history. Tools and more efficient hunting helped produce great change in hominid evolution and made man what he is. Humans continue to be users of increasingly complex tools, such as computers, and perhaps this continued development of technology may determine the future evolutionary path of *Homo sapiens*.

Bibliography

Cann, R. L., M. Stoneking, and C. A. Wilson. "Mitochondrial DNA and Human Evolution." *Nature* 325 (January 1, 1987): 31-36. Though written somewhat for the knowledgeable student of human evolution, this important article presents the results of a major study using DNA to trace genetic differences in widely varied samples of the present population and, by constructing an evolutionary family tree, to propose a time and place for the emergence of modern man. It shows the increasing importance of genetics for the study of the modern human evolution.

Eldredge, Niles, and Ian Tattersall. *The Myths of Human Evolution*. New York: Columbia University Press, 1982. In fewer than two hundred pages the authors give the nonspecialist a brief, comprehensive look at human evolutionary history, while attempting to show that the once-standard expectations of evolution—slow, steady, gradual progress—are not supported by the evidence. According to the authors, fossil evidence shows human evolution to be the result of long periods of stability interrupted by abrupt change, occurring in smaller populations. The thesis is an important consideration presented in well-written form.

Leakey, Richard E. *The Making of Mankind*. New York: E. P. Dutton, 1981. This book of modest size is written, by the son of Louis and Mary Leakey, from the perspective of one who grew up with famous physical anthropologists and scientists who were tracing human origins. The text is complemented with many color photographs. Chapters discussing the development of language and early *Homo sapiens* culture are important. It also distills and synthesizes important ideas of others.

Phenice, Terrell W. *Hominid Fossils*. Dubuque, Iowa: Wm. C. Brown, 1973. This represents one of the best introductory illustrated keys of hominid fossil remains of the Pleistocene epoch. The drawings are all oriented the same way, and each fossil illustration is listed with its measurements and with information concerning tools found at the respective sites. This book (and similar types of atlases) is very helpful to the nonspecialist.

Pilbeam, David. *The Ascent of Man: An Introduction to Human Evolution*. New York: Macmillan, 1972. This classic text by a distinguished expert traces the emergence of *Homo sapiens* from early hominid origins. It contains numerous photographs of fossil discoveries and schema for proposed theories for modern human ancestry. Designed as a college textbook, it does a fine job of discussing human origins in the context of primate evolution, although it is somewhat dated.

Scientific American, ed. *Human Variation and Origins: An Introduction to Human Biology and Evolution*. San Francisco: W. H. Freeman, 1967. This carefully selected collection of twenty-seven articles drawn from several issues of *Scientific American* contains several classics in the areas of human evolution and diversification. Though newer information is lacking, the basic and crucial concepts of human origins and variation are presented. Particularly valuable are early cornerstone discussions of the genetic code by Francis Crick (chapter 7), tools and human evolution by S. Washburn (chapter 16), and the distribution of man by W. Howells (chapter 21). Each article is a separate chapter.

Stringer, Christopher B., and Peter Andrews. "Genetic and Fossil Evidence for the Origin of Modern Humans." *Science* 239 (March 11, 1988): 1263-1268. This major article combines genetic data and data from the late Pleistocene hominid fossil record to discuss the two most important contrasting but competing models on the origins of modern humans: the multiregional model and single-origin, or out-of-Africa, model. Though technical in one or two places, it synthesizes much information succinctly. A healthy list of references at the end is useful.

Waechter, John. *Man Before History.* Oxford, England: Elsevier-Phaidon, 1976. This is a concise, readily accessible volume on the evolutionary history of humans. It contains some of the finest visual and graphic representations (photographs and illustrations) on the subject found in any single work on the evolutionary journey of the human species. It also contains an extensive glossary of terms with numerous illustrations. Particularly strong in its discussion and representation of late prehistoric culture (especially art), it is an excellent reference work geared toward the nonspecialist.

Andrew C. Skinner

Cross-References

Apes to Hominids, 127; Evolution: A Historical Perspective, 903; Convergent and Divergent Evolution, 910; Cultural Evolution, 918; Extinction, 953; Gene Flow, 1097; Human Genetics, 1190; Hominids, 1321; Natural Selection, 1870; Nonrandom Mating, Genetic Drift, and Mutation, 1965; Primates, 2202; Speciation and the Species Concept, 2521; Systematics, 2594.

HORMONAL CONTROL OF BLOOD SUGAR AND FATTY ACIDS

Type of life science: Animal physiology
Other field of study: Biochemistry

The energy needs of the body are integrated through a series of hormonal responses that ensure a continuous supply of nutrients to meet the specific requirements of each tissue. By understanding the relationship between hormonal regulators and their metabolic fuels, scientists can then study responses to such stressful conditions as starvation or exercise.

Principal terms

ABSORPTIVE STATE: the period following a meal when ingested nutrients are being absorbed from the intestine and entering the blood

ANABOLISM: the buildup, or synthesis, of larger organic molecules from their smaller constituent parts

CATABOLISM: the breakdown, or degradation, of the larger, energy-rich organic molecules within cells

GLUCONEOGENESIS: the conversion of amino acids and glycerol into glucose within the cells of the liver or kidney

GLYCOGENESIS: the genesis or synthesis of glycogen from glucose in liver and muscle cells

GLYCOGENOLYSIS: the lysis, or breakdown, of glycogen into glucose and its release into the blood

INTERMEDIARY METABOLISM: those chemical reactions in cells involved in processing metabolic fuels into energy or into chemical intermediates used in the synthesis of vital cell components such as nucleic acids, proteins, and lipids

LIPOGENESIS: the production of energy-rich triglycerides in adipose and liver cells from fatty acids and glycerol

LIPOLYSIS: the breakdown of triglycerides into free fatty acids and glycerol and their release into the blood

Summary of the Phenomenon

All living organisms require metabolic fuel as an energy source for their survival. This energy is used to fuel all the chemical reactions that occur within cells. The major dietary source of energy for humans is carbohydrates, which can be in the form of such simple sugars as glucose or, more commonly, in the form of disaccharides (sucrose) or polysaccharides (starch). Fat is the second major energy source and is the most efficient source of energy. On a per-weight basis, fat provides more than twice as much energy as sugar. It is the fat deposits in the body which allow an animal to tolerate periods of starvation.

Lipolysis, or the breakdown of stored fat, produces free fatty acids that can then be used as an energy source for both muscle and liver tissue. Some cells can utilize alternative fuels such as amino acids, but the brain and nerve cells require a continuous supply of glucose. In the resting state, the brain is the chief glucose-consuming tissue. Because the brain does not store any of this nutrient, brain damage can result within fifteen minutes if its glucose supply is cut off. Prolonged fuel deprivation also results in the production of a substitute form of energy derived from the adipose tissue. The metabolism of fatty acids can produce substances termed ketone bodies. These represent an alternate source of fuel that the brain can use to diminish reliance on glucose.

Approximately 80 percent of the storage form of glucose, glycogen, is found in the muscle. The remaining 20 percent of carbohydrate is stored mainly in the liver but also in some other organs. Liver glycogen plays a key role in responding to the energy needs of the body and is the principal source for the short-term replenishment of glucose to the blood. Normally 70 percent of the glucose output from the liver is derived directly from the breakdown of stored glycogen (glycogenolysis), whereas about 30 percent is generated from the conversion of amino acids from muscle protein (gluconeogenesis).

Human bodies thus alternate between periods of food availability (and the resulting storage of high-energy organic compounds) and periods of fasting (where those energy stores are called upon to provide energy and to maintain plasma glucose concentrations). The body must somehow monitor its own stages—whether it is in an anabolic mode, one in which there is nutrient storage, or in a catabolic mode, one in which degradation of these energy-rich molecules occurs.

The key to understanding this integrated response lies, in part, in the exquisitely sensitive glucose sensors lying in the endocrine cells of the pancreas. Under most circumstances the pancreatic hormones, insulin and glucagon, represent the dominant hormonal regulators that respond to the energy needs of the body. Additional control of nutrient flow is provided by epinephrine, growth hormone, cortisol, and thyroid hormone. The release of glucagon is triggered by a declining blood glucose concentration, whereas the release of insulin is triggered by a rising blood glucose. Insulin can thus be considered an anabolic hormone. In the presence of glucose, insulin will also respond to and lower the concentrations of free fatty acids and amino acids and will promote their conversion into glyocogen, triglyceride, and protein, respectively. In contrast, glucagon is released in response to fatty acids and amino acids in the absence of glucose, whereas glucose itself is a potent inhibitor of glucagon release.

Insulin accomplishes its glucose-lowering effect by four different processes. First, insulin aids in the transport of glucose into most cells. In the absence of insulin, glucose cannot readily penetrate most cell membranes except those of the brain, exercising muscle, and the liver. Insulin is thought to increase the number of specific carriers in the membrane to transport glucose into the cell. Thus, resting muscle cells depend on insulin for the uptake of glucose and its subsequent conversion into stored glycogen. During exercise, however, when blood insulin levels are decreased, both glucose uptake and metabolism are increased in working muscle cells. This mechanism ensures that the actual cells which require an increase in metabolic fuel during periods of need will in fact be able to gain access to this nutrient. Second, insulin promotes glycogenesis, the storage of glycogen in the comparatively large muscle mass, with the rest stored in the liver. Third, insulin prevents glycogenolysis during periods when glucose is freely available so that the breakdown of the previously stored fuel is not wasted. Finally, insulin inhibits gluconeogenesis in the liver and kidney. This is accomplished by reducing the concentration of amino acids in the blood and by inhibiting the activity of the enzymes responsible for the conversion of noncarbohydrate molecules into glucose.

Insulin also exerts multiple effects on blood fatty acids and promotes their storage into triglycerides. In adipose tissue, insulin promotes the transport of glucose into the cell as well as the activation of enzymes that are responsible for the conversion of glucose into fatty acids and glycerol. These small precursor molecules can then be synthesized into triglycerides. Insulin potentiates the uptake of fatty acids from the blood into adipose cells; insulin also inhibits lipolysis during periods of increased availability of fatty acids. Energy is thus not expended in breaking down the already-formed triglycerides into their component parts. Finally, insulin is responsible for reducing blood amino acid concentrations and stimulating protein synthesis, actions which collectively promote growth and development.

The most important function of glucagon is to prevent hypoglycemia, the inappropriate lowering of blood glucose concentration. It accomplishes this by stimulating liver glycogenolysis and gluconeogenesis. Gluconeogenesis is an important factor in replenishing liver glycogen stores and thus in maintaining normal blood glucose levels between meals. Glucagon also stimulates lipolysis in the liver (but has little effect on either muscle or adipose tissue). Glucagon is thus increased during periods of fasting and decreased while food is actively being digested— exactly the opposite of what insulin does. Insulin puts nutrients into storage while their concentrations in blood are increased, whereas glucagon breaks down these energy stores between meals to maintain a normal blood concentration of nutrients, particularly blood glucose.

Epinephrine, like glucagon, mobilizes the carbohydrate and fat stores to provide an immediate source of energy to fuel muscular work. It is released from nerve endings in the adrenal medulla into the bloodstream, where it exerts an effect on its respective target tissues. Its most important actions are on the muscle and adipose tissues, where it stimulates glycogenolysis and lipolysis, respectively. In the liver, epinephrine stimulates both gluconeogenesis and glycogenolysis. Because of differences in the enzyme content of the liver and the muscle, the glycogen in muscle is not converted directly to glucose. Rather, lactic acid is released into the blood as a result of the metabolism of muscle glycogen. The liver, in turn, takes up the lactic acid and converts it into glucose. Thus, epinephrine, through its actions on skeletal muscle, indirectly contributes to an increase in blood glucose levels. Epinephrine also inhibits the release of insulin and stimulates glucogen, further adding to its hyperglycemic action. Under resting conditions, epinephrine plays only a minor role in fuel homeostasis; however, its importance becomes evident in the response to "fight or flight" situations. By mobilizing the body's fuels for immediate action, the release of epinephrine also assures adequate nourishment for the brain. Muscles can use the fatty acids for energy production, but the brain cannot.

Growth hormone can also influence certain aspects of fuel metabolism. Growth hormone, or somatotrophin, is the most abundant hormone produced by the anterior pituitary gland, even in adults, whose growth has already ceased. Growth hormone is an insulin antagonist: It opposes the actions of insulin. Growth hormone increases blood glucose levels by decreasing the glucose uptake by muscles, and it enhances the breakdown of fat stored in the adipose tissue. Muscles use the mobilized fatty acids instead of glucose for their energy needs. The overall response to growth hormone secretion is an increase in blood fatty acids to be used as a metabolic fuel, which spares glucose for glucose-dependent tissues such as the brain. Furthermore, growth hormone enhances protein anabolism in muscle. This protective effect of maintaining body protein may be important during periods of fasting.

The secretion of cortisol by the adrenal cortex plays an important role in intermediary metabolism. The overall effect of cortisol's action is to increase the concentration of blood glucose at the expense of protein and fat stores. Cortisol promotes the breakdown of protein in the muscle, thereby increasing the supply of gluconeogenic precursors to the liver. These mobilized amino acids are also available for repair of damaged tissue or synthesis of new cellular structures. Cortisol also inhibits glucose uptake and use by many tissues, with the exception of the brain. Finally, cortisol stimulates lipolysis, thus releasing free fatty acids into the blood. Adequate concentrations of cortisol are essential for normal fuel metabolism, but changes in cortisol secretion are not important in the metabolic responses to feeding or fasting.

The actions of thyroid hormones are similar to those of cortisol in that they are necessary for normal metabolic responses. The thyroid gland can be likened to the carburetor of a car: If the idle of the car is set high, the car burns fuel at an excessive rate, while at a low setting, fuel intake is decreased. Similarly, if the activity of the thyroid gland is increased, metabolic fuel is burned up at a greater rate than if the activity is low. Thyroid hormone also modulates the rate of many specific reactions involved in intermediary metabolism. For example, the conversion of glucose into glycogen is assisted by small amounts of thyroid hormone, but the reverse, the breakdown of glycogen into glucose, occurs when the concentration of thyroid hormone is high. Thyroid hormone is essential for protein synthesis, but at abnormally high concentrations the overall effect is protein degradation. Thyroid hormones are thus generally catabolic—the consumption, rather than storage, of fuel dominates its actions. This is manifested by depletion of liver glycogen stores, muscle wasting from protein degradation, and depletion of fat stores. Yet, because the actions of thyroid hormone are exceptionally slow in onset, changes in thyroid hormones are not usually important for fuel homeostasis.

The actions of glucagon, epinephrine, cortisol, growth hormone, and thyroid hormone (with the exception of the anabolic effects of growth hormone on protein metabolism) are opposite those of insulin. Because they antagonize the effects of insulin, these five hormones are referred to as "counterregulatory hormones," with insulin being the regulatory hormone. The secretion of these hormones is normally inversely related to the rate of insulin release, with the net result that these hormones act in concert with insulin to maintain normal fuel homeostasis.

Methods of Study

Until comparatively recently, the measurement of insulin activity was limited to crude biological assays. These included measurements of the ability of insulin to lower blood glucose or to stimulate glucose uptake by rat muscle. Using radioactive (labeled) glucose, the rate of uptake of glucose into the rat muscle could be followed. In each of these methods, the concentration of insulin could be estimated by comparing the magnitude of the biological effect with that produced by a known concentration of pure insulin.

A practical method for the measurement of insulin in blood was first developed in 1959. This assay not only revolutionized the study of insulin and its role in the metabolic control of fuel metabolism but also permitted the development of similar assays for the measurement of numerous biologically important molecules. The assay was based on the principle of competition between the insulin in blood and insulin made radioactive (labeled) with a protein (an antibody) specific for binding to insulin. One essential feature of this method is the separation of the insulin bound to the antibody from the free, labeled hormone. Once separated, the radioactivity in each fraction can be counted. The concentration of insulin in a blood sample can then be compared with known standard concentrations of insulin. Availability of this sensitive technique permitted the measurement of insulin release from cultured pancreas fragments as easily as from blood. Compounds and food that affect the release of hormones—and thereby affect fuel metabolism—have thus been studied in this manner.

In 1975, the human insulin gene was one of the first human genes to be cloned. The gene responsible for the synthesis of insulin was isolated from the insulin-producing beta cells and placed in a bacterium. Under these conditions, bacteria can continually produce human insulin such that large quantities of the hormone can be isolated; eventually, the purified preparation can be used to treat diabetic patients. Until the advent of this technology, insulin could be obtained only in minute amounts from animal pancreas tissue. Moreover, because insulin from a cow or pig is structurally different from human insulin, some diabetic patients developed an allergy to it.

Using the same procedure, growth hormone can also be isolated in large quantities from the bacterium. Administration of this material to farm animals improves their efficiency of milk and meat production. Studies have shown that growth hormone increases the animals' feed efficiency, growth rate, and muscle mass while decreasing the amount of carcass fat. In humans, growth hormone is used to treat dwarfism and may be used to treat children with small stature.

Context

Knowledge of the hormonal regulation of glucose and fatty acids in blood has improved scientists' understanding of how the body copes with the challenges of short- and long-term starvation, responds to exercise, and responds to the ingestion of nutrients. In general, it is the change in insulin secretion that is the major determinant of the response to any of these situations.

Normally, the metabolic changes associated with starvation are simply a continuation of the processes that began during the postabsorptive period. The processes that occur serve to meet the energy needs of the normally glucose-dependent tissues, such as the brain, while at the same time they minimize protein degradation. The decline in blood glucose concentrations decreases insulin release while stimulating additional glucagon release from the pancreas. The increase in glucagon secretion early in starvation is important for the maintenance of glycogenolysis as well as the stimulation of gluconeogenesis. Glucagon returns to normal levels by about the third day of starvation, however, and so is unlikely to play a significant role in the adaptation to more long-term starvation.

Growth hormone concentrations are elevated in early starvation but return to normal within a week. There is evidence that growth hormone and cortisol contribute to the maintenance of blood glucose concentrations during starvation. Starvation also results in a decrease in the production of thyroid hormones. Consequently, in response to the decline in metabolic rate, the tissue requirement for metabolic fuels is decreased. The lack of insulin prevents the muscle from using glucose as an energy source, so glucose can be exclusively used by the brain. The production of ketone bodies is increased, however, and it is this metabolic fuel that constitutes the major energy source for the brain.

The metabolic responses to exercise and to stress are similar to each other and depend upon their severity and duration. During mild exercise and the early stages of more rigorous exercise, the muscles rely on muscle glycogen as their primary energy source. Muscle triglyceride also supplements the energy needs of the working cells. Because there is an increase in blood flow to the exercising muscle, there is an increase in delivery of both glucose and free fatty acids. Recall that during periods of exercise the muscle can use blood glucose as a fuel even though insulin levels are depressed. Heavy exercise stimulates glucagon, growth hormone, and epinephrine release and effectively shuts down insulin release. The changes in these hormones stimulate both glucose production from the liver and free fatty acid release from adipose tissue. Muscle contraction can then be sustained by these fuel sources.

The body's overall response to stress is to prepare for "fight or flight." Cortisol, epinephrine, and glucagon mobilize energy reserves to provide additional energy for the brain and muscle. The difference between exercise and stress is that during exercise the increased production of these metabolic fuels is balanced by their consumption in the contracting muscle. Ultimately, there are no marked changes in blood glucose and fatty acid concentrations. In stress, however, these fuels may not be burned, which results in a substantial increase in their blood concentrations.

Bibliography

Kleiber, Max. *The Fire of Life*. Rev. ed. Melbourne, Fla.: R. E. Kriege, 1975. This is a classic text on animal energetics and nutrition. Part 2 is devoted to the metabolic changes during starvation, while part 3 deals with food as a fuel. Definitely an intermediate-level college text with a biochemical approach to fuel metabolism.

Lehninger, Albert. *Principles of Biochemistry*. New York: Worth, 1982. A comprehensive text providing glimpses of how living organisms solve some of their most fundamental physical and chemical problems. The logic behind metabolism and factors that regulate the processing of nutrients are elegantly presented.

Newsholme, Eric, and Tony Leech. *Biochemistry for the Medical Sciences*. New York: John Wiley & Sons, 1983. Chapter 7 specifically discusses changes in fuel metabolism with graded levels of exercise. The reasons for muscle fatigue and exhaustion in marathon runners are clearly discussed.

Norman, Anthony, and Gerald Litwack. *Hormones*. Orlando, Fla.: Academic Press, 1987. Chapter 7, "Pancreatic Hormones: Insulin and Glucagon," provides a concise review of the endocrine pancreas and the factors that regulate insulin and glucagon release. Each section is well illustrated and is formatted in a logical fashion. Provides clear information on the effects of insulin and glucagon at the molecular level and covers their biological effects.

Notkins, Abner. "The Causes of Diabetes." *Scientific American* 241 (November, 1979): 62-73. The etiologies of both Type I and Type II diabetes are presented. Evidence for environmental and genetic factors causing diabetes is summarized. A model for the binding of glucose to proteins helps explain why the diabetic has a lower life expectancy.

Young, Vernon, and N. S. Scrimshaw. "The Physiology of Starvation." *Scientific American* 225 (October, 1971): 14-21. Documents the changes in fuel metabolism in humans during starvation. Blood levels of various amino acids are followed prior to fasting and then for the first forty days of starvation. Major pathways in the metabolism of sugars by the liver in starvation and fed states are clearly diagrammed.

Hillar Klandorf

Cross-References

Catabolism of Fats and Proteins, 337; Testing for Endocrine Functions of Glands

HORMONAL CONTROL OF PROTEIN METABOLISM

Type of life science: Animal physiology
Other field of study: Biochemistry

Hormonal control of protein metabolism underlies the well-being and health of most animals. Because of the structural contributions of proteins to the animal body and because of their role in the regulation of body functions and energy, the hormonal control of proteins is strategically important to the biological status of higher animals.

Principal terms

AMINO ACID: a small organic molecule of which there are about twenty; it constitutes the basic structural unit of proteins

ANABOLISM: a process that is concerned with combination of smaller molecules to form a large molecule; it results in the intensification of energy capacity

CATABOLISM: a process that involves the breakdown of a large molecule into smaller molecules; it is accompanied by a release of energy for utilization purposes

CYTOPLASM(IC): one of the two major compartments in a cell; it is the outer portion, where many cellular processes occur

ENDOCRINE: pertaining to glands in the body that release their products or secretions into the bloodstream; such glands do not possess ducts for such release

ENDOPLASMIC RETICULUM: a membranous network that ramifies throughout the cytoplasm

HORMONE: a regulatory compound that is released from an endocrine gland; it is either a protein, a steroid, or an amino acid derivative

METABOLISM: the sum of all chemical processes in the body; it includes the anabolic, or buildup, and catabolic, or breakdown, changes

PROTEIN: a large organic molecule comprised of linked amino acids; it functions in structural, energy, and regulatory requirements of the body

Summary of the Phenomenon

Protein metabolism, wherein one of the body's most important nutritional requirements is reassembled for invigorating many vital functions, is prominently controlled by regulatory chemical agents known as hormones, which are carried by the blood. The proteins themselves are molecules that are universally known to engage in very useful functions.

Generally, these activities are the maintenance of the body structure, the regulation of body functions, and the provision of energy. Protein metabolism, or the involvement of proteins in these body tasks, is accomplished through two avenues: anabolism, which basically includes amino acids availability, and catabolism. A delicate balance between these two phenomena must be maintained in order to avoid any excess or deficiency in the body's reservoir of proteins.

Of the two constituents of protein metabolism, the less complex is catabolism, a process of degradation whereby the protein molecules are broken down to amino acids, with the liberation of chemical fragments and energy for sustaining the body functions. Anabolism, on the other hand, is a general biological concept whereby amino acids are joined together by energy bonds in order to form larger protein molecules. The anabolic process is the more complicated of the two processes since the incorporation of the amino acids into specific proteins requires the involvement of specified encoded blueprints. These patterns for protein assemblages originate on the deoxyribonucleic acid (DNA) in the nucleus, are then transferred to ribonucleic acid (RNA), and then proceed to the protein synthesizing machinery on the cytoplasmic ribosomal/endoplasmic reticulum complex.

Finally, in line with these concepts, since proteins are fitted together from amino acids, the availability of amino acids to the cells is an important precursory action to the anabolic and the subsequent protein catabolic processes. This accessibility of amino acids is achieved via the absorptive uptake from the small intestines, followed by circulatory transport and entrance into cells across the cell membrane.

The hormones that control these two features of protein metabolism are produced by and released from the endocrine, or ductless, glands, which are widely distributed throughout the body. Regarding anabolism and amino acid availability, insulin is the most outstanding hormonal candidate. This hormone is produced by the pancreas, which is positioned just below the stomach, in the middle region of the abdominal cavity. The well-documented actions of insulin involve promoting the transport of amino acids across the cell membranes. Consequently, insulin stimulates the entry of amino acids into cells, thereby providing the basic units for making proteins. Additionally, insulin also stimulates protein manufacture by two means: by regulating the incorporation of amino acids into proteins and by influencing the DNA-to-RNA-to-protein synthesizing axis.

Next on this list of hormones that influence protein anabolism is growth hormone, or somatotropin. This hormone is released from the anterior pituitary gland located below the forebrain. Another regulatory compound, growth-hormone releasing factor, produced by a specific site in the forebrain, then stimulates the release of growth hormone. Hence, these two hormones operate as a paired regulatory team. Growth hormone performs an important anabolic role. Its action is the basis for all organismic growth. Specifically, growth hormone facilitates the incorporation of amino acids into proteins. This action is accomplished by way of enhancing the production of DNA and RNA, the two compounds that ultimately control the protein-manufacturing process.

Another hormone, thyroxine, produced by the thyroid gland, located in the neck region, is also widely known to stimulate protein synthesis in the body cells.

Finally, the male sex hormone, testosterone, produced by the testes, promotes protein synthesis in many nonreproductive tissues and organs. In a similar manner, the female sex hormone, progesterone, released from the ovaries in the lower abdomen, also induces protein synthesis. The protein-stimulatory activities of these reproductive hormones constitute the basis for growth in both genders. Yet, testosterone and progesterone can negatively affect protein synthesis under certain circumstances.

From a catabolic standpoint, the hormones affecting protein metabolism include glucagon, the glucocorticoids, the catecholamines, and the adrenal steroids. Glucagon, a hormone produced by the pancreas, exerts its catabolic effect by increasing the rate of protein breakdown in the liver. It also limits the rate of incorporation of amino acids into proteins. Then there are the glucocorticoids, which are exemplified by cortisol, or hydrocortisone. These are released from the outer portion of the adrenal gland, found in the vicinity of the kidneys, which are located in the middle-body region. These hormones promote the mobilization of proteins from the body tissues. This action is followed by subsequent breakdown of the proteins and the transport of the constituent amino acids into the liver. The glucocorticoids are capable of stimulating the synthesis of liver enzymes that assist in the breakdown of amino acids.

Yet another group, the catecholamines, illustrated by epinephrine and norepinephrine, and produced by the inner portion of this same adrenal gland, is reputed to induce a general breakdown of liver proteins. Finally, the steroid hormones, also released by the adrenal gland, are believed to lower the rate of protein synthesis and to stimulate the rates at which tissue proteins and amino acids are broken down.

Methods of Study

The hormones that are involved with regulation of protein metabolism fall into three groups: protein, derivatives of amino acids, and steroids that are related to lipid (fat) compounds. The techniques employed for measuring these hormones as they affect protein metabolism are very specific and have allowed for a much better understanding of the operational characteristics and mechanisms of protein metabolism. Radioimmunoassay is probably the most widely used modern technique in this regard. This technique is based on the antigen-antibody binding reaction and is useful in measurements involving small quantities of hormones. Under this method, the hormone performs the role of an antigen. The antibodies or binding proteins are prepared either by the immunization of animals against the hormones or by biotechnological measures that entail bacteria.

The first step in the radioimmunoassay procedure is the mixing of known amounts of the unlabeled (no radioisotopes are added) test hormone plus antibody, with the radioactively labeled hormone in a test tube. Upon incubation of the mixture, there is competition between the unlabeled and labeled hormonal fractions for the binding sites on the antibody. The second step in the procedure involves separation of the free portions. This process is accomplished by filtering, centrifugation, or precipitation. Finally, the level of binding between the labeled hormone and antibody is determined. This binding is used as an indication of the amount of unlabeled hormone which is present.

A modification of the radioimmunoassay procedure is competitive protein binding. Herein, naturally occurring proteins, instead of the antibodies, are used in the binding process. Other recently developed techniques for studying hormonal activities are chromatography, the use of polyclonal or monoclonal antibodies, cellulose filter assays, which compare the filtering efficiency with known standards, perfusion techniques, chromatofocusing, and radioreceptor assays. Chromatography is the most widely used among these more-recent methods. It employs different types of columns and media, and is based on the principle of absorption and separation. This system is classified in accordance with the physical states of its two constituent phases. Hence, on this basis, there are the liquid-solid, liquid-liquid, gas-liquid, and gas-solid types. High-performance liquid chromatography is currently the most advanced and preferred type being used.

Context

Hormonal regulation of protein metabolism is important because it promotes availability of proteins and amino acids to the cells of the body. This accessibility of proteins and amino acids is conducted through anabolic and catabolic mechanisms, which are delicately balanced by the opposing actions of various hormones. This balance in protein metabolism can be shifted in the direction of either catabolism or anabolism should the combined actions of opposing hormones not be coordinated. The necessity for securing this balance in protein metabolism ensures that neither a net decrease nor a net increase could occur in the body pool of proteins. Deviations from this balance could be reflected by undesirable consequences in body mass, in the regulation of the body functions, and in the utilization of energy. It is not surprising, then, that many hormonal systems in the body, either directly or indirectly, work through protein metabolism. They do so because the proper nutritional status involving proteins is essential for biological integrity.

Bibliography

Austin, C. R., and R. V. Short. *Reproduction in Mammals: Mechanisms of Hormone Action*. Cambridge, England: Cambridge University Press, 1979. An advanced-level textbook directed toward readers with a strong background in hormones study. Chapter 6, "Progesterone," generally deals with the actions of this hormone. This publication provides abundant detailed information, along with very good graphs, diagrams, and additional reading lists.

Fox, Stuart Ira. *Human Physiology*. 2d ed. Dubuque, Iowa: Wm. C. Brown, 1987. A textbook written in a very lucid manner with beautiful diagrams and explicit tables. Chapter 19, "Regulation of Metabolism," deals with metabolism from nutritional, energy, and hormonal regulation. Good summaries at the ends of chapters and selected readings are provided. This text is good college-level reading but is also appropriate for high school students.

Goodman, H. Maurice. *Basic Medical Endocrinology.* New York: Raven Press, 1988. Chapter 4, "Islets of Langerhans," furnishes detailed information substantiated by experimental evidence on hormones, insulin, and glucagon. Additionally, chapter 1, "Introduction," briefly covers the main and most successful method, radioimmunoassay, for studying hormones, along with its advantages and limitations. Very precise diagrams are presented. Specific journal articles are included in the bibliography.

Ingbar, Sidney H. *Contemporary Endocrinology.* Vol. 1. New York: Plenum, 1979. A college-level text that covers the entire endocrine system. Chapter 8, "Catecholamines and the Sympathoadrenal System: The Regulation of Metabolism," covers a specific area in controlling metabolism. A rather high order reading book with extensive bibliographies.

Malkinson, A. M. *Hormone Action.* New York: John Wiley & Sons, 1978. Chapter 2, "Peptide Hormones and Catecholamines," furnishes a very general and comprehensive coverage on the actions of hormone. A good book that treats the hormones and their functions in a very readable fashion. It provides very elaborate review of the scientific literature pertaining to hormonal action.

O'Riordan, J. L. H., P. G. Malan, and R. P. Gould. *Essentials of Endocrinology.* Oxford, England: Blackwell Scientific Publications, 1982. Chapter 7, "Pancreatic and Gastrointestinal Hormones," deals with the hormones released by the pancreas in a more specific manner. Chapter 1, "The Endocrine System and the Molecular Basis for Hormone Action," contains a short but clearly written segment concerned with hormonal binding assays. This book is full of detailed, very scientific information. The coverage here is designed for students and readers seeking more precise matter.

Paxton, Mary Jean W. *Endocrinology: Biological and Medical Perspectives.* Dubuque, Iowa: Wm. C. Brown, 1986. Chapter 10, "Hormonal Control of Intermediary Metabolism," covers the nutritional and hormonal aspects of metabolism. This book is especially designed for intermediate college-level readers. It provides exceptionally good diagrams and tables. The reference lists are detailed and current.

Rhoades, Rodney, and Richard Pflanzer. *Human Physiology.* Philadelphia: Saunders College Publishing, 1989. A general physiology textbook written for intermediate-level college readers. Chapter 6, "Energy and Cellular Metabolism," covers the contributions of the nutrients and hormones to metabolism. This text contains very beautifully drawn and clear diagrams with summaries at the ends of chapters. Suggested readings are provided.

Turner, C. Donnell, and Joseph T. Bagnara. *General Endocrinology.* 6th ed. Philadelphia: W. B. Saunders, 1976. A general textbook that thoroughly covers the entire hormonal system and the endocrine glands that produce these hormones. The book furnishes abundant experimental evidence and extensive bibliographies.

Vander, Arthur J., James H. Sherman, and Dorothy S. Luciano. *Human Physiology.*

5th ed. New York: McGraw-Hill, 1990. A very good general physiology textbook with excellent diagrams and very readable explanations of biological matters. Chapter 17, "Regulation of Organic Metabolism, Growth, and Energy Balance," provides a nice section that deals with the hormonal control of metabolism. Excellent summaries and reading lists are presented at the ends of chapters. This work is a good college-level textbook.

Fitzgerald Spencer

Cross-References

Catabolism of Fats and Proteins, 337; Endocrine Functions of the Pancreas, 787; Endocrinology of the Adrenal Glands, 800; Endocrinology of the Pituitary Gland, 807; Endocrinology of the Thyroid and Parathyroid Glands, 814; Eukaryotic Transcriptional Control: Steroid Hormones, 887; Hormonal Control of Blood Sugar and Fatty Acids, 1339; Hormone Mechanisms: Gene Regulation, 1353; Hormone Mechanisms and Second Messengers, 1361; Mammalian Hormones, 1368.

HORMONE MECHANISMS: GENE REGULATION

Type of life science: Genetic regulation in eukaryotes
Other fields of study: Animal physiology, biochemistry, and molecular biology

Steroid hormones are intercellular messengers that modulate life processes as hormone-receptor complexes that cause specific gene expression. Studying them has helped scientists to learn about eukaryotic gene regulation and to treat cancer.

Principal terms

CHROMATIN: a deoxyribonucleic acid (DNA) and protein mixture containing all the hereditary information in an organism; interaction with steroid hormone-receptor complexes changes the DNA segments (genes) used for ribonucleic acid (RNA) synthesis, altering gene expression

ENDOCRINE GLANDS: glands that produce hormones and secrete them into the blood, so they can serve as intercellular messengers in other organs

GENE EXPRESSION: a biochemical process in which segments of the DNA in chromatin, genes, are copied (transcribed) to RNA messages that yield specific proteins via cellular protein-synthesizing machinery

GONADS: endocrine glands in males and females that make steroid sex hormones; male gonads (testes) make androgens, and female gonads (ovaries) make estrogens

HORMONES: chemical messengers made by endocrine glands to stimulate, in other tissues, biochemical processes necessary for life and well-being

MESSENGER RIBONUCLEIC ACID (MRNA): a nucleic acid molecule made by DNA transcription; each one carries the information used for synthesis of an enzyme or some other protein

PROTEINS: amino acid polymers made by cellular protein-synthesizing machinery via translation of mRNAs; they are catalysts called enzymes and are many other key cell components

RECEPTORS: very specific proteins that interact with hormones, enabling them to carry out messenger functions in target organs; steroid hormone-receptor complexes alter gene expression

STEROID HORMONE: a hormone that is a lipidic (fatlike) chemical derived from cholesterol

TARGET ORGAN: a nonendocrine organ that responds to a hormone by changes in its biological capabilities; target organs for steroid hormones exhibit altered levels of key proteins as a result of changed gene expression

Summary of the Phenomenon

The word "hormone" arises from the Greek verb *horman*, which means to urge on or stimulate. This definition is fitting because hormones are chemical messengers that stimulate biochemical processes necessary for the life and well-being of the body as a whole. Hormones are produced in tiny amounts by the organs called endocrine glands; the study of hormones is named endocrinology for this reason. An endocrine gland secretes hormones directly into the blood, which then carries them to other organs, where hormone effects occur. The organs affected by hormones are called target organs. The messenger action of hormones integrates body functions and allows them to occur with maximum flexibility.

The steroid hormones are structurally similar to lipids (fatlike chemicals) that arise from cholesterol. There are two main groups of steroid hormones, corticosteroids and gonadal (sex) hormones. Corticosteroids are made by the outer part (cortex) of the adrenal glands, each a pea-sized organ that sits atop one kidney. Sex hormones are made by the male and female gonads (the testes and ovaries, respectively). Adrenal corticosteroids are subdivided into the glucocorticoids and the mineralocorticoids. There are three classes of gonadal hormones: the androgens, the estrogens, and the progestins. The most active members of the five types of steroid hormones are cortisol (or hydrocortisone), aldosterone, testosterone, estradiol, and progesterone, respectively.

Glucocorticoids, such as cortisol, were named because their first reported effects were antidiabetic actions related to the biological fate of the sugar glucose. Later, they were also shown to possess remarkable abilities to act as anti-inflammatory and antiallergenic agents. Glucocorticoid effects are mediated via changed production of enzymes (biological catalysts) and other proteins in their target organs. Glucocorticoid overproduction, Cushing's syndrome, and glucocorticoid underproduction, Addison's disease, can be fatal unless treated appropriately.

The second class of corticosteroids, mineralocorticoids such as aldosterone, promote sodium retention by the kidneys. In most people, their action helps to maintain the body's normal salt and water balance. In people who have the rare disease hyperaldosteronism, too much mineralocorticoid is produced and the resultant high sodium retention causes high blood pressure. Aldosterone's "sodium-sparing" action in normal individuals is thought to take part in maintaining normal blood pressure. Mineralocorticoids, like glucocorticoids, also mediate their biological effects by causing changes in production of key proteins in their target organ, the kidney.

Sex hormones are grouped into male hormones (androgens) and female hormones (estrogens and progestins). Androgens and estrogens, respectively, stimulate the growth, maintenance, and maturation of the male and female reproductive systems. Yet, they have effects on nonreproductive tissues, too. Estrogens such as estradiol lead to water uptake and body lipid deposits that make women more well-rounded than men. The effect of estrogens on water uptake is one reason that it is more difficult for women to diet successfully than men. In contrast, androgens such as testosterone lead to the larger size, deeper voice, and more extensive musculature seen in men. They are the "anabolic" steroids that weight lifters, athletes, and many people recovering from surgery use to increase their strength and muscle mass quickly. Progestins (for example, progesterone), the second class of female hormones, ready the womb for pregnancy and maintain the developing baby. Sex hormones, like corticosteroids, also mediate their effects by altering the production of key proteins in target organs.

Steroid hormones cause changes in the proteins made by their target organs via stimulation of the expression of specific genes. Genes are segments of giant deoxyribonucleic acid (DNA) molecules, called chromosomes, found in cell nuclei. Genes are strung together in a chromosome as beads are on a string. The chromosome, itself, is actually a DNA-protein complex called chromatin. Depending on the type of cell examined, special proteins in the chromatin block different genes, allowing only some genes to be expressed. The sum of the properties of the genes expressed in a cell explains why multicellular organisms contain different organs. Cells of the eye, for example, differ from liver cells because of the genes that are expressed in their chromosomes. Yet, the DNA in each cell of an organism is exactly the same when all the proteins present in chromatin are stripped away.

Gene expression involves the ability of cells to use unblocked genes to produce a second kind of polymer molecule called messenger ribonucleic acid (mRNA). Each gene can be used to make many copies of mRNA by a process called transcription. The transcribed mRNA molecules are exported from the nucleus into the cytoplasm and used to make proteins by a process called translation. The mRNA made from each type of gene is translated into one particular protein. A gene that is blocked in the chromatin of a particular cell cannot be used to make mRNA. Consequently, that cell loses the biochemical ability that the resultant protein would give it.

In the 1960's, scientists began to understand the mechanism by which steroid hormones caused gene activation. This "receptor" mechanism for hormone action, first identified for estrogens, explains the operation of all steroid hormones. It stipulates that the biological consequences of steroid hormone action depend upon hormone interactions with protein receptors. Before dealing with how the steroid hormones affect gene expression, a theorized receptor mechanism must explain the cellular detection of the tiny amount of any steroid hormone in the body, usually equivalent to a small pinch of salt dissolved in a bathtub full of water; why steroid hormones only affect their target organs, although they enter most body cells; and how different steroid hormones, which are very similar structurally, affect only certain target organs. These explanations come from three properties of receptor proteins: high affinity, limited distribution, and great specificity.

High affinity means that a receptor for a given steroid binds it very avidly. Consequently, cells containing a given hormone receptor will interact with the hormone at levels that make it possible to detect the equivalent of a pinch of salt in a bathtub. The term "limited distribution" means that receptors for individual hormones are present only in cells of target organs. For example, mineralocorticoid receptors are found mostly in cells of their main target organ, the kidney. Because of limited distribution, hormone molecules enter and pass right through most cells. Only in target organs do they react with receptors and cause changes.

The great specificity of hormone receptors, for example, the glucocorticoid receptor, has to do with the ability of various hormone molecules to interact with them to produce complexes capable of altering gene expression. Steroid hormones that are not glucocorticoids do not form adequate amounts of hormone-receptor complex to cause a hormone effect even when they are present at many times the maximum concentration at which they are found in target organs. Second, there is a "pecking order" among the different members of a given class of hormones in that those that produce strong, mild, and weak effects in a target organ have parallel abilities to interact with the receptor. Also, synthetic steroid hormones, more effective than natural hormones of the same class, may have higher affinities for the receptor.

Steroid hormones' mediation of gene expression is a process that begins in target cell cytoplasm. Here, an appropriate hormone molecule enters the cell and interacts with a molecule of specific, high-affinity receptor, which produces a molecule of hormone-receptor complex. Once the complex forms, it can enter the cell nucleus and interact with chromatin, to cause specific genes to produce mRNAs. Alone, neither steroid hormone nor receptor can do that. The mRNAs then leave the nucleus, enter the cytoplasm, and cause the synthesis of key proteins needed for expression of the hormone effect. Examples of such proteins are contractile proteins, enzymes that catalyze important chemical reactions, and various transport proteins that import or export cellular biochemicals.

The effects of different steroid hormones on the chromatin of different target cells cause production of different groups of proteins. The mechanism of these effects is related to chromatin structure. Chromatin contains special sites that bind to steroid hormone-receptor complexes and allow them to turn on specific genes. This binding results in synthesis of mRNAs from the genes. The steroid hormone-receptor binding sites vary in their positions in chromatin from different target organs. Consequently, because a given target organ contains chromatin that will only react with one type of hormone-receptor complex and the sites at which different hormone-receptor complexes bind vary in position, different genes are activated by different hormones. The mechanism of this activation is still not clear, though much research is being done to identify it.

Methods of Study

In 1964, it was proposed that steroid hormones act by increasing gene expression, meaning that they increase RNA and protein production. Experimental data, with rats and other animals, supported this hypothesis as follows. First, in animals injected with chemicals that stop RNA or protein synthesis (inhibitors), hormone administration did not lead to effects seen in animals that had been given the hormone without inhibitors. Second, target organs in animals given hormones and amino acids or nucleotides (chemicals that become proteins or RNAs, respectively) labeled with radioactive atoms produced more radioactive RNA and radioactive protein than those from animals that were not given hormones. Furthermore, inhibitor effects and increased RNA or protein synthesis did not occur in cells of nontarget organs, supporting a special interaction between hormones and target organs.

The specificity of interaction of hormones with their target organs was shown next, when the fate of injected hormones labeled with radioactive atoms was examined. Here, the radioactivity accumulated extensively in the cells of target organs, but little radioactivity was seen in the cells of nontarget organs. Furthermore, the hormone radioactivity localized in the nuclei of target cells. This accumulation of the hormones in target organs and its localization in cell nuclei preceded any observable effects of the hormones, supporting the concept that the basis for steroid hormone action was genetic.

Many studies of hormone accumulation and localization are done by a method called autoradiography. Autoradiography is carried out by placing thin slices of tissues to be examined and pieces of photographic film in contact in a dark container. Emitted radiation exposes the film because it is energy similar to light. Examination of the extent of exposure of film in contact with various tissues is used to compare their hormone content. The patterns of film exposure allow identification of the cellular location of the hormone examined.

Accumulation of injected hormones in target organs suggested that they bound to some cellular chemical. These chemicals, receptors, were expected to be involved in the actions of the hormones. Many researchers began to search for receptors for different hormones. Criteria expected to identify receptors were their presence only in cells of target organs and their avid (high-affinity) binding to a particular type of hormone but not to other types of steroids.

Identification and isolation of cellular steroid hormone receptors was difficult because they are present at very low concentrations. By 1966, however, the estrogen receptor of rat uterus was identified and shown to be a protein. Estrogen receptor had the expected properties. It was found in estrogen target organs but not in nontarget organs. Its concentration was so low that it could only be identified as a complex with the radioactive estrogen, estradiol. It bound estradiol and other estrogens avidly and had much lower affinity for other types of steroid hormones. Soon, corticosteroid, androgen, and progestin receptors were also identified. All these receptors were proteins exhibiting limited distribution, high affinity, and great specificity, as shown by autoradiography and other techniques.

Next, it was shown that receptors carry steroid hormones into cell nuclei, that steroid hormone-receptor complexes bind to chromatin, and that the binding sites are chromatin proteins called acidic nuclear proteins. The specificity of the binding response results from the fact that there are hundreds of different acidic nuclear proteins and that they vary from target organ to target organ. The first two observations were again based on autoradiography and related procedures. The importance of the acidic nuclear proteins was shown when their removal from target organ chromatin drastically decreased its ability to bind to the hormone-receptor complexes.

Different steroid hormone-receptor complexes bind to different acidic nuclear proteins in various target organs. These proteins are located at varying places in chromatin, so they are associated with different genes, which is why androgens, estrogens, progestins, glucocorticoids, and mineralocorticoids activate different genes and lead to production of different proteins. Complex techniques using methods of genetic engineering are being used to identify the basis for the specificity of binding of hormone-receptor complexes to target organs and how the complexes cause increased mRNA production. Many such efforts examine interaction with RNA polymerase, the enzyme that makes RNA.

Context

Knowing the mechanism of steroid hormone action has produced better understanding of eukaryotic gene expression and several important advances in life science. The advances include treatment for certain cancers, identification of the molecular basis for several diseases of previously unknown origin, explanation and design of therapeutic drugs, and models for actions of other hormones and hormonelike molecules. In addition, it is hoped that illumination of the exact way in which steroid hormones bind to receptors and the exact basis for gene activation by hormone-receptor complexes will identify how to prepare still better synthetic hormones and other chemicals with therapeutic abilities leading to safer contraceptives, still better means to fight cancer, and the basic understanding of how the body works.

The techniques involved in investigation of steroid hormone receptors have been particularly valuable to the development of chemotherapy treatments for human breast cancer. It has been shown that many breast cancers are receptor positive, meaning that they contain estrogen receptor. Other, receptor-negative breast cancers do not contain the receptor. Receptor-positive tumors need estrogens to grow, and many of them can be kept from recurring by surgical removal of the ovaries or use of antiestrogens, chemicals related to estrogens that prevent gene activation by natural estrogens. The success of treatment of receptor-positive breast cancer in this way has been high enough that it is now common practice to test excised breast cancers for estrogen-receptor content, to guide choice of postoperative therapy. Measurement of androgen, glucocorticoid, and progesterone receptors is also becoming valuable for diagnostic purposes.

A group of diseases called male pseudohermaphroditism has also been explained via understanding of steroid hormone receptors, though it is not yet treatable. Afflicted people are males, as they possess a Y chromosome. Yet, male traits do not develop at birth, they are identified as females, and they are reared as women. Most often, pseudohermaphroditism causes complete testicular feminization. This is entirely a result of defective androgen receptors and leads to individuals who look like women but possess internal testes. It is believed that future advances in understanding the molecular basis of androgen action will produce means to reverse the disease. Such reversal is frequently desired by people who suffer through painful, incomplete sex-reversal surgery.

Use and planning of drugs to treat cancer or reverse pseudohermaphroditism and other endocrinologically related problems is intimately related to the receptor concept. For example, tamoxifen and clomiphene, two antiestrogens, are used to treat receptor-positive breast cancer. Their action results from binding to the estrogen receptor and forming complexes without effect on gene activation, while preventing estrogen from forming functional complexes, activating genes, and making tumors grow.

Another use of the receptor concept has been in the design of synthetic hormones that are more potent than natural steroid hormones whose actions they mimic. This extra strength is important because the extremely high doses of natural hormones required for therapeutic uses can have dangerous side effects, including high blood pressure, birth defects, and cancer. Furthermore, there are cases in which the receptor concept led to identification of the action mechanism of other important biomolecules, including thyroxine and vitamin D effects. Thyroxine, an amino acid hormone made by the thyroid, stimulates many biological processes throughout the body. Vitamin D participates in control of the calcium content of the bones. Study of these biomolecules, and many others, has proved that they operate via receptor-mediated gene activation. The receptor concept is also expected to be essential to future understanding of other life processes.

Bibliography

Baxter, J. D., and K. M. MacLoed. "Molecular Basis for Hormone Action." In *Metabolic Control and Disease*, edited by P. K. Bondy and L. E. Rosenberg. Philadelphia: W. B. Saunders, 1980. This chapter is an excellent, in-depth summary of hormone-receptor complex formation, the control processes involved in hormone actions, and the biochemical consequences of the interactions between hormone-receptor complexes and other cellular components.

Heftmann, Erich. *Steroid Biochemistry*. New York: Academic Press, 1970. This book presents an introductory survey of the steroid hormones and related chemicals. Its coverage includes their chemical structures, their biochemistry, and their physiological properties.

Lehninger, A. L. *Biochemistry*. New York: Worth, 1975. This edition of the classic college biochemistry text provides excellent coverage of steroid hormones in chapter 29. Lehninger deciphers the chemistry, biochemistry, history, and evolution of hormone action in a scholarly fashion.

_____. *Principles of Biochemistry*. New York: Worth, 1982. Chapter 25 of this text, written at a more general level than *Biochemistry*, covers most of the same topics. It has the advantage of some newer information, lacking in the 1975 book. The two texts are complementary.

O'Malley, Bert W., and Anthony R. Means. "Female Steroid Hormones and Target Cell Nuclei." *Science* 183 (February 15, 1974): 610-620. This article describes many important aspects of the interaction of steroid-receptor complexes with nuclear DNA and the resultant regulation of its transcription into mRNA. Many terms related to gene activation are clarified here.

O'Malley, Bert W., and William T. Schrader. "The Receptors of Steroid Hormones." *Scientific American* 234 (February, 1976): 32-44. This article describes many important aspects of the receptor concept, including its history, receptor interactions with target cells, molecular biological involvements, and uses of the concept in health science. Some very nice graphics clarify many issues.

Zubay, Geoffrey. *Biochemistry.* New York: Macmillan, 1988. Chapter 31 of this text covers well all aspects of animal steroid action. It also describes plant and insect hormones in some detail, adding to the breadth of discussion. Very current coverage of gene expression and steroid properties is to be found in other chapters, if desired.

Sanford S. Singer

Cross-References

DNA Replication, 692; Testing for Endocrine Functions of Glands and Organs, 772; Endocrinology of the Adrenal Glands, 800; Genes and Nucleic Acids, 1134; Lipids, 1598; Proteins, 2272; The Female Reproductive System, 2346; The Male Reproductive System, 2354; Transcription of DNA to Form RNA, 2632; Translation of Messenger RNA to Form Protein, 2647.

HORMONE MECHANISMS AND SECOND MESSENGERS

Type of life science: Animal physiology
Other fields of study: Biochemistry, cell biology (cytology), genetic regulation in eukaryotes, and molecular biology

Many hormones interact with cell membranes to produce second messengers that control cell processes by turning key enzymes on or off. Understanding second messengers has helped scientists learn about control processes and disease.

Principal terms
ADENYL CYCLASE: the enzyme in cell membranes that composes the second messenger
ENDOCRINE GLANDS: glands that produce hormones and secrete them into the blood so that they can serve as intercellular messengers in target organs
ENZYMES: proteins that act as biological catalysts, chemicals that speed up chemical reactions in living organisms
HORMONES: chemical messengers made by endocrine glands to stimulate, in other tissues, biochemical processes necessary for life
KINASE: an enzyme that uses adenosine triphosphate (ATP) to add phosphate to another biomolecule
PROTEIN: a biological amino acid polymer; proteins include catalysts called enzymes, some hormones, and many other key cell components
PROTEIN KINASE: one of a few kinase enzymes that are turned on or off by second messengers
SECOND MESSENGER: a chemical signal made in response to interaction between a hormone and a target-cell membrane that mediates a hormone effect; examples are cyclic AMP and similar chemicals
TARGET ORGAN: a nonendocrine organ that responds to a hormone by changes in its biological capabilities; responses are often the result of second messengers

Summary of the Phenomenon

Hormones are chemical messengers that stimulate biochemical processes necessary for the life and well-being of the whole body. They are produced in tiny amounts by organs called endocrine glands. Endocrinology (the study of the hormones) is named for these glands. Endocrine glands secrete hormones into the blood, which then carries them to other organs. The organs affected by hormones are called "target organs." Messenger action of hormones integrates body functions and allows them to occur with maximum flexibility.

Some hormones, including steroid hormones, cause their effects by a mechanism that involves direct stimulation of the expression of specific genes in their target organs. Other hormones, such as epinephrine and important hormones that are proteins (polymers of amino acids), cause their effects via another mechanism. This mechanism involves "second messengers." A hormone causes the production of another chemical, or second messenger, that produces the effect. Second-messenger effects are not usually caused by gene activation. The best-known second messenger is a chemical called cyclic adenosine-3′, 5′-monophosphate (cyclic AMP); second messengers will be considered later.

The understanding of second-messenger mechanisms began with study of the biological actions of epinephrine, made by the central portion (medulla) of the adrenal glands, twin endocrine glands located on top of the kidneys. Epinephrine is a chemical precursor of the amino acid tyrosine, and its secretion by the adrenal medulla triggers a group of processes often called "fight or flight" responses. These include accelerated heart rate and output, accompanied by increased energy and strength. They may explain, for example, the frantic strength that will sometimes allow a woman weighing 50 kilograms to lift her 90-kilogram husband and drag him to safety when he is rendered unconscious by an accident.

The most prominent biochemical event associated with the fight or flight response is the greatly increased breakdown of the main energy reserve, glycogen (a complex carbohydrate), in muscle and liver. This breakdown readies the body to utilize the energy required for the physical response of fight or flight. In the early 1950s, Earl W. Sutherland, Jr., and coworkers made several key observations that led to understanding of the second messenger mechanism involved. Sutherland's work led to his receiving the 1971 Nobel Prize in Physiology or Medicine.

One of these observations was that the addition of epinephrine to thin slices of liver tissue grown outside the body mobilized the energy reserve as glucose molecules. The glucose molecules then accumulated in the solution in which the liver slices were suspended. Examination of the phenomenology of glucose production showed that it was the result of increased biological activity of an enzyme (a protein biological catalyst) that broke glycogen down to glucose.

For simplicity, glycogen will be depicted as a long string of glucose molecules, GGGGGG . . . G, where G is one glucose molecule and the dots indicate the presence of many more Gs than those shown. Each glucose released can be oxidized in the body to produce energy in the same way that coal or oil produces the energy to run nonbiological machines. The enzyme that catalyzes glucose release from glycogen is called phosphorylase.

Another important observation that researchers made was that mixing pure phosphorylase with epinephrine did not produce added energy. Consequently, the stimulatory effort of epinephrine in liver slices resulted from another factor or factors present in liver cells. Additional examination identified the fact that phosphorylase could exist as either an active (a) form and an inactive (b) form. It appeared possible that epinephrine might stimulate conversion of pure phosphorylase b to phosphorylase a, and that this could explain the action. Thorough study, however, showed that mixing epinephrine with phosphorylase b did not result in the anticipated effect.

Later studies with broken-cell preparations of liver showed that epinephrine stimulated conversion of phosphorylase b to phosphorylase a. This was the first time that a hormone effect had ever been seen in a system that was not composed of whole cells. In addition, use of a broken-cell preparation allowed investigators much greater control of experimental conditions than had been possible before. They were now able to add or remove factors from the system, and narrow down the identities of possible factors involved in the process. They could also separate cell components, such as cell membranes and nuclei to identify sites where control factors were produced.

A major breakthrough next occurred when a small amount of adenosine triphosphate (ATP) was added to broken-cell preparations in the presence of epinephrine. ATP, the main energy source for biochemical processes, greatly stimulated activation of phosphorylase b by epinephrine. The effect was found to be the result of two consecutive events: Epinephrine caused ATP to interact with cell membranes and produce the factor that stimulated activation of phosphorylase b, and the factor caused ATP use to convert phosphorylase b to phosphorylase a.

The factor was soon shown to be a chemical cousin of ATP, cyclic adenosine monophosphate (AMP). Epinephrine function was found to be the stimulation of a cell membrane enzyme to produce cyclic AMP. Cyclic AMP (or cAMP) then caused another enzyme to add phosphate from ATP to phosphorylase b. The mysterious action of epinephrine was actually simple: The hormone messenger caused an enzyme to make cyclic AMP, a second messenger. This second messenger stimulated addition of phosphate to phosphorylase b, activating it. The identified enzymes were named adenyl cyclase and protein kinase. Adenyl cyclase made cyclic AMP, and protein kinase apparently used ATP to add phosphate to phosphorylase b, changing its biological activity.

There is a third step in this phenomenon, the action of another ATP-using enzyme. This enzyme, phosphorylase kinase, adds phosphate to phosphorylase b. The overall organization of the process is as follows: Epinephrine reacts with cell membrane sites (receptors) and causes adenyl cyclase to make cyclic AMP; cyclic AMP activates protein kinase; protein kinase adds phosphate from ATP to phosphorylase kinase, activating it in turn; and the phosphorylase kinase uses ATP to convert phosphorylase b to phosphorylase a, which releases glucose from glycogen molecules.

The advantage of such a system is production of an amplification cascade effect, as follows. One molecule of epinephrine causes production of many cyclic AMP molecules. Each cyclic AMP then turns on a molecule of protein kinase. The protein kinase molecules each turn on hundreds of molecules of phosphorylase kinase. Each phosphorylase kinase molecule then converts many molecules of phosphorylase b to phosphorylase a, and millions of glucose molecules are released from glycogen because of the action of each epinephrine molecule that began the process.

This type of cascade effect is an excellent system for amplification of a hormone response, and hormone mechanisms that use second messengers are found in many places in living organisms. Consequently, a large number of key enzymes in control processes are affected by special kinases like phosphorylase kinase. Several different protein kinases (each controls groups of such processes) are present, furthermore, in different target organs. In many cases, cyclic AMP is the second messenger that interacts with them, although several other second messengers—including cousins of cyclic AMP (cyclic GMP), calcium ion, and inositol triphosphate—are also involved in control processes. Finally, some phosphate additions turn enzymes off in second-messenger cascades. For example, glycogen synthetase kinase adds phosphate to the enzyme, glycogen synthetase, that makes glycogen and this turns off the synthetase, stopping glycogen production.

Methods of Study

The understanding of second-messenger mechanisms arose from observation that epinephrine administration increased blood levels of the sugar glucose. Study of how this came about led to discovery that much of the blood glucose came from the polymeric glucose-storage form, liver glycogen. This focused research on identifying how glycogen was converted to glucose and relevant interactions between epinephrine and liver cell components.

Early examination of the phenomenon began with measurement of the amounts of all chemicals in liver that could become blood glucose. This examination showed that production of only one such chemical, glucose-1-phosphate, was affected by epinephrine. Manufacture of glucose-1-phosphate is the first step in glucose mobilization. It involves splitting off this chemical from glycogen by the enzyme, phosphorylase.

Phosphorylase was then isolated and found to occur in two forms, active phosphorylase a, which makes glucose-1-phosphate from glycogen, and inactive phosphorylase b, which does not. Chemical examination of the two phosphorylase forms showed that they differed in that form b is missing a phosphate. Loss of this phosphate is caused by the enzyme, phosphorylase phosphatase. Phosphorylase b reactivation requires only phosphate readdition, via the enzyme phosphorylase kinase.

The phosphatase and the kinase seemed likely to participate in a control system. Support for this came from discovery of similar activation and inactivation of the phosphorylase in muscle, the other main source of blood glucose from glycogen. It appeared likely that epinephrine effects could have resulted from interaction with phosphorylase, the kinase, or the phosphatase. The hormone had no effect, however, when mixed with samples of any of these three enzymes.

It was then shown that broken-cell preparations, made by mechanical disruption of liver exhibited the epinephrine effect. Because the effect did not require whole cells, study of epinephrine interaction with individual cell components became possible. Such efforts showed that epinephrine caused release, from cell membranes, of a small molecule (a "second messenger") that led to the activation of phosphorylase b.

At first, chemical identification of the second messenger seemed impossible because it was produced only in tiny amounts. Eventually, though, enough of the messenger was collected to demonstrate, chemically, that it was related to ATP, the main energy and phosphate source in cells. Then, in a stroke of good luck, the messenger was shown to be identical to a newly identified cousin of ATP, cyclic AMP.

With cyclic AMP clearly the second messenger for the fight or flight response, researchers began to search for it in other tissues. Soon, chemical analysis identified the presence of cyclic AMP in virtually every type of living cell. Even more important, cyclic AMP levels changed in cells exposed to a great many different hormones. So, cyclic AMP was a widespread second messenger. The picture became more complete when it was shown that cyclic AMP was made from ATP by a cell membrane enzyme, adenyl cyclase, turned on by epinephrine. This was how epinephrine released the second messenger.

The key to action of a particular hormone in a target organ by a second messenger was shown to be that each target organ possessed membrane sites (receptors) that bound the hormone and led to the activation of adenyl cyclase. Epinephrine, for example, causes fight or flight effects in liver and muscle by this mechanism. In contrast, glucagon does this in liver but not muscle. The specificity occurs because liver and muscle contain epinephrine receptor, but only liver has such sites for glucagon. Proof of the existence of binding sites for specific hormones in target organs is accomplished by mixing hormones labeled with radioactive atoms with cell membranes and showing that only some hormones bind to the membranes.

The final linkup was the discovery that cyclic AMP turns on an enzyme, protein kinase, that uses ATP to add phosphate to phosphorylase kinase. This reaction turns on phosphorylase kinase so that it, in turn, can activate phosphorylase b. Protein kinase was soon identified in all cells that respond to hormones in this way, and the delineation of the second-messenger mechanism was complete. The overall effort had required use of chemical analysis of tissues, subcellular fractionation of cells, purification and study of enzymes, and radioisotope binding studies.

Context

Conceptualization of the epinephrine-cyclic AMP second-messenger system has led to fundamental advances in several aspects of life science. These include explanation of the basis for other hormone-mediated processes involving cyclic AMP; identification of additional second messengers; and some clarification of the molecular basis for disease processes. It is hoped that further study of second messengers will identify useful therapeutic chemicals and add to basic understanding of life processes.

Attempts to identify other hormones that operated like epinephrine began after discovery that cyclic AMP is present in many endocrine target organs. Researchers examined effects of protein hormones whose action mechanisms had evaded them because the hormones, like other proteins, did not enter cells. The ability of each hormone to bind cell membranes of target organs was tested and followed by examination of the effect of the binding on adenyl cyclase activity. These efforts identified over a dozen protein hormones as acting via a cyclic AMP-protein kinase cascade (pituitary hormones). It was also found that some of the hormones caused their effects by preventing cyclic AMP production, indicating that variations in second-messenger cascades existed.

The existence of such mechanistic variations led to the search for and the identification of other second messengers. The best known of these are cyclic GMP, cyclic CMP, inositol phosphate, and calcium ion. The action mechanisms of these second messengers are not as well understood as the cyclic AMP systems, but their discovery has added new depth to endocrinology and explained some parts of the molecular basis for action of protein hormones that do not use cyclic AMP as their second messenger.

Biochemical dissection of components of the second-messenger system has also led to potentially exciting revelations concerning disease processes. For example, another aspect of cyclic AMP cascades is an enzyme called cyclic AMP phosphodiesterase. The phosphodiesterase destroys cyclic AMP, allowing living organisms to end the amplification cascade. Caffeine, theophylline, and other drugs related to cyclic AMP prevent the action of this enzyme. Doing so keeps the amplification cascade—and thus hormone responses—going longer.

Such effects, annoying when they are only the nerve-jangling action of too much caffeine, are of more fundamental importance in the case of theophylline, a useful anti-asthma drug. Theophylline action, by turning off phosphodiesterase, is viewed as a valuable explanation of how some asthma drugs work and a beginning to understanding several related processes in the brain. These observations are expected to produce better therapeutic drugs for use in treating asthma and designing probes to be used in study of brain action.

A final aspect of cyclic AMP action that should be mentioned briefly is the belief that it—and other second messengers—is also involved in some aspects of gene regulation related to cancer. This idea began with the observation that, in bacteria, cyclic AMP affects the production of certain enzymes of sugar metabolism via gene activation. This background and other studies of cancer cells has lead to theorization that a number of normal and pathological gene activations in higher organisms occur via cyclic AMP.

Bibliography

Conn, Eric E., Paul K. Stumpf, George Bruening, and Roy H. Doi. *Outlines of Biochemistry.* 5th ed. New York: John Wiley & Sons, 1987. A chapter summarizes concepts involved in second-messenger regulation. It includes coverage of enzyme-mediated metabolic regulation and a description of the second-messenger action of both cyclic AMP and inositol phosphate. The coverage relates messenger interactions and their metabolic consequences in a simple way.

Goldberg, N. D. "Cyclic Nucleotides and Cell Function." *Hospital Practice* 9 (1974): 127-142. This well-rounded article describes several aspects of the second-messenger mechanism as it pertains to cyclic AMP and other cyclic nucleotides. It contains a particularly good description of the important role of protein kinase in glycogen phosphorylase action and in related processes.

Lehninger, Albert L. *Principles of Biochemistry.* New York: Worth, 1982. Chapter 25 summarizes second-messenger regulation as related to epinephrine. Secretion of epinephrine, cyclic AMP, the enzymes of the regulatory cascade, and inactivation of cyclic AMP are dealt with in an easy-to-handle fashion, but at a fairly high level. The rest of the chapter is worth reading for its overall coverage of hormones.

Pastan, Ira. "Cyclic AMP." *Scientific American* 227 (August, 1972): 97-105. This article describes many important aspects of the development of understanding of cyclic AMP action in several aspects of the biochemistry of normal and cancerous cells of higher organisms, and in bacteria. The history of the evolution of the original second-messenger concept by Sutherland and his coworkers is also well developed.

Robison, G. A., R. W. Butcher, and E. W. Sutherland. *Cyclic AMP.* New York: Academic Press, 1971. This work presents a complete review of all aspects of the identification of the second-messenger concept by premier members of the Nobel Prize-winning research group that contributed so heavily to it. All of the aspects of the related enzymology and metabolism are well covered.

Sutherland, Earl W. "Studies on the Mechanism of Hormone Action." *Science* 177 (1972): 401-408. This article explains important aspects of the Sutherland group's development of understanding of cyclic AMP action in epinephrine action. The evolution of the second-messenger concept is well developed by its originator.

Zubay, Geoffrey. *Biochemistry.* New York: Macmillan, 1988. Chapter 31 of this fairly advanced text covers many aspects of animal and plant hormone action well. It describes second messengers and, in context, fits them into the general scheme of hormone action. Several good diagrams show how the regulatory process occurs.

Sanford S. Singer

Cross-References

Cellular Membrane Specializations, 388; Endocrinology of the Adrenal Glands, 800; Hormone Mechanisms: Gene Regulation, 1353; Mammalian Hormones, 1368; Protein Phosphorylation, 2257; Proteins, 2272; Subcellular Fractionation Using Centrifugation, 2552.

MAMMALIAN HORMONES

Type of life science: Animal physiology
Other fields of study: Developmental biology (embryology) and zoology

Mammals use chemical messengers called hormones for information transfer and control between different body regions. These molecules, produced and secreted from endocrine glands into the bloodstream for transport, play important roles in mammalian development from conception to death.

Principal terms

ENDOCRINE SYSTEM: an array of ductless glands scattered throughout the mammalian body that produce and secrete hormones directly into the bloodstream

GENE: a sequence of approximately one thousand DNA nucleotide pairs on a chromosome that encodes a messenger RNA for eventual protein production

HOMEOBOX: a set of genes that encode proteins involved in development of a wide range of animal species, from nematodes to insects to mammals

HOMEOSTASIS: the maintenance of constant conditions within the internal environment of an organism, a process controlled by antagonistic hormone pairs

HORMONE: a chemical messenger, either protein or steroid, that communicates information between different body regions

HYPOPHYSIS: the pituitary gland, or "master" gland, which produces and secretes at least eight protein hormones influencing growth, metabolism, and sexual development

HYPOTHALAMUS: a brain region just below the cerebrum that interconnects the nervous and endocrine systems of mammals, thereby controlling most hormone production and many body functions

NEUROTRANSMITTER: a signaling molecule that provides neuron-to-neuron communication in animal nervous systems; some double as hormones

PROTEIN HORMONE: a hormone type composed of protein, a long chain of amino acids encoded by a gene

STEROID HORMONE: a hormone type derived from cholesterol, a type of fat molecule

Summary of the Phenomenon

Mammals are vertebrate animals that have fur (hair) and that nourish their young with milk by means of mammary glands, which are modified sweat glands. Mammals include, among other animals, primates (such as humans and chimpanzees), cetaceans (such as whales and dolphins), and marsupials (such as kangaroos, koalas, and opossums). Mammals are sexually reproducing and diploid (having two copies of every chromosome). During fertilization, a sperm from the male parent unites with an egg from the female parent to produce a diploid single-celled zygote. The zygote contains all the genetic information for all the cells of the future individual. The zygote divides first into two cells, then four, eight, sixteen, thirty-two, and so on.

As the cells divide, they begin to specialize, so that different groups of cells assume unique functions. Some cells become nerve cells, others skin cells, and others blood cells. A number of factors, including hormones, contribute to differentiation.

Throughout the development of the organism, profound changes such as birth, puberty, menopause, aging, and death occur. Progressive changes in cell functions contribute to these sequential processes. Many of these developmental changes are controlled by hormones, chemical messengers that provide communication between cells located in different portions of the body via the bloodstream.

Hormones fall into the two principal categories of protein hormones and steroid hormones. Protein hormones are composed of protein—long chains of amino acids encoded by genes. Steroid hormones are derivatives of cholesterol. Both hormone types function in the same fashion: They control genes. Hormones are produced and secreted from a source endocrine gland and are then transported through the bloodstream to a target tissue, where they penetrate cells and concentrate on the control regions of genes located on chromosomes. Once at a control region, a given hormone either activates or inactivates the gene. If a gene is activated, messenger RNA will be produced, leading to protein production. If a hormone inactivates a gene, protein production will cease. A given hormone may activate certain genes and inactivate others.

Endocrine glands are ductless glands (glands that lack channels for secreting their products) that produce and secrete hormones into the bloodstream. Major mammalian endocrine glands include the hypothalamus, hypophysis, thyroid, parathyroids, thymus, pancreas, adrenals, and gonads. The hormones secreted from these glands influence many cells and each other during mammalian development.

Homeostasis, the maintenance of a constant internal environment, is a major objective of endocrine hormones. They work antagonistically (against each other) to maintain various body conditions (such as blood sugar and calcium levels) in equilibrium. Endocrine hormones work principally, but not exclusively, by negative feedback. For example, a region of the brain called the hypothalamus reacts to various body conditions by releasing hormones that stimulate the nearby hypophysis (the pituitary gland) to release certain of its hormones. The hypophyseal hormones direct other glands and tissues to respond in a particular fashion. Once bodily conditions are back to normal, the hypothalamus terminates its initial stimulatory hormones, thereby stopping the entire sequence of events.

The hypothalamus controls a number of critical body functions, including the activities of endocrine glands, body temperature, wake and sleep cycles, and appetite. Ultimately, all these functions involve some type of hormones. When various conditions occur in the body (for example, hyperthermia, which is increased body heat), genes in certain hypothalmic cells synthesize special proteins called releasing factors that are sent into the bloodstream to activate target cells in glands (in the example cited, sweat glands) located elsewhere in the body. Often, the target of hypothalmic releasing factors is a nearby endocrine gland called the hypophysis, also known as the pituitary, or "master gland."

The eight hormones known to be released from the hypophysis are vasopressin (the "antidiuretic hormone"), oxytocin, prolactin, growth hormone, thyrotropin, adrenocorticotropic hormone (ACTH), follicle-stimulating hormone (FSH), and luteinizing hormone (LH). Vasopressin is released in response to low water levels in the blood; it stimulates the kidneys to retain water, reduce urine output, and increase blood pressure until blood water levels return to normal, upon which it will no longer be produced. Oxytocin causes muscular contractions in the uterus during childbirth and in the breast for the secretion of milk for an infant. Prolactin is present in males and females, but it is functional only in females. It stimulates milk production from fat deposits in the breast. Growth hormone causes growth in children; it is present in adults, but contributes only to the control of metabolic rate. Thyrotropin stimulates the thyroid gland to produce and secrete various hormones that control metabolism (examples: thyroxine and triiodothyronine). Adrenocorticotropic hormone stimulates the adrenal cortex, located above each kidney, to release its metabolism-controlling steroid hormones. At puberty, follicle-stimulating hormone stimulates the female ovarian follicle to mature and begin producing the steroid hormone estrogen; it directs the male testes to begin producing sperm. Also at puberty, luteinizing hormone stimulates the ovary to begin producing eggs and the steroid hormone progesterone; it directs the testes to begin producing the steroid hormone testosterone.

The hypophyseal hormones, all proteins encoded by genes, have a major impact upon metabolism and development in mammals. This is especially true for the sexual-cycle hypophyseal hormones FSH and LH. In females, puberty begins with the first menstrual cycle, which (in humans) begins in the early teenage years and lasts for the next thirty to forty years, after which it abruptly stops in menopause. Each menstrual cycle is the female body's way of preparing for a possible pregnancy. At the beginning of the cycle, the hypophysis produces high concentrations of FSH, which stimulates the ovarian follicle to develop and produce estrogen, a steroid hormone that increases body fat in regions such as the buttocks and breasts. Simultaneously, increased LH production matures the egg in the ovarian follicle and stimulates progesterone production. Progesterone causes the endometrium (the lining of the uterus) to increase its blood vessel content and thickness for receiving and maintaining a fertilized egg and for the subsequent long gestation period (nine months in humans). If the egg is fertilized by sperm, it will adhere to the endometrium, and progesterone will continue to be secreted to maintain the endometrium and the pregnancy. If the egg is not fertilized, progesterone levels will drop, estrogen levels will rise, the endometrium will be sloughed away (menstrual bleeding will occur), and the cycle will start all over again.

The female menstrual cycle is only one very complex example of how hormones are intricately involved in mammalian developmental processes. There are many subtler aspects of the menstrual cycle that still are not well understood, such as the identity of the hormonal signal from the fertilized egg that stimulates the female ovary to continue progesterone production for continuation of the pregnancy. All mammalian hormones are interconnected by cause-and-effect relationships. Tremendous research remains before a clear and complete picture of hormonally controlled mammalian development will emerge.

The thyroid gland, located in the throat region, produces several hormones (examples: thyroxine and triiodothyronine) that elevate the body's metabolic rate. The thyroid also secretes a hormone called calcitonin, which works antagonistically with the hormone parathormone produced by the adjacent parathyroid glands. When blood calcium is high (as in a condition called hypercalcemia), the calcitonin gene in thyroid cells begins producing the protein hormone calcitonin, which stimulates bone cells called osteoblasts to build more bone, thereby removing calcium from the bloodstream. Once blood calcium levels are back to normal, calcitonin production halts. In hypercalcemia, the parathormone gene in parathyroid cells begins producing parathormone (also a protein hormone) that stimulates bone cells called osteoclasts to break down bone, thereby restoring blood calcium levels but possibly contributing to osteoporosis (bones that are brittle because of calcium deficiency) and other bone-related disorders. Parathormone production is stopped once blood calcium levels are back to normal.

The islets of Langerhans in the pancreas secrete two antagonistic protein hormones, insulin and glucagon. In response to high glucose levels in the blood (as in hyperglycemia), genes in beta cells produce and secrete insulin, which directs body cells, especially liver cells, to absorb glucose and store it as a polysaccharide called glycogen. Insulin production will stop once blood glucose levels are reduced to normal. An insulin deficiency leads to prolonged hyperglycemia, a serious and often fatal disorder called diabetes mellitus. When blood glucose levels are too low (as in hypoglycemia), genes in the alpha cells of the islets of Langerhans produce and secrete glucagon, which directs body cells to break down their glycogen reserves and begin releasing glucose back into the bloodstream until normal blood glucose levels are reached, upon which glucagon production ceases.

Further endocrine glands include the adrenal cortex, located on top of each kidney, which secretes three major classes of steroid hormones: the glucocorticoids such as cortisol, which controls fat and protein metabolism; the mineralocorticoids such as aldosterone, which controls blood sodium levels; and the androgens (male sex steroids). The adrenal medulla, located internally to the adrenal cortex, is derived from nervous tissue and secretes two hormones, epinephrine and norepinephrine, that double as excitatory neurotransmitters at nerve axon endings;

chemical energy transmission between nerve cells occurs at synapses, or gaps, between adjacent neurons. Neurotransmitters are protein hormones that relay electrical impulses from one neuron (nerve cell) to another throughout the trillion-cell nervous systems of mammals. Other neurotransmitters include the excitatory acetylcholine and inhibitors glycine, enkephalin, and gamma-aminobutyric acid.

The kidney secretes the protein hormone erythropoietin when the blood has a low red blood cell level; erythropoietin stimulates the undifferentiated stem cells called hemocytoblasts in the red bone marrow of flat bones (ribs, sternum) to differentiate and develop into mature red blood cells. Platelet-derived growth factor (PDGF) is released from damaged blood vessels to activate platelet cells to begin blood clotting. Macrophage colony stimulatory factor and eosinophil chemotactic factor are two hormones that both activate and attract certain respective immune system cells to the site of an infection or allergic reaction. Histamine is released from damaged tissue and causes blood vessel dilation, so that the vessels are more leaky, thus allowing hormones and other molecules to reach the injury site, eventually leading to the inflammation and itching associated with wound healing.

The hormone prostaglandin helps inflammation and contracts some smooth muscles located throughout the body; nerve growth factor stimulates the growth of sensory nerves throughout the body; and epidermal growth factor stimulates the growth of the epidermis, the outermost skin layer that is constantly being shed and replaced. Sunlight exposure to skin produces cholecalciferol, or vitamin D, which helps to stimulate bone growth and maintenance.

Methods of Study

The tally of mammalian hormones extends well beyond the molecules just discussed. What is most puzzling is how the many hormones are interconnected during the control of development. Hormones control gene activities of target cells and some simple hormone systems act antagonistically (calcitonin-parathormone, insulin-glucagon). Yet there has not emerged a clear and complete picture of the overall interactions. Hormones control an incredibly complex array of cellular activities from conception to death.

Mammalian developmental hormones have been studied using a variety of biochemical and physiological experiments: isolation and purification experiments, injection into experimental animals, studies of metabolic disorders in animals, and molecular genetics experiments. Protein structures based upon genetic and biochemical studies are well understood. Steroid hormone structures have been unraveled from studies of cholesterol biochemistry.

Dissections of experimental animals yield intact endocrine glands (such as the thyroid and pancreas) that can be used to show function. Chemical secretions from these glands can be extracted and separated into the various hormone components by several biochemical techniques such as electrophoresis, chromatography, and centrifugation. The isolated hormones can be further purified by rerunning them through these separatory techniques.

Electrophoresis involves the separation of molecules in an electric field based upon their sizes and charges. Large molecules move slowly, whereas small, compact molecules move more quickly. Protein hormones move from the negative pole to the positive pole in electrophoretic gels. Affinity chromatography involves placing membrane hormone receptor proteins on a vertical column containing a porous resin. The specific hormone type that binds to this particular target receptor protein will stick to the resin. Nonbinding hormones will wash through the column. Finally, ultracentrifugation separates molecules based upon size in incredibly high-spinning gravity fields measuring about 100,000 times the earth's gravity. These three techniques, plus a few others, are very effective in isolating and purifying hormones as well as other important molecules.

Isolated hormones have been injected into experimental organisms and organ extracts, followed by observation and recording of the animal's physiological responses. For example, injection of vasopressin reduces an animal's urine output while simultaneously producing a slight blood pressure rise. Injection of insulin lowers blood sugar levels, which is why diabetics are prescribed insulin. Such experiments require the use of experimental animals, and extracts from these animals, which has sparked considerable controversy and debate concerning animal rights. These studies are important in understanding the physiology of the human body.

Hormone activity and function can also be studied from individuals having deficiencies or excesses of hormone production. Gigantism and dwarfism are different extremes of growth hormone secretion. Goiter and cretinism are each the result of abnormalities in thyroid gland hormone production. Rickets is a bone disorder caused by insufficient cholecalciferol (vitamin D). Diabetes mellitus is a very serious condition caused by an insulin deficiency that results in high blood glucose (hyperglycemia). Diabetes insipidus is caused by a vasopressin deficiency.

Genetic studies such as cloning and DNA sequencing have identified genes that may encode other developmental hormones. Discovery of the homeobox within the genes of all mammals indicates that there are some proteins (hormones) that control basic pattern development in mammals during early embryonic development. Some researchers believe that there may be certain hormones that accelerate aging and cause death in later life.

Context

All mammals start as a single-celled zygote—an egg that has been fertilized by a sperm—that undergoes a rapid sequence of mitotic divisions until it reaches the stage of a hollow, microscopic ball of identical cells called the blastula. Signaling molecules called hormones stimulate the blastula to fold in upon itself and form layers of tissue that gradually become differentiated into organs because of the presence of other hormones, which affect the tissue in sequence. Still other hormones later influence the interactions of organ systems for the smooth function of the organism. Knowledge of the chemical mechanisms and sequences through which hormones exert their effects will provide the key to understanding the action of genes, which in a more fundamental way are responsible for the various stages of life. Hormones direct cellular differentiation and development in the organism for the rest of its life. Hormones will be crucially involved in fetal development, birth, early growth and development, puberty, reproductive cycles, aging, and eventually death. Hormones control virtually all aspects of an organism's life.

If certain relevant mammalian developmental hormones can be identified, then target cells—cells that respond to the hormones in discrete but interrelated ways— may also be determined. A "developmental profile" for any organism would then be a real possibility, and the control of any organism's development, even behavior, could result. This may pose some serious ethical problems, but it also presents some wonderful implications for health and human welfare. Such knowledge of developmental hormones could be used to deactivate cancer cells, for example, or treat diseases such as hemophilia and rheumatoid arthritis. It might even be possible to slow the aging process.

Currently, there is some detailed knowledge of the functions of many developmental hormones. Many hormones remain to be identified, however, and the overall scheme of hormonal control of development is still sketchy. Extensive research will be needed in the future.

Hormones already are used to some extent in the medical treatment of various disorders such as kidney disease, rheumatoid arthritis, and diabetes mellitus. Many diseases nevertheless remain untreatable. One particular mysterious disease is progeria, accelerated aging in which a person dies of "old age" before the age of fifteen. Progeric patients exhibit all characteristics of aging, including heart problems, cancer, and high blood pressure, although within a greatly shortened time frame.

Bibliography

Alberts, Bruce, Dennis Bray, Julian Lewis, Martin Raff, Keith Roberts, and James D. Watson. *Molecular Biology of the Cell.* New York: Garland, 1983. As an intermediate-level undergraduate textbook, this outstanding work is a comprehensive, clear discussion of molecular and developmental biology. It contains excellent photographs and diagrams. Chapter 13, "Chemical Signaling Between Cells," provides detailed information concerning hormones and neurotransmitters.

Gehring, Walter J. "The Molecular Basis of Development." *Scientific American* 253 (October, 1985): 152B-162. As part of a special *Scientific American* issue called "The Molecules of Life," this article is a discussion of research into the homeobox, a region of genetic molecules that control early embryonic development in a variety of organisms, from nematodes to humans. Gehring describes several important experiments and major theories concerning early development.

Raven, Peter H., and George B. Johnson. *Biology.* 2d ed. St. Louis: Times-Mirror/ Mosby, 1989. This clearly written textbook is for beginning biology majors. Chapter 48, "Hormones," provides a concise discussion of protein and steroid hormones, with excellent tables and graphs describing many important human endocrine glands and hormones.

Sang, James H. *Genetics and Development*. London: Longman, 1984. This text is suitable both as a graduate level textbook and as a heavily cited reference source for developmental geneticists. It clearly and precisely presents current theories of determination, differentiation, and development. Chapter 8, "Tissue Origins," and chapter 11, "Sex Differences," are excellent discussions of development.

Snyder, Solomon H. "The Molecular Basis of Communication Between Cells." *Scientific American* 253 (October, 1985): 132-141. As part of a special *Scientific American* issue called "The Molecules of Life," this article is a clear, comprehensive survey of mammalian endocrine systems and hormones, including both protein and steroid hormones. Mechanisms of hormone action, hormone transport, and experimental studies are presented in this beautifully illustrated, well-diagrammed article.

Spence, Alexander P., and Elliott B. Mason. *Human Anatomy and Physiology*. Menlo Park, Calif.: Benjamin/Cummings, 1979. Spence and Mason's textbook is an excellent anatomy and physiology text for biology and allied health majors. The book is clearly written, extensively illustrated, and contains much information. Chapter 17, "Endocrine System," is a thorough survey of endocrine glands, hormone types, hormone functions, mechanisms of hormone action, and hormonal disorders.

Stryer, Lubert. *Biochemistry*. 2d ed. San Francisco, Calif.: W. H. Freeman, 1981. Stryer's classic work is an outstanding textbook for advanced undergraduate students in biology, biochemistry, and physiology. The book is very clearly written and well-illustrated. It has tremendous value as a reference tool. Chapter 35, "Hormone Action," is a thorough survey of hormone types and their mechanisms of action.

Wallace, Robert A., Jack L. King, and Gerald P. Sanders. *Biosphere: The Realm of Life*. 2d ed. Glenview, Ill.: Scott, Foresman, 1988. This is an excellent introductory biology textbook for both science and nonscience majors. It is clearly written and comprehensive in its coverage, although it is not too detailed to be understood by the general reader. Chapter 35, "Chemical Messengers in Animals," is a concise but thorough survey of mammalian hormones.

Zubay, Geoffrey. *Biochemistry*. Reading, Mass.: Addison-Wesley, 1983. As a graduate biochemistry textbook, this work is very detailed, although the illustrations and tables are excellent. Chapter 29, "Hormone Action," provides considerable information for protein and steroid hormone structures and actions, including a good discussion of negative feedback homeostasis.

David Wason Hollar, Jr.

Cross-References

MAGILL'S
SURVEY
OF
SCIENCE

ALPHABETICAL LIST

CATEGORY LIST